The teaching of secondary mathematics

McGRAW-HILL SERIES IN EDUCATION

HAROLD BENJAMIN, Consulting Editor-in-Chief

CURRICULUM AND METHODS IN EDUCATION
Arno A. Bellack, Teachers College, Columbia University, CONSULTING EDITOR

FOUNDATIONS IN EDUCATION
Harold Benjamin, Emeritus Professor of Education, George Peabody College for Teachers, CONSULTING EDITOR

ADMINISTRATION IN EDUCATION
Harlan Hagman, Wayne State University, CONSULTING EDITOR

PSYCHOLOGY AND HUMAN DEVELOPMENT IN EDUCATION
Nicholas Hobbs, George Peabody College for Teachers, CONSULTING EDITOR

GUIDANCE, COUNSELING, AND STUDENT PERSONNEL IN EDUCATION
Walter F. Johnson, Michigan State University, CONSULTING EDITOR

CURRICULUM AND METHODS IN EDUCATION

ARNO A. BELLACK, *Consulting Editor*

BATCHELDER, MCGLASSON, AND SCHORLING *Student Teaching in Secondary Schools*

BENT AND KRONENBERG *Principles of Secondary Education*

BROWN, LEWIS, AND HARCLEROAD *A-V Instruction: Materials and Methods*

BUTLER AND WREN *The Teaching of Secondary Mathematics*

LEFEVRE *Linguistics and the Teaching of Reading*

MARKS, PURDY, AND KINNEY *Teaching Elementary School Mathematics for Understanding*

PHENIX *Realms of Meaning*

STRANG, MCCULLOUGH, AND TRAXLER *The Improvement of Reading*

WINGO AND SCHORLING *Elementary School Student Teaching*

The teaching of secondary mathematics

CHARLES H. BUTLER
Professor of Mathematics
Western Michigan University

F. LYNWOOD WREN
Professor of Mathematics
San Fernando Valley State College
Julia A. Sears Professor of Mathematics, Emeritus
George Peabody College for Teachers

FOURTH EDITION

McGRAW-HILL BOOK COMPANY
New York, St. Louis, San Francisco, Toronto, London, Sydney

THE TEACHING OF SECONDARY MATHEMATICS

Library of Congress Catalog Card Number 64-25596

09329

Preface

AT THE TIME OF the publication of the third edition of our book the effect of the "explosive revolution" in mathematics and the teaching of mathematics was just beginning to be felt. Now, five years later, much of the new philosophy as to curriculum content and organization as well as many of the trends in instructional procedures seem to be fairly well established and, thus, more clearly discernible. These facts, along with the generous reception which the previous editions have received, have made it seem desirable to undertake this, the fourth edition.

All chapters have been revised to some extent and several chapters have undergone extensive revision. A new chapter on geometry has been written to supplement chapters 16 and 17 of the third edition, which were rewritten. In every case the exercises and the bibliographies have been subjected to critical scrutiny and careful revision.

The underlying philosophy which has guided the authors in the preparation of the manuscript has been: (1) to emphasize the desirability of preserving a sane balance between the traditional and the new in the mathematics program of the secondary school; (2) to maintain a sound professional balance in the treatment of theoretically desirable approaches to instructional problems and of practical analyses of subject matter content; and (3) to provide a book which will be found helpful to teachers active in the field as well as to prospective teachers while in their training programs.

The book is divided into two parts. Part I directs its attention to the discussion of those traditional and current educational problems, practices, and issues which give significant character to effective teaching of secondary mathematics. Part II concerns itself with helping prospective and active teachers of secondary mathematics attain a more informed understanding of the basic subject matter to be taught.

Our purpose in writing each edition of this book has been to bring together in one volume the substance of the best contemporary thought on the most significant issues relevant to the teaching and learning of secondary-school mathematics. There is an advantage in having this within the covers of a single book. Such a book can be used as a basic textbook for classes or as a basic source of reference. At the same time, our bibliographies facilitate more intensive exploration of particular problems by bringing together lists of relevant supplementary references. Thus we believe that our book is useful both as a basic textbook for undergraduate or graduate classes for prospective or inservice teachers of mathematics, and also as a helpful source of suggestions and supplementary references for the more intensive study of particular ideas.

For their kind permission to quote from published sources in the present revision, we wish to express our appreciation to those authors, publishers, organizations, and journals from whose works such quotations have been taken. Also we wish to express to Alleyne T. Wren our sincere appreciation for her valuable assistance in the typing and preparation of the manuscript.

CHARLES H. BUTLER
F. LYNWOOD WREN

Contents

Part I

THE PROGRAM AND THE IMPROVEMENT OF INSTRUCTION IN SECONDARY MATHEMATICS

ONE

The evolving program of secondary mathematics

THE AMERICAN public secondary school, which had its beginning in the third decade of the nineteenth century, was preceded by two other significant institutions of secondary education, viz., the Latin grammar school and the academy. The discrimination between the respective periods for which each of these schools represents the predominant educational pattern is not altogether distinct and clear-cut. The transition from the influence of one educational philosophy to that of another has been characterized by a somewhat deliberate effort at reform under the persistent demands of social change. The development of the new institutions and the gradual fading from prominence of the old have been merely the outward evidences of the efforts of educational leaders to keep abreast of the demands of a changing social order. Such a pattern of educational evolution continues to exercise influence in the shaping of the curriculum content and the instructional procedure in the schools of today.

In the three centuries of American secondary education many significant changes have taken place. The early aristocratic policy of selecting students from among a favored few has been replaced by the modern democratic policy of opening the doors of educational opportunity to students from all levels of society. The fundamental philosophy has changed from one which demanded an institution whose principal function was preparation for a single profession to one which calls for an institution whose chief aim is twofold in nature, viz., the provision of terminal training that is functional for all individuals and the provision of propaedeutic training for those who can, and desire to, derive profit from further study in institutions of higher learning.

Mathematics and the changing educational program In the early frontier days the need for mathematics and the motivation for its development were rather limited. The farmer and the ordinary worker needed little beyond the ability to add and subtract. Those boys who aspired to enter some form of trade experience needed to know something of simple computation, and have a slight knowledge of common measure, a few very simple fractions, and the use of English and other European moneys. The seafaring man needed to know the basic principles of navigation; the clergyman found astronomy necessary in fixing the dates of religious festivals; and the public official, when fixing territorial boundaries, found surest recourse in surveying. From this meager source flowed the shallow stream of mathematics in sixteenth-century America. Consequently, it is not surprising that mathematics received little attention in the early elementary schools. They were established for the primary purpose of teaching writing and reading, with an occasional reference to ciphering. In fact, one who could qualify as an "arithmeticker" was likely to be considered as especially endowed, although the sobriquet implied no more than that the individual was able to perform the simplest of computations.

It was not until the latter part of the nineteenth century that real progress began to take place in the development of mathematics in America. By that time there was a fair-sized group of native talent working in the field of mathematics, and there were major influences shaping up to promote significant development in mathematical research. As most important among these influences we might list the vision of the presidents of certain outstanding universities and their appreciation of the need for promotion of interest in mathematics in this country, the founding of the American Mathematical Society, and a closer contact with European scholars. Many of the young men of that era who were interested in mathematics pursued advanced study and sought advanced degrees in mathematics in European universities, in particular, those of Berlin, Göttingen, and Leipzig. Furthermore, many European mathematicians were imported to this country to teach in our universities, some temporarily and others on a permanent basis.

It was well that the leaders in the field of mathematics should have become so concerned with the promotion of mathematical research in this country. The research worker is the producer of mathematics. It is he who must stay out on the frontier in the expansion of the effectiveness, usefulness, and significance of the field of mathematics as an important aspect of our culture and social structure. The investments of effort and planning made by these early leaders have paid excellent dividends to the stockholders in American culture, for today the American corps of mathematicians occupies the vanguard of mathematical thought.

Thus we see that, during the course of approximately four centuries, vision and scholarly effort have produced a strong and impressive superstructure of enlightened research in the field of mathematics in our country. But what of the understructure of effective teaching and intelligent subject-matter planning at the elementary and secondary levels? While the events of recent years have created an international feeling of awe and admiration in the contemplation of the marvelous accomplishments of mathematical research, there have been many pointed expressions of concern over faulty teaching of, and deficient curriculums in, mathematics at the elementary and secondary levels.

Early arithmetic Arithmetic, the only mathematical study of importance in the secondary schools of the United States during the colonial period, made its entrance into the curriculum of the Latin grammar school through the early writing school. Later, in the eighteenth century, we find a tendency toward more general recognition of the value of arithmetic as a school subject. This was due partially to the rise of commercial interests and also to the tendency of the people to be more hospitable toward a subject not supported by tradition.[1] The subject matter of the course was logical in arrangement and consisted primarily of a series of rules to be memorized and dogmatically applied according to rather definite classifications. No attempt was made to adapt the instruction to the pupil, and very little change was made in the nature or content of the subject matter. Under such a system of instruction, the only arithmetic studied was ciphering, which consisted largely of the manipulation of integers.

Textbooks were not generally used until the latter part of the eighteenth century. The master dictated the problems to be solved and stated the rule or rules to be used. No special directions or explanations were given. The rules and problems were recorded in cipher books. In describing two such books used in the study of arithmetic in the state of Illinois between 1804 and 1808, Breslich states that the subject taught was but little more than a mechanical manipulation of figures and a study of rules dogmatically applied.[2]

[1]Elmer E. Brown, "The Making of Our Middle Schools" (New York: Longmans, Green & Co., Inc., 1902), p. 134.

[2]E. R. Breslich, Arithmetic One Hundred Years Ago, *Elementary School Journal*, **25** (1924–1925), 664–674.

By the methods of colonial times each problem was solved as being one of a certain type or as belonging to a particular case, and few pupils were able to solve a problem unless they knew under which case it came. This system and these methods of attack were applied to problems on a variety of subjects. Such an instructional program placed the emphasis almost entirely on the rote memorization of rules and paid very little attention, if any, to basic understanding of concepts and techniques or to the significant characteristics of effective reasoning.

Mental discipline The curriculum of the academy was much broader in its scope than was that of the Latin grammar school and, in general, was less dominated by college entrance requirements. An examination of the annual reports made to the Regents of the University of the State of New York reveals that many different subjects appeared in various academy curriculums during the period from 1787 to 1870; among them were arithmetic, algebra, astronomy, bookkeeping, conic sections, civil engineering, plane geometry, analytic geometry, leveling, logarithms, mapping, mensuration, navigation, nautical astronomy, statistics, surveying, and trigonometry.[3] The particular attention which was given to mathematics during this period was due in part to the possibility of practical applications but principally to the idea of mental discipline, which occupied a very prominent place in educational thought during the early years of American education and exerted a profound influence upon curriculum making and methods of teaching. The attitude prevalent in the minds of textbook writers and teachers of this period was well stated by Joseph Ray:[4]

> The object of the study of mathematics is twofold – the acquisition of useful knowledge and the cultivation and discipline of the mental powers. A parent often inquires "Why should my son study mathematics? I do not expect him to be a surveyor, an engineer, or an astronomer." Yet the parent is very desirous that his son should be able to reason correctly, and to exercise, in all his relations in life, the energies of a cultivated and disciplined mind. This is, indeed, of more value than the mere attainment of any branch of knowledge.

The more extreme views on mental discipline did not go unchallenged, especially in the Middle West. The pioneer life made it necessary for the individual to rely upon his ability to develop the natural resources of this new country, and this called for a type of education which placed more emphasis on the utilitarian values than on the disciplinary or the cultural values. Although the number of mathematical

[3]From Paul Monroe, "Principles of Secondary Education" (New York: The Macmillan Company, 1914), p. 54. By permission of The Macmillan Company, publishers.

[4]Joseph Ray, "New Elementary Algebra" (New York: American Book Company, 1848), p. iii.

subjects in the curriculum remained fairly uniform throughout the life of the academy, the nature and purpose of instruction underwent considerable change.

Foreign influences The English influence predominated in the American schools from the time of the Revolution until 1820. Many of the instructors in the American colleges and academies had received their training in England, and the majority of the texts either were English editions or were copied rather closely from English authors. Hutton's "Mathematics," Bonnycastle's "Algebra," and Playfair's "Euclid" are three of the most frequently mentioned texts of this early period.[5]

The period of French influence may be dated from the appointment of Claude Crozet, who had been trained in the École Polytechnique of Paris, as professor of mathematics at the United States Military Academy in 1817. For a period of approximately fifty years from this date texts by French authors were the most popular for general use, although they never entirely displaced the older English texts.

Contemporaneous with the influx of French mathematics was the revival of interest in elementary education under the influence of the Pestalozzian school. The first incorporation of Pestalozzian ideas in the preparation of an arithmetic text was in Warren Colburn's "Intellectual Arithmetic upon the Inductive Method of Instruction," otherwise known as the "First Lessons."[6] This text, published first in 1821, marked the beginning of a new epoch in arithmetic and the teaching of arithmetic. The pupil was now supposed to replace the studying and memorizing of rules that he did not always fully understand with the setting up of his own rules as generalizations of his actual experiences. He was introduced to new topics by means of practical problems and questions, the order of presentation always being from the concrete to the abstract.[7] Colburn published a more advanced book in 1822 as a "sequel" to his "First Lessons." This text was designed as a practical arithmetic to be studied after the more elementary text. It consisted of topics usually found in the earlier advanced arithmetics except for certain omissions—in particular, the rule of three, rule of position, and powers and roots. The method of presentation was the same in the two texts.[8]

The period from 1821 to 1857 was one of rapid development for the study of arithmetic. One hundred ninety-five texts on the subject were published during that time; of that number, forty-six were designed for

[5]F. Cajori, "The Teaching and History of Mathematics in the United States" (Washington, D.C.: Government Printing Office, 1890), pp. 55–56.

[6]*Ibid.*, p. 106.

[7]Walter S. Monroe, "Development of Arithmetic as a School Subject" (U.S. Office of Education Bulletin 10, 1917), pp. 63–70, 80–88.

[8]Walter S. Monroe, Analysis of Colburn's Arithmetics, *Elementary School Teacher*, **13** (1912–1913), 239–246.

use in colleges and academies and four were direct translations from the French.[9] During the period from 1860 to 1892 there was no essential change in aim or content, and there were few modifications in the methods of teaching.[10] In contrast with the previous period, however, there was significant change in the organization and presentation of subject matter. The arithmetics of the latter period were combinations of the old, as found in colonial arithmetics, and the new, as found in the works of Colburn. The old arithmetics generally rejected reasoning; Colburn's arithmetics rejected rules and encouraged reasoning; the texts of the period 1860 to 1892 gave rules but at the same time gave demonstrations and encouraged pupils to think.

The Pestalozzian influence for reform in content selection and instructional technique was felt in algebra and geometry as well as in arithmetic. Colburn, who published his "Introduction to Algebra upon the Inductive Method of Instruction" in 1832, advanced new ideas on methods of instruction in algebra. His idea was to make the transition from arithmetic to algebra as gradual as possible. Because the learner was expected to derive most knowledge from solving the problems himself, the explanations were made as brief as was consistent with giving what was required. The problems were designed to exercise the learner in reasoning instead of making him a mere listener.[11] Geometry, before the nineteenth century, was taught dogmatically, and the students merely memorized and worked by rule. Although there still remain traces of the dogmatic method of instruction, during the first half of the twentieth century there was a definite increase in emphasis on original exercises with less rote memorization of theorems. In still more recent years this new trend toward greater geometric understanding has been augmented by a marked emphasis on more careful and specific attention to the postulational structure of geometry, more intelligent recognition of the relative educational values of both three-dimensional and two-dimensional geometry, and more thoughtful evaluation of the relative significance and effectiveness of the synthetic and analytic techniques of geometric proof.

The public high school By 1860 the educational philosophy which was to shape the program of the public high school had begun to predominate over that which had fostered both the Latin grammar school and the academy. There was now a strong tendency toward expansion

[9]J. M. Greenwood, "American Textbooks on Arithmetic," *Annual Report of the Commissioner of Education* (Washington, D.C.: Government Printing Office, 1897–1898), vol. I, pp. 796–868.

[10]Walter S. Monroe, "Development of Arithmetic as a School Subject," p. 90.

[11]H. G. Meserve, Mathematics One Hundred Years Ago, *Mathematics Teacher,* **21** (1928), 339.

in both number and content of courses offered, as well as an attempt to blend intellectual and practical training in the same school. Curriculums were organized and expanded rapidly with no particular plan or definite educational objective in view. By 1890 this unrest had reached its highest point.[12] This awkward and unsystematic expansion of the curriculum offered sufficient reason for a demand for reform, and mathematics received its share of the attack. Dissatisfaction arose from several sources relative to the results achieved in the teaching of secondary mathematics. Complaints came from the teachers of mathematics themselves that the subject was not being grasped by the pupils. A study of a large number of representative high schools revealed that the largest percentages of failures were in Latin and mathematics.[13] College faculties were not hesitant in letting it be known that students entered their freshman classes with poor mathematical training. Businessmen were doubtful of the opportunity for the application of high school mathematics, as taught, to problems of everyday life.

The Committee of Ten The Committee of Ten on Secondary School Subjects agreed that a radical change in the teaching of mathematics was necessary. The Subcommittee on Mathematics recommended that a course in concrete geometry, with numerous exercises, be introduced into the grammar school and that systematic algebra should be begun at the age of fourteen. The committee suggested that demonstrative geometry should follow the first year of algebra, that it should be taught along with algebra for the next two years, and that work in solid geometry might be incorporated. Formal algebra was to be studied for 5 hours a week during the first year and for 2½ hours a week for the two following years, during which time it was to parallel work in geometry. Special emphasis was to be placed on literal as well as numerical coefficients. The committee also suggested that those who did not expect to go to college might, after the first year of algebra, turn to bookkeeping and the technical parts of arithmetic, while boys planning to attend scientific schools might profitably spend a year on trigonometry and some more advanced topics of algebra. A hope was expressed by the committee that a place might be found in the high school or college course for at least the essentials of modern synthetic or projective geometry.[14]

[12] I. L. Kandel, "History of Secondary Education" (Boston: Houghton Mifflin Company, 1930), p. 461.

[13] F. P. O'Brien, "The High School Failures," *Contributions to Education* 102 (New York: Bureau of Publications, Teachers College, Columbia University, 1919), p. 21.

[14] "Report of the Committee of Ten on Secondary School Subjects" (New York: American Book Company, 1894), pp. 105–116.

The Committee on College Entrance Requirements In order to bring about a better articulation between the secondary schools and colleges, the Committee on College Entrance Requirements in 1899 recommended the following course:

> Seventh Grade: Concrete Geometry and Introduction to Algebra; Eighth Grade: Introduction to Demonstrative Geometry and Algebra; Ninth and Tenth Grades: Algebra and Plane Geometry; Eleventh Grade: Solid Geometry and Plane Trigonometry; Twelfth Grade: Advanced Algebra and Mathematics reviewed.

Algebra for the seventh and eighth grades was to begin with literal arithmetic, which was to be followed by simple polynomials and fractional expressions, equations of the first degree with numerical coefficients in one and two unknowns, the four fundamental operations for rational algebraic expressions, and simple factoring. One-half of the time of the seventh grade was to be devoted to concrete geometry, while in the eighth grade one-half of the time was to be spent on demonstrative geometry. The important objective of such work was to awaken an interest in demonstrative geometry. The committee recommended that an equal amount of time be devoted to algebra and geometry in the ninth and tenth grades.[15]

The International Commission Another influence for change in the curriculum of secondary mathematics was due to the reports of the International Commission on the Teaching of Mathematics, which were published by the United States Bureau of Education between the years 1911 and 1918. Committee III of the commission, in its study of "Mathematics in the Public General Secondary Schools of the United States," found that every high school offered algebra and geometry for at least one year each. One-half of the schools gave algebra for an extra half year, and less than twenty per cent gave algebra for the full two years. There were very few schools that offered algebra for two and one-half years, and only the larger high schools had courses in solid geometry, plane trigonometry, and advanced algebra.[16]

The sequence in practically all the textbooks in geometry was that of Legendre. Geometrical constructions by the Euclidean method[17] were

[15]A. F. Nightingale, "Report of the Committee on College Entrance Requirements," *Proceedings and Addresses of National Education Association*, 38th Annual Meeting, 1899, pp. 648–651.

[16]Report of Committees III and IV of the International Commission, "Mathematics in the Public and Private Secondary Schools of the United States" (U.S. Office of Education Bulletin 16, 1911), pp. 17–22.

[17]The first three postulates stated by Euclid in his famous "Elements" are: "Let it be granted,

"*a.* That a straight line may be drawn from any one point to any other point:

"*b.* That a terminated straight line may be produced to any length in a straight line:

usually given a logical place among other propositions. The original exercises, which ranged from 600 in one text to 1,200 in another, were rigidly confined to the subject matter of the text.

In addition to subjects usually recognized as secondary school subjects, several high schools offered a course in commercial arithmetic similar to the course frequently given in the elementary school except that the problems were somewhat more difficult and more closely related to commercial life.[18]

In their analysis of the report of Committees III and IV, the American Commissioners of the International Commission found[19] the following very marked tendencies for change in curriculum and method:

1. To omit geometric proofs that are either obvious or too difficult
2. To transfer the more difficult portions of the algebraic matter hitherto given in the first year of the high school to a later year
3. To avoid algebraic manipulations of greater complexity than is requisite to prepare pupils thoroughly for the work that lies beyond
4. To give more prominence to the equation
5. To introduce more problems from physics and other sciences and from practical life
6. To modify the conception of the aim of the teaching to conform to what is understood to be the outcome of recent psychologic research concerning the value of "formal discipline"
7. To attach greater importance to the utilitarian possibilities of mathematics

After their general survey of the field of secondary mathematics, the commission felt[20] that there were two main needs which were dominant, namely,

> The need for the better preparation of teachers and the need to reduce, if not eliminate, the waste of effort involved in independent and often inadequate treatment of fundamental and broad questions by separate schools, colleges, or local systems.

In their study of elementary mathematics in the college the commission found that calculus had become primarily a sophomore study and

---

"*c*. And that a circle may be described from any centre, at any distance from that centre."

The first two of these postulates enable us to draw a straight line, but not lines of a prescribed length except insofar as a line might be drawn to connect two given points. In other words, these two postulates permit all operations possible with an unmarked straightedge. The third postulate allows the use of the compass for the drawing of a circle with a given center and passing through a given point, i.e., with a fixed radius.

Thus "geometrical constructions by the Euclidean method" are those constructions which can be performed by using only the unmarked straightedge and compass.

For further discussion see Richard Courant and Herbert Robbins: "What Is Mathematics?" (Fair Lawn, N.J.: Oxford University Press, 1941), pp. 117–140.

[18]Report of Committees III and IV of the International Commission, *op. cit.*, p. 22.

[19]"Report of the American Commissioners of the International Commission on the Teaching of Mathematics" (U.S. Office of Education Bulletin 14, 1912), pp. 29–31.

[20]*Ibid.*, pp. 39–40.

that it was serving somewhat as "a boundary line between two styles of teaching," the recitation method and the lecture or lecture-quiz method. This difference in the educational problem before and after calculus was further emphasized by the proposal, on the part of some, to relegate the first two years of college work to the high school and, on the part of others, to take care of this work in "a junior college leading to an appropriate degree." The organization of subject matter was still largely compartmentalized, but there was developing a tendency toward fusion, with more emphasis on practical applications. The general outline of material was algebra, trigonometry, analytic geometry, and calculus, with a prerequisite of elementary algebra through quadratics, plane geometry, and sometimes solid geometry. The changing complexion of the school population was recognized as a cause for readjustment of content and instructional technique in the freshman year.[21]

The National Committee of Fifteen on Geometry Syllabus

In 1908 the Mathematics Round Table of the Secondary Department of the National Education Association unanimously called for a committee to study and report upon the problem of a syllabus for geometry. During the same year the American Federation of Teachers of the Mathematical and Natural Sciences authorized the appointment of such a committee, and in 1909 the Secondary Department of the National Education Association authorized the committee to proceed as a joint committee of the association and federation.

In its report[22] the committee recommended that reasonable attention be given to concrete exercises but with no diminishing attention to the logical structure of geometry. It suggested that there be "a quickening of the logical sense" through a distribution of emphasis designed to economize on the time and energy spent in the mastery of theorems and to provide more time and opportunity for the study of geometry in its more concrete relations. It pointed out that there are some terms in geometry which it is best to accept as undefined and recommended that definitions be introduced when needed rather than massed at one place in the text or course of study. The desirability of the use of certain informal proofs was mentioned, as well as the advisability of excluding limits and incommensurables from the requirements for entrance to

[21]*Ibid.*, pp. 41–47.
Report of Committee XII of the International Commission, "Graduate Work in Mathematics in Universities and in Other Institutions of Like Grade in the United States" (U.S. Office of Education Bulletin 6, 1911), pp. 45–47.

[22]Committee of Fifteen, "Provisional Report on Geometry Syllabus," *School Science and Mathematics*, **11** (1911), 330.

college. It was recommended that between one and one and one-half years be given to plane geometry and that it be taught simultaneously with algebra or preceded by at least one year of algebra.

In the treatment of exercises the committee recommended that careful thought be given to their distribution and gradation; it seemed to feel that the tendency had been to overemphasize difficult abstract applications of various theorems in the exercises. It, therefore, suggested concrete exercises along with "a judicious selection of a reasonable number of abstract originals." Material for exercises was to be found in other subject fields, such as architecture, natural design, indirect measurement, and any other source available to the individual teacher. A great deal of emphasis was given to the nature and importance of the concept of locus.[23]

The National Committee on Mathematical Requirements In 1916 the National Committee on Mathematical Requirements was organized under the auspices of the Mathematical Association of America, Inc., "for the purpose of giving national expression to the movement for reform in the teaching of mathematics, which had gained considerable headway in various parts of the country, but which lacked the power that coordination and united effort alone could give."[24]

The committee was instructed to concern itself with making a comprehensive study of the whole problem of mathematical education on the secondary and collegiate levels. One of the major problems was thus to make proper provision for the comparatively new, yet fairly well-established, junior and senior high school programs of instruction. In its final report the aims of mathematical instruction were formulated into three general classes (practical, disciplinary, and cultural),[25] and instead of a detailed syllabus for the junior high school there was a proposal for a general outline by topics, accompanied by a statement that further experimentation was necessary before a standardized syllabus could be determined. Although the committee refused to take a definite stand on the arrangement of topics, it did suggest five plans for distribution of this material, hoping that they might prove helpful in the organization of mathematics curriculums for the junior high school. It further recommended that the mathematics proposed for the grades of the junior high school be required of all pupils.[26]

The committee recommended that provision be made for the specific aims of the mathematics of the senior high school through a body of

[23]*Ibid.*, pp. 434–460, 509–531.

[24]The National Committee on Mathematical Requirements, "The Reorganization of Mathematics in Secondary Education" (Boston: Houghton Mifflin Company, 1923), p. vii.

[25]*Ibid.*, pp. 6–13.

[26]*Ibid.*, pp. 29–42.

elective material which should be open to all pupils who had satisfactorily completed the required work of the junior high school. Fully realizing that the method of organization of this material could be more elastic in nature than that for grades 7 to 9, and also being thoroughly cognizant of the fact that no one best plan had been determined, the committee suggested four different plans, any one of which might be used for the purpose of more efficiently organizing the instructional content of the mathematics of grades 10 to 12.

Additional electives such as elementary statistics, mathematics of investment, shop mathematics, surveying and navigation, and descriptive or projective geometry were suggested for schools where there was a need for such work and where the conditions warranted their inclusion in the curriculum. It was also recommended that extensive use be made of historical and biographical material in the entire teaching program to lend interest and significance to the subject matter studied.[27]

Integrated courses The arrangement of subject matter has always been a problem at least as difficult as its selection. The early tendency was simply to follow the compartment system of organization, and that has continued to be the familiar pattern of the traditional high school course. However, during the twentieth century there has been increasing significance in the attention and effort directed toward the integration of related subject matter. The initial impetus in shaping the underlying philosophy of this new pattern of instruction in mathematics can be traced largely to the efforts of the Committee of Ten and the Committee on College Entrance Requirements during the latter part of the nineteenth century. Although there had been a few scattered instances of such treatment of mathematical subject matter prior to that time, the reports of the two committees seem to carry the first evidence of any concentrated thought devoted to its consideration. In an address before the National Education Association (1902), Newhall expressed the hope that a time would come when the secondary school course would comprise six years and mathematics would not be limited by artificial boundaries, as was the case in the study of algebra, geometry, and trigonometry.[28] Contemporaneous with this address, the influence of Klein in Germany, Tannery and Borel in France, Perry and Nunn in England, and Moore in America made the conditions more favorable for a fairly rapid growth of more general interest in the integration of instructional materials in mathematics.

[27]*Ibid.*, pp. 48–57.

[28]Charles W. Newhall, Correlation of Mathematical Studies in Secondary Schools, *Proceedings of the National Education Association* (1902), pp. 488–492.

However, the effort to present the mathematics of even the junior high school in a fused course has not been without its rather severe critics. There are those who feel that it is too much of a hodgepodge of superficialities that tends to general weakening of the subject content. Some critics have felt that too much emphasis is given to fusion of subject matter and not enough attention is paid to the significance of the individuality of different topics. Nevertheless, the fact that two of the fundamental services of the junior high school have been to provide for exploration and for contact with minimum essentials has helped to concentrate interest in integrated mathematics courses in its curriculum.

The effort to evolve a functional mathematical program well adapted to the education of the masses has also brought about significant changes in the content and instructional techniques of senior high school mathematics. The mathematical content for the later years of secondary instruction is more specialized in nature than that of the three previous years and, as a consequence, has not been so readily adapted to a fused method of organization. One of the most difficult of the problems which confront the teachers of senior high school mathematics is that of so organizing and presenting subject content as to preserve its intrinsic characteristics and yet to introduce the desired continuity.

In recent years there has been a great deal of experimentation in the use of different types of instructional materials arranged in varying course patterns by such groups as the School Mathematics Study Group (SMSG), the University of Maryland Mathematics Project (UMMP), the University of Illinois Committee on School Mathematics (UICSM), the Ball State Teachers College Experimental Program, the Boston College Mathematics Institute, the Developmental Program in Secondary Mathematics at Southern Illinois University, the Syracuse University Madison Project, and the Greater Cleveland Mathematics Program (GCMP). This effort has resulted not only in the introduction of new material but also in an emphasis on integrated organization and treatment of subject matter at both the junior and senior high school levels of instruction.

In the development of the mathematics curriculum of the junior college there are definite indications of a trend toward a more integrated pattern of content organization in these first two years of the college program. The best evidence of the truth of this statement is to be found in the many different types of integrated texts now in use, in particular, texts on "Unified Algebra and Trigonometry" and "Analytic Geometry and Calculus," and also in the recommendations of the Committee on the Undergraduate Program in Mathematics (CUPM) of the Mathematical Association of America.[29] Many teachers feel that students taking such courses get a deeper appreciation of the fundamental interrelationships of mathematical material and consequently have a better idea of the real meaning of mathematics than do those who take the traditional compartmentalized type of course. They also claim that such a student will attain just as satisfactory a degree of mastery of the fundamentals, if not a better one.

College Entrance Examination Board The problem of the curriculum of secondary mathematics has always been closely related to the question of college entrance requirements. The entire program of the Latin grammar school was defined in terms of preparation for college. The academy, however, early expanded its program to include not only preparation for college but also a terminal type of program for the non-college-bound pupil. In meeting the demands of this new function of secondary education, the academy gradually encroached upon the educational program of the colleges. The natural consequence of this was a material increase in college entrance requirements.

At the close of the eighteenth century the only mathematics required for admission to college was "a knowledge of the rules and processes of vulgar arithmetic." The statutes of 1807 prescribed that the requirements for admission to Harvard should include the rules of arithmetic dealing with simple and compound notation, addition, subtraction, multiplication, division, reduction, and the single rule of three. In 1820 these requirements were extended to include the algebra of simple equations, roots and powers, and arithmetical and geometrical progressions. Columbia added algebra to her entrance requirements in 1821; Yale, in 1847; and Princeton, in 1848. In 1844, candidates for admission to Harvard College were examined in arithmetic, algebra, and geometry (up to the book on proportion). Geometry was made an entrance requirement at Yale in 1865; at Princeton, Michigan, and Cornell in 1868; and at Columbia in 1870. By 1870 the admission requirements at Harvard had been extended to include higher arithmetic, algebra through quadratic equations, logarithms, and the elements of plane geometry. Yale and Princeton specified only to quadratic equations in algebra. While Yale specified the first two books of Playfair's "Euclid" (or an acceptable equivalent), Princeton specified only the first book. Similar requirements existed at the other leading universities of that period.[30]

[29]Report of the Committee on the Undergraduate Program in Mathematics, *American Mathematical Monthly*, **63** (1955), 511–520. Also see subsequent reports and bulletins distributed through the central office of the committee, P.O. Box 1024, Berkeley, Calif.

[30]E. C. Broome, "A Historical and Critical Discussion of College Admission Requirements" (New York: The Macmillan Company, 1903), pp. 41–53.

The National Committee on Mathematical Requirements in its 1923 report recognized the far-reaching influence of college entrance requirements upon the teaching of secondary mathematics. It criticized the prevailing type of examination as overemphasizing "the candidate's skill in formal manipulation." In an effort to make desirable modifications in the prevailing type of college entrance examination, members of the national committee met with members of a committee from the College Entrance Examination Board and drew up a list of recommendations which were incorporated in the 1923 report. While attention was paid to the problem of reducing the excessive "difficulty and complexity of the formal manipulative questions," two of the most significant recommendations were as follows:[31]

1. An effort should be made to devise [algebraic] questions which will fairly test the candidate's understanding of principles and his ability to apply them, while involving a minimum of manipulative complexity.
2. The examinations in geometry should be definitely constructed to test the candidate's ability to draw valid conclusions rather than his ability to memorize an argument.

Early in 1921 the College Entrance Examination Board appointed a commission to study the problem of college entrance requirements and make recommendations for desirable revisions in the definitions of requirements in elementary mathematics. In their reports[32] published in 1923 the commission eliminated from the list of requirements in algebra the extended and useless manipulation of polynomials, reduced factoring to three types, and simplified the requirements in fractions. Increased recognition was given to the formula and the graph, and two notable changes were made in the simplification of the material dealing with surds and in the introduction of numerical trigonometry. For plane geometry only eighty-nine theorems were included in the syllabus, and of these only thirty-one were starred to be used for purposes of proofs. In the case of the unstarred propositions the candidate was expected to be familiar with content so that he might answer questions related to substance or use the propositions in solving originals. Similar provisions were made for solid geometry. A new type of examination was one designed to take care of a one-year course in plane and solid geometry. The committee made the effort to reorganize the examination material in such a way that the demands on the candidate's memory would be lightened and increased opportunity for the development of geometrical understanding would be given. These examinations functioned to set up more definite goals of instruction as well as pro-

[31]The National Committee on Mathematical Requirements, *op. cit.*, pp. 76–77.
[32]College Entrance Examination Board, *Documents* 107 and 108 (New York: College Entrance Examination Board, 1923).

vided a principal pattern of textbook construction. The work of the board has helped to clarify the problem of entrance requirements and provide for better articulation between the work of the senior high school and that of the freshman year of college.

In 1935 the Commission on Examinations in Mathematics, a commission of the College Entrance Examination Board, completely revised the examinations in mathematics. In the new ones, known as alpha, beta, and gamma, the effort was made "to combine the advantages of the longer essay-type, multiple-step question with those of the single-step question."[33] Two of the significant differences between the new and the old form of entrance examinations were the increased objectivity in scoring and the reduced emphasis upon the traditional compartmentalized treatment of subject matter.

The commission postulated that "the examinations should be such as to determine: (*a*) the candidate's understanding and appreciation of the fundamental principles and characteristic modes of approach of mathematics; (*b*) his technical equipment and his knowledge of mathematical facts."[34] Furthermore, in recognition of the different interpretations of the meaning of "fitness for college," the commission attempted to provide examinations for the three following groups:[34]

(α) Those who are not ready to carry on in college the study of mathematics or natural science, but who base their claim to be admitted to college in part upon the study of mathematics in the secondary schools
(β) Those who intend to fulfill at least the minimum college requirement in mathematics or natural science
(γ) Those who look forward to more advanced undergraduate work in mathematics and science

In presenting these new examinations the commission stated that while, in specifying the scope of the examinations, it desired to exercise sufficient definiteness to avoid uncertainty on the part of the teacher, it was "strongly influenced by the wish to leave teachers of mathematics in secondary schools free to guide the development of their pupils in such ways as seem to them most desirable."[35]

Soon after the introduction of these examinations there began to develop a rather general demand from schools that there be provided an examination suitable for candidates whose first two years had been devoted primarily to the study of algebra. In response to this demand

[33]College Entrance Examination Board, "Description of Examination Subjects" (New York: College Entrance Examination Board, 1940), pp. 34–37. An earlier draft of this document, later edited, was published in *Mathematics Teacher*, **28** (1935), 154–166.

[34]*Ibid.*

[35]*Ibid.*

the Committee of Examiners in Mathematics of the College Entrance Examination Board introduced in June, 1942, Mathematics 2*A* (Alternative Alpha).

After the discontinuance in 1943 of the alpha, beta, and gamma tests, the board went through five distinct but unsatisfactory phases of testing. Each phase represented a definite effort to work out a satisfactory combined use of the Scholastic Aptitude Test and various types of achievement tests in mathematics. The final plan, which was put into use in 1950, called for two distinct phases: (1) the Scholastic Aptitude Test, taken by mathematics candidates along with all candidates during the morning session, and (2) two 1-hour achievement tests in mathematics (Intermediate Mathematics and Advanced Mathematics) in the afternoon.

In 1955 the board assumed the responsibility for continuing the work on the Advanced Placement Program, which originated in 1952 in the School and College Study of Admission with Advanced Standing, a project sponsored by the Fund for the Advancement of Education. The first administration of the program was held in May, 1956, and the program has since continued to be administered yearly by the Educational Testing Service. Advanced placement is defined[36] by the board to mean:

(1) Exemption from prescribed courses and placement in an advanced college course instead of in an elementary course which would otherwise have been required, or
(2) the award of college credit in recognition of achievement in covering the work ordinarily required in a course of college level, or
(3) both advanced placement and college credit.

In 1955 another important action was taken by the board in the interest of improved instruction in mathematics. The Commission on Mathematics[37] was appointed

> . . . (1) to study the present secondary school mathematics curriculum with a view toward the recommendation of a realignment of the entire secondary mathematics program to provide adequate preparation for the study of present-day college and advanced mathematics; and (2) . . . to investigate the Board's activities in the testing of mathematics and to recommend any possible improvement therein.

Believing that "the improvement of secondary school mathematics instruction . . . would be greatly facilitated and the colleges in nowise

[36]College Entrance Examination Board, "Fifty-third Annual Report of the Director" (New York: College Entrance Examination Board, 1955), p. 20.

[37]College Entrance Examination Board, "Fifty-fifth Annual Report of the Director" (New York: College Entrance Examination Board, 1957), p. 10. The report of the commission was published in April, 1959.

handicapped," the commission strongly recommended that the traditional requirements in elementary algebra, intermediate algebra, advanced algebra, plane and solid geometry, and trigonometry be replaced by a new formulation of entrance requirements in mathematics. The new program would designate the new requirements in terms of length of time spent in study. The titles suggested for courses to be given in four successive high school years were Elementary Mathematics I, Elementary Mathematics II, Intermediate Mathematics, and Advanced Mathematics. The group then proceeded to define in rather specific detail the subject-matter content of each year's program,[38] and in order to help implement the recommendations for revised and renewed emphases in the content of instruction, a separate volume of appendixes was published concurrent with the report.

The commission, recognizing the need for a "context of reference" for the proper interpretation of its recommendations, closed its report with the following brief summary[39] of all the commission's recommendations:

> College preparatory mathematics should include topics selected from algebra, geometry (demonstrative and coordinate), and trigonometry—all broadly interpreted. The point of view should be in harmony with contemporary mathematical thought; emphasis should be placed upon basic concepts and skills and upon the principles of deductive reasoning regardless of the branch of mathematics from which the topic is chosen. In every case, the standard of substance and content should be commensurate with that of the courses outlined in Chapter 4 [on pages 20–47]. Courses designed for other purposes (e.g., consumer mathematics, business mathematics, shop mathematics) are not acceptable.

The commission did not overlook the importance of the well-prepared teacher; a considerable portion of the report is devoted to the discussion of both preservice and in-service training of both elementary school and secondary school teachers of mathematics.[40]

In the light of these and other impending recommendations for change in the college and high school mathematics programs the Educational Testing Service, in the spring of 1958, began initial planning for a new series of end-of-course Cooperative Mathematics Tests.[41] These plans culminated in the 1962 announcement of "new-course-oriented achievement tests in arithmetic (grades 7, 8, and 9), elementary algebra, intermediate algebra, and high school geometry."[42]

[38]"Report of Commission on Mathematics" (New York: College Entrance Examination Board, 1959), pp. 20–47.

[39]*Ibid.*, pp. 60–61.

[40]*Ibid.*, pp. 48–58.

[41]Sheldon S. Myers, Cooperative Mathematics Tests: A Progress Report, *American Mathematical Monthly*, **69** (1962), 223–225.

[42]New Cooperative Mathematics Tests, *American Mathematical Monthly*, **69** (1962), 917.

National organizations No discussion of the forces that have had significant influence in the evolution of the program in secondary mathematics would be complete without mention of the Mathematical Association of America, the National Council of Teachers of Mathematics, and the Central Association of Science and Mathematics Teachers.

The Mathematical Association of America. This group was organized at Columbus, Ohio, in December, 1915, and incorporated under the laws of the state of Illinois on September 8, 1920. In the interest of improved instruction in collegiate mathematics the association has sponsored the following:

1. The publication of the *American Mathematical Monthly,* a high-grade mathematical magazine devoted to the interests of collegiate mathematics.
2. The organization of a large number of sections in which papers in mathematical research are presented and instructional problems in collegiate mathematics are discussed.
3. The organization of many undergraduate clubs in colleges and universities. These clubs have been very effective in motivating interest in mathematics.
4. The appointment of many committees for the study of problems related to the content and methods of mathematical instruction and the better training of teachers of mathematics. Some of the committees have been independent committees of the association; others have been joint committees with representation from other interested groups.

Each year, in addition to the sectional meetings, the association holds two regular national meetings at which papers are read and instructional problems are discussed. Further evidences of the interest of the association in the promotion of mathematics are (1) annual subsidies paid to journals that are interested in the publication of mathematical research, (2) the publication in December, 1929, of the Rhind Mathematical Papyrus, (3) the publication of the *Carus Monograph Series,* (4) the awarding of the $100 Chauvenet Prize, the purpose of which is to stimulate expository contributions in mathematical journals, (5) the sponsoring of various committee studies of secondary school and college mathematics programs, (6) the sponsoring of competitive tests at the college and high school levels, and (7) the promotion, under grants from the National Science Foundation, of two programs of visiting lectures, one at the college level and one at the high school level.

The National Council of Teachers of Mathematics. This group was organized at Cleveland, Ohio, on February 24, 1920, and incorporated under the Illinois laws on April 28, 1928. The purpose of the council is to promote interest in mathematics, especially in the elementary and secondary fields, by the following means:[43]

[43]Frank B. Allen, The Council's Drive to Improve School Mathematics, *Mathematics Teacher,* **56** (1963), 386–393; *Arithmetic Teacher,* **10** (1963), 368–375.

1. The holding of meetings for presentation and discussion of papers. The annual meeting is usually held during the month of April. During the summer a meeting is held in conjunction with the National Education Association, of which the council, while retaining its identity and independent status, became a department on July 8, 1950. Occasional meetings are held during the Christmas season in conjunction with the American Association for the Advancement of Science. Also, through its policy of cosponsored meetings there are regional meetings held in conjunction with sponsoring affiliated groups.

2. The publication of three journals and of books, pamphlets, monographs, and reports for the purpose of vitalizing and coordinating the work of local organizations of teachers of mathematics and of bringing the interests of mathematics to the attention and consideration of the educational world. There are two official journals: the *Mathematics Teacher,* the only magazine in the United States whose interests are devoted entirely to the improvement of instruction in mathematics at the secondary level, and the *Arithmetic Teacher,* the only magazine in the United States whose interests are devoted entirely to the improvement of instruction in arithmetic. The council also publishes the *Mathematics Student Journal,* which provides enrichment and recreational material for pupils in grades 7 to 12. A further significant contribution to the literature of better instruction in mathematics is the *Yearbook,* published at intervals since 1926 by the council, which is devoted to the discussion of important aspects of the teaching of elementary and secondary mathematics. There is a continuing Yearbook Planning Committee which gives a great deal of thought to the planning of the yearbook program.

A new venture in the interest of mathematics and its place in the modern educational program is the series of supplementary publications. The purpose of this series of publications is to enrich the instructional background of the teacher of elementary and secondary mathematics and to provide supplementary instructional aids and enrichment materials for students.

3. The promotion of the affiliation of local organizations of teachers of mathematics with the council and of close cooperation with other professional organizations. Recently the council has become somewhat international in nature through such affiliation with groups from certain provinces of Canada.

4. The promotion of investigations for the purpose of improving the teaching of elementary school and secondary school mathematics.

The Central Association of Science and Mathematics Teachers. Although it is a sectional organization, this group has exerted a national influence over the teaching of secondary school mathematics. The Central Association was organized in April, 1903, and incorporated in July, 1928. Since its organization, it has sponsored a very active program in the interest of improved teaching of science and mathematics in the secondary schools of our nation. Its program has been carried forward through annual meetings and the publication of *School Science and Mathematics,* "a journal for all science and mathematics teachers." The annual meetings, held during the Thanksgiving holiday season, are characterized by programs which are inspirational and informative as well as pedagogical in nature.

In this connection there should be mentioned also the *Mathematics Magazine,* published in Los Angeles, California. This magazine devotes a portion of each issue to The Teaching of Mathematics, a section in which are discussed teaching problems as they are primarily related to the junior college.

The Joint Commission to Study the Place of Mathematics in Secondary Education In the fall of 1933 a Commission to Study the Place of Mathematics in Secondary Education was appointed by the Mathematical Association of America; later this commission was incorporated into a Joint Commission of the Mathematical Association and the National Council of Teachers of Mathematics. In its final report[44] the commission undertook to define the place of mathematics in the modern educational program and then organize a mathematical curriculum for grades 7 to 14 (secondary education was defined to include the junior college) in terms of the major mathematical fields which would provide for continuity of development and flexibility of administration.[45]

> It is the opinion of this Commission that the obvious difficulty of providing for both continuity and flexibility has been the great stumbling block in the development of a nation-wide mathematical program of instruction. Accordingly, in this Report is described a program for mathematics in grades 7 to 14 that definitely aims to provide for continuity of development, and that at the same time respects the reasonable demands for flexibility on the part of school administrators and teachers.

The proposed program was based upon an assumed "normal mathematical equipment of the American pupil who has satisfactorily completed the work of the sixth grade," which was defined[46] as follows:

1. A familiarity with the basic concepts, the processes, and the vocabulary of arithmetic

[44]Joint Commission of the Mathematical Association of America, Inc., and the National Council of Teachers of Mathematics, "The Place of Mathematics in Secondary Education," *Fifteenth Yearbook* (Washington, D.C.: National Council of Teachers of Mathematics, 1940). (Hereafter referred to as the Joint Commission.)

[45]*Ibid.*, p. 53.

[46]*Ibid.*, p. 54.

2. Understanding of the significance of the different positions that a given digit may occupy in a number, including the case of a decimal fraction
3. A mastery of the basic number combinations in addition, subtraction, multiplication, and division
4. Reasonable skill in computing with integers, common fractions, and decimal fractions
5. An acquaintance with the principal units of measurement, and their use in every day life situations
6. The ability to solve simple problems involving computation and units of measurement
7. The ability to recognize, to name, and to sketch such common geometric figures as the rectangle, the square, the circle, the triangle, the rectangular solid, the sphere, the cylinder, and the cube
8. The habit of estimating and checking results

In recognition of existing differences in educational philosophies and practices and in an effort to make "a definite step toward educational harmony," the commission set up a tentative list of guiding principles to be followed in organizing the mathematical program for grades 7 to 12.

In the light of these principles two classifications of the materials of mathematical instruction were made.[47]

1. *The subdivision according to major subject fields*
   - I. The field of numbers and computation
   - II. The field of geometric form and space perception
   - III. The field of graphic representation
   - IV. The field of elementary analysis
   - V. The field of logical (or "straight") thinking
   - VI. The field of relational thinking
   - VII. The field of symbolic representation and thinking
2. *The subdivision according to certain broad categories enumerated as follows:*
   - I. Basic concepts, principles, and terms
   - II. Fundamental processes
   - III. Fundamental relations
   - IV. Skills and techniques
   - V. Applications

In Chapters V and VI of the report the commission proposes and discusses in considerable detail two alternative curriculum plans. The two differ somewhat in detail and emphasis, but both give recognition to the guiding principles enumerated and are consonant with the foregoing dual classification of subject matter. For one of these plans a grade placement chart displays a suggested allocation and organization of the subject matter in each year for grades 7 to 12.[48]

[47]*Ibid.*, p. 61.
[48]*Ibid.*, pp. 72–119, 246–251.

The report contains suggestions for modification of the program to give flexibility to the curriculum, and it also contains a discussion of the problems of both retardation and acceleration in their bearing upon the program of mathematical instruction. In this connection there is presented a second grade placement chart, which gives a proposed selection and grade allocation of subject matter for slow students in grades 7 to 9.[49]

In the discussion of the mathematics program for grades 13 and 14 (the junior college) the commission points out that the preparatory type of student is in the minority and that the mathematical needs of this type of student are adequately provided for in the traditional courses. Accordingly, the discussion deals mainly with the problem of providing for the terminal type of student. Two programs, somewhat different in nature, are proposed as possible terminal courses for students who do not plan to pursue the study of mathematics further. These courses are based on the commission's belief that the junior college curriculum should make provision for a mathematical course of at least one year in extent for all students.

The commission emphasized that in no sense was this recommended program of mathematical instruction to be regarded "as a final unchanging yardstick inhibiting personal initiative and further experimentation." The intention was, rather, that it might prove to be a step forward in securing "for mathematics the place in education it so richly deserves" and a safe standard for comparison in the program of curriculum experimentation and change.

The Progressive Education Association Committee on the Function of Mathematics in General Education In 1932 the Executive Board of the Progressive Education Association established the Commission on Secondary School Curriculum. This commission subsequently established several committees to explore the respective contributions of various subject fields to general education at the secondary level; among them was the Committee on the Function of Mathematics in General Education. The complete report of this committee was issued in tentative (mimeographed) form in 1938 and published in final form in 1940.[50]

The report is in four parts. The first of these presents the educational philosophy which guided the committee in the formulation of the

[49]*Ibid.*, pp. 120–148, 252–253.

[50]Maurice Hartung and others, Commission on Secondary School Curriculum of the Progressive Education Association, "Mathematics in General Education," *Report of the Committee on the Function of Mathematics in General Education* (New York: Appleton-Century-Crofts, Inc., 1940).

report. Central in this philosophy is the premise that mathematics, in order to justify its place in the secondary school curriculum, must contribute to the satisfaction of the needs of the students. These needs are enumerated in terms of the following four "basic aspects of living":[51]

1. Personal living
2. Immediate personal-social relationships
3. Social-civic relationships
4. Economic relationships

This part of the report closes with a discussion of the role of mathematics in satisfying the needs of people with respect to these four aspects of living.

Part II is the most extensive section of the report. It consists of an elaborate discussion of certain broad concepts or understandings which find application in problem solving, whether this be in situations that are peculiarly mathematical or not. In the discussion of these concepts an effort is made to show applications to situations encountered in ordinary living as well as to strictly mathematical situations. In other words, much emphasis is placed upon the *generality* of the concepts and upon various broad aspects involved in their understanding. Separate chapters are devoted to the consideration of the following major concepts:

Formulation and solution
Data
Approximation
Function
Operations
Proof
Symbolism

Part III is concerned with an explanation of the nature and development of mathematics.

Part IV considers the problem of understanding the student and stresses the need for considering not only overt behavior but also the various influences which have operated to shape the student's personality. It contains a section on implications for teaching. The report closes with a chapter on the evaluation of student achievement. This chapter discusses the purposes of evaluation and contains some interesting suggestions of new and unique means and devices for organizing an evaluation program in terms of instructional objectives previously set up.

This report confines itself mainly to the discussion of a program of mathematical education in terms of broad outlines and general principles and does not attempt to set forth any detailed organization of subject matter. It recognizes frankly that the formulation of a series of courses based upon the report's proposals would require years of

[51] *Ibid.*, p. 20

experimentation and that such experimentation would probably eventually modify some of the suggestions made. It looks to the future instead of trying to set up a practical program for the immediate present.[52]

It is with respect to this point that the task undertaken by this Committee differed from that of the Joint Commission of the Mathematical Association of America and the National Council of Teachers of Mathematics. In preparing its report of *The Place of Mathematics in Secondary Education*, the Joint Commission, after discussing the general aims of education, sought to outline a program of the sort being offered at the moment by some schools in advance of the great majority. Most of its suggestions have been tested to some extent in practice, and the Joint Commission took a practical rather than experimental point of view.

The AAAS Co-operative Committee on the Teaching of Science and Mathematics Concomitant with the great increase in size in the program of secondary education in the United States during the last three centuries there has been a vast expansion of purpose. Modern educational problems are rooted in the context of mass education, which seems to nurture extensive, and at times seemingly excessive, curriculum design. These problems will always remain complex; there is no way to simplify them. The only hope for an intelligent approach to their solution is through the cooperative effort of duly organized groups who are interested in the formulation and promotion of that program in our schools which will be most significant when evaluated in terms of the educational needs of a school population that is highly heterogeneous as to abilities, aptitudes, and interest.

An important step in this direction was made in 1941 when the representatives of several scientific societies created the Co-operative Committee on Science Teaching "to work on educational problems the solution of which can be attained better by co-operative action than by any single scientific group working alone." The Mathematical Association of America was one of the societies represented on the original committee before its reorganization, in 1944, as a committee of the American Association for the Advancement of Science (AAAS). As presently constituted, the committee consists of representatives from fourteen national scientific societies, two of which are the Mathematical Association of America and the National Council of Teachers of Mathematics.

Since its organization, the committee has given attention to the problem of the preparation of teachers of science and mathematics. In 1946

[52]*Ibid.*, p. 14.

it published its recommendations relative to this important problem in a report on The Preparation of High School Science and Mathematics Teachers, in which the following proposals were made:[53]

(1) A policy of certification in closely related subjects within the broad area of the sciences and mathematics should be established and put into practice.
(2) Approximately one-half of the prospective teacher's four-year college program should be devoted to courses in the sciences.
(3) Certificates to teach general science at the 7th-, 8th-, or 9th-grade level should be granted on the basis of not less than forty-two semester hours of college courses in the subjects covered in general science.
(4) Colleges and certification authorities should work toward a five-year program for the preparation of high-school teachers.
(5) Curriculum improvements in the small high school should go hand in hand with improvement in teacher preparation.

The committee not only has directed its attention to many other problems and projects but also has projected a rather active future program of study and service.[54] Among the most important projects undertaken was the study of the effectiveness of the teaching of science and mathematics at all levels, which served as the basis for a report incorporated as Appendix II of Volume 4 of the report on *Science and Public Policy* made by the President's Scientific Research Board.[55] In this study appraisals of the science and mathematics programs from grades 1 to 12 were made. These served as the basis for certain recommendations for improvement, among which were the following which pertained to mathematics:[56]

(1) A complete appraisal should be made of science and mathematics teaching in secondary schools. This should include a survey of curriculum offerings, student enrollments, available laboratory and demonstration equipment, methods of instruction, the workweek of the teachers, and the total preparation of teachers for their responsibilities.
(2) The secondary-school mathematics curriculum should be studied to determine the effectiveness of present offerings with regard to the general education needs of all students and the special needs of students talented in science and mathematics. New courses in mathematics should be designed wherever indicated by this study.
(3) The secondary-school science curriculum should be reorganized so as to permit . . . at least 3 years of science for students with special talents in science and mathematics. . . .

[53]Report of the AAAS Co-operative Committee on the Teaching of Science and Mathematics, The Preparation of High School Science and Mathematics Teachers, *School Science and Mathematics*, **46** (1946), 107–118.

[54]The Co-operative Committee on the Teaching of Science and Mathematics: Its Organization and Program, *Science*, **106** (July 11, 1947), 28–30.

[55]"Science and Public Policy" (Washington, D.C: President's Scientific Research Board, 1947), **4**, 47–149.

[56]*Ibid.*, pp. 93–94.

(4) . . .

(5) Studies should be made concerning the place, value, and effective use of biographical and historical materials relating to science and mathematics.

(6) Studies should be made of the various curricular and administrative arrangements employed in small and large communities to meet the needs of talented youth. Reports should be prepared to make more teachers acquainted with best practices.

(7) Studies should be made of the guidance procedures used in secondary schools. . . . Bulletins revealing effective materials and practices concerning science and mathematics should be prepared for and studied by secondary-school teachers and counselors.

(8) Studies should be made to determine the most effective ways to use demonstration, laboratory, project, shop, and field experiences and such facilities as library materials, audio-visual aids, etc., in the teaching of science and mathematics.

(9) A study should be made of the administrative devices which will encourage greater use of community resources in the teaching of science and mathematics.

(10) The work of science and mathematics supervisors, special consultants, visiting teachers, and other special advisory personnel should be studied with a view to making more prevalent the practices and techniques most effective in developing sound programs involving science and mathematics for general education, and in providing optimum opportunities for the development of students with special talents.

The report also included many very pertinent recommendations for the recruitment and training of teachers of science and mathematics in the elementary and secondary schools.[57]

In 1959 a second report on the preparation of teachers of science and mathematics was published. This report concerned itself with the problems inherent in the new curriculums and patterns of instruction in secondary schools. One of its primary concerns was with the many types of demands made on the beginning teacher. Several typical curriculums, in both science and mathematics, were outlined and presented as highly desirable basic training programs.[58]

The emergency of World War II During the past quarter of a century, there has been an increasing amount of evidence which points to the inadequacy of the mathematics program in our schools. This inadequacy became very conspicuous in the light of the deficiencies in mathematics discovered among the inductees into the war training program of World War II. To meet the emergency of the situation, the U.S. Office of Education in cooperation with the National Council of

[57]*Ibid.*, pp. 107–109.

[58]Alfred B. Garrett, Recommendations for the Preparation of High School Teachers of Science and Mathematics, *School Science and Mathematics,* **59** (1959), 181–189; Preparation of High School Science Teachers, *Science,* **131** (April 8, 1960), 1024–1029.

Teachers of Mathematics appointed two committees to give the problem careful study. The first committee worked in close cooperation with the Army, Navy, and Civil Aeronautics Administration. Its report[59] was based on a detailed analysis of approximately fifty unit courses used in the Federal-state program of Vocational Training for War Production Workers, twenty Navy training manuals, and fifty Army instructional manuals. The committee gave attention to the entire program of secondary mathematics and made specific recommendations for a Special One-year Course and a Special One-semester Course designed as an emergency refresher course for high school pupils near graduation or induction but not studying mathematics.

The report[60] of the second committee served as an extension of that of the first committee in that it was designed to supplement the earlier report "by amplifying the suggestions offered for the *lower* levels of mathematics as represented in the Special One-year Course." The procedure used by this committee consisted of conferences "with Army officers directly in charge of training enlisted men" and observation of "the basic training process itself during the first thirteen weeks of the inductee's Army life." A rather detailed outline of minimum essentials was given, along with a presentation of "general suggestions with respect to instruction." Although this report was directed entirely to the wartime emergency, its summary[61] of the "minimum essentials" has definite implications for civilian needs.

> Young men about to enter the Army must be taught . . . the ability to meet quantitative problems effectively, confidently, and sensibly. They must be able (*a*) to identify the quantitative aspects of the situations which confront them, (*b*) to deal with these situations by approximation and estimation when computation is not required, (*c*) to recognize and use the simpler symbolisms of mathematics, (*d*) to tell when and how mathematical symbolism, concepts, and processes are to be employed, and (*e*) to compute accurately, quickly, and intelligently when computation is called for.

These two reports are given special prominence because of their specific and important implications concerning the teaching of mathematics in the elementary and secondary schools. The War Preparedness Committee (appointed in 1940) and the War Policy Committee (appointed in 1943) were joint committees of the American Mathematical Society and the Mathematical Association of America. Their interests were primarily in the organization and direction of manpower in mathematical research for most efficient and effective service to the war effort. A similar committee was the National Committee of

[59]National Council of Teachers of Mathematics, Report on Pre-induction Courses in Mathematics, *Mathematics Teacher*, **36** (1943), 114–124.

[60]National Council of Teachers of Mathematics, Report of the Committee on Essential Mathematics for Minimum Army Needs, *Mathematics Teacher*, **36** (1943), 243–282.

[61]*Ibid.*, p. 246.

Physicists and Mathematicians, appointed in 1943. Some of the reports of these committees had significant import for mathematics at the secondary level.[62]

The Commission on Post-War Plans At its annual meeting in February, 1944, the Board of Directors of the National Council of Teachers of Mathematics created the Commission on Post-War Plans for the purpose of planning for effective programs in secondary mathematics in the post-war period. As originally constituted the commission consisted of five members. This number was expanded later to include thirteen members from eleven widely scattered states. The commission found significant background for its thinking and planning in the work of the first two of the above-mentioned committees of the war period.

In its first report[63] the commission announced its plan of organization and solicited help from the interested public in these words: "We are asking discerning school people and thoughtful laymen for good ideas and definite suggestions from which a sensible report may later stem that will provide adequate training in mathematics for *all* students in our schools – each according to his needs." With the hope of helping to crystallize thinking and "in order to promote discussion . . . in workshops and professional courses" the commission proposed, and discussed briefly, the following five recommendations which it felt "should be carefully considered by many persons in planning our work for the postwar years:"

1. The school should insure mathematical literacy to all who can possibly achieve it.
2. We should differentiate on the basis of needs, without stigmatizing any group, and we should provide new and better courses for a high fraction of the schools' population whose mathematical needs are not well met in the traditional sequential courses.
3. We need a completely new approach to the problem of the so-called slow learning student.
4. The teaching of arithmetic can be and should be improved.
5. The sequential courses should be greatly improved.

The commission's second report[64] contained its recommendations for the improvement of mathematics in grades 1 to 14. These recommendations were presented in the form of thirty-four theses. The first thesis

[62]William L. Hart, On Education for Service, *American Mathematical Monthly,* **48** (1941), 353–362. Also published in *Mathematics Teacher,* **34** (1941), 297–304.

Marston Morse and William L. Hart, Mathematics in the Defense Program, *Mathematics Teacher,* **34** (1941), 195–202.

William L. Hart et al., Universal Military Training in Peace Time, *Mathematics Teacher,* **39** (1946), 17–23.

[63]Commission on Post-War Plans, First Report, *Mathematics Teacher,* **37** (1944), 226–232.

[64]Commission on Post-War Plans, Second Report, *Mathematics Teacher,* **38** (1945), 195–221.

stated that: "The school should guarantee functional competence in mathematics to all who can possibly achieve it." Realizing the desirability of being explicit as to the implications of "functional competence in mathematics," the commission proceeded to delineate its essentials in the form of a check list consisting of twenty-eight items. This list was later expanded in the "Guidance Pamphlet"[65] to include twenty-nine items. While full significance of the check list can be had only by reference to the questions listed in it, some idea can be obtained from the following list[66] of key ideas or concepts of each of the twenty-nine items:

1. Computation
2. Per cents
3. Ratio
4. Estimating
5. Rounding numbers
6. Tables
7. Graphs
8. Statistics
9. The nature of a measurement
10. Use of measuring devices
11. Square root
12. Angles
13. Geometric concepts
14. The 3-4-5 relationship
15. Constructions
16. Drawings
17. Vectors
18. Metric system
19. Conversion
20. Algebraic symbolism
21. Formulas
22. Signed numbers
23. Using the axioms
24. Practical formulas
25. Similar triangles and proportion
26. Trigonometry
27. First steps in business arithmetic
28. Stretching the dollar
29. Proceeding from hypothesis to conclusion

The remaining theses of the second report were presented according to the following outline:

1. *Mathematics in grades* 1 *to* 6. Theses 2 to 8 give emphasis to the consideration of arithmetic as a content subject as well as a tool subject and as having both mathematical and social aims, the need for more careful attention to meanings and wiser use of drill, the realization of the importance of readiness and the futility of incidental teaching, and the desirability of more careful evaluation of learning.
2. *The mathematics of grades* 7 *to* 8. Theses 9 to 11 point out the uniqueness of the demands of the unified program for all students for these two grades.
3. *Mathematics in grade* 9. Theses 12 and 13 emphasize the need for a double-track program in mathematics and also for a careful consideration of the content of the algebra program in the ninth grade.
4. *Mathematics in grades* 10 *to* 12. Theses 14 to 20 treat of the main objectives and essential characteristics of the sequential courses of these three years in the high school program.
5. *Mathematics in the junior college.* Theses 21 to 23 call attention to the different demands likely to be made on the mathematics program of the junior

[65]Commission on Post-War Plans, Guidance Report, *Mathematics Teacher*, **40** (1947), 315–339. Later published as the "Guidance Pamphlet in Mathematics."
[66]*Ibid.*, pp. 318–319.

college by three different groups of students: those with cultural interests only, those with prevocational needs, and those who have major interests in mathematics.

6. *The education of teachers of mathematics.* Theses 24 to 32 discuss in fairly full detail some of the significant problems of teacher preparation at the various levels of instruction.
7. *Multisensory aids in mathematics.* The last two theses of the report briefly emphasize the significance of multisensory aids in effective instruction in mathematics at all levels.

In 1942 the Consumer Education Study was organized with two chief purposes in mind: (1) to investigate what should be taught and how it could best be organized and objectively presented and (2) to facilitate the work of the schools by providing instructional materials. It was recognized that mathematics has an important contribution to make to consumer education, both in the elementary school and in the secondary school. The Commission on Post-War Plans was invited to make recommendations on what this contribution might and should be. In 1945, in conjunction with the Consumer Education Study, the commission published a pamphlet entitled "The Rôle of Mathematics in Consumer Education."[67] In this report the commission first analyzed the nature and purposes of consumer education in general. It then proceeded to point out the relation of elementary school and secondary school mathematics to this total program and also to suggest to administrators and teachers a form for organization of materials as well as methods of instruction.

One of the recognized major problems in modern secondary education is that of intelligent guidance of pupils as they plan their school programs in the context of the actualities of the present and the horizons of the future. It is a well-established fact that in no subject-matter area have high school students suffered more from erratic and unwise guidance than in the field of mathematics. The Commission on Post-War Plans made a significant attempt to correct this unfortunate situation in the publication of the previously mentioned "Guidance Pamphlet," in the preparation of which they were aided materially by the counsel of representatives from the U.S. Office of Education, who were men of wide experience in the problems and techniques of educational guidance. The pamphlet was addressed to the high school student in the spirit suggested by this opening paragraph:

> Why should I study mathematics? What good will mathematics be to me? Perhaps you have asked yourself these two questions. If so, you have a right to good answers, and you will find them in the following pages.

[67]Commission on Post-War Plans, *The Rôle of Mathematics in Consumer Education* (Washington, D.C.: The Consumer Education Study, National Association of Secondary School Principals, 1945).

The commission then proceeded in simple style to present to the high school student significant information within the framework of the following carefully determined outline, from which it suggested that the reader should select only those areas in which he is interested:

I. Mathematics for Personal Use
II. Mathematics Used by Trained Workers
III. Mathematics for College Preparation
IV. Mathematics for Professional Workers
V. Women in Mathematics
VI. Mathematics Used by Civil Service Workers
VII. Mathematical Organizations
VIII. Graduate Schools Offering the Doctorate in Mathematics
IX. Selected References on Mathematical Careers

This pamphlet, through subsequent revisions, has continued to render service in the guidance of young people as they seek to chart their educational course through the secondary school and college.

Mathematics in general education During the early 1950s, the demands of a program of "general education" began to make their imprint upon the curriculum from the elementary school through the junior college. This new emphasis in educational philosophy was in essence a reaction against the emphases of an age of specialism. The claim was made that the college graduate was educated in the sense that he had acquired competencies in some particular occupation yet fell short of the demands of active citizenship in his community.[68] There were many who felt that the graduate of the secondary school could be characterized similarly. The trend toward specialization had led to the introduction of many courses and varied curriculums in both the secondary school and the college. The net result of such emphases had been a decreasing opportunity on the part of the student to participate in a program from which he might derive an "integrated view of human experience." As an antidote to the trend toward specialization there evolved a plan of general education which emphasizes a program designed to develop the abilities, attitudes, understandings, and behavior patterns which should be the common experience of all educable men and women.

What contribution can mathematics make to such a program? There is a body of mathematical content that is of significance to every individual capable of intelligent participation in the educational program, whether it be at the level of the elementary school, secondary school, or college. It is the professional obligation of informed groups to determine what this content is, how it should be organized and presented, and what basic training is essential to prepare teachers to meet the

[68]"Higher Education for American Democracy," vol. I, "Establishing Goals" (Washington, D.C.: President's Commission on Higher Education, 1947), p. 48.

challenge and responsibility of the program. This continues to constitute a major problem in mathematics instruction, the significance of which is discussed in the next chapter.

Other activities At its meeting in December, 1956, the Board of Directors of the National Council of Teachers of Mathematics appointed the Secondary School Curriculum Committee (SSCC) with the commission "to make a comprehensive and critical study of the curriculum and instruction in mathematics in secondary schools with relation to the needs of contemporary society." The membership of the committee was selected from secondary school and college teachers of mathematics, research workers in pure and applied mathematics, and personnel from business and industry. The committee work was carried out through the use of subcommittees appointed to make intensive studies in each of the following areas:[69]

1. The place of mathematics in a changing society and the implications of contemporary mathematics
2. The aims of mathematics education and the pedagogy of mathematics
3. The nature of mathematical thought in grades 7–12
4. How geometry should be introduced and developed
5. Content and organization of junior-high-school mathematics
6. Foreign mathematics programs
7. Adjustment of the mathematics program to pupils of average and below-average ability
8. Aids to teaching
9. The organization of the mathematics program
10. The administration of the mathematics program
11. Programs of instruction for the mathematically gifted pupil

The Committee on the Undergraduate Program in Mathematics (CUPM) of the Mathematical Association of America was appointed in January, 1953. This committee was directed "to consider the problems of making available in our society the values of modern mathematics" and "to attack the problem with broader scientific and cultural objectives than could be expressed through another mere study of curriculum revision."

Under this mandate the following books have been published: *Universal Mathematics, Elementary Mathematics of Sets with Applications*, and *Modern Mathematical Methods and Models* (volumes I and II, designed primarily for biology and social science majors). The committee also sponsored the publication of a paperback edition of the notes used by Emil Artin in a freshman honors course at Princeton University.

[69]The report of the Secondary School Curriculum Committee was published in the May, 1959, issue of *Mathematics Teacher*, pp. 389–417.

Sensitive to its inability to keep abreast of the rapid changes in mathematics, the committee asked to be dismissed so that a new committee might be formed with a much broader program. In January, 1959, the CUPM was reconstituted and organized into four panels: The Panel on Teacher Training; The Panel on Mathematics for the Physical Sciences and Engineering; The Panel on Mathematics for the Biological, Management, and Social Sciences; and The Panel on Pre-Graduate Training.[70] Each panel, whose membership was augmented by the addition of invited experts from its respective area, has the assigned responsibility of making recommendations for curricular change in its particular area of interest and of making consistent effort to implement these recommendations. The committee, which operates under grants from the National Science Foundation and the Ford Foundation, also has established a Consultants Bureau and a Library Committee to assist colleges in updating their curriculums and strengthening their library holdings.[71] The committee proposed to write completely new materials for experimental tryouts with the hope that ultimately from these would evolve an undergraduate college program in mathematics which would retain from the traditional and introduce from the new that mathematical content of established significance. This significance was to be evaluated in the context of the extended mathematical needs of engineering, physical science, biological science, social science, and high-speed digital automata. Outlines have been published and some actual writing of materials has been accomplished for the first two years; the outlines for the third and fourth years are still in a somewhat nebulous stage.

The American Association for the Advancement of Science, in 1955, inaugurated its Science Teaching Improvement Program (STIP). This was to be "an action program to increase the number of well-qualified science and mathematics teachers at the secondary-school level." In January, 1957, a plan for regional consultants in science and mathematics was inaugurated. The purpose of this plan was to stimulate regional efforts to recognize problems related to improved instruction and to initiate plans and programs designed to solve these problems on a regional basis. The program, made possible under a grant from the General Electric Educational and Charitable Fund, was in effect for eighteen months and was instrumental in shaping the plans of the American Association for a continuing program in the interest of improved instruction in science and mathematics. This program was extended in 1959 by a new three-year grant from the Carnegie Corpora-

[70]Conference of the Committee on the Undergraduate Program, *American Mathematical Monthly,* **66** (1959), 213–220.

[71]The activities of the committee and its panels are publicized through a series of reports and pamphlets which are available through the central office of the Committee on the Undergraduate Program in Mathematics, P.O. Box 1024, Berkeley 1, Calif.

tion of New York. One of the major activities of the extended program was the Study on the Use of Special Teachers of Science and Mathematics in Grades 5 and 6.

Another grant in 1959 from the Carnegie Corporation of New York to the AAAS was for a study of certification requirements for teachers of secondary school science and mathematics. The study was to be made in cooperation with the National Association of State Directors of Teacher Education and Certification (NASDTEC). The report of this study was published in 1961.[72] A second grant from the Carnegie Corporation was made in 1961 for the extension of the study and use of the guidelines for secondary school programs and to underwrite a study of programs in mathematics and science for elementary school teachers.

The National Science Foundation was authorized by an act of Congress in 1950. It has two distinct sets of functions: (1) the support of research and education through grants, fellowships, and other means; and (2) the development of national science policy and the evaluation and correlation of the research activities of the Federal government as well as the correlation of its own program with those of other agencies, both public and private.[73] The foundation's programs in science and mathematics education are developed and carried out by the Division of Scientific Personnel and Education within the following organizational structure:

1. The Fellowships Section
2. The Institutes Section
3. The Special Projects in Science Education Section
4. The Course Content Improvement Section
5. The Scientific Personnel and Education Studies Section

This organization has rendered and is still rendering a tremendous service in improving and strengthening the programs of science and mathematics in the secondary schools and colleges of our country.

In June, 1963, a group of professional mathematicians and mathematics users gathered in Cambridge, Massachusetts, under the auspices of Educational Services, Incorporated, and the National Science Foundation. The purpose of this meeting was to consider problems of curricular reform in the mathematics program for grades K through 12 in the context of "exploratory thinking with a view to a long-range future." The principal results of their deliberations, as presented in the report of the conference,[74] are separated into two major categories:

[72]NASDTEC-AAAS Studies, "Guidelines for Preparation Programs of Teachers of Secondary School Science and Mathematics" (Washington, D.C.: The American Association for the Advancement of Science, 1961).

[73]Alan T. Waterman, National Science Foundation: A Ten-year Resumé, *Science,* **131** (May 6, 1960), 1341–1354.

[74]Report of the Cambridge Conference on School Mathematics "Goals for School Mathematics" (Boston: Houghton Mifflin Company, 1963).

Curriculum for Elementary School (K–6) and Curriculum for Grades 7–12. It was the consensus of the group that this thirteen-year program should provide a level of training for the student comparable to a current three-year college program which would contain two years of calculus and one semester each of modern algebra and theory of probability.

The curriculum proposed for the elementary school is designed to make each student of the elementary grades familiar with the structure of the real number system and the basic ideas of both synthetic and analytic geometry. Also, significant attention is to be given to inequalities in the program of the elementary school after a very early introduction: "immediately after learning to count." The outline for the early grades is separated into two parts: one outline of topics for grades K through 2, with great emphasis on very informal treatment, and one for grades 3 through 6, continuing the informal pattern but with more direct concern for fundamental preparation for the mathematics program of the high school. The content of both programs is outlined under the following broad topics: the real number system, geometry, logic, and applications, with the additional topic area of "theory of real functions" for grades 3 through 6.

For the development of this program a great deal of "premathematics" and spiral treatment is recommended. The term "premathematics" is defined to mean "general heuristic cognitive patterns."

It is hoped that the student graduating from the sixth grade of such a program as that proposed will be so thoroughly grounded in arithmetic and intuitive geometry that he will be prepared to undertake a strong program in algebra, deductive geometry, calculus, linear algebra, and probability when he enters high school. With this in mind the report presents two proposed outlines for grades 7 through 12. The similarities and dissimilarities of the two programs are discussed at length. The two outlines in broad-topic form are presented here in separate columns.

Grade	*Proposal I*	*Proposal II*
7 and 8	Algebra Probability	Algebra Geometry Probability
9	Geometry	Algebra Geometry Calculus
10	Geometry Topology Linear Algebra	Analysis Probability Linear Algebra
11 and 12	Analysis	Analysis

One should not pass judgment, whether positive or negative, on the program proposed by the conference until after making a very careful study not only of the content of the program but also of the intent of the recommendations. The conference group emphasized that their ideas are exploratory and are not to be taken as prescriptive. The report goes further, saying: "We propose an ambitious program, aware that it may be impossible, but still convinced that it is worth shooting toward."

Along with other efforts and movements in the interest of improved instruction in secondary mathematics, there should be mentioned the increasing interest in television as an instructional medium, the use of films and other types of audio-visual materials, teaching machines and programmed instruction, the "Continental Classroom," the national and state contests in mathematics, and the intensive programs in curriculum improvement and teacher training being promoted in several states. The National Defense Education Act of 1958, which is administered by the U.S. Office of Education, provides funds to be used by the schools of the country in the purchase of equipment for aid in teaching science, mathematics, and foreign languages. The act also makes provision for financial assistance to state departments of education in the employment of supervisors in these three areas of the school program.

This is indeed an era of revived and concerned interest in the real import of mathematics as an integral part of the American program of education, from the early elementary grades through the total program. It is the sincere hope of all concerned that the study now being given to the problem of improved instruction will be sufficiently intensive and extensive to produce a curriculum and a pattern of teaching that will offer to the boys and girls of our land unexcelled opportunities to become significantly informed in the field of mathematics.

EXERCISES

1. What have been some of the more important aspects of the evolving philosophy of education in the United States?

2. Cite evidences of the effect that each of the points of view called for in exercise 1 has had on the mathematics curriculum.

3. What was the mathematics curriculum of the Latin grammar school?

4. How did the mathematics curriculum of the academy differ from that of the Latin grammar school?

5. At approximately what time did textbooks begin to be used extensively in mathematical instruction?

6. Name four important mathematics texts of the Latin grammar school period and also four of the academy period.

7. Briefly trace the influence of college entrance requirements in mathematics on the secondary school mathematics curriculum.

8. What were some of the more important causes of change in the mathematics program of the Latin grammar school and the academy?

9. What evidences are there of French and English influences on the instruction in mathematics during the early periods of American education?

10. In what way did the Pestalozzian movement affect the teaching of mathematics?

11. Name the early texts that most vividly reflected the Pestalozzian influence.

12. Name four texts that played a very important part in shaping the early instruction in algebra and geometry.

13. Name six influences that have been significant in the evolution of the mathematics curriculum of the secondary school. Give the major contribution of each.

14. What was the purpose and what were the main recommendations of the Committee of Fifteen on Geometry?

15. Briefly outline the recommendations for secondary mathematics made in the report, "The Reorganization of Mathematics in Secondary Education."

16. What classification of aims was given in the report, "The Reorganization of Mathematics in Secondary Education"?

17. Point out the distinguishing characteristics of each group of aims called for in exercise 16. Also, indicate the extent to which the groups overlap.

18. Briefly outline the recommendations of the Joint Commission concerning the program of secondary mathematics.

19. Contrast the recommendations of the Joint Commission with those of the National Committee on Mathematical Requirements.

20. What do you understand by the general-mathematics movement? By what other names has this movement been designated?

21. Compare the value of general mathematics in the senior high school with its value in the junior high school and in the junior college.

22. In what ways has the junior college movement affected the curriculum of secondary mathematics?

23. What is your evaluation of the Joint Commission's discussion of the role of mathematics in civilization and the place of mathematics in the educational program?

24. What are some of the more significant aspects of the nature and work of the Commission on Mathematics of the College Entrance Examination Board?

25. Briefly outline the work of the Commission on Post-War Plans.

26. Briefly summarize the most important of the implications of the thirty-four theses of the second report of the Commission on Post-War Plans.

27. What are some of the more significant aspects of the Report of the Secondary School Curriculum Committee (SSCC)?

28. What are some of the more important recommendations of the Committee on the Undergraduate Program in Mathematics (CUPM)?

29. What are some of the more important activities of the School Mathematics Study Group (SMSG)?

BIBLIOGRAPHY

Allen, Frank B.: The Council's Drive to Improve School Mathematics, *Mathematics Teacher*, **56** (1963), 386–393; **57** (1964), 370–378.

Baird, George H.: The Greater Cleveland Program, *Mathematics Teacher*, **54** (1961), 31.

Beatley, Ralph: Coherence and Diversity in Secondary Mathematics, "Eighth Yearbook" (Washington, D.C.: National Council of Teachers of Mathematics, 1933), pp. 165–215.

Blyth, John W.: Teaching Machines and Logic, *American Mathematical Monthly*, **67** (1960), 285–287.

Brumfiel, Charles, Robert Eicholz, and Merrill Shanks: The Ball State Experimental Program, *Mathematics Teacher*, **53** (1960), 75–84.

Cambridge Conference on School Mathematics, Report of: "Goals for School Mathematics" (Boston: Houghton Mifflin Company, 1963).

Commission on Mathematics, Report of: "Program for College Preparatory Mathematics" (New York: College Entrance Examination Board, 1959).

Commission on Post-War Plans, Second Report: *Mathematics Teacher,* **38** (1945), 195–221.

Davis, Robert B.: The Syracuse University "Madison Project," *American Mathematical Monthly,* **67** (1960), 178–180.

Fehr, Howard F.: New Thinking in Mathematical Education, *Mathematics Teacher,* **53** (1960), 424–429.

Forbes, Jack E.: Programmed Instructional Materials: Past, Present, and Future, *Mathematics Teacher,* **56** (1963), 224–227.

Hale, William T.: UICSM's Decade of Experimentation, *Mathematics Teacher,* **54** (1961), 613–618.

Heimer, Ralph T.: Some Implications of Programmed Instruction for the Teaching of Mathematics, *Mathematics Teacher,* **54** (1961), 333–335.

Hlavaty, Julius H.: Mathematics in Transition, *Mathematics Teacher,* **54** (1961), 21–22, 26–30.

Hutchinson, C. A.: Mathematics Instruction for Purposes of General Education, *American Mathematical Monthly,* **48** (1941), 189–197.

Jackson, L. L.: "Sixteenth Century Arithmetic," *Contributions to Education* 8 (New York: Bureau of Publications, Teachers College, Columbia University, 1906).

Joint Commission of the Mathematical Association of America, Inc., and the National Council of Teachers of Mathematics: The Place of Mathematics in Secondary Education, *Fifteenth Yearbook* (Washington, D.C.: National Council of Teachers of Mathematics, 1940).

Kemeny, John G.: Report to the International Congress of Mathematicians, *Mathematics Teacher,* **56** (1963), 66–78.

Matchett, Margaret S.: Teaching Machines or What? *Mathematics Teacher,* **55** (1962), 351–355.

McGarvey, Paul: Programmed Instruction in Ninth-grade Algebra, *Mathematics Teacher,* **55** (1962), 576–578.

Mock, Gordon D.: The Perry Movement, *Mathematics Teacher,* **56** (1963), 130–133.

Monroe, W. S.: A Chapter in the Development of Arithmetic Teaching in the United States, *Elementary School Teacher,* **13** (1912–1913), 17–24.

———: Analysis of Colburn's Arithmetics, *Elementary School Teacher,* **13** (1912–1913), 239–246, 294–302.

Moore, E. H.: On the Foundations of Mathematics, *First Yearbook* (Washington, D.C.: National Council of Teachers of Mathematics, 1926), pp. 32–57.

National Committee on Mathematical Requirements: "The Reorganization of Mathematics in Secondary Education" (Boston: Houghton Mifflin Company, 1923).

Newsom, C. V.: A Course in College Mathematics for a Program of General Education, *Mathematics Teacher,* **42** (1949), 19–24.

On the Mathematics Curriculum of the High School, *American Mathematical Monthly,* **69** (1962), 189–193.

Perry, John: The Teaching of Mathematics, *Educational Review,* **23** (1902), 158–181.

Pickard, Willis L.: "Evolution of Algebra as a Secondary School Subject," *Contribution to Education* 397 (Nashville, Tenn.: George Peabody College for Teachers, 1947).

Pieters, Richard S., and E. P. Vance: The Advanced Placement Program, *Mathematics Teacher,* **54** (1961), 201–211.

"Revolution in School Mathematics, The" (pamphlet) (Washington, D.C.: National Council of Teachers of Mathematics, 1961).

Rosenbloom, Paul D.: Implications for the Colleges of the New School Program, *American Mathematical Monthly,* **69** (1962), 255–259.

Secondary School Curriculum Committee of the National Council of Teachers of Mathematics, Report of: The Secondary Mathematics Curriculum, *Mathematics Teacher,* **52** (1959), 389–417.

Seybolt, R. F.: Notes on the Teaching of Elementary Mathematics in Colonial America, *Journal of Educational Research,* **11** (1925), 359–367.

Simons, L. G.: "Introduction of Algebra into

American Schools in the Eighteenth Century" (U.S. Office of Education Bulletin 18, 1924).

Smith, D. E., and Jekuthiel Ginsburg: "A History of Mathematics in America before 1900," *Carus Monograph* 5, The Mathematical Association of America, Inc. (La Salle, Ill.: The Open Court Publishing Company, 1934).

Stone, Marshall: The Revolution in Mathematics, *American Mathematical Monthly*, **68** (1961), 715–734.

Teaching Machines and Mathematics Programs, *American Mathematical Monthly*, **69** (1962), 552–565.

Wagner, John: The Objectives and Activities of the SMSG, *Mathematics Teacher*, **53** (1960), 454–459.

Wills, Herbert: The UICSM Programmed Instruction Project, *American Mathematical Monthly*, **69** (1962), 804–806.

Young, G. S.: The NASDTEC-AAAS Teacher Preparation and Certification Study, *American Mathematical Monthly*, **67** (1960), 792–797.

TWO

Mathematics in general education

GENERAL EDUCATION has been defined as that portion of the educational program which deals "mainly with preparation for life in the broad sense of completeness as a human being, rather than in the narrower sense of competence in a particular lot."[1] Thus, the total program of education is broadly considered as divided into two distinct, yet complementary, patterns, one for general education and one for special education. No onus of disrepute nor halo of respect is to be ascribed to the one in comparison with the other. Each program has its distinct function to perform and is to be evaluated only in the context of its determinate responsibility to the total educational program.

The large numbers of students at all levels of instruction, from the elementary school through the junior college, constitute part of the educational problem which confronts educators today. The other part of the problem, and equally important, is the kind of education that is to be provided to prepare these students to live more effectively as responsible members of their social order. In such a total program, general education and special education are not to be distinguished from each other so much in subject matter as in point of view and method of treatment. At all levels, general education will attempt to develop those abilities, attitudes, understandings, and behavior patterns which should be within the common experience of all educable

[1]Report of Harvard Committee, "General Education in a Free Society" (Cambridge, Mass.: Harvard University Press, 1945), p. 4.

people. On the other hand, special education, at appropriate levels, will attempt to fashion programs leading to the development of competencies in special areas of interest and endeavor.

A basic philosophy of general education For some students the real responsibility of the educational program is to make provision for challenging their special interests and abilities and developing their individual competencies and understandings. For all students, however, there exists the potential of becoming rational, trustworthy, and useful individuals. The basic concern of general education is to help each student realize and accept the challenge of his individual potential and lay the foundation for successful pursuit of special interests and aptitudes so that he can develop to his full stature as a responsible citizen. The purposes of general education are thus fourfold: (1) to contribute to the preparation for life needs, not only those which the student realizes but also those he must be taught to realize; (2) to establish basic relevance between knowledge and everyday experience; (3) to provide a nonspecialized type of training characterized by wide application, universal value, and great intellectual appeal; and (4) to lay the foundation of basic information essential to later intelligent pursuit of individual interests and special aptitudes.

The objectives of a program provided to meet such educational responsibilities should be designed to help the student (1) think effectively, (2) communicate thought, (3) discriminate among values, (4) make relevant judgments, (5) improve and maintain health, (6) do his part as an active and responsible citizen, (7) choose a vocation intelligently, (8) gain skill in adding to his previous knowledge, (9) find self-expression in, and create an appreciation for, things of beauty, (10) make sound emotional and social adjustments, (11) choose avocational interests wisely, (12) realize and appreciate his cultural heritage, and (13) understand his physical environment.

The program in mathematics can and must make significant contribution toward the attainment of these basic objectives of general education. It must make provision for:

1. Competence in the basic skills and understandings for dealing with number and form
2. Habits of effective thinking – a broad term involving analytical, critical, and postulational thinking, as well as reasoning by analogies and the development of intellectual curiosity
3. Communication of thought through symbolic expression and graphs
4. Development of the ability to make relevant judgments through the discrimination of values
5. Development of the ability to distinguish between relevant and irrelevant data

6. Development of intellectual independence
7. Development of aesthetic appreciation and expression
8. Development of cultural advancement through a realization of the significance of mathematics in its own right and in its relation to the total physical and social structure

It is in this context that there does exist a body of mathematical subject matter that is of significance to every educable individual at any and all levels of instruction.

The junior high school It is true that the primary force behind the demand for a program of general education was a revolt against the elective system which characterized for many years the instructional program of our colleges. However, it is of interest to note that the basic philosophy of the evolving pattern for the contribution of mathematics to general education at the collegiate level of instruction is fundamentally the same as that expressed in 1923 by the National Committee on Mathematical Requirements as a guide for the general mathematics program of the junior high school. As witness to the truth of this statement compare the definition of general education, quoted previously from the Harvard Committee,[2] and its implications for mathematics education with the following statement from the National Committee's report:[3]

> The primary purposes of the teaching of mathematics should be to develop those powers of understanding and of analyzing relations of quantity and of space which are necessary to an insight into and a control over our environment and to an appreciation of the progress of civilization in its various aspects, and to develop those habits of thought and of action which will make these powers effective in the life of the individual.

To implement this stated purpose, the National Committee recommended that the program of study for grades 7 to 9 contain the fundamental ideas of arithmetic, algebra, intuitive geometry, numerical geometry, and an introduction to demonstrative geometry. Furthermore, the report recommended that this body of mathematical subject matter be required of all pupils in these grades, since it was felt that its content included the mathematical knowledge and skills likely to be needed by every citizen.

The members of the committee seemed to have conceived of the program of mathematics in general education as performing two basic functions: (1) to give the students a broad view of the field of elementary mathematics in order to explore their interests and test their

[2] *Loc. cit.*

[3] National Committee on Mathematical Requirements, "The Reorganization of Mathematics in Secondary Education" (Boston: Houghton Mifflin Company, 1927), pp. 13–14.

abilities and (2) to give the students the mathematical information and skills most likely to be useful to them in their vocational pursuits.

While no effort was made to recommend grade levels for the treatment of specific topics, several optional plans of organization which did have certain implications for grade placement were presented. Basically these recommended patterns of subject-matter organization have prevailed through the intervening years. Support of the fundamental philosophy and specific recommendations of grade content were included in the 1940 report of the Joint Commission of the Mathematical Association of America and the National Council of Teachers of Mathematics.[4] The major modification found in this second report consisted of a recommended two-track program in which the basic differentiation consisted of a possibility of two distinct patterns in grade 9: algebra for some and general mathematics for others. Both committees agreed in their recommendation that the mathematics program through grade 9 be required of all pupils. These recommendations were given further confirmation in the following theses of the 1945 report of the Commission on Post-War Plans:[5]

Thesis 9. The mathematical program of grades 7 and 8 should be essentially the same for all normal pupils.

Thesis 10. The mathematics for grades 7 and 8 should be planned as a unified program and should be built around a few broad categories.

Thesis 11. The mathematics program of grades 7 and 8 should be so organized as to enable the pupils to achieve mathematical maturity and power.

Thesis 12. The large (more than 200 pupils) high school should provide in grade 9 a double track in mathematics, algebra for some and general mathematics for the rest.

Thesis 13. In most schools first-year algebra should be evaluated in terms of good practice.

In support of thesis 13 the commission quotes a statement which was incorporated in the request for funds to underwrite the work of the National Committee on Mathematical Requirements. The statement is as follows:[6]

The situation that needs to be met may best be illustrated by the case of algebra. Our elementary algebra is, in theory and symbolism, substantially what it was in the seventeenth century. The present standards of drillwork, largely on non-essentials, were set up about fifty years ago. A considerable number of teachers, both in the secondary schools and the colleges, believe that the amount

[4]Joint Commission of the Mathematical Association of America, Inc., and the National Council of Teachers of Mathematics, "The Place of Mathematics in Secondary Education," *Fifteenth Yearbook* (Washington, D.C.: National Council of Teachers of Mathematics, 1940).

[5]Commission on Post-War Plans, Second Report, *Mathematics Teacher,* **38** (1945), 204–207.

[6]*Ibid.*, p. 207.

of time spent by pupils on abstract work in difficult problems in division, factoring, fractions, simultaneous equations, radicals, etc., is excessive; that such work leads to nothing important in the sciences and adds but little to facility in the manipulation of algebraic forms.

Although this statement was written about 1920, it carries generally the same message as that found in professional periodicals and committee reports of modern vintage. There is, however, a basic difference in the implications of the present-day pronunciations. The modern demand for change is paying much more attention than that of former years to emphasis on such basic concepts as relation, function, structure, mathematical systems, more precise terminology and definition, greater significance of the nature and techniques of induction and deduction, the need for study of inequalities as well as equations, and the construction of mathematical models. It is paying much less attention to the learning of rules, mere manipulation of formulas and equations, development of computational skills, and the measurement of geometric configurations. This change in emphasis not only has affected the algebra program of the junior high school but also has tended to revise the program of the general mathematics track. The basic philosophy underlying the program of mathematics in general education has not undergone any great change under the pressure of the demands for a more modern program of mathematics in our schools. There have been, however, some very marked changes in the interpretation of the implications of this philosophy for attaining the fundamental objectives of general education. In particular, this is true at the junior high school level of instruction.

Some of the dissatisfaction with the junior high school mathematics program finds its origin in the feeling on the part of many that the selection and treatment of subject matter is not only inadequate but also, in many cases, quite inappropriate. For example, many people feel that in the eighth grade there has been more emphasis on social applications than on the development of appropriate mathematical content and that in the ninth-grade algebra course there has been more emphasis on mechanics than on appropriate considerations of basic structure. It might be added that for the ninth-grade general mathematics course there exists the same basic criticism as that expressed for the content of the eighth-grade mathematics course. Such topics as banking, taxation, stocks and bonds, and public utilities offer opportunities for pertinent applications of mathematical principles and skills, but they should not be used as the basic pattern for the organization and presentation of mathematical subject matter at any grade level. *It is the job of the mathematics teacher to teach mathematics, and this cannot be done incidentally.* A primary use of applications should be for the purpose of guiding the immature thinker toward recognition of ways and means of putting his acquired mathematical knowledge to effective use. Pertinent applications sought from many different sources should be fashioned in the natural framework of problem situations, i.e., in variable patterns calling for realization of what the unknown elements are and what the problem situation is, discrimination between relevant and irrelevant data, determination of whether there is a need for any additional data, recognition of relationships between the data and between the known and unknown elements, selection of the most appropriate operations, and estimation of answers as a guide to reasonableness of results. This, however, should come only after the necessary mathematical concepts, principles, and skills have been developed. Only through the proper development of basic mathematical concepts, principles, and skills can the proper foundation be laid for true appreciation of mathematics as an important element of our culture and for the intelligent use of mathematics in solving many of the problems which occur in our daily lives. The curriculum maker and the classroom teacher must keep in mind the fact that much of the subject matter of present-day mathematics has evolved from the demands of significant problem situations of the past.

Although the philosophy in the report of the National Committee on Mathematical Requirements (1923) calling for change is pretty much the same as the modern philosophy demanding reform, there is one important difference, at least in implication. The basic emphasis on general mathematics (better said, mathematics in general education) of the 1923 report, the report of the Joint Commission (1940), and that of the Commission on Post-War Plans (1945) is reflected in this quotation from the Commission on Post-War Plans: ". . . general mathematics is *organized* differently, . . . it offers a greater *variety* of topics and . . . it is related *more directly* with immediate application."[7] As stated previously, the basic emphasis of the modern demand for a program in general education is that general education and special education are not to be distinguished from each other so much in subject matter as in point of view and method of treatment. This implies that, while there may be differentiation in tracks, in the two-track program of the junior high school there will not be any differentiation in basic subject matter or basic preparation of teachers. The appropriate development of relevant basic mathematical skills, concepts, and principles will be the first responsibility of teachers regardless of track. The differentiation will come in the interpretation, supplementation, and enrichment of this development. For one track this aspect of the program will be oriented in the context of the user of mathematics; in the other it will assume the point of view of a for-

[7]Commission on Post-War Plans, *op. cit.* The italics are in the original, and the comparisons are made with the algebra program of the ninth grade.

ward look toward more advanced work in mathematics. There are some who are proposing still a third track to make provision for a still slower-paced mathematics program for pupils of very low-level competence. Regardless of track, the teachers of mathematics in the junior high school will have to be equally well informed in mathematical subject matter, in the history of mathematics, in the psychology of individual differences, and in effective techniques of presentation of materials and evaluation of results.

The senior high school The inception of the idea of dividing the six-year secondary education program of grades 7 to 12 into the junior high school and the senior high school dates from the early 1900s. Since that time, the primary function of the senior high school has been defined in terms of the provision of opportunities for the beginning of content specialization and the pursuance of one's aptitudes and special interests. While this has been generally accepted as the basic philosophy in the formulation of the senior high school program in mathematics, there have been those who have argued for the need to make provision for continuance of the general-education emphasis into the senior high school. It has been their contention that young people are graduating from high school with tragic inadequacies in the fundamentals of elementary mathematics. From World War II to the present, emphasis on the reality of this situation has been increasing. It has come from military personnel, businessmen, and people in industry, as well as from teachers of mathematics. The accusations have been substantiated further by repeated experimentation.

No program in mathematics for general education has as yet been designed for the senior high school. There have been a few efforts in preparing texts which might provide content for a general-education program in mathematics at the eleventh- or twelfth-grade level. The Secondary School Curriculum Committee took the position that it is desirable for all graduates from the high school to have attained at least a certain minimal degree of mathematical competency and recommended that some means should be provided to determine whether or not prospective graduates have done so. Further, it recommended that possibly grade 11 is the best place to subject the candidate to this check in order that a required program might be pursued in grade 12 by those who fail to measure up to the basic mathematics requirements of general education.[8] It remains to be seen whether the evidence of mathematical inadequacy and the public concern which it has provoked will influence the groups engaged in the intensive restudy of secondary mathematics to propose a program of mathematics for

[8]Secondary School Curriculum Committee, The Mathematics Curriculum, *Mathematics Teacher*, **52** (1959), 413.

general education specifically designed for the senior high school. Here again the pattern of individual differences can well call for a multiple-track program. If it is to have significance to the individual, the general-education program should not be allowed to degenerate into one of remedial efforts. Furthermore, the mathematically gifted should be given the opportunity to work in an atmosphere of full challenge and maximum interest. There should be differentiation on the basis of need and ability without "burdening with a stigma" or "investing with a halo" any one group as compared with another.

After an intensive study of the American high school, James Bryant Conant recommended[9] a program of instruction structured in three categories, as follows:

> First, there are the courses that should be *required* of *all* students, irrespective of their academic ability or their vocational goals. Then, there are two types of elective programs – the nonacademic and the academic.
>
> The required program should occupy about half of every student's time. It should include four years of English, three or four years of social studies including two of history, at least one year of mathematics and one year of science. These courses are intended to provide the groundwork for citizenship in a democracy. . . .
>
> The nature of the nonacademic elective program will depend almost entirely on the community. There may be a considerable number of parents who are interested in having their children whose talents are nonacademic, take vocational courses geared to employment opportunities in the community. In that case, such courses should be offered. . . .
>
> I am convinced . . . that, on a national basis, something like 15 per cent of the youth of high-school age have the ability to study effectively and rewardingly advanced mathematics, science, and a foreign language. And I think those academically talented students should be urged by the counselors to elect a minimum academic elective program that includes four years of mathematics, four years of *one* foreign language, and three years of a science.

These recommendations are directed toward four-year high school programs, but they have important implications for those programs which are on a 3-3 pattern of junior high school and senior high school.

The success of any such program of mathematics education will depend to a very great extent upon the preparation and experience of the teacher. Whether his instructional responsibilities are directed toward general education or toward the more specialized nonacademic and academic programs, he should be a person with a strong mathematical background, acquainted with the demands of individual differences, and informed on the relative merits of appropriate teaching techniques. These more highly specialized attributes of a good teacher should be supported by the cultural, disciplinary, and practical qualities of a sound program in general education.

[9]James Bryant Conant, A Hard Look at Our High Schools, *Look*, **23** (Feb. 3, 1959), 31–32.

The junior college The name "junior college" is here used to apply to grades 13 and 14, whether they are attached to the high school, organized as a separate two-year unit, or constitute the first two years of a four-year college program. At this level of instruction there exists, somewhat as at the junior high school level, the need to have concern for at least two large groups of students. There are those who, for various reasons, will desire to terminate their college program at the end of the two years, and there are those who will plan to go on to the more advanced work of later years. Also, from the point of view of mathematics, there are those who, even though they continue for four years or more of college and university work, do not have any special interest in and aptitude for mathematics. Recognition of this fact, and of the fact that in our modern technological society mathematics has a responsible contribution to make to the program of general education, has given concern to educators and mathematicians alike. What is the most effective contribution which mathematics can make to the program of general education at the college level? There is not as yet any real agreement on the answer. Committees have given, and still are giving, concentrated attention to the problem of finding the most appropriate answer. In particular, the work of the Committee on the Undergraduate Program in Mathematics is to be noted.[10] The professional journals have also carried many articles expressing individual points of view on the content of such a program. Despite the wide differences of opinion, there seems to be universal agreement on one fundamental characteristic of the program; namely, *the content of the course must be mathematics, not just about mathematics.*

Texts that reflect different points of view have begun to appear. The most generally accepted program seems to be developed around the broad areas of the basic notion of number, measurement, probability and statistics, function, and the nature of proof. The discussion of number seems to be concerned with the following: (1) the historical background of our number system, paying special attention to the concepts of one-to-one correspondence, place value, and order, (2) number systems with nondecimal bases, (3) the basic properties of real numbers, (4) extension of number systems from natural numbers to complex numbers, including the concepts of sets, groups, and fields, (5) congruences and modular number systems, (6) the number line, and (7) rectangular coordinates. The approximate nature of measurement is developed along with the concepts of precision and accuracy; significant digits and standard notation; linear, area, volume, and capacity measurements; direct and indirect measurement; and computation with approximate numbers. The introduction to probability and statis-

[10]Report of Committee on the Undergraduate Program in Mathematics, *American Mathematical Monthly*, **63** (1955), 511–520.

tics is restricted to the basic patterns of probability and the simpler measures of central tendency and variability. There is some consideration of basic characteristics of a normal distribution and the product-moment correlation. Sets, relations, and functions form an important part of the language and the subject matter of this program. More precise definitions of constant, variable, and function are given. Simple algebraic and trigonometric functions are introduced, and appropriate techniques, including graphs, are used for deriving their properties. The study and use of the basic rules of logic and simple truth tables are introduced as a foundation for a clearer understanding of the nature of proof as it applies to various mathematical areas. The importance of intuition and the necessity of deduction are developed. Contrasts are drawn between the algebraic and the purely geometric types of proof, as well as between direct and indirect methods. Careful attention is also paid to the basic nature of postulates, with some extensions to Boolean algebra being made.

This not too carefully delineated outline of topics can be considered a rough indication of what might be thought of as a required program in mathematics for a general-education program at the college level. An analysis of the outline will disclose an implementation of the generally accepted basic assumption upon which such courses are to be built; namely, the course must be mathematics, not just about mathematics.

There is no doubt that mathematical content for such a course can be developed in a very meaningful manner that is quite compatible with the scholastic aptitude of all college students. Just as in any instructional area, the final responsibility for the effectiveness and value of any such course is that of the teacher. No course designed for the program of general education should be relegated to the apprentice teacher or the graduate assistant. Teachers of such courses must be prepared specifically for the job. The teacher preparation program must provide learning experiences in advanced subject matter which will help the prospective teacher see more elementary content in the richer context of the more advanced and to interpret the more advanced in the language and understanding of the more elementary. It must help the prospective teacher see the profession of teaching as an opportunity to make a rich and valuable contribution to the field of mathematics, a contribution no less genuine than that which lies open to the person trained for research in pure or applied mathematics. Such a program of preparation must be carried out with advanced courses in mathematics and related areas which have been designed to develop basic interrelationships as well as specific properties, and it must emphasize the necessity to recognize the limitations of individual aptitudes as well as encourage the setting of high standards of endeavor. In the hands of a teacher so prepared the mathematics course in the general-education program can make a truly significant contribution to the intellectual growth of every educable individual.

EXERCISES

1. Distinguish between general education and special education.

2. What are the basic purposes of a program in general education?

3. What general abilities should a program in general education be designed to help students develop?

4. In what ways can the program in secondary mathematics contribute toward the attainment of the objectives of general education?

5. What should be the basic objectives in mathematics for a general-education program at the level of the junior high school? The senior high school? The junior college?

6. Contrast the implications for general education as contained in the Harvard Committee's definition (page 43) with those for junior high school mathematics as contained in the statement from the National Committee on Mathematical Requirements (page 45).

7. What are some basic changes which need to be made in the Commission for Post-War Plans' check list for functional competence in order to bring it in line with current thinking about the content of secondary mathematics?

8. What are some of the principal arguments for modification of the program in junior high school mathematics?

9. What are the arguments for and against the thesis that the relative order of emphasis in the teaching of mathematics at the junior high school level is (1) basic understandings of concepts, principles, and techniques of mathematics and (2) ability to apply acquired mathematical understandings and skills to the interpretation of social situations?

10. Discuss the thesis of exercise 9 for senior high school mathematics.

11. Discuss the thesis of exercise 9 for junior college mathematics.

12. Argue the merits of the following thesis as a fundamental principle upon which any sound program of mathematics for general education should be based: The content of the program must be mathematics and not just about mathematics.

13. Give some of the arguments both for and against placing emphasis on each of these content areas in a mathematics program for general education: the number concept, measurement, the nature of proof, functionality, statistics.

14. Are there other content areas than those listed in exercise 13 which should be included in a mathematics program for general education?

BIBLIOGRAPHY

Alberty, E. J.: Role of Mathematics in Core-program Development, *School Review*, **64** (1956), 300–306.

Bryan, J. C.: Mathematics in General Education, *School Science and Mathematics*, **58** (1958), 249–255.

Burr, H.: Are We Providing for the Non-college Pupil in Mathematics? *California Journal of Secondary Education*, **30** (1955), 405–406.

Dixon, L. J.: Mathematics and General Education, *Mathematics Teacher*, **48** (1955), 204–208.

Fehr, Howard F.: Goal Is Mathematics for

All, *School Science and Mathematics*, **56** (1956), 109–120.

Green, L. W.: From Knowledge into Power: A Philosophy of General Education, *Journal of General Education*, **11** (1958), 151–156.

Hannon, H. H.: Mastery of Certain Aspects of Mathematics for General Education, *Journal of Educational Research*, **50** (1957), 363–371.

Hartung, M. L.: Mathematics in the Total School Program, *Mathematics Teacher*, **51** (1958), 336–343.

Harvard Committee, Report of: "General Education in a Free Society" (Cambridge, Mass.: Harvard University Press, 1945).

"Higher Education for American Democracy," vol. I, "Establishing the Goals" (Washington, D.C.: President's Commission on Higher Education, 1947).

Layton, W. I.: Mathematics in General Education, *Mathematics Teacher*, **50** (1957), 493–497.

Leonhardy, A.: Mathematics Used in the Biological and Physical Science Areas in a College Program of General Education, *School Science and Mathematics*, **51** (1951), 265–274.

_____: Mathematics Used in the Humanities, Social Science, and the Natural Science Areas in Program of General Education on the College Level, *Science Education*, **36** (1952), 252–253.

McFarland, Sister Mary F.: Mathematics, Our Common Heritage, *Journal of General Education*, **11** (1958), 170–181.

Mires, K. C.: General Mathematics for College Freshmen, *Mathematics Teacher*, **50** (1957), 513–516.

Rowe, Jack L.: General Mathematics for Terminal Students in California Junior Colleges, *Mathematics Teacher*, **52** (1959), 105–106.

Simpson, T. M.: Mathematics in the College General Education Program, *Mathematics Teacher*, **50** (1957), 155–159.

Stone, D. R., and H. C. Bateman: Basic Elements in Defining General Education, *Junior College Journal*, **27** (1956), 90–92.

Summerer, K. H.: College Mathematics for the Non-science, Non-mathematics Major, *School Science and Mathematics*, **56** (1956), 39–43.

Trimble, H. C.: Mathematics in General Education, *Mathematics Teacher*, **50** (1957), 2–5.

Trowbridge, H.: Forty Years of General Education, *Journal of General Education*, **11** (1958), 161–169.

Ullsvik, B. R.: Basic Learnings in Mathematics, *Educational Leadership*, **12** (1955), 199–204.

Wilson, J. D.: Mathematics in General Education at San Francisco State College, *Twenty-second Yearbook* (Washington, D.C.: National Council of Teachers of Mathematics, 1954), pp. 288–303.

Zant, J. H.: Critical Thinking as an Aim in Mathematics Courses for General Education, *Mathematics Teacher*, **45** (1952), 249–256.

THREE

The impact of modern mathematics

IT MAY BE somewhat trite to remark that the mathematics programs of the elementary and secondary schools have been and still are undergoing tremendous change. Anchored in the clear recognition of the need for careful evaluation of the educational merits of both the traditional and the new in mathematics, the thought engendering this change has been essentially bifocal in nature. One point of view has focused attention on a redirection of emphasis in the treatment of the portion of traditional subject matter that has been accepted as having valid current educational value. This new emphasis pays greater attention to basic structure and less attention to mere operational facility. The other point of view seeks ways and means for employing more recently developed concepts and techniques to clarify, simplify, and enrich the presentation of the mathematical content of both the elementary and the secondary curriculum. Thus, modern mathematics may be said to be characterized by both a new point of view and a new body of subject matter.

Modern mathematics as a point of view The origin of what might be called the modern point of view in mathematics can be traced to the pioneering efforts of Gauss, Bolyai, Lobachevski, and Riemann in the creation of non-Euclidean geometries. By daring to challenge that which for two millennia had been accepted as absolute, they freed the intellect to reject the evidence of the senses for the sake of what the mind might produce. The modern postulational method of mathematics finds its source in the publication by Lobachevski (1830) and Bolyai (1832) of a seemingly self-consistent geometric system which contradicted the Euclidean fifth postulate of parallelism while keeping all other postulates intact. It was further enhanced through the publication by Riemann (1854) of still another such non-Euclidean geometry based upon a still different contradiction of the fifth postulate and the non-Euclideanism of "curvature of space." Subsequent refinements by Pasch, Peano, and Hilbert succeeded in establishing the purely hypothetico-deductive nature of geometry. In fact it has been said that Hilbert's work "firmly implanted the postulational method, not only in the field of geometry, but also in nearly every other branch of mathematics of the twentieth century."[1]

This new method no longer recognizes postulates (axioms) as "self-evident truths," but merely as "acceptable assumptions." They are individual creations of the investigator's mind and are to be used as the basic hypotheses for some type of intellectual venture. The investigator may or may not be concerned about their material truth or falsity; he is concerned with their consistency and is curious about their implications. After he is convinced of the validity of his conclusions, he may become interested in the possibility of existence of physical or social situations which would provide a context of "truth" for his assumptions. In such cases the same aura of usefulness would encompass his conclusions. The validity and consistency of results rather than the practicality of results, however, are the major concerns of the mathematician.

The new method also places emphasis on the necessity for clear distinctions between that which is defined and that which must remain undefined. It is recognized that concepts and terms are defined through the use of other concepts and terms. Therefore, to avoid undesirable circuity of definition, the necessity for undefined, or irreducible, elements is created. The experience of the individual usually serves as the basic orientation for the specification of such undefined elements and the selection of fundamental postulates. Thus the modern point of view concerning geometry is that it is a creation of man's intellect, its distinctive structure being delineated by the basic postulates, the undefined elements, the dimensionality of the space of orientation, and the techniques of investigation.

In essentially contemporaneous development with geometry, algebra too was being freed from the shackles of authoritative tradition. The English mathematician George Peacock was the first, in about 1835, to think of algebra as a hypothetico-deductive system. This concept of algebra as an abstract science was developed further, in England,

[1]Howard Eves and Carroll V. Newsom, "An Introduction to the Foundations and Fundamental Concepts of Mathematics" (New York: Holt, Rinehart and Winston, Inc., 1958), p. 86.

by D. F. Gregory and Augustus De Morgan and, in Germany, by Hermann Hankel. The central thought of this development had its origin in the recognition and abstraction of the fundamental properties which characterize the algebra of positive integers (natural numbers). Such abstraction provided the symbolization which led to the realization that these same properties could very well characterize operations with elements other than the positive integers. If the operations are addition and multiplication and if a, b, and c represent positive integers, distinct or not, then the properties may be stated in the following manner:

Closure: If a and b are positive integers, then $a + b$ and $a \times b$ are positive integers.

Associative: $a + (b + c) = (a + b) + c$
$a \times (b \times c) = (a \times b) \times c$
Commutative: $a + b = b + a \qquad a \times b = b \times a$
Distributive: $a \times (b + c) = (a \times b) + (a \times c)$

Sir William Rowan Hamilton, a British mathematician, did for algebra what Lobachevski and Bolyai did for geometry. In 1834 he made known his new quaternion algebra, in which he had dared to contradict the commutative property of multiplication. Other noncommutative algebras followed, notably Grassmann's (1844) classes of algebras of still greater generality than Hamilton's quaternion algebra and Cayley's (1857) matrix algebra. Of more recent date are the nonassociative algebras, such as those of Jordan and Lie.

From such considerations of algebraic structure there have evolved postulate sets for fields, rings, integral domains, and groups, each of which has great potential for significant contribution at the level of the secondary school to the better understanding of the essential nature of algebra as a body of mathematical subject matter.

In any hypothetico-deductive system the question of consistency is the problem of major concern. How can one be assured that, among all the implications derivable from the basic postulates, there can never occur conflicting statements? Consistency can be of two types: *relative* and *absolute*. In the above statements concerning the consistency of Lobachevskian and Riemannian geometries the only implication is that, at the time of publication, no internal inconsistencies had been discovered. This, of course, did not rule out the possibility of the eventual detection of contradictory theorems implied by the basic postulates. Since 1868 there has been the added significance of relative consistency. This was established in rather brilliant fashion by E. Beltrami, who demonstrated[2]

[2]E. T. Bell, "The Development of Mathematics," 2d ed. (New York: McGraw-Hill Book Company, 1945), p. 307.

> . . . that plane hyperbolic [Lobachevskian] geometry can be interpreted as that of the geodesics [curves of shortest length] on a surface of constant negative curvature [pseudosphere or tractoid], and likewise for spherical geometry [plane Riemannian geometry] and a surface of constant positive curvature [sphere]. Since pseudospheres and spheres are familiar surfaces in Euclidean space, it was felt that the consistency of the classical non-Euclidean geometries had been demonstrated.

Of course, the implication is merely that the geometries of Lobachevski and Riemann are just as consistent as is that of Euclid, no more and no less. Euclidean geometry merely serves as a mathematical model of the non-Euclidean geometries, since it was found possible to find unique representation in Euclidean geometry of the postulates and undefined terms of the non-Euclidean geometries. For example, the controversial fifth postulate of Euclid was represented in each non-Euclidean geometry by its respective substitute; point was identified with point and the straight lines of Euclidean geometry with the geodesics of non-Euclidean; two straight lines (geodesics) intersect in one point in Euclidean and Lobachevskian geometry but in two points in Riemannian geometry. (Arcs of great circles on the surface of a sphere intersect in the two poles.)

When a mathematical system contains an infinite number of primitive elements, no better than relative consistency can be established. This is not always as nebulous as it may seem. For example, since the points of Euclidean plane geometry can be identified with ordered pairs of real numbers and algebraic meanings can be assigned to the five primitive terms (point, line, on, between, and congruent), it follows that Euclidean geometry, and hence the non-Euclidean geometries mentioned above, are as consistent as the real-number system.[3] Similarly, the consistency of many mathematical systems can be checked against that of the real-number system.

When a mathematical system contains only a finite number of primitive elements, concrete representation can be found in the domain of reality and, thus, absolute consistency of the system can be established.[4]

Since finite postulational systems can be checked for consistency against the concrete expectations of reality, the basic problem of consistency of postulational systems is that of infinite systems and, therefore, primarily that of the consistency of the real-number system. Through the inspirational researches of Peano, Dedekind, and

[3]Eves and Newsom, *op. cit.*, pp. 96–102.

[4]See, for example, Burton W. Jones, Miniature Number Systems, *Mathematics Teacher*, **51** (1958), 226–231, and Miniature Geometries, *ibid.*, **52** (1959), 66–71. Also see Eves and Newsom, *op. cit.*, pp. 158–161, 164.

G. Cantor the consistency of the real-number system has in turn been related to that of the system of natural numbers, thus giving[5]

> . . . the mathematician a considerable feeling of security concerning the consistency of most of mathematics. This attitude follows from the fact that the natural number system seems to have an intuitive simplicity lacking in most other mathematical systems, and the natural numbers have been very extensively handled over a long period of time without producing any known inner contradictions.

The quest for a solution of the problem of consistency of infinite mathematical systems may be analyzed into five significant phases:

1. The study of the absolute consistency of finite systems. An exhaustive examination of all elements in a model of such a system can detect inconsistencies or establish consistency.
2. The relative proofs of consistency. For example, Beltrami's use of the techniques of differential geometry to establish the relative consistency of Euclidean, Lobachevskian, and Riemannian geometries and Hilbert's use of Cartesian coordinate geometry to draw the conclusion that his geometry was as consistent as algebra.
3. Hilbert's efforts to construct "absolute" proofs for which he stipulated that there should be no reference to the consistency of other systems, to an infinite number of structural properties of formulas, or to an infinite number of operations with formulas. The thought behind these stipulations was that if every mathematical system could be exhibited as a pattern of formulas linked together in a finite structure, an exhaustive analysis could establish whether or not contradictory theorems could be deduced from the accepted postulates of each respective system.
4. The 1931 paper by Gödel, which established that it is quite unlikely that an absolute proof of consistency, satisfying Hilbert's conditions, can ever be found for all deductive systems, particularly arithmetic; also that there are an infinite number of arithmetical truths which can never be deduced from a given set of postulates within the restrictions of a finite set of rules of inference.[6] This means that if the arithmetic of real numbers is consistent, this fact cannot be established within its own formal structure.
5. Proofs of the consistency of arithmetic by Gerhard Gentzen, of the Hilbert school, and others. Although these proofs were not accomplished in accordance with Hilbert's stipulations, they are of logical significance.

[5]Eves and Newsom, *op. cit.*, p. 195. The authors present a very interesting discussion on The Postulational Approach to the Real Number System, pp. 190–216.

[6]Ernest Nagel and James R. Newman, "Gödel's Proof" (New York: New York University Press, 1960), p. 98.

The basic substance of the modern point of view in mathematics is described effectively by Bell[7] in these words:

> In precisely the same way that a novelist invents characters, dialogues, and situations of which he is both author and master, the mathematician devises at will the postulates upon which he bases his mathematical systems. Both the novelist and the mathematician may be conditioned by their environments in the choice and treatment of their material; but neither is compelled by any extra-human, eternal necessity to create certain characters or to invent certain systems.

Modern mathematics as new subject matter The new subject matter, like the modern point of view in mathematics, had its origin in the field of geometry. It has been said that analytic geometry "constitutes the greatest single step ever made in the progress of the exact sciences."[8] The analytic geometry of Fermat (1629) and Descartes (1637) in a very real sense remade geometry by removing the bane of Greek classicism and making modern geometry possible. Though it was, in essence, only a technique to be used in geometric investigations, Cartesian geometry became the key to unlock the floodgates through which flowed the stream of modern mathematics. With the publication in 1637 of Descartes' "Discours de la méthode," *analysis* became the characterizing technique of modern mathematics as contrasted with the *synthesis* of the old. It opened up new vistas in the field of geometry, provided stimulus for the invention of the differential and integral calculus by Newton (1666, 1684) and Leibniz (1673, 1675), and served as an aid in clarifying concepts and simplifying techniques in algebra and arithmetic.

Fermat also combined his mathematical talents with Pascal's to lay the foundation for the theory of probability in the joint solution of a game-of-chance problem proposed to Pascal by Chevalier de Méré. In this episode of 1654 the mathematics of chance had its beginning; since then it has continued to develop to such stature that it has become basic in many areas of modern living and scientific investigation. Something of its significance is implied by the fact that the Commission on Mathematics of the College Entrance Examination Board has published an experimental text for high school use entitled "Introductory Probability and Statistical Inference for Secondary Schools." Out of this initial effort there has evolved a continuing pattern of emphasis in this subject area at both the high school and college levels of instruction, underscored by inclusion of the television program "Continental Classroom" as a significant unit.

[7]Bell, *op. cit.*, pp. 305–306.

[8]John Stuart Mill, "An Examination of Sir William Hamilton's Philosophy" (London: Longmans, Green, Reader, and Dyer, 1878), p. 617.

The seventeenth century is also marked by three other distinct developments in the field of mathematics. Desargues and Pascal made significant contributions toward the beginnings of synthetic projective geometry; Pascal foreshadowed the modern fabulous era of computing machines with his invention of the first adding machine; Leibniz improved on Pascal's adding machine by extending the operational possibilities to include multiplication and laid the foundations for modern symbolic logic in his efforts to "reduce all reasoning of whatever kind to a universal 'characteristic' or . . . a symbolic mathematical science."[9] His inspiration seemed to have come from Descartes' reduction of geometry to a universal method.

In contrast to the positive stimulation of Leibniz to new endeavors, the great significance of the Cartesian approach to the study of geometry so overshadowed the work of Desargues and Pascal that their new projective geometry was lost temporarily in an oblivion of pure metric geometry. There it remained until revived by the publications by Carnot (1803, 1806) and Poncelet (1822). Further impetus was given to this area of investigation through the announcement by Gergonne (1825–1827) of the principle of duality "which, with its generalizations, left as substantial a residue of new and useful methods in geometry, algebra, and analysis as any mathematical invention of the nineteenth century."[10]

In 1872 Felix Klein announced his famous Erlanger program. In the address announcing this program he incorporated a definition of geometry which served to restore order, as it were, to the confusion existing in geometry. He appealed to algebra to give him the concept needed and defined a geometry as "the system of definitions and theorems invariant under a *group* of transformations." While this synthesis of geometrical thinking no longer seemed adequate after the advent of the general relativity theory, it does still serve to provide an effective approach to the better understanding of the real significance of geometry at the level of the secondary school. Invariance is an extremely important property of geometrical configurations which is of sufficiently simple structure to be comprehensible at the secondary level of instruction yet sufficiently abstract to open up new vistas of mathematical endeavor of challenging interest.

Probably the most significant and most basic of all the newer concepts of modern mathematics is that of *set*. An aggregate, ensemble, assemblage, class, or set is merely a collection of elements which are thought of as having some characteristic coherence. Some examples of sets are a set of dishes, a swarm of bees, a flock of sheep, a herd of cows, the fingers on one hand, the letters of the alphabet, all the posi-

[9]Bell, *op. cit.*, p. 133.
[10]*Ibid.*, p. 316.

tive integers, all the integers, the rational numbers, the real numbers, the points of a line, the points of a plane. The symbol used to indicate a set is illustrated by $A = \{a,b,c,d,e\}$, which is a set of five elements. A basic relation existing between sets is that of *equivalence*, or *one-to-one correspondence* between elements. For example, the set A, above, is equivalent to the set of fingers on a normally shaped hand because to each finger there corresponds one and only one element of the set A and, conversely, to each element of the set A there corresponds one and only one finger. This basic concept of equivalence of classes (sets) was recognized by Galileo. In 1638 he published a work in which he not only recognized this basic principle of equivalence of sets containing finite numbers of elements but also announced the fundamental distinguishing characteristic of infinite sets, namely, an infinite set is one whose elements can be placed in one-to-one correspondence with only a portion of the elements of the set. Stated in better language, an infinite set is a set which is equivalent to a *proper subset* of itself. The set B is a proper subset of the set C if every element of B is an element of C and there is at least one element of C which is not an element of B. Galileo exhibited a one-to-one correspondence between the set of all positive integers and the proper subset of positive integers which are perfect squares. Thus the set of all positive integers was exhibited as an infinite set.

In contrast, a finite set is a set for which a one-to-one correspondence cannot be established with any of its proper subsets. For example, the set S of all the letters of the English alphabet is a finite set. A bit of thought should make it evident that a one-to-one correspondence cannot be established between the set S and the set $A = \{a,b,c,d,e\}$ or any other proper subset of S.

The significance attached to the concepts of set and equivalence of sets was relatively incidental until toward the latter part of the nineteenth century. Although Bolzano (1850) had earlier postulated the basic distinction between finite and infinite sets and Boole (1847, 1854) had made an algebraic approach to the study of the theory of sets, it was G. Cantor (1895) who recognized the nonintuitive character of the concept of set and proceeded through the structure of a theory of sets of points to make significant contributions toward the modernization of the field of mathematical analysis.

Following in close sequence, Fréchet (1906) generalized the Riemannian (1854) point-set approach to the study of geometry through his introduction of a theory of abstract spaces. Such a space consisted merely of a set of undefined elements, usually points, and a set of relations involving these elements. The geometries which evolved as distinct theories of such spaces served to provide effective techniques for the development of Einstein's general relativity theory. It was this type of geometry which did not adapt necessarily to effective classification under Klein's transformation theory.

Further evidence of the fundamental significance of set theory lies in the fact that it is possible to define natural numbers in terms of sets. Such a definition not only reduces the number of undefined terms necessary for the structure of mathematical systems but also relates the consistency of such systems to the problem of the possibility of the structure of the theory of sets as a consistent postulational system.

Although the principal orientation of the early development of the concept of set was in the field of mathematical analysis, there probably has been no other concept that has so thoroughly permeated the whole domain of mathematical thought. The modern mathematical theory of sets has made significant contributions toward clarification, simplification, and abstraction of concepts and techniques in arithmetic, algebra, geometry, and analysis alike. It has become a powerful instrument for interpreting and clarifying the significant of the old in mathematics as well as an effective vehicle for simplification and adaptation of the pertinent of the new.[11]

Nature of deductive methods One of the most significant of all the new emphases affecting the modern program in mathematics directs more explicit and careful attention to the basic postulational structure of mathematics. From the point of view of logic, a fundamental criterion directing such considerations of structure is that the number of properties necessary to be assumed should be minimized, thus maximizing the number to be proved. Pedagogically, however, it is desirable, at times, to relax this criterion in order to present an equivalent structure more readily comprehensible to the immature mind.

For example, a postulational basis for the natural numbers was first announced in 1889 by the Italian mathematician G. Peano. This was a minimum set of postulates from which can be deduced the properties not only of the natural numbers but also, through proper extensions, of integers, the rational numbers, the real numbers, and the complex numbers. A less abstract, but equivalent, set of postulates which adapts itself to greater ease of comprehension by the immature student is the following:[12]

For our primitive, or undefined, terms take a set N of elements called *natural numbers*, together with two binary operations on the set, called *addition* and *multiplication* and denoted by $+$ and $\times$ [having the property of closure and] satisfying the following ten postulates.

[11]For an excellent discussion of some of the basic concepts of set theory see E. J. McShane, Operating with Sets, *Twenty-third Yearbook* (Washington, D.C.: National Council of Teachers of Mathematics, 1957), pp. 36–64.

[12]Eves and Newsom, *op. cit.*, p. 195.

$N1$. If a and b are in N, then $a + b = b + a$.
$N2$. If a and b are in N, then $a \times b = b \times a$.
$N3$. If a, b, c are in N, then $(a + b) + c = a + (b + c)$.
$N4$. If a, b, c are in N, then $(a \times b) \times c = a \times (b \times c)$.
$N5$. If a, b, c are in N, then $a \times (b + c) = (a \times b) + (a \times c)$.
$N6$. There exists a natural number 1 such that $a \times 1 = a$ for all a in N.
$N7$. If a, b, c are in N and if $c + a = c + b$, then $a = b$.
$N8$. If a, b, c are in N and if $c \times a = c \times b$, then $a = b$.
$N9$. For given a and b in N one and only one of the following holds: $a = b$, $a + x = b$, $a = b + y$, where x and y are in N.
$N10$. If M is a set of natural numbers such that (1) M contains the natural number 1 and (2) M contains the natural number $k + 1$ whenever it contains the natural number k, then M contains all the natural numbers.

In the statement of the above postulates the relation of *equality* was used. Such a relationship between two or more natural numbers is characterized by the following five basic properties:

$E1$. *Reflexive Property.* If a is in N, then $a = a$.
$E2$. *Symmetric Property.* If a, b are in N and $a = b$, then $b = a$.
$E3$. *Transitive Property.* If a, b, c are in N such that $a = b$ and $b = c$, then $a = c$.
$E4$. *Addition Property.* If a, b, c are in N and $a = b$, then $c + a = c + b$.
$E5$. *Multiplication Property.* If a, b, c are in N and $a = b$, then $ca = cb$.

These five properties are stated here as characterizing the relationship of equality between natural numbers. They also hold for equality between all numbers. The first three properties (reflexive, symmetric, and transitive) are the properties which characterize the more general *equivalence* relation. They hold for such relations as similarity and congruence of geometric figures, equality of areas, perimeters, and volumes, equality of line segments and angles, and many other types of relations, both mathematical and nonmathematical in nature.

From the ten postulates of the system of natural numbers and the five characteristic properties of equality all the familiar properties of the system of natural numbers can be deduced as theorems. Certain appropriate definitions of terms will facilitate such development. For example, postulate $N9$ states that there are three basic relationships between any two given natural numbers a and b. They are:

$a = b$	(a relationship of equality)		(1)
$a + x = b$	for x in N	(relationships of inequality	(2)
$a = b + y$	for y in N	between a and b)	(3)

When the relation (2) holds, a is said to be less than b ($a < b$), and when relation (3) holds, a is said to be greater than b ($a > b$).

As an illustration of the use of the above set of postulates in the development of other basic properties of the system of natural numbers, consider the familiar property frequently stated as the axiom: If equals are added to equals, the sums are equal. This may now be stated and proved as follows:

Theorem: If a, b, c, and d are in N and if $a = b$ and $c = d$, then $a + c = b + d$

Proof:

1. The sum of any two of the elements a, b, c, and d is in N.	1. *Closure property.*
2. $a = b$.	2. *Hypothesis.*
3. $a + c = c + a$.	3. *N1.*
4. $c + a = c + b$.	4. *E4 and hypothesis.*
5. $c + b = b + c$.	5. *N1.*
6. $c = d$.	6. *Hypothesis.*
7. $b + c = b + d$.	7. *E4.*
8. Therefore, $a + c = b + d$.	8. *Steps 3, 4, 5, 7, and E3.*

The fact that, through appropriate definitions and extensions, the properties of systems, other than the system of the natural numbers, can be developed from this basic list of postulates[13] caused the algebraists to become interested in the possibilities of further abstractions. They recognized that these same properties would be valid for any system consisting of a set of elements and two defined operations for which the system of postulates N1–10 held. The desire for further abstractions led to the consideration of still other postulational systems, the sets of elements and the operations upon the elements being defined only in terms of the restrictions specified by the basic postulates. The body of theorems and properties implied by logical deduction from such a postulational system thus becomes a mathematical model for the analysis of situations amenable to the fundamental postulates. Herein lies the basic concept of the significance of *mathematical structure*.

From the point of view of the secondary school, one of the most important of such postulational systems is an *integral domain*, defined as follows:

A set I of elements for which the operations of addition and multiplication are defined is called an *integral domain* if the following postulates are satisfied:

I1. *Closure.* If a and b are in I, then $a + b$ and $a \times b$ are in I.

I2. *Uniqueness.* For a, b, c, and d in I, if $a = b$ and $c = d$, then $a + c = b + d$ and $a \times c = b \times d$.

I3. *Commutative Property.* If a and b are in I, then $a + b = b + a$ and $a \times b = b \times a$.

[13]Eves and Newsom, *op. cit.*, pp. 194–216; Ivan Niven, The Concept of Number, *Twenty-third Yearbook* (Washington, D.C.: National Council of Teachers of Mathematics, 1957), pp. 7–35.

$I4$. *Associative Property.* If a, b, and c are in I, then
$$(a + b) + c = a + (b + c) \qquad \text{and} \qquad (a \times b) \times c = a \times (b \times c)$$
$I5$. *Distributive Property.* If a, b, and c are in I, then
$$a \times (b + c) = (a \times b) + (a \times c)$$
$I6$. *Zero.* I contains an element 0 such that, if a is in I, then $a + 0 = a$.
$I7$. *Unity.* I contains an element 1 ($\neq 0$) such that if a is in I, then $a \times 1 = a$.
$I8$. *Additive Inverse.* If a is in I, then there is an element $-a$ (a inverse or negative a) in I such that $a + (-a) = 0$.
$I9$. *Cancellation Law.* For a, b, and c ($c \neq 0$) in I if $ca = cb$, then $a = b$.

This postulational system derives its name from the fact that the most elementary set of elements meeting the conditions of the definition is the set J consisting of all integers (positive and negative and zero), with the operations being the customary processes of addition and multiplication. A less familiar example of an integral domain is defined as follows:

1. The set I consists of all irrational numbers of the form $a + b\sqrt{2}$, where a and b are elements of the set J.
2. Addition and multiplication are defined as ordinary binomial addition and multiplication. Namely, for all a, b, c, and d in J,
$$(a + b\sqrt{2}) + (c + d\sqrt{2}) = (a + c) + (b + d)\sqrt{2}$$
$$(a + b\sqrt{2}) \times (c + d\sqrt{2}) = (ac + 2bd) + (ad + bc)\sqrt{2}$$
where the form ac is used in the same sense as $a \times c$.
3. $a + b\sqrt{2} = c + d\sqrt{2}$ if, and only if, $a = c$ and $b = d$.
4. 0 is defined to be $0 + 0\sqrt{2}$.
5. 1 is defined to be $1 + 0\sqrt{2}$.

The reader should verify that the two systems described in the above paragraph do satisfy the conditions for an integral domain.

The concept of a field is rated by many as the most important of all the concepts of elementary algebra. A field is a postulational system satisfying the postulates $I1-8$ of an integral domain plus the additional postulate of a multiplicative inverse. The postulates of a field, thus, are:

$F1-8$ the same as $I1-8$, except that for identification purposes the set of elements will be referred to as F rather than I.

$F9$; multiplicative inverse.[14] If a is a nonzero element of F, then there is an element a^{-1} (a inverse) in F such that $a^{-1} \times a = 1$.

The system consisting of the set J of all integers, positive, negative, and zero, and the ordinary processes of addition and multiplication does not form a field, while the system consisting of the set R of all real numbers with addition and multiplication does constitute a field. Why?

[14]With the postulate of the multiplicative inverse $F9$ the cancellation property $I9$ becomes an easily derived theorem. For if a,b,c are in F and $c \neq 0$, then c^{-1} is also in F. Then, if $ca = cb$, we have by equality property $E5$ that $c^{-1} \times (ca) = c^{-1} \times (cb)$. The associative property implies $(c^{-1} \times c) \times a = (c^{-1} \times c) \times b$, or, by $F9$, $1 \times a = 1 \times b$. Whence, by $F7$ and $F3$, $a = b$.

One or two simple illustrations will point up the basic significance of the concept of field. In the field of complex numbers the two binomials $x^2 - y^2 = (x - y)(x + y)$ and $x^2 + y^2 = (x - iy)(x + iy)$ are factorable, while in the field of real numbers only $x^2 - y^2$ is factorable. The equation $x^2 + 1 = 0$ has no solution in the field of real numbers but has two solutions, $+i$ and $-i$, in the field of complex numbers. In other words, in the field of real numbers the solution set for $x^2 + 1 = 0$ is the null set, while in the field of complex numbers it is $\{i, -i\}$. The solution set for the equation

$$6x^2 + x - 2 = 0$$

is $\{1/2, -2/3\}$ in the field of rational numbers, the field of real numbers, or the field of complex numbers. Why is this not a correct statement: The solution set for the equation $6x^2 + x - 2 = 0$ is $\{1/2\}$ in the field of positive rational numbers? What is a correct statement describing the situation which would restrict the solution set of the equation to $\{1/2\}$?

One of the simplest of all significant algebraic structures is that of a *group*. In a form suitable for the secondary school a group may be defined in either of two ways:

1. A *multiplicative group* is a closed system consisting of a set of elements G and the ordinary operation of multiplication satisfying the four postulates:

$G1$. If a and b are in G, then $a \times b = b \times a$.
$G2$. If a, b, and c are in G, then $a \times (b \times c) = (a \times b) \times c$.
$G3$. There is an element 1 in G such that $a \times 1 = a$ for a in G.
$G4$. If a is in G, then there exists an element a^{-1} in G such that $a^{-1} \times a = 1$.

A familiar set of elements which form a multiplicative group is

$$\{1, -1, -i, i\}$$

where $i^2 = -1$. The multiplication table is as shown in the accompanying table. $G3$ is obviously satisfied. Since $-i \times i = i \times -i = 1$, $-i$ is the inverse of i and i is the inverse of $-i$. Similarly, for 1 and -1, each is its own inverse. Thus $G4$ is satisfied. Since the table is symmetric with

$\times$	1	-1	$-i$	i
1	1	-1	$-i$	i
-1	-1	1	i	$-i$
$-i$	$-i$	i	-1	1
i	i	$-i$	1	-1

respect to its principal diagonal, from the upper left corner to the lower right corner, $G1$ is satisfied. As an example that $G2$ is satisfied, $-1 \times (i \times -i) = -1 \times (1) = -1$ and $(-1 \times i) \times -i = -i \times -i = i^2 = -1$.

Therefore, $-1 \times (i \times -1) = (-1 \times i) \times -i$.

2. An *additive group* is a closed system consisting of a set of elements G' and the ordinary operation of addition satisfying the four postulates:

$G'1$. If a and b are in G', then $a + b = b + a$.
$G'2$. If a, b, and c are in G', then $a + (b + c) = (a + b) + c$.
$G'3$. There is an element 0 in G' such that $a + 0 = a$ for a in G'.
$G'4$. If a is in G', then there exists an element $-a$ in G' such that $(-a) + a = 0$.

A simple illustration of such a group is the set $W = \{0, 1, 2, 3, 4, 5, 6\}$, with addition defined as ordinary addition modulo 7. In modular arithmetic 23 is said to be *congruent to* 2 modulo 7, $23 \equiv 2 \pmod 7$, and $33 \equiv 1 \pmod 4$, since $23 = 3 \cdot 7 + 2$ and $33 = 8 \cdot 4 + 1$. Thus by "ordinary addition modulo 7," we have, for example, $4 + 6 \equiv 3 \pmod 7$, since $4 + 6 = 10 = 1 \cdot 7 + 3$; also $5 + 2 \equiv 0 \pmod 7$, since $5 + 2 = 7 = 1 \cdot 7 + 0$. The accompanying table is constructed after the fashion of these examples.

A check of the table will establish the fact that postulates $G'1$–4 are all satisfied. A single example must suffice for $G'2$. It can be extended to all such sums of elements of the system. $(4 + 2) + 5 = 6 + 5 = 11 \equiv 4 \pmod 7$, and $4 + (2 + 5) \equiv 4 + 0 = 4 \pmod 7$. Therefore $(4 + 2) + 5 \equiv 4 + (2 + 5)$. $G'3$ is satisfied, since 0 is an element in the set such that $a + 0 = a$ for each element of the set. Since 0 occurs in each row of the table, $G'4$ is satisfied; each element of the set has an inverse element in the set. Also, $G'1$ is satisfied, since the table is symmetric with respect to its principal diagonal.

+	0	1	2	3	4	5	6
0	0	1	2	3	4	5	6
1	1	2	3	4	5	6	0
2	2	3	4	5	6	0	1
3	3	4	5	6	0	1	2
4	4	5	6	0	1	2	3
5	5	6	0	1	2	3	4
6	6	0	1	2	3	4	5

The above illustration of an additive group may seem a bit artificial, but it is a mathematical model which can be used effectively in calendar reckoning. This can be accomplished by labeling the days of the week as follows: Sunday, 0; Monday, 1; Tuesday, 2; Wednesday, 3; Thursday, 4; Friday, 5; and Saturday, 6. Such questions as What day is 5 days from today? and What day was 4 days ago? are answered through simple arithmetic computation. For example, if today is Saturday, or 6, the answer to the first question is Thursday, since $6 + 5 \equiv 4$, and the answer to the second question is Tuesday, since $2 + 4 = 6$.

The groups, as defined and illustrated here, are *Abelian groups*. If postulates $G1$ and $G'1$ were removed, the definitions would be those of non-Abelian groups. The illustrations are of finite groups. The set of all nonzero rational numbers with the operation of ordinary multiplication is an example of an infinite Abelian group.

An interesting example of a finite geometry as a postulational system which exhibits absolute consistency can be constructed in the following manner:[15]

1. Consider "point" and "line" as the undefined elements and "lies on" as the undefined relation. Such concepts have meanings derived intuitively from concrete experiences of our daily life.
2. Use as the fundamental postulates of this system the following statements:
   - *FG*1. If P_1 and P_2 are distinct points, there is at least one line on which they both lie.
   - *FG*2. If P_1 and P_2 are distinct points, there is not more than one line on which they both lie.
   - *FG*3. Any two lines have at least one point which lies on both lines.
   - *FG*4. There exists at least one line.
   - *FG*5. For every line there are at least three distinct points which lie on it.
   - *FG*6. All points do not lie on the same line.
   - *FG*7. No more than three distinct points lie on any one line.

Figure 3-1 exhibits a model satisfying all seven postulates, thus establishing the absolute consistency of the system. (*Note:* The three points P_2, P_4, and P_6 lie on the curved line.)

Figure 3-1

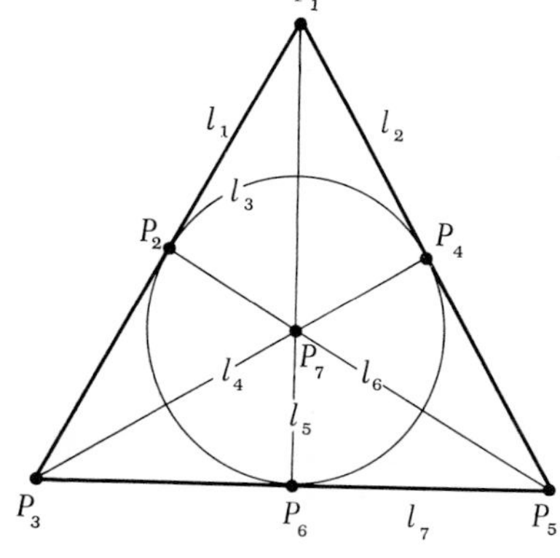

By using these postulates, the following theorems can be proved:

Theorem 1. Any set of points satisfying the postulates *FG*1–7 contains at least seven points.

Theorem 2. For any two distinct points there exists one and only one line on which they both lie.

Theorem 3. There exist three points which do not all lie on the same line.

Theorem 4. For any two lines there is one and only one point which lies on both lines.

[15] O. Veblen and J. W. Young, "Projective Geometry" (Boston: Ginn and Company, 1910), vol. I, pp. 1–7.

To illustrate the pattern of deduction, theorem 1 is proved.

Proof:

1. There exists one line, call it l_1. — 1. *FG4.*
2. There are exactly three points on l_1, say, P_1, P_2, and P_3. — 2. *FG5, 7.*
3. There is at least one point not on l_1, say, P_4. — 3. *FG6.*
4. Since P_4 is distinct from P_1, P_2, and P_3, there exist unique and distinct lines $l_2(P_1P_4)$, $l_3(P_2P_4)$, and $l_4(P_3P_4)$. — 4. *FG1, 2, 3.*
5. There exists one and only one point on l_2 distinct from P_1 and P_4. — 5. *FG5, 7.*
6. This point is also distinct from P_2 and P_3; call it P_5. — 6. *FG1, 2 and step 2.*
7. Similarly, P_6 lies on l_3 and P_7 on l_4. — 7. *FG1, 2, 5, 7 and step 4.*
8. P_1 now must lie on line P_6P_7 (call it l_5); P_2 on line P_5P_7 (call it l_6); and P_3 on line P_5P_6 (call it l_7). — 8. *FG1, 2, 3, 5, 7, and steps 2 and 4.*
9. All postulates are now satisfied and there is a minimum of seven points, so the proof is complete.

The reader should provide proofs of the remaining three theorems.

While the above postulational system is oriented in the context of geometry, it can serve as a mathematical model for problems in distinctly different contexts. Consider the following problem.

Example: What is the minimum number of airplanes necessary to stage a demonstration designed to meet the following specifications?

1. There are to be formation patterns such that each two airplanes are to fly together in one and only one formation.
2. For any two formations there must be at least one airplane which flies in both formations.
3. There are to be exactly three airplanes which fly in each formation.
4. All airplanes cannot fly in the same formation.

If "airplane" is identified with "point," "formation" with "line," and "flies in" with "lies on," then it becomes evident that the specifications of this problem can be identified with postulates *FG*1–7. Therefore, the answer to the question posed in the problem is this: A minimum of seven airplanes will be necessary to fly the specified formations.

Techniques of deduction

The new emphasis on the postulational structure of mathematical subject matter lends emphasis to the need for clearer understanding of the basic techniques used in valid patterns of deductive thinking.[16] Such a pattern of argumentation is essentially one of combining statements, or propositions, into still other propositions. There are four basic operations for making such combinations

[16]For an excellent discussion of such techniques see Carl B. Allendoerfer, Deductive Methods in Mathematics, *Twenty-third Yearbook* (Washington, D.C.: The National Council of Teachers of Mathematics, 1957), pp. 65–99.

in order that they might lead to valid results. They are *conjunction* ($\wedge$, read "and"), *disjunction* ($\vee$, read "either . . . or"), *implication* ($\rightarrow$, read "implies" or "if . . . then"), and *equivalence* ($\leftrightarrow$, read "is equivalent to" or "if and only if"). Rules for the use of these operations, known as *truth tables*, are given here. The symbols p and q represent propositions, where by a "proposition" is meant a sentence so clearly stated that it can be declared unequivocably to be true or false. The label T indicates that the proposition whose symbol is at the top of the column of any given table is to be considered as true, and F is the corresponding label for false.

Conjunction

p	q	$p \wedge q$
T	T	T
T	F	F
F	T	F
F	F	F

Disjunction

Inclusive "or"

p	q	$p \vee q$
T	T	T
T	F	T
F	T	T
F	F	F

Exclusive "or"

p	q	$p \veebar q$
T	T	F
T	F	T
F	T	T
F	F	F

The conjunction of two propositions ($p \wedge q$) is considered true only if both of the two propositions being combined. The exclusive-"or" type disjunction ($p \vee q$) is true if the label T can be applied to either one or both of the two propositions being combined. The exclusive-"or" type of disjunction ($p \veebar q$) is considered true only when T is the label to be applied to one or the other *but not both* of the two propositions. For example, consider the two propositions:

p: I shall go home.
q: I shall go to the show.

The conjunction $p \wedge q$ (I shall go home and I shall go to the show) is considered a true statement only if I go to both places. The disjunction $p \vee q$ (I shall go either home or to the show) will be true if I go to either one or both places. The disjunction $p \veebar q$ (at three o'clock either I shall

Implication

p	q	$p \rightarrow q$
T	T	T
T	F	F
F	T	T
F	F	T

Equivalence

p	q	$p \leftrightarrow q$
T	T	T
T	F	F
F	T	F
F	F	T

Negation

p	$\sim p$
T	F
F	T

go home or I shall go to the show) manifestly is true only if I am at one place or the other; for I cannot be at both places at the same time.

The first two rows of the truth table for "implication" are quite acceptable from a purely intuitive point of view. If we start with a true proposition and use a valid process of reasoning, it is quite natural to feel that we should arrive at a true conclusion. That is the meaning to be derived from these first two lines. A bit of reflection will convince one of the rationality and warn one of the danger pictured in the last two rows. For example, consider the three following propositions concerning natural numbers:

p: $3 = 8$, which is false.
q_1: $11 = 11$, which is true.
q_2: $7 = 12$, which is false.

Let us now investigate the validity of these two theorems:

Theorem 1. If $3 = 8$, then $11 = 11$ ($p \to q_1$).
Theorem 2. If $3 = 8$, then $7 = 12$ ($p \to q_2$).

Theorem 1. $p \to q_1$. *Theorem* 2. $p \to q_2$.

Proof: In each theorem we agree to accept p, though false, as the hypothesis.

1. $3 = 8$.	1. *Hypothesis.*	1. $3 = 8$.	1. *Hypothesis.*
2. $8 = 3$.	2. *By E2 (p. 64).*	2. $4 = 4$.	2. *E1 (p. 64).*
3. $11 = 11$.	3. *Theorem (p. 65).*	3. $7 = 12$.	3. *Theorem (p. 65).*

The law of the syllogism now justifies the conclusion (see Table 3-1):

4. $(3 = 8) \to (11 = 11)$, or $p \to q_1$. A *false* hypothesis, through valid reasoning, has led to a *true* conclusion. This is the justification of line three of the truth table for "implication."

4. $(3 = 8) \to (7 = 12)$, *or* $p \to q_2$. *A false hypothesis, through valid reasoning, has led to a false conclusion. This is the justification of line four of the truth table for "implication."*

Rows 3 and 4 of this truth table underscore the futility of reasoning from a false hypothesis. Not only are the results questionable but the consequences dangerous.

The truth table for "equivalence" is to be interpreted as indicating that two statements are equivalent when and only when the same label applies to each, independently of context. In the table, for example, in the rows where the statement $p \leftrightarrow q$ is labeled T, when p is true, so is q; when p is false, so is q; and conversely.

The table for "negation" is used simply to emphasize the statement made earlier that a proposition is a sentence that can be labeled as either true or false, in the sense of the exclusive "or." Note that the symbol for the negation of a proposition p is $\sim p$, read "not p."

One of the most important principles of the process of deductive rea-

TABLE 3-1

$[(p \to q) \wedge (q \to r)] \to (p \to r)$

1	2	3	4	5	6	7	8
p	q	r	$p \to q$	$q \to r$	$[(p \to q) \wedge (q \to r)]$	$p \to r$	$[(p \to q) \wedge (q \to r)] \to (p \to r)$
T	T	T	T	T	T	T	T
T	T	F	T	F	F	F	T
T	F	T	F	T	F	T	T
T	F	F	F	T	F	F	T
F	T	T	T	T	T	T	T
F	T	F	T	F	F	T	T
F	F	T	T	T	T	T	T
F	F	F	T	T	T	T	T

soning is the law of the syllogism, used above in the argument of theorems 1 and 2. This law is of the form: If proposition p implies proposition q and proposition q implies proposition r, then it follows that proposition p implies proposition r. This may be stated much more elegantly in symbolic form as $[(p \to q) \wedge (q \to r)] \to (p \to r)$. Table 3-1, the truth table for this proposition of implication, illustrates a very important property of the law of the syllogism. Columns 1, 2, and 3 display all the possible combinations of true and false of the three basic propositions p, q, and r. Columns 4 and 5 display the combinations of true and false for the two propositions whose conjunction is the hypothesis of the implication being investigated; column 6 records the analysis of the hypothesis; and column 7 records the analysis of the conclusion. The final column exhibits the fact that the proposition being investigated is true regardless of the status of the original propositions p, q, and r as to truth or falsity. A proposition formed by combining other propositions is a *tautology* if it is true independently of whether the component propositions are true or false.

One of the real trouble spots in the techniques of deductive reasoning is the proper use of related or derived implications; in particular this is true concerning the converse, inverse, and contrapositive propositions of a given implication. If the given implication is $p \to q$, the *converse* is the implication $q \to p$, where hypothesis and conclusion have been interchanged; the *inverse* is $(\sim p) \to (\sim q)$, where both hypothesis and conclusion have been negated; the *contrapositive* is $(\sim q) \to (\sim p)$, where the hypothesis and conclusion have been both negated and interchanged. The truth table, Table 3-2, makes clear that *only* the contrapositive proposition is equivalent to the original proposition. If one is true, so is the other; if one is false, so is the other. This is not true for

TABLE 3-2

p	q	$\sim p$	$\sim q$	Proposition, $p \to q$	Converse, $q \to p$	Inverse, $(\sim p) \to (\sim q)$	Contrapositive, $(\sim q) \to (\sim p)$
T	T	F	F	T	T	T	T
T	F	F	T	F	T	T	F
F	T	T	F	T	F	F	T
F	F	T	T	T	T	T	T

either the converse or the inverse. For these two propositions separate investigations are necessary to determine whether they are true or false.

The following is a simple but interesting exercise. First guess the answer to the question and then check your guess by the construction of the proper truth tables.

Example: Given the statement: If the sun shines, then the school will have a picnic ($p \to q$). Which of the following is the negative of the given statement?

1. If the sun shines, then the school will not have a picnic [$p \to (\sim q)$].
2. If the sun does not shine, then the school will have a picnic [$(\sim p) \to q$].
3. The sun is shining and the school is not having a picnic [$p \wedge (\sim q)$].
4. If the sun does not shine, then the school will not have a picnic [$(\sim p) \to (\sim q)$].
5. The sun is not shining and the school will have a picnic [$(\sim p) \wedge q$].

A great deal more can be said about the techniques of deduction; the effort here has been simply to point out some of the fundamental patterns and basic principles.

The nature of proof

Mathematics is primarily a deductive science in that propositions are proved by showing that they are implied by propositions that have been proved, definitions that have been stated, and postulates that have been accepted. The definitions of fundamental terms should be phrased to conform with experience, experiment, and common and universal usage. The principal characteristics of good definitions are clarity, simplicity, and brevity. In the last analysis there necessarily will be certain undefined terms which are accepted as established elements of common knowledge. For example, there is no clarification of concepts gained by setting up formal definitions of point, line, plane, and space in the approach to the study of geometry. Similarly, in any deductive science there necessarily will be a basic list of fundamental assumptions. It should be emphasized that these assumptions are merely statements accepted as true because of their conformity with common experience and sound judgment and that they are in no sense to be considered as "self-evident truths." From a pedagogical point of view the principal characteristics of such a body of assumptions are:

1. Consistency. There should be no contradictory statements in the list.
2. Simplicity of statement. The assumptions should be free from ambiguous statements and should be in a form that will permit ready deductions.
3. The assumptions should present no conflict with established knowledge or observable facts.

When a mathematical system has been clearly structured by the selection of the undefined elements, the definition of basic terms, and the acceptance of a fundamental set of assumptions, then the proving of theorems, i.e., derivable propositions, becomes the major concern. Every theorem has two characteristic properties, a hypothesis and a conclusion. The hypothesis is a statement, simple or compound, of the accepted relationships existing between elements of the given structure which are to be used in the search for the new relationships which are summed up in the conclusion, again a simple or compound statement. The *proof* of the theorem consists in the establishment of the truth of the conclusion through implications and inferences that find their original source of justification in the hypothesis. There are three distinct processes to be used in establishing the proof of any given theorem.

Synthetic process. The synthetic process consists in the drawing of a series of necessary conclusions until the desired conclusion is reached. The hypothesis implies, as a necessary consequence, the hypothesis of some axiom, postulate, or previously established theorem; these hypotheses imply the conclusions associated with them, which in turn make further implications, and this chain of necessary deductions is pursued until the desired conclusion is reached. Although the simplicity, elegance, and rigor of this form of argument make it highly desirable, it is far from desirable as a sole procedure to be followed in deriving mathematical proofs. As a technique it makes no provision for the pupil to understand the reason for making significant constructions or applying auxiliary theorems. As a simple illustration let us consider a synthetic proof for the following theorem from geometry.

Figure 3-2

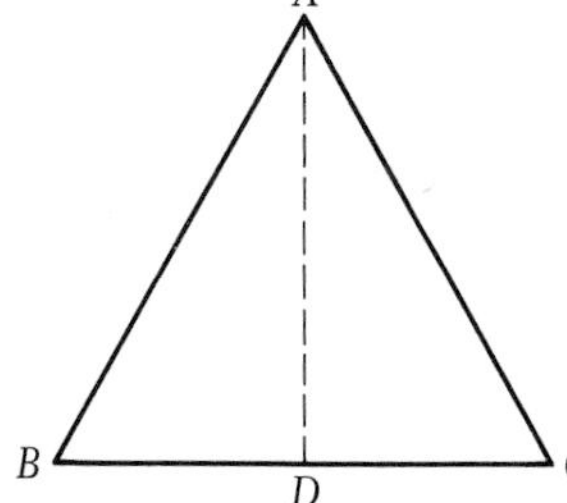

Theorem: If two sides of a triangle are congruent, the angles opposite these sides are congruent.

Given: $\triangle ABC$, in which $\overline{AC} \cong \overline{AB}$.

To prove: $\angle B \cong \angle C$.

	Statements	Reasons
Proof:	1. Draw $\overline{AD}$ bisecting $\angle BAC$ and meeting $\overline{BC}$ in D.	1. *To bisect a given angle.*
	2. In $\triangle BAD$ and CAD, $\overline{AB} \cong \overline{AC}$.	2. *By hypothesis.*
	3. $\angle BAD \cong \angle CAD$.	3. *By construction.*
	4. $\overline{AD} \cong \overline{AD}$.	4. *Common side.*
	5. $\therefore \triangle BAD \cong CAD$.	5. *Two triangles are congruent if two sides and the included angle of the one are respectively congruent to two sides and the included angle of the other.*
	6. $\therefore \angle B \cong \angle C$.	6. *Corresponding angles of congruent* $\triangle$.

The hypothesis of the given theorem, *through the auxiliary construction*, implies the conditions of the hypothesis of the congruence theorem (side, angle, side), which in turn implies through its conclusion the desired conclusion of the theorem, viz., the angles opposite the congruent sides are congruent. The inexperienced student, who has had no more insight into this theorem than that pictured here, is likely to become quite confused with the content of the very first step. Where did the author get the line segment $\overline{AD}$? How did he know to draw it? Why not draw some other line segment? Many questions such as these are likely to arise, and they are certain indicators of a lack of understanding and self-confidence in the pursuit of geometric information. The neophyte in the techniques of deductive thinking needs more exercise of his intuition and opportunity for discovery than such a procedure provides.

Diagrammatically, the chain of reasoning may be written $H_1 \rightarrow H_2 \rightarrow C_2 \rightarrow C_1$, where the symbol $\rightarrow$ is to be read "implies" and H_i and C_i represent hypotheses and conclusions, respectively.

Analytic-synthetic process. The analytic-synthetic process is not only a principal research tool in the hands of the mature mathematician but also an effective technique for guiding the immature student in the ways of discovery and validation of results. The analysis is the process of discovery of ways and means of arriving at desired results. The investigator considers the desired conclusion and raises the question: What relation or property *is sufficient* to justify the use of this conclusion as a true statement? Once this relation or property is found, he analyzes it for the same purpose, with the hope in mind that ultimately he will arrive at the hypothesis of the theorem as the source of the chain of sufficient reasons. This process does not constitute a proof, however, until it has been established that the steps are reversible. The reverse argument is the *synthesis*.

The analytic approach to the theorem given above would be as follows:

Questions	Answers
1. By what methods can two angles be proved congruent?	1. *Among other methods, two angles can be proved congruent if they*

	can be shown to be corresponding angles of congruent ⚠.
2. Is it possible to introduce two congruent ⚠ into the figure?	2. *Since* $\overline{AB} \cong \overline{AC}$ *by hypothesis, I see that by drawing the bisector of* $\angle BAC$ *I shall have the two congruent* ⚠ *BAD and CAD.*

Analytic process. In a sense the analytic process is a condensed form of the analytic-synthetic process. The investigator considers the desired conclusion and reasons that *it is implied* by the conclusion of some proposition. He follows such a chain of reasoning back to the hypothesis of the unproved theorem, thus closing the logical chain necessary to establish the validity of the desired conclusion. Diagrammatically, this type of proof may be written $C_1 \leftarrow C_2 \leftarrow H_2 \leftarrow H_1$, where the symbol $\leftarrow$ is read "is implied by." Of course, the chain of implications can become much more complex than that indicated here, but the basic pattern remains the same regardless of the degree of complexity.

Another important type of analytic argumentation in geometry is that which places its orientation in a Cartesian coordinate system. This enables one to make use of the properties and techniques of algebra and, at more advanced levels, those of calculus as methods of study and investigation instead of using geometric intuition and deduction. In the ordinary geometry of two or three dimensions, points are represented by ordered pairs or ordered triples, respectively, of real numbers; lines (whether curved or straight), planes, and surfaces are represented by equations and formulas involving independent and dependent variables whose common domain is the set of all real numbers. Concepts such as "angle," "on," "between," and "congruent" are given algebraic meanings. Within such a context the interrelationships between points, lines, and planes which shape and characterize significant geometric configurations become subject to the laws and techniques of the field of real numbers. The proving of geometric theorems becomes transformed into the proving of corresponding algebraic theorems or the deriving of valid implications contained in systems of equations.

The two most important types of proof are *direct proof* and *indirect proof.* Direct argumentation takes place when we try to prove a truth as stated. The attempt is made to start with a hypothesis and proceed through a chain of syllogistic reasoning to the implication of the desired conclusion. As pointed out above, it is frequently the case that a critical analysis of possible chains of sufficient conditions is *necessary* before an appropriate chain of necessary conclusions can be constructed.

Indirect reasoning (or indirect proof) is a method of reaching a desired conclusion through the process of investigation and elimination of *all other mutually exclusive possibilities.* Although teachers of mathematics have been inclined to neglect it, this form of argument is one of the most powerful and one of the most natural techniques of deduction. One prominent logician has estimated that about half of all our reasoned conclusions are arrived at through the method of indirect reasoning.[17] Another has said that "the process of *reductio ad absurdum* is of the greatest importance. It is the most prominent of all the methods by which men learn those truths of Nature that are unitedly known by the name of Science."[18]

A simple illustration of the technique of indirect reasoning is the following:

> One evening Mr. Jones was reading when his light went out. He immediately set about to discover the source of the trouble. His first thought was that the current was out all over town, but a glance at his neighbor's house, where the lights were burning, eliminated that possible explanation. Next, he thought that the lights were out all over his house, but by trying a nearby lamp he found that it gave light, so another possibility was eliminated. By trying another lamp through the same floor plug, the light bulb of his lamp in another lamp, and his lamp with a light bulb known to be good, he finally eliminated all possibilities except the fact that there was something wrong with the wiring in the particular lamp he was using. Further investigation centered on the wiring of the lamp revealed the defect, which could then be corrected.

The characteristics of indirect reasoning that are put into play in the illustration are the use of contradictory possibilities and the gradual elimination of those which can be established as inconsistent with conditions which are known or can be shown to exist. First, Mr. Jones assumed (1) the current is out all over town or (2) the current is not out all over town. The error of the first of these assumptions was established by a glance at his neighbor's house, where the lights were burning. Second, he assumed (1) the lights are out all over the house or (2) the lights are not out all over the house. The fact that another lamp would light eliminated the first of these two possibilities. Similarly, in each succeeding case he was able to contrast two contradictory assumptions and test them for their validity until he was finally able to locate the source of the trouble definitely. Such pairs of contradictory propositions have the following characteristics:

1. They cannot both be true at the same time.
2. They cannot both be false at the same time.
3. If one of them is false, the other must be true.
4. If one of them is true, the other must be false.

If we wish, then, to prove one of two contradictory propositions true, it is sufficient to prove that the other one is false. This, in summary, is

[17] W. S. Jevons, "The Principles of Science" (London: Macmillan & Co., Ltd., 1920), p. 82.
[18] Alfred Milnes, "Elementary Notions of Logic" (London: W. Swan Sonnenschein and Co., 1884), p. 93.

the essence of indirect proof in its simplest and most elemental form. It is based upon two fundamental and complementary laws or postulates of logic which, in turn, rest upon a third principle of logic for their application. These two laws are known as the *law of contradiction* and the *law of the excluded middle*. The law of contradiction asserts that a thing cannot both be and not be. The law of the excluded middle asserts that a thing must either be or not be. The above-mentioned characteristics of a pair of contradictory propositions are corollaries to these two postulates of logic and really give us our definition of contradictory propositions. This, of course, is to the effect that, if there exist two propositions having these characteristics, one of them must be true and the other one must be false.

The application of these two laws depends, as has been said, upon a third postulate of logic which asserts that there are only two ways in which a false conclusion may be reached. Either (1) the reasoning may be incorrect or (2) at least one of the assumptions upon which the reasoning is based may be false. If neither of these conditions exists in a given case, the conclusion which is reached must be correct. If either or both exist, the conclusion may be false. If, then, one reaches a false or inconsistent or contradictory conclusion and if he can be sure that he has reasoned correctly, it must follow that he must have started out with at least one false assumption.

There are at least two points of distinction to be noted between the method of indirect reasoning used by Mr. Jones in detecting the trouble with his floor lamp and the method of indirect proof as applied to propositions in mathematics. In the first place, propositions in mathematics are generally so stated that one knows at the outset the particular thing which he is required to establish, e.g., Prove that *under such and such conditions* so and so will be true. In the case of the lamp, as in many practical situations, it was not so simple as this at the outset. It was not a case of "prove that the trouble is in the lamp," but rather, a case of "find out in which of several possible places the trouble is located." In life situations the problems are generally not so strictly defined and delimited as they are in most propositions in mathematics. Moreover, it is generally easier in mathematical situations than in life situations to be sure that we have included all possibilities in our setup of the problem.

Second, the procedure is not identical in the two cases; it is usually more formal in mathematics. We set up our pair of contradictory statements, assume as true the one which we wish to prove untrue, and then set about showing, through a chain of logical reasoning, that this supposition necessarily leads to a contradiction or an inconsistency. This is the recognized and well-defined procedure. On the other hand, in a practical situation we rarely set down our possibilities in the manner of formal contradictory statements. We generally proceed more or less intuitively. But even if we should formalize the problem, our investigation of possibilities will often be more in the nature of open-minded experiment than by way of establishing a preconceived opinion by logical reasoning. For example, the light bulb was tested, not with the idea of proving logically that it was defective or with the idea of proving that it was good, but rather with the idea of *seeing whether or not* it was defective. Such experimentation often requires less mental effort than the formal proof of the falsity of a mathematical proposition, so that, while indirect proof in mathematics is generally less complicated in its setup, this advantage is probably more than offset in many cases by the difficulty of the intellectual effort required in the investigation. This may explain why many people who have difficulty in using formal indirect proof in mathematics are able to apply more or less informal indirect reasoning in nonmathematical situations quite successfully.

The technique of indirect proof in mathematics may be conveniently analyzed into four very specific steps to be followed:

1. Set up a pair of contradictory propositions, one of which you desire to prove true. Select the latter at the outset.
2. Assume, for the time being, that the other of the two is true and test the consequences by deductive reasoning to see whether this assumption leads to a contradiction or an inconsistency.
3. If the assumption of step 2 does lead, by correct reasoning, to an inconsistency or a contradiction, conclude that it was a false hypothesis.
4. Under the conditions of step 3, conclude that the contradictory proposition selected in step 1, i.e., the one you want to prove true, is necessarily true, since the only alternative proposition has been shown to be false.

It should be noted that, when the proposition to be proved is in the form of an implication, the pattern of argumentation by indirect proof is essentially identical with that of argumentation by use of the contrapositive proposition.

Two other forms of proof, which are of limited significance, are the *existence proof* and the *enumeration proof*. The existence proof consists in setting up an example which establishes the truth of the proposition. For example, suppose the statement is that every quadratic equation with complex coefficients has two roots of the form $a + bi$, where a and b are real numbers. The general quadratic equation in its simplest form is $x^2 + px + q = 0$, with p and q both real. The two values $(-p + \sqrt{p^2 - 4q})/2$ and $(-p - \sqrt{p^2 - 4q})/2$ can be verified as solutions, and they are of the form $a + bi$. The enumeration proof, which has application in a situation involving only a small number of cases, consists in checking each case for the truth of a given proposition. For example, it would not be a very difficult job to verify that multiplication is commutative for the positive integers modulo 4.

The mathematician frequently is involved in efforts to disprove a proposition rather than prove it. The use of *counterexamples* is an effective method for disproving statements. For example, the statement that $p = n^2 - n + 41$, for n a positive integer, will always produce a prime number can be disproved by the fact that, when $n = 41$, $p = (41)^2$, which is not prime. Unfortunately, this technique is of no value in the proof of the truth of a general statement. Another effective method for disproof is that of *contradiction*. This technique involves assuming the truth of some statement and then showing that a chain of logical deductions from this assumed truth leads to the contradiction of some previously established truth. This is, of course, quite similar to the method of indirect proof.

The nature and significance of induction[19] Although the deductive process provides the technique for drawing valid conclusions and deriving necessary consequences, the inductive process provides the means for imaginative inquiry and daring discovery. The investigation of specific cases and the observation of characteristic behavior can lead to conjectured generalizations. Such induction has played a very significant role in the history of mathematical research. Euler is credited with having said:[20]

> The properties of the numbers known today have been mostly discovered by observation, and discovered long before their truth has been confirmed by rigid demonstration. There are even many properties of the numbers with which we are well acquainted, but which we are not yet able to prove; only observations have led us to this knowledge.

Two of the most famous illustrations of the lasting truth of the above statement are Fermat's last theorem, "The equation $a^n + b^n = c^n$ is not solvable in integers for any $n > 2$," and Goldbach's conjecture, "Every even number greater than 2 is the sum of two prime numbers." Neither of these statements has been either proved or disproved, but each has challenged many mathematicians to engage in significant research. The immature pupil needs guidance in learning how to profit from considered guesses and significant hunches. He needs to be taught to search experience and experimentation for basic information upon which to base pertinent inductions.

[19]For a very helpful and enlightening treatment on the significance of induction as a mathematical process see G. Pólya, "Mathematics and Plausible Reasoning" (Princeton, N. J.: Princeton University Press, 1954), vols. I and II.

[20]Pólya, *op. cit.*, vol. I, p. 3.

When a pupil measures the interior angles of several triangles and finds that in each case the sum of their measures approximates two right angles, or when he cuts out these angles and fits them together and finds that they make a straight angle, he has the background for the induction that the sum of the measures of the interior angles of any triangle is the same as that of two right angles. If an individual had two containers, one conical in shape and the other cylindrical but of the same height and diameter, it would be a very simple experiment to show that the conical container held only one-third as much as the one which was cylindrical in shape. The induction might possibly follow for this individual that such a relationship between the contents of a cone and a cylinder of the same dimensions would always hold. Such inductions are important in the discovery of mathematical truths regardless of the area of interest.

On the other hand, there are many dangers involved in making use of the inductive process. It is always dangerous to make generalizations from specific cases. In the case of the above-mentioned formula $p = n^2 - n + 41$, each of the values of n from 1 through 40 will produce a value for p which is a prime number. The one counterexample, however, when $n = 41$, is sufficient to destroy the generalization one might be tempted to make. Discoveries by induction are in the realm of probable truths. Thus by induction the pupil who experiments with the angles of a triangle or the relationship between a cone and cylinder of like dimensions can only say, in the respective cases, that (1) it is probably true that the sum of the measures of the interior angles of any triangle is the same as that of two right angles, and that (2) the volume of a cone is probably equal to one-third the volume of a cylinder of the same dimensions.

Such experiments as these lay the foundations for inductive generalizations which in turn call for deductive demonstrations to establish validity and universality of application.

Consequences of the impact Whatever else may have resulted from the impact of modern mathematics, it certainly has brought about the introduction of significant new concepts and techniques, a greatly increased emphasis on structure, a reconsideration and refinement of definitions, a clearer attention to the deductive process, a better balance in the treatment of equations and inequalities, a broadening of the concepts of algebra and geometry, a revised treatment of trigonometric functions and techniques, a fundamental treatment of probability and statistical inference, and a re-evaluation of the significance of many of the manipulative procedures at all levels of instruction. There has been a very wholesome revival of inquiry into the curriculum content and instructional techniques in both elementary and secondary mathematics. In the continuing effort to improve these programs teachers and curriculum workers alike must keep in mind that there are good and bad in both the old and the new in mathematics. The possible contributions of each to the mathematics program of our schools must be weighed in the scales of effective and efficient teaching in mathematics in an era when technological patterns are subject to rapid and drastic change. Also it is essential to remember that the inclusion in the curriculum of a concept or principle is not justified by the mere fact that it can be of value to the student of mathematics. Consideration must also be given to such criteria as the following: How well does it meet the needs of the over-all program of secondary education? How well is it adapted to student aptitude? What is its potential for stimulation of interest? Is the necessary level of treatment too formal or sophisticated for the secondary student? Is it so far removed from possible student experience or need that there is danger of obstructing the student's interest and understanding? These and many other questions must be answered as a part of the professional effort to derive the maximum benefit from the impact of modern mathematics.

EXERCISES

1. Give two illustrations of "modern mathematics as a point of view."

2. Give two illustrations of "modern mathematics as new subject matter."

3. What is meant by the basic structure of arithmetic? Of algebra? Of geometry?

4. What are the basic postulates of Lobachevskian geometry? Of Riemannian geometry? Of Euclidean geometry?

5. What are the implications of this statement: One man's postulate may be another man's theorem?

6. What is meant by the consistency of a system of postulates?

7. What is meant by a mathematical model?

8. Distinguish between relative consistency and absolute consistency.

9. What is the principle of duality for two-space? For three-space?

10. State the plane dual of the following: (*a*) A triangle consists of three noncollinear points and their three lines of join. (*b*) The opposite sides of any simple hexagon whose vertexes lie on a conic intersect (are joined) in three points which lie on a line.

11. State the space dual of the following: (*a*) A tetrahedron consists of four noncoplanar points, no three of which are collinear, and their six lines of join. (*b*) A triangle consists of three coplanar but noncollinear points and their three lines of join.

12. Why are triangles and tetrahedrons said to be self-dual figures?

13. Exhibit a method of setting up a one-to-one correspondence between the positive even integers and the natural numbers.

14. Why is the geometry exhibited on pages 69 to 70 called a finite geometry?

15. Establish that the relations of similarity and congruence of geometric figures are relations of equivalence.

16. Which of the following relations are equivalence relations? (*a*) "Is as tall as,"

(*b*) "is shorter than," (*c*) "is less than or equal to" (≦), (*d*) "is the father of," (*e*) "is identical to," (*f*) "has the same area as."

17. Two complex numbers $a + bi$ and $c + di$ are said to be equal if and only if $a = c$ and $b = d$. Show that this relation between complex numbers satisfies the five properties of equality of numbers.

18. Show that numbers of the form $a + bi$ (with a and b real and with the usual definitions of equality, addition, and multiplication of complex numbers) constitute an integral domain.

19. Which of the following sets of numbers, with the usual definitions of addition and multiplication, constitute a field? (*a*) Positive integers, (*b*) all integers, (*c*) rational numbers, (*d*) real numbers, (*e*) complex numbers.

20. Do the positive integers 1, 2, 3, 4 with addition modulo 5 form a group? With multiplication modulo 5?

21. Construct the truth table in each case:

a. $[(p \to q) \wedge (p \to r)] \to (q \to r)$,
b. $[\sim(p \vee q)] \leftrightarrow [(\sim p) \wedge (\sim q)]$,
c. $[\sim(p \to q)] \leftrightarrow [p \wedge (\sim q)]$.

22. Which of the statements of exercise 21 are tautologies?

23. First express each of the following statements symbolically and then construct the truth table.

a. If Ann is informed and Sue is uninformed, then Ann will win the prize.
b. Ann will win the prize if and only if she is informed or Sue is uninformed.
c. If Sue is uninformed but Ann fails to win the prize, then Ann is uninformed.
d. It is not true that Ann is uninformed if and only if Sue is uninformed.

24. Which of the two following arguments is valid? Verify your answer symbolically.

a. If Ann is informed, then Sue is uninformed. Sue is informed only if Ann does not win the prize. Therefore, if Ann wins the prize, she is informed.
b. If Ann is informed, then Sue is uninformed. Ann will not win the prize only if Sue is informed. Therefore, if Ann does not win the prize, she must not be informed.

25. How many men will it take to form committees meeting the following conditions?

a. If M_1 and M_2 represent two different men, then there is one and only one committee on which both M_1 and M_2 serve.
b. Any two committees have at least one man in common.
c. There is at least one committee.
d. Not all men serve on the same committee.
e. Each committee consists of three and only three men.

26. What is the smallest number of committees that can be formed under the conditions of exercise 25?

27. What is meant by the deductive process?

28. Distinguish between induction and deduction, synthesis and analysis.

29. Why, in a deductive science, must there be undefined terms and accepted assumptions?

30. Distinguish between the implications of (*a*) a self-evident truth and (*b*) an accepted assumption.

31. Distinguish between direct proof and indirect proof.

BIBLIOGRAPHY

Adler, Irving: The Changes Taking Place in Mathematics, *Mathematics Teacher*, **55** (1962), 441–451.

———: "The New Mathematics" (New York: The John Day Company, Inc., 1958).

Allendoerfer, Carl B.: The Narrow Mathematician, *American Mathematical Monthly*, **69** (1962), 461–469.

Andree, Richard V.: Modern Trigonometry, *Mathematics Teacher*, **48** (1955), 82–83.

———: How Modern Mathematical Concepts Shed Light on Elementary Mathematics, *Mathematics Magazine*, **28** (1955), 173–176.

Bergamini, David: "Mathematics," Life Science Library (New York: Time, Inc., 1963).

Blumenthal, L. H.: "A Modern View of Geometry" (San Francisco: W. H. Freeman and Company, 1961).

Botts, Truman, and Leonard Pikaart: Mathematics from the Modern Point of View, *Mathematics Teacher*, **54** (1961), 498–504.

Brother U. Alfred, F.S.C.: Prevalence of the Set Concept, *School Science and Mathematics*, **62** (1962), 473–479.

Bruck, R. H.: Recent Advances in the Foundations of Euclidean Plane Geometry, *American Mathematical Monthly*, **62** (1955), 2–17.

Brune, Irvin H.: Symbols and Functions, *Mathematics Teacher*, **51** (1958), 232–235.

Cogan, Edward J.: The Handmaiden Becomes of Age, *American Mathematical Monthly*, **70** (1963), 554–560.

Commission on Mathematics of College Entrance Examination Board: "Introduction to Algebra from the Point of View of Mathematical Structure" (Princeton, N.J.: Educational Testing Service, 1958). (Pamphlet.)

Duren, W. L., Jr.: The Maneuvers in Set Thinking, *Mathematics Teacher*, **51** (1958), 322–335.

Evenson, A. B.: "Modern Mathematics" (Chicago: Scott, Foresman and Company, 1962).

Eves, Howard, and Carroll V. Newsom: "An Introduction to the Foundations and Fundamental Concepts of Mathematics" (New York: Holt, Rinehart and Winston, Inc., 1958).

Exner, Robert M., and Myron F. Rosskopf: "Logic in Elementary Mathematics" (New York: McGraw-Hill Book Company, 1959).

Fujii, John N.: "An Introduction to the Elements of Mathematics" (New York: John Wiley & Sons, Inc., 1961).

Graves, Lawrence M.: The Postulates of Algebra, and Non-Archimedean Number Systems, *Mathematics Teacher*, **52** (1959), 72–77.

Gray, James F.: "Sets, Relations, and Functions" (New York: Holt, Rinehart and Winston, Inc., 1962).

Hamilton, Norman T., and Joseph Landin: "Set Theory, the Structure of Arithmetic" (Englewood Cliffs, N. J.: Allyn and Bacon, Inc., 1961).

Henkin, Leon W., Norman Smith, Verne J. Varican, and Michael J. Walsh: "Retracing Elementary Mathematics" (New York: The Macmillan Company, 1962).

Jones, Burton W.: Miniature Number Systems, *Mathematics Teacher*, **51** (1958), 226–231.

———: Miniature Geometries, *Mathematics Teacher*, **52** (1959), 66–71.

———: "Elementary Concepts of Mathematics" (New York: The Macmillan Company, 1963).

Kane, Robert B.: Linear Programming: an Aid to Decision Making, *Mathematics Teacher*, **53** (1960), 177–179.

Keedy, Mervin L.: "A Modern Introduction to Basic Mathematics" (Reading, Mass.: Addison-Wesley Publishing Company, Inc., 1963).

Kelley, John L.: "Introduction to Modern Algebra" (Princeton, N.J.: D. Van Nostrand Company, Inc., 1960).

Kemeny, John G.: Rigor vs. Intuition in Mathematics, *Mathematics Teacher*, **54** (1961), 66–74.

Levi, Howard: "Foundations of Geometry and Trigonometry" (Englewood Cliffs, N.J.: Prentice-Hall, Inc., 1960).

May, Kenneth O.: What Does "If" Mean? *Mathematics Teacher*, **48** (1955), 10–12.

Meder, Albert E., Jr.: Modern Mathematics and Its Place in the Secondary School, *Mathematics Teacher*, **50** (1957), 418–424.

———: What Is Wrong with Euclid? *Mathematics Teacher*, **51** (1958), 578–584.

Meserve, Bruce E.: New Trends in Algebra and Geometry, *Mathematics Teacher*, **55** (1962), 452–461.

——— and Max Sobel: "Mathematics for Secondary Schools" (Englewood Cliffs, N.J.: Prentice-Hall, Inc., 1962).

Mosteller, F., R. E. K. Rourke, and G. B. Thomas, Jr.: "Probability and Statistics" (Reading, Mass.: Addison-Wesley Publishing Company, Inc., 1962).

National Council of Teachers of Mathematics: Insights into Modern Mathematics, *Twenty-third Yearbook;* and The Growth of Mathematical Ideas, *Twenty-fourth Yearbook* (Washington, D.C.: National Council of Teachers of Mathematics, 1957 and 1959).

Niven, Ivan: "Numbers, Rational and Irrational" (New York: Random House, Inc., 1961).

Northrop, E. P.: Modern Mathematics and the Secondary School Curriculum, *Mathematics Teacher,* **48** (1955), 386–393.

Pedley, Arthur H.: Complex Numbers and Vectors in High School Mathematics, *Mathematics Teacher,* **53** (1960), 198–201.

Pólya, G.: "Mathematical Discovery" (New York: John Wiley & Sons, Inc., 1962).

Rees, Mina: The Nature of Mathematics, *Mathematics Teacher,* **55** (1962), 434–440.

Ringenberg, L. A.: Numbers and Number Systems, *Mathematics Magazine,* **31** (May–June, 1958), 265–276.

Robinson, George A.: Useful Generalizations of the Concept of Function, *Mathematics Teacher,* **52** (1959), 444–448.

Rosenberg, Herman: The Changing Concept of Trigonometry as a School Subject, *Mathematics Teacher,* **51** (1958), 246–252.

Rourke, Robert E. K.: Some Implications of the Twentieth Century Mathematics for High Schools, *Mathematics Teacher,* **51** (1958), 74–86.

——— and Myron F. Rosskopf: What Do We Mean? *Mathematics Teacher,* **49** (1956), 597–604.

Selby, Samuel M., and Leonard Sweet: "Sets – Relations – Functions: An Introduction" (New York: McGraw-Hill Book Company, 1963).

Tierney, John A.: Trigonometric Functions of a Real Number, *Mathematics Teacher,* **50** (1957), 38–39.

———: The Law of Contraposition, *Mathematics Teacher,* **53** (1960), 189–190.

Wiebe, Arthur J.: "Foundations of Mathematics" (New York: Holt, Rinehart and Winston, Inc., 1962).

Wiseman, John D., Jr.: Introducing Proof with a Finite System, *Mathematics Teacher,* **54** (1961), 351–352.

FOUR

Modern curriculum problems in mathematics

THE CURRENT INTEREST in and demand for change in the mathematical program of the secondary school springs from four clearly defined sources: (1) the great hiatus existing between the mathematics curriculum of the past and the spirit and genius of modern mathematical thought, (2) the misdirected emphases in instructional patterns, (3) the mathematical inadequacies of so many high school graduates, and (4) the increased mathematical needs of high school graduates who enter college. Some have argued that in spite of the fact that mathematics is one of the fastest growing of all the sciences, it is being taught in our schools as though nothing new had happened in at least three centuries. Others have felt that the program of instruction has tended to overemphasize the manipulative aspects of mathematics, with entirely too little attention being paid to the conceptual and structural aspects of the subject. Expressions of concern over the mathematical inadequacies of high school graduates have been heard for many years, but they are given new point and urgency because of the increased and growing proportion of high school graduates who go to college and the greater mathematical demands made upon them when they get there.

Concern over the mathematical program in our schools is both widespread and acute. It is found among laymen as well as among professional people. The significance of this important current educational problem is emphasized by the work of committees representing the thinking of prominent professional organizations and by extensive experimentation being carried on for the purpose of discovering appropriate modification of curriculum content and instructional procedures.

Although the mathematics program of the elementary school is receiving considerable attention amid all this professional activity, the major interest and concern has been directed toward improving the mathematics curriculums of the junior high school, the senior high school, and the junior college. An important facet of this program is the discovery of effective and realistic ways of making suitable provision for individual differences among students.

Grades seven and eight The mathematics program of grades 7 to 9 has been a problem of great concern for many years. The varying patterns of administrative organization (6-3-3, 6-6, 7-5, and 8-4) contribute confusion to the basic educational philosophy which should underlie the program of the junior high school; distorted interpretations of educational values becloud the objectives of instruction; unrealistic standards of competency for promotion from lower grades tend to temper the challenge of instruction; and inadequate preparation of teachers restricts the depth of understanding in presentation of materials. It is a well-known fact that, during these impressionistic years, many boys and girls lose interest in mathematics. Some observers feel that this is due, in large measure, to the overemphasis on "socialized arithmetic" in the seventh and eighth grades. The Secondary School Curriculum Committee states:[1]

> In grades seven and eight much of the time is given to so-called social applications, some of which seem inappropriate at this level. Few new mathematical ideas are introduced. Teachers often report that the traditional courses at this level offer little challenge to the upper 50 per cent of the pupils, and that review and maintenance provided for the lower 50 per cent usually serve only to deaden their interest because emphasis usually is on drill, with little provision for bringing out deeper insight and understanding.

The Commission on Mathematics of the College Entrance Examination Board recommends a program for grades 7 and 8 which it feels the college-capable can cover in 1½ years. The outline of this program is as follows:[2]

(1) *Fundamental operations and numeration*—whole numbers and fractions (common and decimal), place value in the decimal system and other systems (particularly the binary), arithmetic mean, and a knowledge of square root including methods of approximating square roots of whole numbers.
(2) *Ratio*—making comparisons and scale drawings, per cent with moderate treatment of applications.

[1]Report of the Secondary School Curriculum Committee, *Mathematics Teacher*, **52** (1959), 403.

[2]"Report of the Commission on Mathematics of the College Entrance Examination Board" (New York: College Entrance Examination Board, 1959), p. 19.

(3) *Measurement* – English and metric systems, geometric measurements, use of ruler and protractor, indirect measurement of lengths, areas, volumes, etc.
(4) *Relationships among geometric elements* – parallel, perpendicular, intersecting, and oblique lines (in a plane and in space), various types of angles and triangles, Pythagorean relation, sums of interior angles of polygons, symmetry about a point and a line.
(5) *Graphs and formulas* – reading and construction of bar graphs, line graphs, pictograms, circle graphs, and continuous line graphs, meaning of a scale, basic formulas.

Other proposals have come from other sources. Experimentation at the University of Maryland involved the writing and experimental trial of courses for these grades. These courses included all the points mentioned in the foregoing outline of the commission's recommendations, with orientation toward the concepts, terminology, and notation of sets and formal logic. Also, large-scale and continuing experimental studies looking to the improvement of the mathematics curriculum in grades 7 and 8 have been undertaken by the School Mathematics Study Group (SMSG) and by the University of Illinois Committee on School Mathematics (UICSM).

The content and pattern of instruction in the eighth grade has created a problem of greater concern than has that of the seventh grade. There are many who feel rather strongly that, particularly in this grade, the mathematics program is impaired very seriously because of its incidental relationship to the analysis and solution of social problems which, at best, are of questionable interest and value to immature boys and girls. Mathematics cannot be taught effectively at any grade level when presented only in such incidental fashion. The programs of both grades 7 and 8 thus constitute a fundamental curriculum problem of current interest and significance. Scattered experimentation is investigating, for appropriateness of presentation and challenge, units from such areas as nondecimal numeration, factoring and primes, nonmetric geometry, techniques of deductive reasoning, averages, finite systems, measurement, approximations, and probability and statistics.

Some feel that the first course in algebra should become the program for the eighth grade. Others would rather extend the instruction in this grade to more advanced properties of number and more general treatment of graphs. Many feel that, whatever the curriculum content of the mathematics program for grades 7 and 8 might be, it must be mathematics, with the emphasis on adaptation to social usage held incidental and used only as an instructional aid in the systematic development of the fundamental mathematical concepts and principles of pertinent concern.

The curriculum content and instructional techniques of grades 7 and 8 are thus seen to present many problems of current concern. The problems are of such great educational consequence that they demand wide experimentation and intense investigation before intelligent proposals can be made for their significant solution.

Grade nine The philosophy of the junior high school has been defined in terms of four fundamental principles or broad objectives: (1) better articulation between the elementary school and the secondary school; (2) exploration, revelation, and guidance; (3) interpretation and control of environment; and (4) motivation. Under the influence of this philosophy and the inspiration of such men as Felix Klein of Germany, John Perry of Scotland, and E. H. Moore of America, there developed early in this century a demand for a noncompartmentalized form of organization of subject matter in the mathematics program of the secondary school.

Through the early pioneering efforts of a few individuals, a start in this direction had been made for the courses in the junior high school by 1920. This movement was strengthened and given great impetus by the 1923 Reorganization Report of the National Committee on Mathematical Requirements. Within a few years noncompartmentalized courses called "General Mathematics" had come to represent the typical offering in grades 7 and 8, and had also gained a firm foothold as an alternative to elementary algebra in a two-track program for the ninth grade. The recommendations of the Committee on Mathematical Requirements (1923), the Joint Commission (1940), and the Commission on Post-War Plans (1945) all gave support to the significance of such a program in general mathematics for grade 9. The basic purposes of such a program, as designed by its original proponents, were to show the interrelationships between the fundamental structure and techniques of the major areas of mathematical endeavor and to build for the individual an understanding and competence in mathematics essential for intelligent living amid the quantitative demands of a technological environment. It was thus designed as a second-track program for those pupils who had neither aptitude nor interest to justify their pursuing the course in first-year algebra.

While the two-track approach has continued to characterize the program of the ninth grade in most schools, it is unfortunately true that narrow interpretations of some of the implications of the pragmatism which has predominated in our educational philosophy of recent years succeeded in serious misdirection of the emphasis in presentation of the program in general mathematics. This diversion of basic purpose has followed two patterns: (1) The mathematical content has been made incidental to the social situation, and (2) the content has been allowed to degenerate in many areas into that of a refresher program of drill, trivial problem solving, and repetition of the mechanics of operation. This fact has caused great concern among those interested in a bona fide program in mathematics which can be of distinct benefit to educable boys and girls of ninth-grade stature.

The consensus of committee reports, experimentation, and professional point of view seems, at present, to favor one program in algebra but with varying degrees of emphasis and levels of attainment. For example, the Secondary School Curriculum Committee states:[3]

> All students may eventually study the same algebra, but not at the same depth of understanding, at the same time and rate, with the same application, nor necessarily in the same sequence. Thus, for example, in the ninth school year, one group may be doing a development of the number system from an axiomatic point of view, another group may be studying positive and negative numbers as usually presented in an inductive manner, while a third less able group may be making use of the basic concepts of algebra to help strengthen their understanding of arithmetic processes.

While the emphasis seems to be to make drastic modifications in the general-mathematics program of the ninth grade, the algebra program is also being subjected to rather critical survey. Here the principal emphasis is more in the direction of modernization of content and treatment. New concepts from the language of sets will be used for refinement of basic definitions and principles; relative importance of different areas of subject matter will be weighed and new concepts and techniques will be introduced; mechanical manipulation no longer will predominate the instructional pattern but will allow for attention to basic structure. The Commission on Mathematics makes this statement:[4]

> In the proposed program, the mechanics or formal manipulations in algebra will be the same as hitherto taught, and the subject matter is largely the same. The difference is principally in concept, in terminology, in some symbolism, and in the introduction of a rather large segment of new work dealing with inequalities, treated both algebraically and graphically. Solution sets of inequalities involving two variables are also studied.
>
> The new emphasis in the study of algebra is upon the understanding of the fundamental ideas and concepts of the subject, such as the nature of number systems and the basic laws for addition and multiplication (commutative, associative, distributive). The application of these laws in various number systems, with emphasis on the generality of the laws, the meanings of conditional equations and identities and inequalities is stressed. The nature of a function—in particular, the linear, the quadratic, exponential, and logarithmic functions—is also discussed.

[3]Secondary School Curriculum Committee, *op. cit.*, pp. 408–409.
[4]Commission on Mathematics, *op. cit.*, pp. 21–22.

There are many problems of curriculum content and instructional procedure in the revision of the mathematics program of grades 7 to 9. Only through the considered deliberation and careful experimentation of interested and informed groups can effective solutions be found.

The senior high school One of the major criticisms directed against the mathematics program of the senior high school is that it has consisted largely of unrelated specialties and manipulative procedures. Artificial barriers have existed among arithmetic, algebra, geometry, and trigonometry. The needed extensions of our number system from the domain of the positive rational numbers of the elementary school have been made mostly by rule and rote rather than by discovering and understanding. Algebra still has had the ring of the seventeenth-century pattern of learning the proper tricks to perform in order to arrive at the solution of problems. Geometry, when compared with Euclid's "Elements," of 300 B.C., has presented basically the same subject content but a psychologically thinned presentation, which too frequently has removed significant challenge rather than providing better motivation and learning conditions. Trigonometry continued to emphasize computation and triangle solving and to give too little attention to the analytic aspects and behavior of the circular functions.

Contemporary thinking seeks ways of correcting these defects by stressing broad, pervasive unifying concepts which thread through all the branches of mathematics and which can give coherence and structure to the whole subject.

The modern emphasis in mathematics points out that the true essence of mathematics lies in logic, decision making, and systematic search for the underlying structure of any given system or situation. Instruction in mathematics formerly tended toward the search for the solutions of various types of quantitative problems as they arose. There were some who even recommended the grouping of problems by types and adapting the solution techniques to the individual characteristics of respective types. Now the emphasis is directed toward the search for underlying principles and basic structure as guides to fundamental generalizations and abstractions. "Technology is subject to rapid change. Training in specifics can, and may, soon become obsolete. On the other hand, a person with fundamental training in mathematics will have the background for making adaptations to applications, even to those not now foreseen."[5] This quotation might very well be considered the basic theme directing the thinking and activity of those interested in essential revision of the mathematics curriculum of the secondary school. This should not be taken to imply that applications

[5]Secondary School Curriculum Committee, *op. cit.*, pp. 411–412.

and the techniques of problem solving are to be abandoned. These should and will continue to be very significant parts of all the courses, but, relatively, the structural aspects of mathematics will be the main focus of instructional efforts.

The content of algebra will no longer be defined largely in terms of manipulative skills; rather, it will emphasize a study of mathematical structure. Attention will be directed to the postulational structure of algebraic systems and to the use of deductive techniques in the development of the basic properties of such a system. Such concepts as group, integral domain, and field will be used to clarify and simplify algebraic language. The language of sets will be used also for clarification, simplification, and unification of concepts and techniques. For example, a *variable* may be defined as a symbol which represents any one of a set of elements. The *set of elements* is called the domain of the variable. Similarly a *relation* may be defined as a set of ordered pairs (x,y) such that to each value of the first element x there corresponds at least one value for the second element. The domain of the first element is called the domain of the relation, and that of the second element, the range of the relation. If to each value of the first element there corresponds one and only one value of the second element, then the relation is called a *function.*

Equations and inequalities may be thought of as sentences which make statements about the variables included. These statements may be thought of as *set selectors,* in that they select values of the variables for which the sentence is true. Thus, if the *universal set,* the set from which all usable values are to be selected, is the set of all integers, the sentence $x + 1 = 5$ selects the value 4; the sentence $y = x^2$, when x is assigned arbitrary values, selects all integral squares. To each first element x there corresponds one and only one second element y. Thus $y = x^2$ defines a function, although there are two distinct first elements which produce the same second element. For example (2,4) and (−2,4) both make $y = x^2$ a true statement. The sentence $y > x^2$ also selects values of y for any given x, but in this case to each first element x there correspond infinitely many values of the second element y. For example, if $x = 2$, then y can be any integer greater than 4. Thus $y > x^2$ defines a relation and not a function.

Inequalities will receive the recognition they are due. Simultaneous systems involving both equations and inequalities will be treated, and careful attention will be given to the graphical solution of such systems. For example, in Fig. 4–1 the point (−2,3) is the graph of the *solution set,* or truth set, of the system of equations

$$\begin{aligned} x + 2y &= 4 \\ 3x - 2y &= -12 \end{aligned}$$

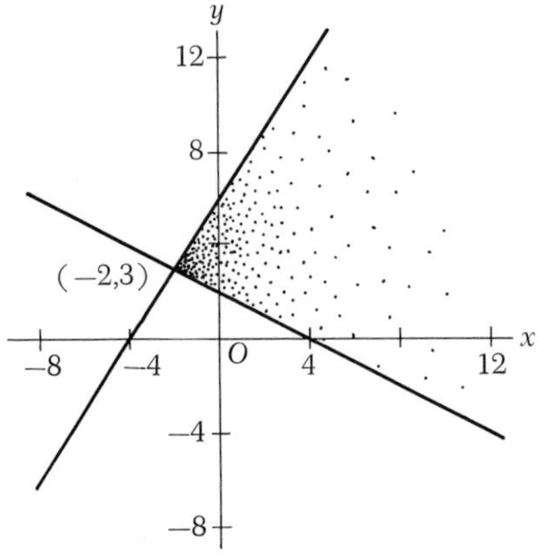

Figure 4-1

The shaded portion of Fig. 4–1 represents the graph of the infinite set which is the solution set of the system of inequalities

$$x + 2y > 4$$
$$3x - 2y > -12$$

The program in geometry has been of growing concern for many years. The basis for this concern has been sixfold in nature: (1) the recognition of the existence of logical defects in the Euclidean structure, (2) the failure to make appropriate adaptations of Cartesianism to simplify and enrich geometric study, (3) the failure to emphasize the postulational nature of Euclidean geometry and the possibility of the existence of non-Euclidean geometries, (4) the failure to emphasize the basic projective properties of geometric configurations, (5) the possible overemphasis on the restriction of geometric constructions to only those possible by straightedge and compass alone, and (6) the inadequate attention paid to three-dimensional geometry.

How to make corrections for these inadequacies in the high school geometry program has created a curriculum problem of no mean consequence. The Commission on Mathematics has proposed a year's program in geometry in their Elementary Mathematics II for grade 10.[6] This program is summarized in the following words:[7]

> The program proposed by the Commission envisages an informal and intuitive introduction to geometric ideas, followed by an informal discussion of the nature of deductive reasoning. The course would then take up a short but important sequence of theorems, studied deductively, culminating in the Pythagorean Theorem. In the treatment of this sequence, both the geometric and the logical ideas previously introduced informally would be illustrated, consolidated, and confirmed by more formal study. Specific postulates, including in addition to the usual assumptions the congruence properties of triangles, would be introduced.
>
> With the Pythagorean Theorem and theorems about similar triangles established, it is possible to proceed with coordinate geometry. The essential topics to cover are:
>
> 1. Location of points by coordinates
> 2. Length and slope of a line segment
> 3. Division of a segment in a given ratio
> 4. Equation of a line
> 5. Equation of a circle

[6]Commission on Mathematics, *op. cit.*, pp. 38–39. Also see report appendices 11, 12, and 14–16 for additional discussion of specific aspects of the proposal.

[7]*Ibid.*, pp. 27–28.

> The remainder of plane geometry can now be developed by using both synthetic and analytic methods. Emphasis should be placed on the development of skill in analyzing a situation and a valid proof of either kind.

This summary fails to indicate that the proposed program is designed as "a course in plane and solid geometry." The outline includes suggestions concerning the drawing of three-dimensional figures and basic definitions, theorems, and formulas related to solid figures.

The report of the Secondary School Curriculum Committee supports a stronger emphasis on synthetic geometry than does that of the Commission. It, too, recommends a combined treatment of solid geometry with the plane, the principal emphasis being directed to the configurations of the plane. Suggestions are made of "elements of geometry [which] are regarded as appropriate at the various grade levels." The point of view of the committee with reference to the total geometry program of the high school is summarized in these words:[8]

> It is the considered opinion of this committee that elements of geometry should be taught throughout the secondary sequence (grades seven to twelve) and that one year should be devoted to synthetic geometry with particular emphasis on the geometry of the plane. This does not imply any desire to minimize the importance of co-ordinate geometry. Indeed the study of co-ordinate systems should permeate the entire secondary sequence beginning with the idea of one-to-one correspondence between numbers and points on a line in grade seven. The year devoted to synthetic geometry should be no exception. For example it is instructive to extend the study of loci to the co-ordinate plane. . . . It is also desirable to use analytic methods, on occasion, to provide alternative proofs for certain theorems which have been proved synthetically. Such proofs give pupils confidence in their ability to use analytic methods.
>
> During the year course some teachers with superior classes may find it possible to include a considerable amount of solid geometry along with the plane geometry without sacrificing the essential values of the latter. Indeed some references to space geometry do much to enhance the pupils' understanding of relations which were first considered in the plane. The first consideration should be the presentation of a thorough course in plane geometry in which pupils receive intensive training in the solution of a large number of miscellaneous problems. In this situation the pupil needs time for contemplation, time for the formulation of conjectures, and time to test these conjectures for consistency with known facts. On the other hand, there is no point in pursuing an endless elaboration of originals which are confined to the plane. At some point during the year the good student will find it both natural and profitable to consider solid geometry in a systematic manner and not merely as counterpoint for plane geometry.

Both committees agree that a full half-year program in solid geometry is no longer justified. Also, both committees agree that it is highly

[8]Secondary School Curriculum Committee, *op. cit.*, pp. 404–405.

desirable that more careful attention be given to deductive techniques and to the possibilities of other geometries than the metric geometry of the Euclidean plane.

Thus, despite some differences in the details of their recommendations, it is clear that both of these committees took the position that Euclidean geometry must continue to hold a prominent place in the mathematical program of the senior high school. This position is further supported by the action taken in three important experimental projects[9] in preparing experimental courses and textbooks in Euclidean geometry. While these, too, differ in details of organization, and while the treatment of the subject in all three cases has a strongly modern orientation, their participation in these experimental projects implies general agreement that the traditional content of Euclidean geometry deserves the prominent place which it has held and now holds in the high school curriculum.

In trigonometry the primary objective has shifted away from the numerical aspects of the subject and toward its analytic aspects. There is still value in the use of trigonometric techniques to acquaint the immature student with the basic characteristics of indirect measurement, and the solution of triangles will still have some importance as a medium for introducing the more elementary techniques of computing with approximate data and as training in the use of tables. But the main importance of trigonometry lies no longer in its usefulness as a computational tool. It lies, rather, in the contribution which the analytic aspects of this subject can make to subsequent work in mathematics. For most students, trigonometry can no longer be properly regarded as a terminal course. The variation and the periodic nature of the trigonometric functions, the relations among the functions, properties of the inverse trigonometric functions, the solution of trigonometric equations, the representation of complex numbers as vectors and their treatment by trigonometric methods, and the circular functions of real numbers are among the topics which henceforth should receive important emphasis in the study of trigonometry. The proposed modifications of this course create curriculum problems demanding careful study.

The program for the twelfth year offers almost limitless possibilities and poses many significant curriculum problems. The program for this year is more of an elective program than those of previous years. It is also true that the tight sequence of mathematical study begins to break down a bit at this level. These two facts make it both possible and desirable that the planning of the mathematics curriculum for grade 12 should provide for variation in interests and aptitudes for mathe-

[9]The School Mathematics Study Group, the University of Illinois Committee on School Mathematics, and the Ball State Experimental Program in Mathematics.

matically capable students. Furthermore, the twelfth grade should make provision for potential graduates who do not yet meet the minimum requirements in mathematics to have the opportunity to meet such requirements.[10]

The literature carries descriptions of experiments and suggestions for topics to be used as instructional units in the program for this grade. Possibly the most carefully considered and the most authoritative recommendation of a program for the mathematically capable is that given by the Commission on Mathematics. Their recommendation is for "a course to be called Elementary Functions," for the first semester, to be followed by a second semester "devoted either to introductory probability with statistical applications or to an introduction to modern algebra (fields and groups)."[11] They also state that there are other just as satisfactory possibilities. "Indeed, any serious mathematics, creatively and imaginatively taught, would be appropriate."[12]

The junior college From one point of view, at least, the program of the junior college is analogous to that of the junior high school. For many students the two years of junior college will be the final years of their formal educational careers. Others, though they continue in college, are not interested in further work in mathematics. On the other hand, a fairly large and increasing proportion of students who enter college do plan to specialize in fields of study which require an extensive program in mathematics for which a strong background in analytic geometry and calculus is only a beginning prerequisite.

These facts combine to present a curriculum problem which is both important and complicated. Should all junior college students be expected to take some work in mathematics? If not, who should be excused from this requirement, and for what reasons? If so, how much mathematics should be required of all, and what should be the content of this minimum course? What should be the content and arrangement of the regular systematic freshman and sophomore courses for those who plan to continue their work in mathematics through or beyond the junior college? These are a few of the questions that have to be considered. They are not new, but they are becoming ever more acute and more important.

Although the wise determination of a minimum curriculum in mathematics is of major concern, it is but one of several critical problems which have challenged the best thinking of professional groups interested in improved instruction in mathematics. Also calling for careful study are the demands for change in character of content and for

[10]Secondary School Curriculum Committee, *op. cit.*, p. 413.
[11]Commission on Mathematics, *op. cit.*, pp. 30–33, 42–47.
[12]*Ibid.*

increased intensity of application of the mathematics prerequisite to the natural sciences and engineering. Too, there are increasing demands for pertinent prerequisite training in mathematics from less technical areas, such as the social sciences and psychology, as well as from business and industry. Furthermore, there exists an urgent need for the establishment of a closer affinity between the mathematics of these first two college years and that which serves as the foundation of modern scientific research.

The Joint Committee of the American Society for Engineering Education and the Mathematical Association of America recommended that colleges should raise standards for mathematics performance, pay more attention to the fundamentals of probability and statistics, and provide for pre-engineering students more course electives in mathematics as well as a more intensive program of problem solving.[13]

While the Commission on Mathematics was interested in the college-capable students of the high school and directed its report entirely in the direction of such students, it did not overlook the fact that "the colleges have contributed to the high school curriculum problem by their inertia." The report further states that "the Commission sees no hope of effective curriculum reform at the secondary level unless this reform is supplemented by a related effort at the college level."[14] There is gratifying evidence that many colleges now are taking steps in this direction. This is reflected to some degree in the large and increasing number of textbooks that have appeared since about 1960, which exhibit innovations in the organization of the courses or in the treatment of the subject matter.

The most concentrated effort toward modification of the junior college program has been that of the Committee on the Undergraduate Program in Mathematics (CUPM). In assessing the need for revision, it not only called attention to the widespread dissatisfaction with existing programs but also pointed out that any program of revision must take into account not only the expanding needs of engineering and the physical sciences but also those of the biological and social sciences and the relatively new field of numerical analysis.[15]

As a part of its work, this committee established certain writing groups of mathematicians charged with the responsibility of preparing some new experimental courses for the freshman and sophomore years. This work culminated in the publication by the committee of four experimental textbooks. Taken in pairs, these four books were designed

[13]Report of the Joint Committee of the American Society for Engineering Education and the Mathematical Association of America, *American Mathematical Monthly*, **62** (1955), 385–392.

[14]Commission on Mathematics, *op. cit.*, p. 62.

[15]Report of the Committee on the Undergraduate Program in Mathematics, *American Mathematical Monthly*, **62** (1955), 511–520.

to represent two different courses for the two semesters of the freshman year, each of which would be quite unlike the traditional courses. One of these was thought to be appropriate for all students. The other was designed with a view to meeting the special needs of students planning to major in the biological or social sciences.

Much of the work which has been done and is being done toward improvement of the freshman and sophomore courses in mathematics has undoubtedly been initiated directly or indirectly as a result of the activities of the CUPM.

Experimental curriculum and course projects Changes in curriculums and in individual courses originate in the minds of individuals or in the collective thinking of groups of individuals. Every textbook for a course in mathematics reflects the ideas of its author or authors as to what content and plan of organization is most appropriate, what things should be emphasized, and what kind of presentation will contribute most effectively to learning. Reports of course or curriculum committees reflect the collective opinions of groups of persons about these things.

While the recommendations of certain committees and commissions in the past have had far-reaching influence in reshaping curriculums and courses in mathematics, most of those that were made before the middle of this century were characterized by two things. For the most part they looked toward the rearrangement and adaptation of traditional subject matter, and they were based largely upon collective opinion rather than upon experimental evidence of their validity.

The impact of modern mathematics, however, brought into the picture concepts, terminology, notation, and emphases which hitherto had been lacking in the secondary school courses. Hence the validity, propriety, and feasibility of these innovations for the secondary school curriculum could not be evaluated on the basis of long years of experience and mature observation. As a result, a number of significant experimental projects aimed at producing, trying out, and appraising new courses and methods have come into being since 1950. These projects have varied both in extent and in their detailed objectives and activities, but they have all aimed at providing new and basic information which could be helpful in curriculum revision.

The following list of such experimental projects related to the improvement of mathematics curriculums and courses was reported, with brief descriptions of the projects, by the National Science Foundation in October, 1962,[16] and gives some idea of the scope and nature of these experimental projects.

[16]"Science Course Improvement Projects," 1, Courses, Written Materials, Films, Studies Supported by the National Science Foundation, NSF 62-38, October, 1962.

Syracuse University-Webster College Madison Project (elementary and secondary); Coordinated Science and Mathematics Curriculum for Grades K–9 (elementary and secondary); Survey of Recent East European Literature in School and College Mathematics (elementary, secondary, and college); School Mathematics Study Group (SMSG) (elementary and secondary); Regional Orientation Conferences in Mathematics (elementary and secondary); University of Illinois Committee on School Mathematics (UICSM) (elementary and secondary); Evaluation of Secondary School Mathematics Curricula (secondary); Experimental Films in Mathematics (secondary and college); Films for Mathematics Teachers (secondary); Committee on the Undergraduate Program in Mathematics (CUPM) (college); Experimental Teaching Program in Algebra (college); Experimental Pregraduate Programs in Mathematics (college); New Undergraduate Courses in Mathematics (college); Mathematics Courses for Prospective Elementary School Teachers (two separate projects) (college); Power Series and the Elementary Functions (secondary and college); Coordinated Program for Mathematics and Physics Majors in Freshman and Sophomore Years (college); Films in Mathematics for Elementary School Teachers (elementary); Introductory Course in Probability, Matrices, and Calculus for Students in the Biological and Social Sciences (college); Course in Mathematics for Prospective Junior High School Teachers (college).

The foregoing list includes only projects which have received financial support from the National Science Foundation. In addition to these, any list of significant experimental projects should surely include reference to a number of others such as the Boston College Mathematics Institute (BCMI), the Greater Cleveland Mathematics Program (GCMP), the University of Maryland Mathematics Project (UMMaP), the Ontario Mathematics Commission (OMC), the Ball State Mathematics Project, and the Development Project in Secondary Mathematics at Southern Illinois University. All these are extensive undertakings aimed at the common goal of improving the mathematics curriculum. Of course there are also many experimental studies of mathematics curriculums and courses which have been and are being conducted at local levels within individual school systems.

In 1959 the National Council of Teachers of Mathematics set up the Committee on the Analysis of Experimental Mathematics Programs. This committee was given responsibility for investigating ways in which the National Council could be of help to teachers or schools in considering changes in their mathematics programs. The first report[17] of this committee was published in 1963. In this report the following

[17]"An Analysis of New Mathematics Programs" (Washington, D.C.: National Council of Teachers of Mathematics, 1963).

eight experimental programs are considered: the Boston College Mathematics Institute, the Greater Cleveland Mathematics Program, the Syracuse University-Webster College Madison Project, the University of Maryland Mathematics Project, the Ontario Mathematics Commission, the School Mathematics Study Group, the Developmental Project in Secondary Mathematics at Southern Illinois University, and the University of Illinois Committee on School Mathematics. For each of these programs a brief description is given, and this is followed by a concise analysis (not evaluation) of the program with respect to eight different criteria: "Social Applications," "Placement," "Structure," "Vocabulary," "Methods," "Concepts vs Skills," "Proof," "Provision for Evaluation."

The Committee on Analysis of Experimental Programs is a standing committee. It is expected that additional reports dealing with other experimental programs will be published at appropriate times.

Of all these experimental projects perhaps the UICSM project and the SMSG project, because of their impressive scope and massive scale, seem likely to have the greatest impact upon impending course and curriculum revision in school mathematics. Both are continuing projects. Under each of these projects numerous experimental courses have been written, tried out on a large scale, and extensively revised and rewritten before being released in textbook form; and large numbers of teachers who were to use these experimental materials in participating schools have been given special training for this work. Efforts have also been made to evaluate the experimental courses with respect to both their feasibility and their desirability.

Individual differences The recognition of, and the making of proper provision for, individual differences in learning potential and performance through the years has been, and will continue to be, a major curriculum problem in the shaping of the secondary school program in mathematics. It is a well-known fact that this problem intensifies at the level of the secondary school. Here there are to be found wide variations in ability, ranging from the academically gifted to the very slow learner. It is indeed a problem of serious concern which confronts teachers as they attempt to deal with individual pupils and with groups in accordance with their ability to learn. The classification of pupils (slow learner, average, academically talented) should be the result of cooperative effort on the part of the administrator, the guidance personnel, the teacher, and the parents. It should be based on information from a cumulative record begun in the elementary school and containing results from intelligence and achievement tests, interest and aptitude inventories, and other types of information pertinent to social adjustment and school progress.

There are certain distinguishing characteristics which should be helpful in recognizing the slow learner in mathematics and the mathematically gifted in contradistinction to each other and to the average group. Although there are many possible exceptions to any given pattern, the following[18] might be safely listed as characteristics of the slow learner:

1. Intelligence quotient below 90
2. Has little drive
3. Has short span of attention
4. Has weak association memory
5. Is a poor reader
6. Has difficulty with abstractions
7. Is not logical
8. Lacks imagination
9. Is unable to detect his own errors
10. Has little power to transfer training
11. Is not creative in his thinking

In contrast, the Secondary School Curriculum Committee gives the following lists of general and special characteristics which mark the mathematically gifted:[19]

1. General characteristics
   - *a.* Makes associations readily and retains them indefinitely
   - *b.* Recognizes similarities and differences quickly
   - *c.* Has excellent memory, good vocabulary, broad attention span, and high reading ability
   - *d.* Has a relatively mature sense of values
   - *e.* Pursues interests with tremendous energy and drive
   - *f.* Uses his spare time productively
2. Special characteristics
   - *a.* Recognizes patterns readily and enjoys speculating on generalizations
   - *b.* Prefers to think on higher levels of abstraction
   - *c.* Classifies particular cases as special cases of more general situations with relative ease
   - *d.* Follows a long chain of reasoning, frequently anticipating and contributing
   - *e.* Frequently asks profound questions
   - *f.* May be reading mathematics books years ahead of his class
   - *g.* Is frequently impatient with drill and details that he thinks are not important

Though the identification of the relative-ability groups is a problem of tremendous responsibility, there remain other problems of just as great concern and difficulty. What mathematics program is the most

[18]Mary Potter and Virgil Mallory, "Education in Mathematics for the Slow Learner" (Washington, D.C.: National Council of Teachers of Mathematics, 1958), pp. 11–12.

[19]Secondary School Curriculum Committee, *op. cit.*, p. 410.

significant for each of the three groups (slow learner, average, and mathematically gifted)? Is there a close similarity or a wide variation in the content of the program for each group? There seems to be rather general agreement that the basic content must be the same for all three groups but must vary in amount, pattern of organization, manner of presentation, and intensity of attention. For the slow learner the manner of presentation must emphasize the approach to abstractions through a large amount of concrete experience bolstered by frequent reviews and intensive practice. Furthermore, the abstractions must be kept in simple form. The minimum program must be carefully defined to protect the boys and girls against the demands of an age that is becoming more and more technological in nature.

From the point of view of greatest potential for service to our society, the academically talented students are the ones who place the most serious demand on curriculum designers for careful thinking and imaginative planning. The College Entrance Examination Board has taken cognizance of this fact in the report of its Commission on Mathematics[20] and in the sponsoring of the Advanced Placement Program for admission to college with advanced standing.[21] Other groups have studied the problem and made recommendations for solution.[22]

The Secondary School Curriculum Committee seems to have summarized and underscored the best thought on this extremely important problem in these words:[23]

> All schools should provide opportunities for the gifted. Ability grouping is a widely acceptable and desirable practice, and special classes for the able are recommended where organizational and staff facilities permit. Honors classes, seminars, and special projects provide excellent means for challenging the gifted. A policy of acceleration is followed in some areas. Two basically different patterns are used: (1) A narrow type, or "mere speed-up" plan, in which pupils are allowed to "cover" the requirements of one year's program to get into that of the next year, for example: two years of algebra in one year; and (2) a broad type or "faster growth-in-depth" plan, where more mature understandings and procedures are expected sooner.

[20]Commission on Mathematics, *op. cit.*

[21]College Entrance Examination Board, "Fifty-third Annual Report of the Director" (New York: College Entrance Examination Board, 1955), p. 20.

[22]Report of the Joint Conference of the Cooperative Committee on the Teaching of Science and Mathematics of the American Association for the Advancement of Science and the United States Office of Education, "Education for the Talented in Mathematics and Science" (U.S. Office of Education Bulletin 15, 1952, reprint 1953).

E. P. Vance (Editor), "Program Provisions for the Mathematically Gifted Student in the Secondary School" (Washington, D.C.: National Council of Teachers of Mathematics, reprint 1959).

Report of the Joint Conference of the National Education Association and the National Council of Teachers of Mathematics, "Mathematics for the Academically Talented Student" (Washington, D.C.: National Council of Teachers of Mathematics, 1959).

[23]Secondary School Curriculum Committee, *op. cit.*, pp. 410–411.

There is some question about the advisability of the "mere speed-up plan." A sophomore pupil, for example, who is undertaking senior mathematics could easily be a triple loser. He could be so completely out of step with the educational pattern that he would be confronted with unnecessary confusion in planning for the future; secondly, he could have lost material benefits by not having had the opportunity to make significant explorations below the surface of mere satisfactory accomplishment; and thirdly, he could have missed the inspiring challenge that can come from inquisitive search into the rationale of procedures, the foundations of concepts, and the implications of principles. On the other hand, a carefully planned acceleration program of the "faster-growth-in-depth" type can benefit the able pupil very materially through the provision of opportunities for deeper investigation of foundations, broader contact with related areas of cultural and utilitarian value, and more significant appreciation of basic interrelationships as well as advancement in grade-level accomplishment.

Any program of enrichment for the mathematically gifted not only should provide real challenge to excellent accomplishment but also should provide basic information essential to top-level performance in mathematics, both for the present and for the future. This can be accomplished in better fashion by less emphasis on drill and on delineation of applications, in order to provide more opportunity for discovery of significant patterns and formulation of generalizations. Under informed guidance such pupils should be encouraged to read widely, to investigate significant topics which offer them challenge, participate in competitive endeavors, and seek occasion to meet with other mathematically gifted pupils both within their own school and from other schools.

Since the purpose of ability grouping in mathematics is to increase the efficiency of learning, it behooves teachers to adjust their methods of teaching in order to take maximum advantage of homogeneity of the several groups and to gear instruction to the learning level of the students in each group. Furthermore, administrators should strive (1) to develop in their staffs an understanding of the basic purposes of ability grouping and the desirability of taking advantage of it, (2) to adjust class size for optimum benefits from such grouping, and (3) to reduce non-teaching duties so that all teachers will have better opportunity for taking care of individual differences at all levels of instruction.

The individual classroom teacher As is evident from the discussion of this chapter, many questions are being asked and many problems are being considered, all of which are pertinent to intelligent planning for the curriculum reforms so urgently needed in secondary mathematics. What can the classroom teacher, as an individual, contribute as his part in the total effort toward curriculum revision? The recommendations of committees and the verifications of experimentation all will be of no avail unless implemented by teachers in the classrooms of the nation. Each teacher should consider it a personal challenge and a professional opportunity and obligation to evaluate recommended new ideas and procedures in the context of his particular situation and to make the most effective use of those which are found to be appropriate and pertinent.

The leaders in curriculum planning must strive to think clearly in the mixed perspective of ideal growth in mathematical insight and realistic restriction of unselected student personnel. The classroom teacher must, in turn, strive to make maximum adaptations of approved curriculum content and instructional procedures within the limitations of local pupil potential and individual teaching proficiency. Only through a closely coordinated program of such professional teamwork can the goal of effective curriculum revision in mathematics be accomplished.

EXERCISES

1. To what factors do you attribute the intensity of the current demand for reshaping the mathematics curriculum of the secondary schools? Be as explicit as you can.

2. What, in your opinion, are the chief problems associated with the improvement of the mathematics curriculum for grades 7 and 8? Discuss at least one of these in some detail.

3. Give a somewhat detailed report on the content and nature of the experimental courses for grades 7 and 8 which were developed in the Maryland Study or one of the other major experimental projects, and point out ways in which these courses differ from the traditional courses for these grades.

4. Examine several commercially published seventh- and eighth-grade textbooks of recent date to see to what extent and in what ways they have been oriented toward modern mathematics.

5. Compare the recommendations of the Secondary School Curriculum Committee and those of the Commission on Mathematics with respect to the mathematics programs for grades 7 and 8. Point out any similarities and any major differences that you find.

6. What special problems are associated with the mathematics program for grade 9?

7. The double-track program in mathematics for grade 9 has been widely adopted. Discuss the theoretical justification of such a program, and point out some safeguards that should be set up in conducting such a program.

8. Discuss the special importance of wise counseling of students in the administration of a double-track program in mathematics for grade 9.

9. Compare some recent textbooks in beginning algebra with others published before 1950, noting any differences in the major topics included and the ways in which the subject is developed. Report on these differences.

10. Compare the recommendations of the Commission on Mathematics with those of the Secondary School Curriculum Committee with respect to the course in geometry for the high school. What significant differences, if any, do you find?

11. Examine with some care the experimental textbook on geometry prepared and published by the SMSG. What differences do you find between this and some conventional textbooks in geometry published before 1950?

12. Repeat exercise 11, but this time with reference to the experimental textbook on geometry prepared and published by the UICSM.

13. What similarities and what differences do you find between the experimental courses in geometry published by the SMSG and the UICSM?

14. Select two trigonometry textbooks published since 1960 and two that were published before 1950. Compare the more recent books with the earlier ones as to the topics included and the relative emphasis given to logarithms and the solution of triangles.

15. Discuss the problems that arise in connection with the program in mathematics for grade 12. What do you think would be the most desirable program? Justify your choice.

16. Find out all you can about the history, objectives, and activities of the UICSM, and make a report.

17. Find out all you can about the history, objectives, and activities of the SMSG, and make a report.

18. Find out all you can about the Maryland and the Ball State experimental projects in mathematics, and make a report.

19. Enumerate some of the problems that must be faced in modernizing the junior college curriculum in mathematics. Discuss one of these.

20. Many colleges offer trigonometry and intermediate algebra (essentially high school courses) and allow college credit for them, while others do not allow college credit for these courses. Discuss whether this presents a curriculum problem to the high schools.

21. What curriculum problems in mathematics are presented by the students who are "slow learners"?

22. Describe some of the recommended patterns of instruction designed to challenge mathematically gifted students.

23. What is the Advanced Placement Program sponsored by the College Entrance Examination Board? (See Vance reference in chapter bibliography.)

24. Assuming ample staff and facilities, what are some of the arguments for and against ability grouping of mathematics students in the high school?

BIBLIOGRAPHY

Adler, Irving: Some Changes Taking Place in Mathematics, *Mathematics Teacher*, **55** (1962), 441–451.

Baker, Russell R.: Program Provisions in Michigan Junior High Schools for Superior Students in Mathematics, *Mathematics Teacher*, **55** (1962), 556–559.

Barker, I. C.: Not What Can Be Taught, but What Should Be Taught, *American Mathematical Monthly*, **69** (1962), 426–428.

Begle, E. G.: A Study of Mathematical Abilities, *American Mathematical Monthly*, **69** (1962), 1000–1002.

Bernstein, Allen L.: Recent Research in Mathematics Teaching, *Michigan Education Journal*, **60** (1962), 262, 273.

Brown, Robert S.: Survey of Ohio College Opinions with Reference to High School Mathematics Programs, *Mathematics Teacher*, **52** (1959), 245–247.

Brumfiel, Charles, Robert Eicholz, and Merrill Shanks: The Ball State Experimental Program, *Mathematics Teacher*, **53** (1960), 75–84.

Cairns, Stewart Scott: Mathematical Education and the Scientific Revolution, *Mathematics Teacher*, **53** (1960), 66–74.

Commentary on the Mathematics Curriculum of the High School, *Mathematics Teacher*, **55** (1962), 191–198. (Three short articles which should be read together.)

"Commission on Mathematics, Report of" (New York: College Entrance Examination Board, 1959).

Experimental Programs (a regular continuing department of the *Mathematics Teacher*).

Fehr, H. F.: Mathematics Curriculum for the High School of the Future, *Teachers College Record*, **59** (1958), 258–267.

———: Breakthroughs in Mathematical Thought, *Mathematics Teacher*, **52** (1959), 15–19.

———: New Thinking in Mathematical Education, *Mathematics Teacher*, **53** (1960), 424–429.

Fraser, Dorothy M.: "Current Curriculum Studies in Academic Subjects" (Washington, D.C.: National Education Association, 1962).

Grossman, George: Advanced Placement

Mathematics: For Whom? *Mathematics Teacher,* **55** (1962), 560–566.

Hale, William T.: UICSM's Decade of Experimentation, *Mathematics Teacher,* **54** (1961), 613–619.

Jones, Burton W.: Silken Slippers and Hobnailed Boots, *Mathematics Teacher,* **52** (1959), 322–327.

Keedy, M. L.: The University of Maryland Project, *Mathematics Teacher,* **52** (1959), 281–282.

Kemeny, John G.: Report to the International Congress of Mathematicians, *Mathematics Teacher,* **56** (1963), 66–78.

Kenner, Morton R.: The Developmental Project in Secondary Mathematics, *American Mathematical Monthly,* **68** (1961), 797–798.

Kline, Morris: The Ancients versus The Moderns: A New Battle of the Books, *Mathematics Teacher,* **51** (1958), 418–427.

Leissa, Arthur W., and Robert C. Fisher: A Survey of Teachers' Opinions of a Revised Mathematics Curriculum, *Mathematics Teacher,* **53** (1960), 113–118.

Marlin, Lillian: SMSG: One Point of View, *Mathematics Teacher,* **55** (1962), 476–478.

Mayor, John, and John Brown: New Mathematics in the Junior High School, *Educational Leadership,* **18** (1960), 166.

Meder, A. E.: The Ancients versus the Moderns: A Reply, *Mathematics Teacher,* **51** (1958), 428–433.

Meserve, Bruce E.: New Trends in Algebra and Geometry, *Mathematics Teacher,* **55** (1962), 452–461.

Meyer, William (Moderator): Report of the Committee on High School Mathematics Courses, *California Schools,* **31** (1960), 3–15.

Myers, Sheldon, and Marion G. Epstein: Mathematical Reform and the College Entrance Examination Board, *American Mathematical Monthly,* **70** (1963), 665–667.

National Council of Teachers of Mathematics: Insights into Modern Mathematics, *Twenty-third Yearbook* (Washington, D.C.: National Council of Teachers of Mathematics, 1959).

———: The Growth of Mathematical Ideas, *Twenty-fourth Yearbook* (Washington, D.C.: National Council of Teachers of Mathematics, 1960).

———: Enrichment Mathematics for the Grades, *Twenty-seventh Yearbook* (Washington, D.C.: National Council of Teachers of Mathematics, 1963).

———: Enrichment Mathematics for the High School, *Twenty-eighth Yearbook* (Washington, D.C.: National Council of Teachers of Mathematics, 1964).

———: Report of the Secondary School Curriculum Committee, *Mathematics Teacher,* **52** (1959), 389–417.

———: "The Revolution in Mathematics" (Washington, D.C.: National Council of Teachers of Mathematics, 1961).

National Science Foundation: "Science Course Improvement Project," 1, NSF 62-38, Courses, Written Materials, Films, Studies (Washington, D.C.: National Science Foundation, 1962).

Phillips, Jo McKeeby: The Baby and the Bath Water, *School Science and Mathematics,* **63** (1963), 291–304.

Pieters, Richard S., and E. P. Vance: The Advanced Placement Program in Mathematics, *Mathematics Teacher,* **54** (1961), 201–211.

Rappaport, David: Proposed Revision and Acceleration of the High School Mathematics Program, *School Science and Mathematics,* **60** (1960), 214–221.

Rosenberg, Herman: Great Challenges of Mathematics Education, *Mathematics Teacher,* **55** (1962), 360–368.

Rosskopf, Myron F. (Chairman of Editorial Committee): New Developments in Secondary-school Mathematics, *Bulletin of the National Association of Secondary-School Principals,* **43** (1959).

Rourke, Robert E. K.: Some Implications of Twentieth Century Mathematics for High Schools, *Mathematics Teacher,* **51** (1958), 74–86.

Schneider, Helen, and Burton W. Jones: "The New Mathematics Curricula: What and Why" (Washington, D.C.: National Council of Teachers of Mathematics, 1963). (Pamphlet.)

Stone, Marshall: The Revolution in Mathematics, *American Mathematical Monthly*, **68** (1961), 715–734.

Taylor, Angus E.: Convention and Revolt in Mathematics, *Mathematics Teacher*, **55** (1962), 2–9.

Taylor, Ross: First Course in Algebra—UICSM and SMSG: A Comparison, *Mathematics Teacher*, **55** (1962), 478–481.

Thwaites, Bryan: "On Teaching Mathematics" (New York: Pergamon Press, 1961).

Vance, E. P., and others: "Program Provisions for the Mathematically Gifted Student in the Secondary School" (Washington, D.C.: National Council of Teachers of Mathematics, 1958).

Wagner, John: The Objectives and Activities of the School Mathematics Study Group, *Mathematics Teacher*, **53** (1960), 454–459.

Willerding, Margaret F.: A Critical Look at the New Mathematics for Seventh Grade, *School Science and Mathematics*, **62** (1962), 215–220.

Wilson, Jack: What Mathematics for the Terminal Student? *Mathematics Teacher*, **53** (1960), 518–523.

Zant, James H.: Improving the Program in Mathematics in Oklahoma Schools, *Mathematics Teacher*, **54** (1961), 594–599.

———: Effect of New Mathematics Program in the Schools on College Mathematics Courses, *American Mathematical Monthly*, **70** (1963), 200–202.

FIVE

Stimulating and maintaining interest in mathematics

IT MAY BE taken as axiomatic that students will work most diligently and most effectively at tasks in which they are genuinely interested. To create and maintain interest becomes, therefore, one of the most important tasks of the teacher of secondary school mathematics. It is also one of the most difficult problems which the teacher encounters. The interest of students of secondary school age is capricious. It is easily caught by any new thing, but it is as easily distracted to other new things. Ordinarily it cannot be depended upon to maintain itself for any great length of time unless the work has been carefully and deliberately planned to that end, and even then it usually needs occasional stimulation. Thus the motivation of the work in mathematics has two aspects, viz., that of creating or arousing interest and that of maintaining the interest after the novelty of the work in hand has worn off.

As a rule, students readily *become interested* in things which are new or exciting, in things for which they can perceive practical values or applications to situations and fields of study in which they are already interested, and in things which involve puzzle elements or elements of mystery. Other things being equal, the possession of a background of related information tends to intensify interest in new work, but this is neither a necessary condition nor a sufficient guarantee for the awakening of interest. Novelty is sometimes more compelling than familiarity. The elements of novelty, usefulness, and sheer intellectual curiosity are the primary stimuli for the awakening of interest.

It is easier to interest students in their work than it is to keep them interested after the work has got under way and the novelty has worn off. In this connection it is worthwhile to observe that students tend to *remain interested* in those things which they can do most successfully and which they understand most completely. Inability to understand is likely to beget a condition of listlessness, inattention, and general loss of interest. On the other hand, the work should not be diluted and should not evade the intellectual stretching without which there can be no mathematical growth. The work should present a continual challenge, but it should be a challenge in a real sense and not mere drudgery at tasks devoid of meaning or inexcusably difficult. Consequently, it is of the greatest importance that work in mathematics be so organized and conducted as to emphasize the values and the inherent intellectual challenge of the subject and to ensure understanding and a reasonable degree of competence by keeping the subject matter and the activities at a level of difficulty appropriate to the intellectual maturity of the students. Within these conditions are to be found the motives basic to hard and effective work in mathematics. Interest in the subject can be effectively augmented by numerous special devices and activities, some of which can be used in connection with class instruction while others, such as mathematics clubs and special programs, are essentially coordinate and supplementary activities.[1]

Hartung's analysis of the problem of motivating learning in mathematics In what is probably the most penetrating and thorough published analysis of motivation as related to the learning of mathematics, Hartung[2] distinguishes between motives and incentives. In making this distinction, motives are considered to be states or conditions or "drives" residing within the student, while incentives are external impelling factors. Both can lead to purposeful activity and perhaps toward the same goal. *Interests* are described as motives which serve as important influences in producing both activities and attitudes that are favorable to learning. A strong interest in mathematics then would tend to produce a favorable attitude toward the subject, and such an attitude would in turn probably lead to or enhance the desire to study mathematics in a serious and productive way. Thus the development and stimulation of interest in mathematics becomes an important concern of the teacher.[3]

[1]Walter H. Carnahan, Maintenance of Interest in Mathematics, *Bulletin of the National Association of Secondary-School Principals*, **38** (1954), 110–116.

[2]Maurice L. Hartung, Motivation for Education in Mathematics, *Twenty-first Yearbook* (Washington, D.C.: National Council of Teachers of Mathematics, 1953), pp. 42–67.

[3]*Ibid.*, pp. 51–52.

Interests are motives that almost all teachers try to use to promote learning. The literature on mathematical education contains numerous references to the importance of arousing the interests of students, and dozens of suggestions as to means of doing so. Unfortunately, many of these suggestions seem to stem from a relatively narrow conception of the nature of interest in mathematics.

Genuine interest in mathematics probably depends basically upon the problem solving aspect of the subject. Problems, once recognized or sensed, leave an individual in a state of perplexity, uneasiness, or tension until they are solved. When a solution has been found, tension-reduction and satisfaction results. If mathematics is properly taught, it presents the student with an abundance of problems, and it also provides him with certain general modes of thought and a supply of techniques which enable him to attack these problems successfully. With each successful solution he receives a dividend of satisfaction – he feels good when he gets the answer. As a result, he seeks more experiences of the same kind, and displays other desirable types of behavior which were described earlier in defining interest.

As the student grows in mathematical maturity, he obtains satisfaction also from contemplation of the power of his methods and the sharpness and beauty of his tools. The term "appreciation" is often used in this connection. The behavior is relevant to interest, however, because it leads the student to seek more experiences with mathematics, to discuss it favorably with other people, and to value it for what it does for him personally.

A good many of the devices recommended for arousing interest seem to be based on the assumption that mathematics itself is uninteresting and hence learning must be encouraged by extraneous elements such as the mystery of a puzzle or the competition of a game. When, however, the subject preferences of children are investigated by objective methods, mathematics is often found to rank high on the list. . . .

No mere summary can do full justice to this excellent analysis of the problem of motivating learning in mathematics, but since it cannot be reproduced in full here, it seems desirable to mention at least a few additional observations and conclusions given therein.

Incentives may serve to build motive or "inner drive" and thus to promote genuine interest in mathematical work, but the use of incentives cannot guarantee this. Incentives are only means to an end; they should not be regarded as ends in themselves, and they should not be used indiscriminately or thoughtlessly. Unless they are used judiciously, some incentives such as marks and rewards of various kinds may, indeed, even produce undesirable attitudes. Whether they produce desirable motivation or not depends on the kinds of incentives used and the ways in which they are used.

Most of the suggestions discussed in the literature on mathematics education deal with devices which are essentially thought of as incentives. Among these are such things as mathematical games and contests; tricks, puzzles, and other recreations; films and multisensory aids of various kinds; laboratory projects; applications; information about the need for and the uses of mathematics in certain vocations and professions; historical material; and mathematics clubs. All of these can be useful if presented in proper perspective and with proper concern for the real objective. Some of them, e.g., games, puzzles, and recreations, may fail to contribute much beyond transient attention getting unless care is taken to emphasize the mathematical aspects. They can serve as interesting settings for mathematical principles, but they should not be allowed to obscure those principles. Hartung says:[4]

> If tricks and puzzles are overemphasized, the students are likely to get a distorted idea of the nature of mathematics. They think that mathematics consists largely of a bunch of tricks. . . . If a theoretical explanation of a trick or puzzle is accessible to the student, the discovery of it may, of course, become a genuine problem. Investigating whether a trick which works for a particular set of numbers will work for others, or in general, may be much more interesting than many practical problems. It is to be noted, however, that in this case the interest is derived not from the trick as a trick, but from the more general mathematical or problem-solving behavior that is evoked.

Mathematics clubs constitute one form of special activity which is always desirable. They provide extra avenues of interest for students who are already well motivated, and even if the programs are largely concerned with puzzles and special problems not related to the regular classwork, nothing is lost. The students who belong to mathematics clubs nearly always do so voluntarily, and they are usually among the better students.

Multisensory aids and laboratory and field experiences in mathematics are often regarded as means for motivation, and it is proper that they should be so regarded. They are, however, more than mere motivating devices; they are indeed avenues through which important learning can and should take place.

The most powerful and enduring motivation for learning mathematics comes from genuine understanding of the subject itself. The more fully students understand mathematics, the more they want to learn about it. Lack of understanding leads to continued frustration and to negative attitudes, but understanding and successful experience contribute powerfully toward the development of self-confidence, pride in accomplishment, and desirable attitudes toward the work.

The following check list from Hartung[5] is proposed as suggesting kinds of questions which teachers might well have in mind in deciding upon or evaluating motivational procedures or devices.

[4]*Ibid.*, p. 53.
[5]*Ibid.*, pp. 65–66.

1. Is the proposed procedure likely to be effective?
   a. Does it draw upon motives actually present in the learner?
   b. Is it designed to utilize a combination of several motives in the learner?
   c. Is it appropriate for the age level of the learner?
   d. Is it based upon recognition of a goal by the learner, and does the learner believe he can achieve his goal?
   e. Does it motivate many students or just a few?
   f. How long is the motivation likely to persist?
2. Is the motivation of a desirable type?
   a. Does it lead the student to value the learning experience itself rather than external rewards?
   b. Will it widen and deepen the interests of the learner?
   c. Does it tend to develop desirable attitudes toward the content or skill and toward the teacher?
   d. Are the goals which are set actually attainable?
   e. Does the motivation tend to strengthen attitudes necessary for democratic citizenship?
   f. Is the motivation consistent with the promotion of good social relations between students?
3. Is the procedure practicable?
   a. Is the required expenditure of time and money within the means of the school?
   b. How well can the procedure be controlled in practice?
   c. Does the teacher know how to administer the procedure?

In concluding his article,[6] Hartung distills the essence of the problem of motivation as follows:

> We may reflect that the interests and attitudes of most children when they enter school are favorable to learning mathematics. Some of them learn to *like* it. Others learn to *dislike* it. To change an unfavorable attitude once formed into a favorable one is a difficult assignment. Efforts on the part of teachers to arrange conditions so that unfavorable attitudes are not learned will, in the long run, probably pay generous dividends.

Motivation through the use of multisensory aids and devices Most people gain new impressions more vividly through sensory experiences than they do through reading or abstract reasoning. The remarkable growth and public acceptance of motion pictures, radio, and television leave no doubt of the interest-getting power of these audio-visual media. Advertisements in newspapers and magazines and on billboards and television commercials are found to be more effective when they have eye appeal than when they are confined to mere statements in words, even though the con-

[6]*Ibid.*, p. 66.

nection between the picture and the subject may be pretty farfetched. Thus, a pleasant wooded lake and an attractive young lady seem to be standard adjuncts in advertising almost anything from soap, cigarettes, and beer to refrigerators, automobiles, and waterfront lots.

Teachers of mathematics have been slower than their colleagues in English, geography, science, history, and the social studies to take advantage of this eye-and-ear appeal as a means of stimulating interest among their students. This has been partly due to the nature of the subject, which is essentially one of ideas rather than things. That, in turn, accounts in large measure for the fact that not very many really good pictorial or physical representations of mathematical topics have been commonly available. Commercially, such devices have been limited mainly to a few good sound films and filmstrips and a number of not-so-good ones and to certain rather expensive models and mechanical devices for illustrating theorems in geometry. For one reason or another, these aids and devices have not been very widely used, though as they are improved it can be expected that their use will increase.

Multisensory aids, however, are not limited to motion pictures and filmstrips, and in the past decade increasing attention has been given to the employment of other sensory devices both for motivation and for instruction. Evidence of this is found, for example, in the efforts to improve the effectiveness of textbooks through more and better diagrams and illustrations, the improvement of type face and format, and the liberal use of color. It is also seen in the number of suggestions in textbooks and elsewhere for stimulating interest in mathematics through projects involving the use of instruments and the construction and use of visual or mechanical devices for illustrating mathematical concepts, facts, and principles. Activities of this kind are commonly called "laboratory work in mathematics." Part of the next chapter will be devoted to discussion of such work as an important avenue to learning. Its importance, however, even from the standpoint of motivation alone, is so great that it must not be overlooked in this connection.

Motivation through application to other fields of study The relation of mathematics to other fields of study often provides an important means of stimulating interest. At all levels of secondary education from the junior high school to the junior college the contribution which mathematics has made and can make to the more adequate development and understanding of many subjects is coming to be recognized more fully than ever before, and teachers should not fail to stress its importance from this standpoint. There is no lack of material bearing upon this matter. Many articles discussing the relation of mathematics to other fields of study can be found in such magazines as the *Mathe-*

matics Teacher and *School Science and Mathematics* and in some of the yearbooks of the National Council of Teachers of Mathematics, as well as in other publications.

The basic importance of mathematics in relation to other fields of study has been nowhere more emphatically or more strikingly portrayed than in the mural entitled "The Tree of Knowledge" which was displayed in the Hall of Science at the Century of Progress Exposition in Chicago in 1933 (see Fig. 5-1). In this picture mathematics is represented as the main root of the tree, and springing from it are the other roots, stems, and branches representing the various basic and applied sciences. Copies of this painting can be secured at a nominal charge,[7] either in color or black and white, and in a size suitable for framing to hang on the walls of mathematics classrooms or in a small size suitable for pasting in the front of individual textbooks. This affords an excellent means of keeping before the students a continual reminder of the contribution which mathematics makes to these other subjects and fields of study.

The dependence of physics, chemistry, and astronomy upon mathematics is so manifest that it is hardly necessary to dwell upon it here. Mathematics is literally indispensable in the study of these subjects, and no informed person would question its instrumental value in this connection. It has only been in comparatively recent years that biologists have begun to realize the vast possibilities arising out of the application of mathematics to their science. The work of Quételet, Galton, and Pearson and their followers has opened up new avenues of approach and innumerable possibilities for systematizing and expanding this science and for the investigation and interpretation of biological phenomena through the formulation of precise mathematical expressions of the relationships and changes involved. Remarkable advances have been made through the application of mathematical procedures to advanced studies in genetics, heredity, nutrition, growth and maturation, senescence, metabolism, fatigue, the effects of various stimuli on organisms, and many other special phases of biological and physiological study. Indeed, it is hardly too much to say that it is no longer possible to pursue the study of biological phenomena very far beyond the early descriptive stages without the aid of mathematical analysis and treatment.

The social sciences are also beginning to draw heavily upon mathematics, particularly statistical and graphic methods, for the investigation and interpretation of social phenomena. Some of the mathematics used in connection with these subjects is so simple and so enlightening

[7]Inquiries and orders should be mailed to the Business Manager of the Museum of Science and Industry, Jackson Park, Chicago, Ill.

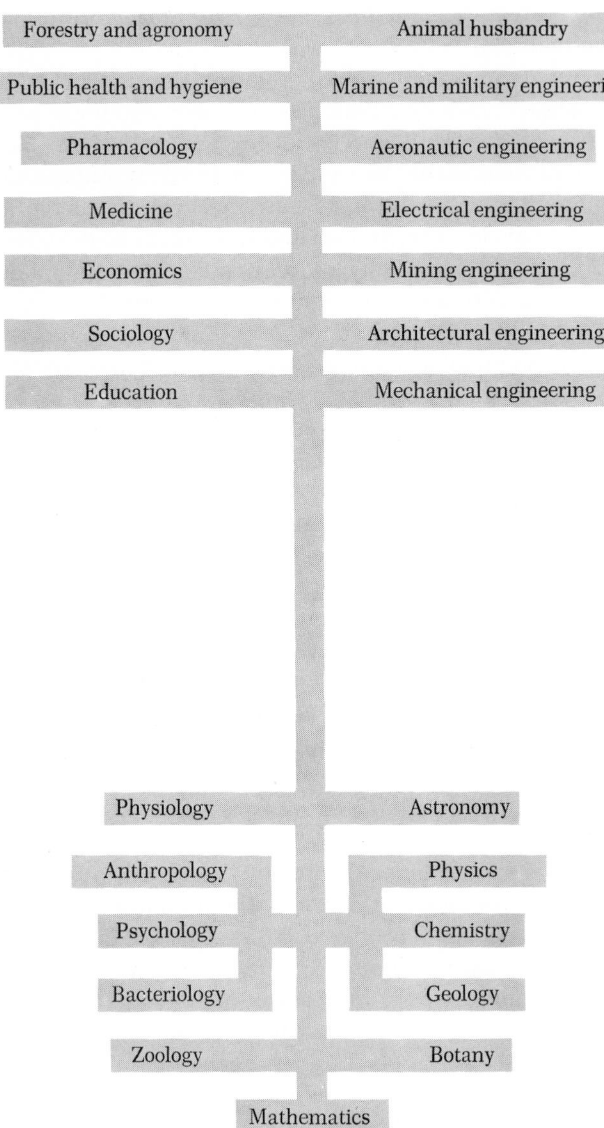

Figure 5-1
Adaptation of "A Century of Progress," mural by John Norton, 1933. (Copyright Museum of Science and Industry, Chicago; adapted by special permission of Museum of Science and Industry, Chicago.)

that it can be incorporated easily and very appropriately even in junior high school courses in which are studied such matters as public health, safety campaigns, thrift, population trends, expenditure of public moneys, and other topics which deal in simple fashion with social and economic phenomena. Economics and sociology deal essentially with mass phenomena, and there is a widespread feeling that the only mathematics which is used in connection with these subjects is statistics. It is quite true that statistics, including graphics, is more extensively and more obviously used than other mathematical procedures in the elementary work in these fields, but in some of the more advanced work, especially in theoretical studies related to social and economic phenomena, there are important applications of mathematics such as high-speed computation, stochastic processes, linear programming, and game theory, which are nonstatistical in nature.

In one way or another mathematics leaves its imprint upon the foundations of many of the school subjects. Its applications are more manifest in some than in others, but seldom, indeed if ever, are they lacking altogether. We have seen that they are not limited to the physical sciences but have important bearings upon the biological and social sciences as well. The industrial arts require mathematics. Psychology is finding more uses for it all the time. Even English, the foreign languages, and the fine arts are enriched by an understanding of the mathematical principles of form and number, of symmetry and order, upon which they are based. By continually impressing upon the students the relationships and applications of mathematics to other school subjects, teachers can stimulate interest in the study of mathematics and can at the same time give the students a more comprehensive and complete idea of the nature of the other subjects.

Motivation through showing the application of mathematics to business, industry, and the professional fields Another important means of stimulating interest in mathematics is through pointing out the applications of mathematics to fields of work through which people gain their livelihood. Students are interested in this not only from an academic standpoint but for practical reasons as well. All boys and many girls must look forward to the intensely practical problem of selecting an occupation and earning a living, and they are generally interested in learning something about the opportunities and requirements in different fields. The extent to which mathematics enters into the upper levels of many lines of work is not realized by most people. Many articles can be found, however, which discuss the applications of mathematics in various vocational fields, and there are even numerous textbooks with titles such as "Business Mathematics," "Mathematics of Finance," "Shop Mathematics," "Mathematics for Printers," "Mathematics for Electricians," and "Mathematics for Agriculture." By pointing out these applications, teachers can perform valuable service in the way of guidance to the students and at the same time stimulate their interest in mathematics itself.

It should be emphasized that professional work in a number of fields requires extensive training in and, indeed, continual use of mathematics. In a preceding section the application of mathematics to the natural and social sciences has been discussed, and it is obvious that individuals desiring to take up professional work in teaching or research in these sciences will be either entirely prevented from doing so or greatly handicapped in their work unless their interest and aptitude for such work are implemented by the ability to adapt mathematical techniques to the circumstances and problems peculiar to their particular lines of study. In this connection the attention of students should be called to the fact that mathematics is now coming to be recognized as a necessary part of the professional equipment in such fields as anatomy, physiology, psychology, psychiatry, and medicine.

Students scarcely need to be told that mathematics is the foundation of engineering. While mechanical devices such as the integraph and handbooks of tables and formulas have reduced the need for the actual applications of calculus and differential equations in much routine engineering work, there will inevitably arise from time to time situations to which no ready-made formula will apply. In such cases the engineer needs to be able to size up the situation and detect the principles and relationships involved and express and investigate them by means of mathematics. A good working knowledge of college algebra, trigonometry, analytic and descriptive geometry, and calculus and a considerable familiarity with differential equations are generally regarded as essential for carrying on or directing engineering work.

Industry and commerce have made less extensive demands upon individuals for mathematical training than have the fields which have just been discussed. However, it will stimulate the students to a sense of the usefulness of mathematics, even in the field of business, if they are impressed with the fact that executive positions generally require the ability to analyze and interpret complex statistical data and that the businessman who has been trained in statistical methods and the mathematics of large-scale finance has a notable advantage over the man who lacks such training. Also, the recent, sudden, and almost explosive impact upon large-scale business and industry of the electronic computer with its allied field of programming offers another important avenue for stimulating students' interest in mathematics. The coding and programming of data for these computers represents a new, interesting, and highly remunerative field in which it now appears that the demand for mathematically trained personnel is destined to exceed the available supply for many years to come.

Calling attention to these matters is both a legitimate and an important way of stimulating students to an interest in their present courses in mathematics as necessary steps in the hierarchy of courses leading to work of professional stature in these fields. It will probably provide a greater stimulus to the more capable students than to those with less ability. Such information is important not only as background for proper guidance of the individual students but in the public interest as well.

Motivation through interest in mathematics as a career Until near the middle of this century the opportunities for careers in mathematics were far fewer, more circumscribed, and financially less attractive than they are today. The professional mathematician found little demand for his services outside the field of teaching, and even in teaching good jobs were not always easy to find.

Now, however, the situation is different. Whereas before 1940 there were almost no business or industrial job opportunities for professional mathematicians as such, today there are literally thousands, and the number is still growing, both in volume and diversity. The demand for professionally trained mathematicians in business and industry is greater than the supply, and the demand is increasing faster than the supply. The capable young man or woman who wishes to make a career in the field of mathematics and who is willing to take the time and make the effort needed to secure the necessary professional training will find a variety of opportunities open to him. He will not need to worry about whether or not he can get a job when he has finished his training. Moreover, because of the scholarships and subsidies which are available at most universities for promising young mathematicians, he may find the financial burden of securing an advanced degree considerably less than he might have expected.

These changed conditions have come about as a result of the explosive growth of mathematics itself and of the applications of mathematical ideas to problems in many fields. Whole new segments or branches of mathematics have come into being. New ideas are being applied to both new and old problems. Old ideas are being applied to new problems and to old problems in new ways. New practical problems stimulate new research in pure mathematics, and new discoveries in mathematics suggest new theoretical developments and new practical applications.

The remarkable developments in mathematical statistics and high-speed computing and data processing, and the great variety of striking applications of these developments, have made these branches of mathematics more widely known and appreciated than some of the others. The fact is, however, that the whole spectrum of mathematics offers career opportunities to young men and women with professional training in the subject. Among such opportunities are careers in teaching at various levels from the high school to the university, in computer theory and techniques, in pure and applied statistics, in operations research in pure mathematics. Many doors are invitingly open to high school students who show high ability and interest in mathematics and who wish to make it their profession.

Motivation through emphasis on cultural and educational values While the practical motive for the study of mathematics is a powerful one, teachers should not neglect to point out the cultural and general educational values. It should be the responsibility of the teachers to emphasize continually that it is an essential part of culture and education to understand the background and the nature of the developments which are going on in the world. It is no easy task, however, to keep oneself informed in these matters in a world in which social, economic, and especially scientific changes are taking place with the rapidity characteristic of the present time. Students should be impressed with the fact that many of these important developments which directly affect our daily lives cannot be adequately understood except through an understanding of scientific principles whose development, expression, and interpretation depend, in turn, upon mathematical principles. They should be led to see that mathematics will aid them even in such matters as interpreting social and economic phenomena and that it is indispensable to the understanding and development of scientific theory.

Students will sometimes argue that it is not necessary to understand these things, that one can operate an automobile effectively without knowing the adiabatic formula or can turn on a radio and enjoy the program without knowing even of the existence of Maxwell's equations. All of which, of course, is true. The thing which students so often fail to realize, however, and which should be impressed upon them continually, is that to limit their interest in such things to the bare utilitarian aspect is to miss the real thrill and wonder of them as well as to run the risk of setting up a barrier to subsequent intelligent study of their characteristics. It is not necessary to be able to solve difficult differential equations in order to be able to *appreciate* the role which mathematics plays in the development of modern science, but such appreciation can hardly be attained without some considerable study of mathematics beyond that which is needed to compute the area of a field or keep oneself from being shortchanged. Indeed, without such a background it is impossible to read understandingly not only a great many scientific articles of general interest but also a rather large number which are written for popular consumption.

Aside from the technical aspects of the subject, the *postulational method* of mathematics has a major contribution to make to the cultural education of the individual. If students are kept aware of the nature and the universal applicability of this method, it will be found to provide an exceedingly strong motive for the study of mathematics, not only from the standpoint of its cultural significance but also because of its intrinsic interest. An appreciation of the significance of the "if-then" type of reasoning is one of the most important potential educational and cultural values of the study of mathematics. When once attained, it in turn not only makes mathematics infinitely more meaningful but infuses a keener interest into the study and provides one of the most powerful motives for the continued pursuit of work in this field.

In one important sense of the word, the cultural values of mathematics may be likened to what we think of as the cultural values of fine music or art or literature. They constitute something which derives from the medium in question and gives enduring intellectual satisfaction colored with esthetic and even emotional overtones, and which at the same time deepens the appreciation and refines the taste. This is a very important facet of the cultural value of mathematics, but one of which people have been too little aware. The reason for this is probably that mathematics is so seldom taught in such a way as to reveal its beauty, its delicacy, its universality, its vagaries, its surprises, even its little jokes. To teach it in such a manner requires rich background and high artistry, but the dividends in intellectual and esthetic satisfaction are tremendously worthwhile. Probably no better or more delightful essay on this aspect of the cultural value of mathematics can be found than that given by Clifton Fadiman in his commentary on a set of books, to which reference is made elsewhere in this chapter, so it seems appropriate to conclude this section with some excerpts from his article.[8]

> In the mysterious metaphors we have agreed to call mathematics all creation is involved, from the symbol-happy logician down to those cunning geometers, the bees. When I trust myself to a ladder I lean upon an equation. Every baby is a formula baby, for when we say that its growth is a function of its nourishment, what are we citing but a case of the calculus? The toddler, gratified to discover a correspondence between the toes of his right foot and those of his left, has taken his first steps in number theory. . . .
>
> The mass of us who quail before the word mathematics are often merely suffering from a bad persistent case of early pedagogy. We were poisoned in our youth by the notion that mathematics is identical with problem-solving. But in truth it is no more equivalent to problem-solving than is music to counterpoint.
>
> As Scott Buchanan puts it in his wonderful little book *Poetry and Mathe-*

[8]Clifton Fadiman, Party of One, *Holiday*, **21** (January, 1957), 8.

matics: "The structures with which mathematics deals are more like lace, the leaves of trees, and the play of light and shadow on a meadow or a human face." The fact is (I quote from G. H. Hardy's *A Mathematician's Apology*) " . . . most people have some appreciation of mathematics just as most people can enjoy a pleasant tune." . . .

James Newman has edited a four-volume collection of mathematical writings called *The World of Mathematics*. His title is just: mathematics is not a subject, it is a world. Within his 2500 pages you will, it is true, encounter a few Greek letters and a few eccentric symbols. But you will also meet soap bubbles, calculating prodigies, chess playing machines, the mathematics of golf, the astonishing mind of a superman named Gauss, birds who count, the laws that govern poker, a professional teataster, Bernard Shaw on the vice of gambling and the virtues of insurance, assorted infinities, a one-sided strip of paper, and even some fiction, odd or brilliant, involving mathematics. . . .

Being incapable, I cannot talk about mathematics itself. But I can talk about the charm of reading about and around mathematics, for I have sensed that charm as vividly as one may sense the charm, without ever being quite able to define it, of a lovely face or voice or piece of architecture. . . .

It is a curious circumstance that, though mathematics is but a set of marks on paper, it should have such numberless connections with what is called the real world. This airy structure, shimmering like a heat haze in the minds of a few men, is also a kind of hub of the universe from which radiate the spokes of a hundred arts and sciences. Or it is like a circular window opening on 360° of thought. It points toward everything else, from a Bach fugue to the propulsion of a spitball, from soap films to diplomacy. Study the myriad spirals of nature and at once you meet the logarithm. Look into D'Arcy Thompson's *On Growth and Form*, and see how mathematics enters into the growth of wild goats' horns, the architecture of a snowflake, the shape of eggs. The mathematical concept of symmetry is tied up not alone with music but with women's veils, flower petals, and the activities of bees. Mathematics is part and parcel of modern war, not merely in the gross concerns of ballistics but in the subtler ones of strategy and tactics. There are few human concerns on which it does not throw some light. . . . It is this marvelous connectivity of mathematics, its bewildering universal-jointedness, that leads the shallowest student to echo Einstein's wonderment: "How can it be that mathematics, being after all a product of human thought independent of experience, is so admirably adapted to the objects of reality?"

Motivation through mathematical recreations and clubs

In the minds of a good many people the concept of motivation has become identified with, and in some cases limited to, the idea of games, puzzles, plays, anecdotes, and other interesting, but sometimes more or less trivial and unrelated, matters often referred to under the generic title of "mathematical recreations." It is unfortunate that this should be the case, because motivation implies a much broader and more significant connotation than this and takes place through various avenues. At the same time such mathematical recreations and peripheral activities, if kept within proper perspective, can be valuable and legitimate in relieving the tedium of necessary routine work and in presenting an aspect of mathematics the existence of which is at times not even suspected. It is a rare individual, especially child, who is not interested in games or in things which are unusual or unsuspected and which contain elements of surprise or mystery. While mathematical puzzles, contests, and games cannot be permitted to pre-empt too much of the time allotted to regular classwork, there is abundant evidence that the moderate and appropriate employment of such devices does add much of interest and zest to the courses.[9]

Mathematics clubs provide an excellent means of stimulating and fostering mathematical study. Membership in these clubs is usually voluntary, and for this reason the clubs are composed mainly of students who have a real interest in mathematics and who desire to obtain a view of the subject which is somewhat different from that gained in the classroom. Such clubs offer excellent opportunities for free consideration of matters of special interest to the members without the necessity of having the programs follow any particular organic sequence of topics such as is generally necessary in regular class instruction. Secondary school pupils, like all others, are dependent upon each other in their mental, physical, social, domestic, and other relationships. They listen to ideas expressed by others and add their own; they criticize and are criticized. The fact that they do not always agree stimulates interest and motivates discussion. A mathematics club offers an ideal place for a free exchange of mathematical ideas and for frank and helpful criticism of these ideas. The club also makes possible an informality and a social atmosphere which the classroom can hardly provide. The club should be an organization of, by, and for the students, the teacher being a sympathetic counselor whose main function is to foster a continuance of interest and to cooperate in guiding the activities of the club along appropriate lines.

The principles of organization of a mathematics club should be neither numerous nor involved. The objectives should be clearly stated and understood by all the members. Emphasis should be on active participation of the members. There should be a faculty sponsor who should be inconspicuous but ready to advise and help when needed. In general, any criticisms that he might have to make concerning programs should be given in private to the individual students

[9]Louis Grant Brandes, Why We Use Recreational Mathematics in Our Secondary School Mathematics Classes, *School Science and Mathematics*, **54** (1954), 289–293.

concerned. It is desirable that each club limit its membership to such size that there will be opportunity for all to participate and that all meetings be held at regularly scheduled times.[10]

The programs of mathematics clubs may cover a wide range of topics, many of which have been listed and discussed in numerous books and in articles in such periodicals as the *Mathematics Teacher*, *School Science and Mathematics*, the *Pentagon*, and the *Mathematics Student Journal*. These will include topics drawn from the history of mathematics, including biographical sketches and interesting anecdotes; the evolution and development of certain aspects of present-day mathematics; topics from algebra, geometry, arithmetic, or trigonometry; games and contests; and applications to other subjects and fields of activity. Discussion of some elementary aspects of modern mathematics may well rate some priority in club programs. The nature of the programs and topics to be discussed will of necessity depend considerably upon the age and advancement of the members of the club. Some subjects which could be discussed with interest and profit by students in the junior college or in the upper years of the senior high school would not be appropriate for junior high school clubs, whereas certain activities in which these clubs could well engage would be too elementary to hold much interest for the older students. The membership of the mathematics club should be, so far as possible, fairly homogeneous as regards age and grade level in order that programs which will be of interest to all the members may be arranged.

There is now an extensive and rapidly growing bibliography on mathematical recreations, clubs, and books and articles of popular interest. It is growing so fast that such a bibliography is likely to be somewhat incomplete even by the time it is published. Several such bibliographies and a great many individual articles and books of popular interest have been published in the past few years.

Motivation through intellectual curiosity Many teachers and textbook writers have never recognized the power of sheer intellectual curiosity as a motive for the highest type of work in mathematics, and as a consequence they have failed to organize and present the work in a manner designed to stimulate the student's interest through a challenge to his curiosity. A notable instance of this is to be found in the fact that practically all theorems of demonstrative geometry are set up as exercises in establishing certain prestated conclusions rather than as exercises for free exploration and investigation of the consequences of certain hypotheses. Thus the element of discovery of the central fact or relationship in each theorem is removed at the outset,

[10]Annie John Williams, Organizing a Mathematics Club, *Mathematics Teacher*, **49** (1956), 149–150.

whereas this element of discovery could in many cases be retained and used to quicken the interest of the students. For example, the statement, "Prove that an inscribed angle is measured by half of its intercepted arc," sets forth a task to be performed while the question, "What relation, if any, exists between the measure of an inscribed angle and the measure of its intercepted arc?" is designed to whet the curiosity of the student instead of satisfying it at the outset.

As a rule, secondary school students are not intellectually lazy. That they may often appear to be so is due in large measure to the fact that their work is so largely set up for them as tasks to be done rather than as situations to be investigated, and they simply become bored and indifferent. Most students in the secondary school are persistently curious individuals, and they will work, and work hard, at things that interest them. They do not hate mathematics, as some seem to think; they hate only drudgery and boredom and frustration. Teachers need to remind themselves continuously that to bring out the best in their students they must appeal to interest motives that are strong and that intellectual curiosity is one of the strongest, as well as the most desirable, of these motives. The range of the potential intellectual interests of these students is practically unlimited. The writers of modern detective fiction have recognized this and have capitalized on it. The enormous popular response which has brought this type of fiction to the front rank in sales and library withdrawals can be attributed only to the general reader's insatiate interest in the development and denouement of a problem situation.

Evidence that mathematics is not devoid of strong appeal to the curiosity and interest of people can be found in the appearance and widespread sale, over the past few years, of a large number of books on mathematical recreations and popular mathematics for the general reader. Even the more serious among these books are attaining sales records far beyond expectation. Indeed, in one instance an expensive four-volume set of books on mathematics[11] achieved a sales record seldom if ever equalled in the history of publishing, when more than 100,000 sets were sold within less than three weeks after publication.

Further convincing evidence of the power of intellectual curiosity as a motive is found in the success which has accompanied the introduction of some of the concepts, notation, and terminology of "modern" mathematics into the mathematics courses of the junior high school. The testimony of teachers who have used such material in the ninth grade, and even in the seventh and eighth grades, is that its challenge to the sheer intellectual curiosity of the students almost invariably provides a powerful stimulant and motive to their study of mathematics.

[11] James R. Newman, "The World of Mathematics" (New York: Simon and Schuster, Inc., 1956).

Mathematical situations lack, of course, the lurid human interest of the ordinary mystery novel, but they do not lack the essential curiosity-provoking possibilities. "Think-of-a-number" games are popular at parties, even among people who anticipate or recall the study of algebra with dread, yet the games are nothing except algebra somewhat obscured, perhaps, by a screen of mysticism which only serves to stimulate curiosity. People are interested in seeing how numbers behave, and algebra is essentially the science of the behavior of numbers. Puzzle problems in mathematics have often been criticized as being unreal or having no genuine application to life situations. A little experience in teaching algebra, however, will soon convince the most skeptical critic that problems which purport to represent "real" situations may not be interesting to students and that, on the other hand, problems may be quite interesting without being "real." As a matter of fact, it is quite possible that the presence of the puzzle element in problems is often a greater stimulus to *interest* than those elements of so-called reality which authors of textbooks try so hard to incorporate in problems.

Obviously there must be system and organization in mathematics. Arithmetic and algebra cannot and should not consist entirely of number games and puzzles, nor demonstrative geometry of incidental and undirected investigations. These are sequential subjects and must be developed in sequential form. Haphazard or piecemeal work will achieve nothing of value. But within the framework of the systematic organization of a course in mathematics at any level of secondary instruction there are many opportunities for motivating the work by deliberate stimulation of the curiosity of the students along the lines indicated. The greater the extent to which this is done, the greater will be the interest, understanding, and assiduity with which the students will work and the more meaningful and worthwhile will the work become to them.

A final word

The means and devices which have been discussed in the foregoing pages will be found helpful in stimulating and maintaining interest in mathematics. In themselves, however, they cannot be regarded as panaceas or guarantees. In the last analysis the first and greatest factor in creating interest is a sympathetic, well-informed, competent, and inspiring teacher. Not all the devices in the world can bear the fruit of a continuing and enthusiastic student interest if they are grafted upon the dead stump of instruction in the hands of an incompetent or uninterested teacher. The truly inspiring teacher must first of all be thoroughly grounded in the subject matter of mathematics, well beyond the level of any material which he is expected to teach, in order that he may inspire the confidence and respect of his students. He must have a sympathetic understanding of student difficulties and must be always ready and willing to offer proper guidance and stimulation. Finally, he must have an enthusiastic interest in his subject and in teaching it. He must believe in its values and its contribution to the educational well-being of the students. Enthusiasm is contagious, and sane enthusiasm backed by sympathetic and enlightened competence is the only real guarantee of the effective maintenance of student interest. Devices are helpful, but they are not sufficient unto the task. The inspiring teacher is the real *sine qua non.*

EXERCISES

1. The rapid development of rocketry, satellites, and other scientific achievements associated with the space age has produced public concern with respect to the improvement of school mathematics. To what extent do you think this concern is reflected in the attitudes of students?

2. Try to find out something about the particular jobs or kinds of mathematical work that are available in the computer field, and the levels of training required for each, so that you can discuss these matters with students who may be interested.

3. Drill work in arithmetic and algebra is necessary but often dull and uninteresting to students. Devise and describe a way of increasing the interest of students during periods of drill in arithmetic or elementary algebra.

4. Construct a design that has some mathematical basis as well as esthetic appeal. Explain the mathematics involved.

5. Make a slide rule for addition and subtraction and show how it works.

6. Give some examples of applications of mathematics to the social sciences.

7. Devise numerical exercises to illustrate these algebraic identities: $a^2 - b^2 = (a - b)(a + b)$; $(a + b)^2 = a^2 + 2ab + b^2$.

8. Give geometric illustrations of the identities of exercise 7. Do you think such illustrations would be very useful in stimulating students' interest through giving them better insight into the meanings of the identities?

9. Construct a piece of demonstration apparatus to illustrate the principle that all angles inscribed in a given segment of a circle are equal.

10. Construct a simple nomograph, and show how it works and why.

11. Prepare at least two recreations, in the form of mathematical fallacies, for presentation to the class.

12. Most children are interested in simple probability and the laws of chance. Make up some simple experiments in drawing numbers from prearranged sets so that the calculated probabilities can be tested experimentally by the students. Try out these experiments on your class.

13. Select five mathematical recreations which you think would be good to use with junior high school students and five which you think would be good to use with senior high school students. Present one or more of these to the class.

14. Make a device to show that it is possible to have a surface which is curved at every point and yet is made up entirely of straight lines.

15. Discuss both the possibilities and the limitations of mathematics contests as means of motivation.

16. Make a list of suggestions which you think would be helpful in organizing or sponsoring a mathematics club of high school students.

17. See if you can prepare a talk on modular arithmetic which you think would be interesting and understandable to a junior high school mathematics club.

18. It has been asserted that if high school students could be made to see what algebra is really about, the problem of motivation would be solved. Discuss this.

19. Explain how various simple numbers would be written in a system of notation using five as the base. Also show how to add and multiply numbers in this system.

20. Repeat exercise 19, using a binary notation where the only numerals are 1 and 0.

21. Explain how an understanding of numerals written in systems of notation using bases other than ten can help students to gain insight into the workings of our common decimal number system and its notation and thereby increase their interest in mathematics.

22. Without using arabic numerals find the sum of CDXXXVII, XLVI, and CCXIX. Check by writing the numbers in arabic numerals and finding the sum. In a similar way find and check the product of XLIX and IV. This exercise affords a good opportunity to point out some of the advantages of our own decimal system of numeration.

23. Many proofs of the Pythagorean theorem are known, but the converse of this theorem is often assumed without proof, although it can be proved in several ways. As a matter of stimulating interest, devise or find two proofs of the Pythagorean converse.

24. Show how the study of inequalities, concurrently with the study of equations in high school algebra, can give added interest and insight into the study of equations.

25. Discuss some ways in which an understanding of the rules and structure of an algebra of sets can help to clarify a student's understanding of the rules and structure of ordinary school algebra and thereby increase his interest in it.

26. Explain in what ways the study of a finite geometry of, say, seven points can help to give insight into ordinary plane geometry and thereby increase interest in this subject.

27. Discuss the proposition that students are more interested in new ideas and procedures than in ideas and procedures with which they are familiar. Give an example in which you think this would be true, and tell why. Give an example in which you think this would not be true, and tell why.

28. It has been observed that many students who seem bored with traditional arithmetic and algebra become keenly interested in sets and set operations and other topics oriented to "modern" mathematics. How do you explain this?

29. Genuine insight into the meaning of the subject matter and into the nature of mathematics itself probably gives the most powerful and enduring motivation of all. To what extent do you think the failure of teachers to develop such insight in their students is due to their own lack of it?

BIBLIOGRAPHY

Abbott, E. A.: "Flatland: A Romance in Many Dimensions" (New York: Dover Publications, Inc., 1953).

Abraham, R. M.: "Winter Nights Entertainment" (New York: E. P. Dutton & Co., Inc., 1933).

_____: "Diversions and Pastimes" (New York: E. P. Dutton & Co., Inc., 1935).

Adler, Irving: "The New Mathematics" (New York: The John Day Company, Inc., 1958).

_____: "The Giant Golden Book of Mathematics" (New York: Golden Press, 1960).

Anderson, Raymond: "Romping through Mathematics" (New York: Alfred A. Knopf, Inc., 1961).

Asimov, Isaac: "Realm of Number" (Boston: Houghton Mifflin Company, 1959).

_____: "Realm of Measure" (Boston: Houghton Mifflin Company, 1960).

Ball, W. W. Rouse: "String Figures and Other Monographs," 3d ed. (New York: Chelsea Publishing Company, 1960).

_____ and H. S. M. Coxeter: "Mathematical

Recreations and Essays," 11th ed. (New York: The Macmillan Company, 1960).
Beiler, Albert H.: "Recreations in the Theory of Numbers" (New York: Dover Publications, Inc., 1964).
Boehm, George A. W.: "The New World of Math" (New York: The Dial Press, Inc., 1959).
Bowers, Henry, and Joan E. Bowers: "Arithmetical Excursions" (New York: Dover Publications, Inc., 1961).
Breuer, Joseph: "Introduction to the Theory of Sets," translated by Howard F. Fehr (Englewood Cliffs, N.J.: Prentice-Hall, Inc., 1958).
Court, Nathan A.: "Mathematics in Fun and in Earnest" (New York: The Dial Press, Inc., 1958).
Cundy, Martyn H., and A. P. Rollett: "Mathematical Models" (Fair Lawn, N.J.: Oxford University Press, 1961).
Dudeney, Henry E.: "Amusements in Mathematics" (New York: Dover Publications, Inc., 1958).
Fadiman, Clifton: "The Mathematical Magpie" (New York: Simon and Schuster, Inc., 1962).
Gardner, Martin: "The 2nd *Scientific American* Book of Mathematical Puzzles and Diversions" (New York: Simon and Schuster, Inc., 1961).
Hess, Adrien L.: "Mathematics Project Handbook" (Boston: D. C. Heath and Company, 1962).
Jones, Burton W.: "Elementary Concepts of Mathematics," 2d ed. (New York: The Macmillan Company, 1963).
Kenna, L. A.: "Understanding Mathematics with Visual Aids" (Paterson, N.J.: Littlefield, Adams & Company, 1962).
Mathematical Association of America, Inc.: "Professional Opportunities in Mathematics," 5th ed. (Buffalo, N.Y.: University of Buffalo, 1961).
Mathematics in the Modern World, *Scientific American*, **211** (1964), pp. 40–224.
"Mathematics and Your Career," rev. 1962 (U.S. Office of Education).
Menger, Karl: "You Will Like Geometry" (Chicago: Museum of Science and Industry, 1961).
Menninger, K. W.: "Mathematics in Your World" (New York: The Viking Press, Inc., 1962).
National Council of Teachers of Mathematics: Its two journals, its yearbooks, and its numerous supplementary publications contain many articles bearing upon motivation in mathematics. Information about these publications can be secured from the National Council of Teachers of Mathematics, 1201 Sixteenth St., N.W., Washington, D.C.
Newman, James R.: "The World of Mathematics" (New York: Simon and Schuster, Inc., 1956).
Ogilvy, Stanley: "Through the Mathescope" (Fair Lawn, N.J.: Oxford University Press, 1956).
———: "Tomorrow's Math: Unsolved Problems for the Amateur" (Fair Lawn, N.J.: Oxford University Press, 1962).
Ranson, William R.: "Thirty Projects for Mathematical Clubs and Exhibitions" (Portland, Me.: J. Weston Walch, Publisher, 1961).
Salkind, Charles T.: "The Contest Problem Book" (New York: Random House, Inc., and Yale University, 1961).
Shuster, Carl N., and Fred A. Bedford: "Field Work in Mathematics" (distributed by Yoder Instruments, East Palestine, Ohio).
Stein, Sherman K.: "Mathematics: The Man-made Universe" (San Francisco: W. H. Freeman and Company, 1963).
Steinhaus, H.: "Mathematical Snapshots" (Fair Lawn, N.J.: Oxford University Press, 1960).

SIX

Means to effective instruction and guided learning

SCHOOLS EXIST for the primary purpose of promoting learning, and teachers of mathematics have as their primary objective the promotion of learning in mathematics. This is not a simple or routine task. The things that are to be learned and the maturity of the students vary from grade to grade, and learning has varied aspects and can take place through many avenues. The students may not all learn things in the same ways, or at the same speed, or with the same facility and completeness. Yet the teacher has the dual task of setting appropriate objectives with respect to the things to be learned and of planning kinds of learning activities which in his judgment give promise of providing his students with the kinds of experiences that can bring them to the attainment of the objectives. To this end, it is necessary that the teacher have a good understanding not only of the desirable mathematical objectives themselves but also of the ways in which children learn mathematics. Moreover, he must remember that there are phases, or stages, in learning as well as degrees of learning and that initial understanding or mastery of skills can deteriorate through disuse or lack of review or application. Such considerations should impel him to consider carefully the instructional means and devices which he plans to use and to adapt them for optimum effectiveness in enabling the students to attain the desired objectives.

Considerations with respect to the learning of mathematics

As has been said, the problem of instruction is that of promoting learning. Since the learning must be done by the student, the problem of instruction becomes that of guiding the activities of the student in such ways that proper learning will take place. This cannot be stereotyped. The teacher who gives thought to ways in which children learn mathematics will be more likely to attain effective results than the one who does not. It seems reasonable, therefore, that some important considerations with respect to how mathematics is learned should be set forth at the outset. It would be difficult to give a better statement of such considerations than that given in the following quotation from a thought-provoking chapter in the *Twenty-first Yearbook* of the National Council of Teachers of Mathematics:[1]

> Children do not grow and develop in mathematical knowledge in a vacuum of such knowledge. Quantitative thinking is acquired in active mental dealing with quantitative situations. The quantitative aspects of a situation can go unnoticed unless they are deliberately brought to the sphere of attention of the student. . . . The child grows and develops in a numerical and geometric environment in which he changes his behavior to ever more complex organized patterns.
>
> But progress is not made along a straight line from the fundamentals to the generalized theorems. This is the way the final learning can be organized, and is frequently so organized in texts, but it is not the way most students grow in wisdom. Our initial learnings in algebra are not Peano's axioms, nor is our initial learning in geometry Hilbert's postulates. Rather, the initial learning is in an area in which exploration first takes place. We count, measure, draw, and make preliminary statements which are refined downward toward the foundations and upward toward more abstract, complex, and generalized relations. After a while we discard many particular theorems for one more generalized theorem, and in advanced states of learning only is the area of exploration reorganized as a straight line mathematical development.
>
> The growth in mathematical knowledge by each individual student thus calls for direction by a skillful teacher who has a balanced emphasis on the various phases of learning. He uses the heuristic method only so far as pupils need directed questions in the quest of their learning. He has an experimental attitude that allows freedom of approach in learning to the degree that the experiment is headed toward a desired concept, or relationship, and directs the experiment back to fruitful approaches when the student is adrift. He recognizes that drill can be dangerous and boring as well as good habit formation procedure He balances each step from concrete experience to semiconcrete representations, to words and symbols, to generalized abstract theorems through proper evaluation and by appropriate attainable challenges. He recognizes also that

[1]John R. Clark and Howard F. Fehr, Learning Theory and the Improvement of Instruction: A Balanced Program, *Twenty-first Yearbook* (Washington, D.C.: National Council of Teachers of Mathematics, 1953), pp. 346–348.

not all learning begins in concrete material objects, but that much new learning may start in already learned abstractions. Thus algebraic fractions are referred back to the abstractions learned in the study of arithmetic fractions and not back to parts of concrete objects. Geometry is related to geometrical drawings, trigonometry is related back to geometry and algebra.

It is just because of this sequential aspect of mathematical knowledge that proper balance becomes the all important aspect in its learning. Unless a clearly and correctly formed mathematical concept emerges from a learning situation and it is related to other phases of already learned mathematics through sufficient practice to gain skill in the use of the concept, the learning of all later mathematics dependent upon this concept is seriously (and sometimes totally) impaired. The lack of correct concepts in arithmetic may be one of the great reasons for the difficulty algebra presents to so many of our students. It is this balance that is indirectly referred to in every chapter in this text (*sic*): a mathematical problem within the comprehension of the student, but still a problem as the start of learning; motivation, sufficient to send him on toward the solution; the challenge to abstract, to generalize, to form concepts; the proper use of sensory aids, of drill, of appropriate language; not doing too much nor failing to do enough; and adapting these measures to the various individual differences in learning. To gain such balance is to become a master teacher—the goal of all professionally minded educators.

Learning is an active process. It is achieved not in any single way but through a variety of activities and is approached through a variety of avenues: reading, listening, asking questions, working with material objects, writing, drawing, comparing, analyzing, interpreting, computing, etc. The one thing which all these activities need to involve is thinking. These activities need to be so planned that they will bring the learner along the path toward understanding and mastery of the subject at his level of advancement. Each is important and each should contribute to the attainment of some aspect of mastery.

Effective instruction cannot be guaranteed by any single simple formula. It goes without saying that, if instruction is to be really effective, the subject matter must be selected and organized in such a way as to make it appropriate and suited to the age and intellectual development of the students. Further than this, it must be presented in an understandable and interesting way, and there must be provision for ample practice. Skills and concepts once developed must be maintained through reapplication and not allowed to deteriorate through disuse. Since students do not learn with equal facility or at equal rates, there must be provision for individual differences. If the instruction is to attain a maximum of usefulness, it must be carried on with the deliberate purpose of securing a maximum of transfer and in such a way that the relation of mathematics to other fields of learning and activity is made manifest. These considerations involve careful planning and adequate testing of outcomes.

Four fundamental problems of teaching mathematics Mathematics is a cumulative and a continuously expanding subject in both its organization and its applications. With every new topic the teacher is confronted with four basic instructional problems: (1) helping the students acquire initial understandings of new concepts and relationships, (2) helping them to strengthen and deepen these well beyond the point of mere "threshold" understanding, (3) helping them maintain understandings and skills already attained, and (4) helping them build the background for significant transfer of these skills and understandings to their physical, social, and intellectual environment. These four phases of teaching should be interwoven as far as possible into a unified instructional program, but their implications are essentially distinct and supplemental rather than identical. The teaching of new material necessarily draws upon the already established background as a frame of reference and to this extent serves as a means of maintenance, but such maintenance is relatively incidental to the mastery of the new material and must be so regarded. Adequate maintenance and maximum transfer, especially of skills, cannot be assured by incidental contacts but require an instructional program designed especially for their attainment.

Teaching for understanding: developmental teaching

As generally conceived, the foremost problem of direct instruction in secondary school mathematics is the teaching of new material. It is this phase of instruction that makes the heaviest demand upon the skill and artistry of the teacher. The primary jobs are to explain, to make clear, to challenge, to guide to discovery, to develop understanding. In order to meet these responsibilities, the teacher must not only consider the logical relationships involved in the unit or topic but also be keenly aware of the relation of the new concepts to the experiential background of the students. He must be able to anticipate probable difficulties and detect and clear up actual difficulties as they occur in the course of the development. He must be able and continually willing to view the unfolding and (to the students) unfamiliar subject matter not merely through his own experienced eyes but from the standpoint of immature students to whom it is all new and strange.

Inventory and preview When new work is taken up with a class it is usually assumed that the students are wholly unfamiliar with the new material, but this is not always the case. It is a good thing, in starting a new unit, to find out what, if anything, the students already know about it. This need not take long. It can sometimes be done by a few well-chosen questions. In other cases brief written inventory tests are more useful. Sometimes the information secured may save time and be of significant help to the teacher in planning and conducting the work.

In presenting a new unit of work it is well to give the students an overview of the unit as a whole in order that they may see the main concepts and principles in their relations to each other and to previous parts of the work. A preview of this sort not only gives meaning and relevance to the larger ideas of the unit but also gives significance and motive to the detailed study which must make up most of the students' work in mastering the unit. The importance of this has not always been recognized by teachers. Too often the new work is simply taken up detail by detail with little thought of relating the details to the structure of the unit as a whole.

The preview should generally be given in the form of a well-organized talk by the teacher. In most cases it should not be a long talk. The teacher should present the ideas that he wishes to emphasize in a coherent account in which clear, concise statements are embellished by supplementary discussion only insofar as this will aid in making the ideas and statements clear and understandable to the students.

The preview may be followed by a brief test to determine how effective the presentation has been and whether there is need for rediscussion of the unit or any of its parts before the class proceeds to a detailed study of the unit.

Teaching new material No mere lecture procedure such as is commonly used in college classes will suffice for the job of teaching secondary school mathematics. It is a common fault of teachers to employ too extensively the method of "telling" or of giving a coherent discussion of a topic and then proceeding as if on the assumption that the discussion has been followed and completely understood by the students. This assumption is almost never justified. Secondary school students are seldom able to assimilate adequately and immediately any lengthy, one-sided teacher-given discussion of unfamiliar subject matter. Points of difficulty will inevitably arise, and unless they are cleared up promptly, they will fail to register with the students; failure to get these points cleared up may easily result in blocking the understanding of the subsequent parts of the discussion.

This does not mean that telling is always and entirely out of place. On the contrary, there are many times when judicious telling or explanation may be not only proper and valuable but absolutely necessary, as, for example, in making clear the meaning of new terms and concepts. Such use of the telling, or lecture, method in secondary school mathematics, however, should generally take the form of explanations or illustrations, and these should not be protracted longer than necessary. Moreover, the discussion should not be one-sided; it should be interspersed with frequent questions by the teacher, who should also strive to elicit questions and contributions from the class.

It is not always easy to get students to raise questions, because all too often the difficulties which arise in their minds are not well enough defined to enable them to put them into words. Many students are quite sensitive about appearing slow of perception or "dumb" in the eyes of their classmates, and rather than run the risk of embarrassment, they commonly let these matters pass in silence. For no better reasons than these, students will frequently allow statements to go unchallenged even though they do not understand them. Such barriers to freedom of inquiry on the part of the students can be broken down only by tact and sympathetic encouragement. The teacher should never resent an interruption of discussion when it is caused by the raising of a legitimate question or inquiry. On the contrary, students should be given every encouragement to raise such questions at any time that they are unable to follow the discussion clearly.

At best, however, students cannot be depended upon to bring up all points which may need special attention in the course of a discussion or explanation. The teacher must anticipate these as far as possible and be always alert to detect them as they become apparent. This can often be done by noting that the students wear puzzled expressions even though they may not actually raise questions. Always at such times, and frequently in any case, the teacher should check the understanding of the discussion by means of questions addressed to members of the class, and at the completion of the discussion of any new topic a check test of some sort should be given before passing on to other activities. Merely to present a finished discussion, closing with some such general question as Is that clear to all of you? or Are there any questions? is entirely inadequate. The silence with which such a question is generally received is absolutely no assurance that the class has followed the discussion at all, though as a rule this interpretation is wrongfully placed upon it. It may simply mean that the students have not followed the discussion even well enough to be able to ask intelligent questions about it.

On the other hand, when by well-chosen questions students can be led to discover facts or relationships for themselves, the advantage is manifest. This makes the student a more active participant in the learning process. It provides a spur to quicken his interest, since it casts him in the role of at least a quasi investigator rather than a mere passive recipient of information. That he has been guided toward his discoveries by the helpful and stimulating questioning of the teacher should not detract from his justifiable pride in his achievement.

Laboratory work in mathematics The use of multisensory aids, when well coordinated with the other classroom learning activities, can serve a double purpose: it not only serves to stimulate interest but provides a most effective means of clarifying many mathematical concepts and relations through the experience of associating them directly with physical things. Thus it serves as a highly important avenue for organic learning as well as for motivation. Such practice is often referred to as "laboratory work in mathematics." The title is just, for the activities which do, or could, take place in the mathematics laboratory bear much the same relation to the mathematics courses as their counterpart activities in the physics or biology laboratory bear to those courses. It is true that the idea of the mathematics laboratory has not yet received the same general acceptance as the science laboratory has, but this may well be because mathematics teachers have not themselves recognized and insisted upon its importance as the science teachers have. Actually, most mathematics teachers have been very passive in this respect. Teachers of science, art, music, home economics, and other subjects do not hesitate to ask for space and equipment for this type of work, and they get it. But most mathematics teachers do not even ask for it, though to do so would be both reasonable and proper.

In spite of this, however, laboratory work in mathematics is receiving increasing attention. New classrooms are being designed with this as one of the primary considerations. Textbooks, teachers' manuals, and professional journals for teachers are giving more suggestions for such work than they ever have before. Special courses are being given to equip teachers and prospective teachers for such work, and the mathematics laboratory has become almost a standard adjunct of institutes and professional meetings for mathematics teachers. Its importance in the learning of mathematics may be compared to the importance of laboratory work in the learning of physics, chemistry, and biology and that of field work in biology and geography. In view of the significant contribution which it can make and the fact that teachers have only begun to exploit its possibilities, it must be given more than passing mention here.

As the name implies, the underlying idea of the mathematics laboratory is that students will develop new concepts and understandings particularly well through experimental activities dealing with concrete situations such as measuring and drawing; counting, weighing, averaging, and estimating; taking readings from instruments; recording, comparing, analyzing, classifying, and checking data; and obtaining original data or impressions from concrete physical situations and working with such data. Most work of this nature will involve the use of various kinds of physical equipment and will entail such activities as those listed here. Some of this work can be done in the classroom that is suitably arranged and equipped; some can take the form of elementary field work such as determination of angles and distances and the mapping of small areas. Most students find such work highly interesting, and it is doubtless true that through it they can develop many mathematical concepts and insights with an interest and a clarity often not attained through a strictly intellectual approach. It is also likely that these concepts and principles become more enduring and more functional and meaningful when they are seen in relation to actual applications.

There is, of course, some danger that, unless proper precautions are taken, laboratory work in mathematics may degenerate into more or less aimless playing with instruments, models, and gadgets. Activities which are mere busywork and which contribute nothing toward understanding are practically worthless and a waste of time. To be productive of learning, the activities must be carefully planned, closely supervised, and guided toward definite ends. Responsibility for the effectiveness of whatever laboratory-type work is done rests squarely with the teacher, and the discharge of that responsibility depends upon adequate planning and supervision of the activities.

The activities involved in laboratory-type work in mathematics fall broadly into two classes which, though not mutually exclusive, may be called respectively "demonstrations" and "experimental activities." By the term "demonstration" we have in mind the illustration and explanation to the teacher or to the class of some mathematical concept or relation by a method in which some physical equipment or device is used to illustrate and help clarify the explanation. Thus the term is used here in the sense in which it is commonly used in connection with classes in physics or chemistry. For example, various physical devices have been used for the following purposes: to illustrate operations with positive and negative numbers, or the manner in which the trigonometric functions vary; to confirm the identification of the center of gravity of a flat triangular solid with the geometrical centroid of a triangle of the same shape and size; and to verify the geometric description of the locus of the vertex of an angle whose sides pass through two fixed points. Demonstration activities therefore are associated with the "giving out," or transmitting to others, of information and ideas already acquired by the demonstrator. The demonstrator may be either the teacher or a student; or perhaps a small group of students may cooperate in giving a demonstration. Any demonstration which is well planned and effectively carried out involves a real learning experience.

Although it is ostensibly aimed at the receiving audience, every experienced teacher knows that the students giving the demonstration will probably learn even more through the deeper and clearer insight engendered by the activity itself.[2]

In speaking of *experimental activities* we shall have in mind any kind of activity which (1) is carried on individually or by small groups working together and (2) is aimed primarily at helping the experimenters themselves to clearer understandings. This sort of activity can take many forms. A student who has obtained timed temperature readings in a physics class in an experiment on the cooling rate of a liquid may, by working with these data in tabular and graphic forms, be helped to a clear understanding of the law of cooling and its mathematical representation. Checking the solutions of simultaneous equations by accurately made large-scale graphs can serve to clarify and deepen the interpretation of graphs as well as make the algebraic solutions seem concrete and realistic. By estimating and then measuring distances or angles, students clarify their concepts of a yard, a rod, 100 feet, or an angle of elevation of 15° or 45°. Real appreciation of how many things make 1,000 will be sharpened by outlining on a piece of cross-section paper a rectangle containing 1,000 squares and then drawing a little ring in each one. The axioms for solving linear equations can be given point and meaning by the use of a pair of balances. A model cut from a large potato can be used to point up the proof that the volume of a triangular pyramid is one-third that of the prism in which it is inscribed. Indeed, the illustration of many theorems of plane and solid geometry by means of physical devices adds a satisfying tangibility to the formal proofs. In the junior high school the properties of geometric figures and concepts of distances, angles, weights, areas, volumes, and loci can be given a more vivid impact through work of this experimental nature than through any other means.[3]

Space limitations make it impossible in this book to extend the discussion of laboratory work in mathematics, though a great deal more could be said about it. Fortunately, there are now available a number of excellent references dealing with this subject in many of its detailed aspects.

Developmental teaching Just as there is no single method through which new concepts are learned, so there is no single method of teaching which fits all learning situations. In order to develop new material successfully, the teacher must adapt his procedure to the situation as

[2]For specific suggestions on conducting such activities, see the article by Emil J. Berger, Principles Guiding the Use of Teacher- and Pupil-made Learning Aids, *Twenty-second Yearbook* (Washington, D.C.: National Council of Teachers of Mathematics, 1954), pp. 160–163.

[3]*Ibid.*

he finds it and modify his procedure in accordance with the changing requirements of the situation. Developmental teaching is an art. It can be neither standardized nor stereotyped. Procedures which are used successfully by one teacher may prove to be unsuccessful when tried by another, or perhaps even by the same teacher under different circumstances. Much depends upon the personality of the teacher, upon his enthusiasm, tact, understanding of children, and upon his ability to sense intuitively the procedures which will serve best to capitalize the psychological classroom situation of the moment or modify it in such a way that it may be made to contribute most powerfully in the drive toward the objective which has been set. That teacher will be most successful in developmental work who has at his command *various* methods of procedure and who uses them in such a way as to make them supplement each other most advantageously as occasion may indicate.

One of the greatest mistakes which many teachers make is to try to cover too much ground in a given period of time or to try to cover a given amount of material in too short a period of time. This nearly always results in superficial learning or in no learning at all. Particularly in the developmental teaching of new material, the teacher should avoid forcing the process too rapidly. The development of new concepts and principles is a slow process, and it always requires a certain amount of discussion. Sometimes it will be necessary for the teacher to carry the burden of the discussion in building up and coordinating the necessary background and in giving a first presentation of the new material, but so far as possible this should be done in such a way as to avoid lecturing. When it is feasible to guide students into exploratory activities through appropriate questioning or laboratory exercises so that they may discover things for themselves, it should be done. When it is necessary for the teacher to give direct information, it should be given briefly and concisely and should be checked by pointed and searching questioning. New understandings, as they are developed, should be given permanence, clarity, and interest by means of adequate illustration and application.

Developmental work is not the job of the teacher alone. In order to be successful, it requires the continuous interaction of the students' best efforts with those of the teacher. The aim at all times is to develop in the students a broadening background of mathematical understanding and foster a continuing interest in the subject to the end that the students will gain added appreciation of its nature and usefulness and will acquire increasing ability to do independent thinking in the field. The teacher must plan and direct the activities of the class toward these goals. He must strive to secure the highest possible degree of cooperative effort on the part of the students. He must be tactful and sympathetic, helping when necessary, encouraging, guiding, checking, and always stimulating the students to put forth their own best efforts. Such a program of developmental teaching may be expected to yield highly satisfactory results not only in developing mastery of the new subject matter immediately in hand but also in building up an added appreciation of mathematics and its contributions, in developing an increasing ability to do independent mathematical thinking, and in stimulating interest in the pursuit of further mathematical study.

Teaching for assimilation: directed study

The preceding sections of this chapter have dealt with the *development* of new material, i.e., with methods of presenting new material to the students, of discussing it with them, and of giving them their first basic understandings of it. It is well to re-emphasize here that many of the difficulties which students encounter in mathematics can be traced to the inadequacy of the developmental work which precedes the period of independent study. Obviously, students will not be able to make much independent progress toward the assimilation of concepts, principles, and relationships of which they have not even gained a basic understanding. Adequate developmental teaching is an absolute prerequisite to successful assimilative study in mathematics. The teacher who neglects to assure himself that his developmental work has been reasonably effective is likely to find his students groping helplessly for light on matters of which they have gained but an imperfect understanding. It is therefore of the utmost importance that, before the students are set to independent study of new material, measures be taken to test their understanding of the ideas which the teacher has tried to develop with them as a preliminary basis for their work during the assimilation period. The results of such a test will often be extremely illuminating to the teacher by revealing points where further developmental work is needed. Any such points should be cleared up immediately by thorough reteaching.

This, however, is only one step toward real and adequate mastery. Concepts are not ultimately mastered without many illustrations in varied contexts, nor principles without repeated application, nor processes without extensive practice, nor any of these without protracted and sustained intellectual effort on the part of the students themselves. The purpose of developmental teaching is to give the students adequate bases of understanding and appreciation and motive upon which to build, but the process of mastery can by no means be thought of as ending with this step. On the contrary, this is merely a beginning which must be followed by an extensive period in which the student must devote himself to the task of assimilation and fixation of the ideas, principles, and processes which have been brought out in the developmental work.

Lest the foregoing statement be misunderstood, we do not mean that the activities of the assimilation work will necessarily be divorced from discussion, illustration, demonstration, experiment, and other kinds of work usually associated with developmental work. Assimilation can take place through many avenues, although the principal one is individual directed study. Let it be emphasized too that the term "directed study" as used here refers to a type of classroom activity rather than a method of teaching; it is to be thought of as a *phase* of teaching rather than a method. There is no reason why part of a class period cannot be devoted to developmental work on new concepts or processes and part of the same period be given to assimilation work on this or previously developed ideas. The assimilation period need not, and probably should not, be an unbroken succession of class periods devoted wholly to study and devoid of everything else. The thing to be noted especially is that the fundamental objective here is different from that in developmental teaching. In the developmental phase of the work the principal aim is to produce threshold *understanding* of new material. In the assimilative phase the aim is to produce fuller and deeper insights, greater familiarity, and improved facility; in short, the aim is to produce real mastery and a comfortable sense of feeling at home and at ease with the material. The objectives, of course, will imply the methods or activities through which they can best be attained, and we shall see that the activities of the assimilative phase will, in general, differ somewhat from those of the developmental phase.

The teacher necessarily has a somewhat active role in at least some parts of the developmental work. In the assimilative stage, however, the situation is different. From this point on, the teacher's role, while no less important than before, is much less obvious. The students and their activities now occupy the center of the stage, while the teacher serves as a sort of prompter and director operating from the wings. Of course there will need to be some general discussion from time to time for purposes of motivation and for clearing up points which offer persistent difficulties, but such discussions should, for the most part, be incidental to the directed study which is the characterizing activity in this part of the work. In the process of assimilation through directed study the students themselves are the main participants so far as overt activity is concerned. The task of the teacher now should be that of guiding and directing their work, stimulating them, encouraging them, helping them over hard spots, evaluating their progress, and in every way possible striving to get them to put forth their best efforts to achieve a permanent and functional mastery of the material upon which they are working.

Directed study in mathematics At first thought it may appear that directed study in mathematics makes little or no demand upon the teacher. It is true that the teacher's role is much less prominent than it is in developmental teaching, but it is hardly less important. Directed study does not reduce teaching to an entirely individual basis, but it does attempt to combine the main advantages of individual instruction for those students who need it with the economy of time and other advantages generally recognized as accruing to group instruction. Directing study involves much more than maintaining order. If it is to be really effective, the teacher must be continually in touch with the work of each individual student. This requires repeated inspection and quick sizing up of the difficulties and needs of the various students. The teacher must be adept, not only at spotting key difficulties and in helping the students to clear them up, but also in discriminating between students who are experiencing real difficulties and those who are merely disinclined to work for themselves.

Many teachers make the mistake of rushing to the assistance of students at the first sign of difficulty and virtually doing their work for them. This is bad practice for two reasons. In the first place it does the students little or no good. Mastery can come only through individual effort, and it is not likely to be gained by the student who is unwilling to assume substantial personal responsibility for results and who relies to an excessive extent upon the teacher's assistance. There will always be such students, and if the directed study program is to be effective, the teacher must be able to detect them. He should decline to extend them assistance unless he is convinced that they are seriously in need of it, and he should make every effort to get them to modify their attitude so that they will be willing to take a larger share of responsibility upon themselves and rely less upon assistance from him.

In the second place, if the teacher allows students to impose unduly upon his willingness to help them, he will soon find himself so swamped with demands of this nature that he will be unable to take care of them all in a satisfactory manner. If he allows himself to be so hurried that he has to rush from student to student, not only will many students waste time waiting for him, but inevitably he will tend to give direct information instead of helping students to think their own way through their problems; therefore, such ostensible assistance as he can give under such circumstances will largely defeat its own purpose. In addition to this, the pressure and stress will almost certainly leave him physically tired, mentally and emotionally disorganized, and generally unfitted for effective work. The only way in which these evil effects can be avoided is for the teacher to confine his assistance to those students who, in his opinion, really need it, and even then to the key difficulties which they encounter. Perhaps the mere explanation of a word will be sufficient. In any case, it is extremely important that the teacher be able to lead the student to disclose just what is causing his difficulty so that it may be cleared up without allowing extraneous matters to befog the issue and without unnecessary waste of time.

On the other hand, the teacher must not be niggardly with assistance when it is really needed. It is a fine art to determine just who really needs help, just what and how much assistance is needed, and in what manner it should be given. It can be done successfully only by a teacher who has a sympathetic understanding of the attitudes and abilities of his students, who has a good knowledge of the difficulties to be expected and the errors commonly made in the work underway, and who possesses a trained insight which will enable him to get directly at the root or key of the student's difficulty, even though the student himself may not know precisely what it is that is causing him trouble.

Students often employ wasteful and inefficient procedures in studying mathematics. Sometimes they do not know how to begin their work, and they fail to form the habit of depending upon themselves. They waste time waiting for someone to get them started or in aimlessly trying one thing after another. They are unsystematic. They allow their attention to be distracted and their work interrupted by trivial things. They are careless in their reading, in their listening, and in their written work. They become impatient and do not take time for deliberate analysis and planning before starting their work. It is not surprising to find these characteristics in young students, but they must be helped to form more mature and stable characteristics. If the students are to acquire the ability to do effective independent study, they need specific instruction in methods and habits of study.

It seems clear, therefore, that one of the most important tasks of the mathematics teacher is to help his students acquire both general habits which are conducive to the improvement of study and specific ideas and practices which may be helpful in studying particular parts or aspects of mathematics.

Teaching for permanence: drill, review, and maintenance

The developmental and assimilative phases of instruction represent essentially the stages during which actual learning of new material takes place. Any subject matter, however, is likely to be forgotten, no matter how well it has been initially mastered, unless it is maintained by repeated application and practice. This is particularly true of mathematical skills and relationships. Skills need to be perfected and maintained through systematic drill, and concepts and relationships must be reviewed and applied at frequently recurring intervals. The instructional effort which is directed toward these ends may well be called *teaching for permanence*. While it generally involves material that has already been learned rather than new material, its importance as a means of strengthening and maintaining learnings is commensurate with the importance of the developmental and assimilative phases of instruction as means of *acquiring* new learnings. Its avenues are drill, review, and application.

The function of drill The place of drill in mathematics has been a much discussed issue in recent years. The reaction against excessive use of abstract rote drill, which came along with the reorganization movement and with the increased emphasis on concepts and meanings, was certainly justified and doubtless overdue. However, it caused many educators to go to the other extreme and inveigh against all drill as being futile and without value. The old pedagogy undoubtedly laid too much emphasis upon memorization and mechanical learning and to a considerable extent neglected meanings. In such a scheme mechanical drill played an important part because it afforded a convenient and fairly efficient medium for the rapid memorization of details and the automatization of processes. The fact that these do not necessarily imply understanding, and that proficiency acquired without understanding is not likely to endure very long, was apparently not recognized, since it did not seem to cause much concern. Eventually, however, a strong reaction set in, with the extremists taking the position that meanings alone have value, that the development of new concepts and understandings is all that matters, and that drill, in its restricted sense, has no place in the educational process. This point of view overlooks the important element of fixation, without which it would be manifestly impossible to organize and relate concepts or to carry on any process at a reasonable level of efficiency.

An enlightened present-day view of mathematical instruction must reject both of these extreme positions as untenable. Drill must be recognized as an essential means of attaining some of the desired controls, just as a strong emphasis upon concepts and meanings must be regarded as essential for understanding. Both are necessary and neither alone is sufficient. Many of the operations of mathematics need to be performed not only correctly but with considerable facility and speed if they are to be very useful. Some of them need to be actually automatized. The acquisition of facility in such operations can be secured only through systematic and repeated practice, i.e., through drill.

If instruction is to be valuable, however, understanding must go hand in hand with operational facility. With a few possible exceptions children should not be drilled on procedures which they do not first understand. Drill under such circumstances lacks both significance and motive. It may indeed produce temporary facility, but facility will be without value unless it is associated with meaning. If understanding and motive are lacking, drill becomes little more than drudgery.

Principles of drill Educational psychology in recent years has done much to provide us with well-established principles whereby drill may be made interesting and effective, and authors and publishers have combined to make available materials specially designed to facilitate the application of these principles. In the following paragraphs some important considerations relating to drill in mathematics will be enumerated and briefly discussed.

Drill, to be most effective, must be well motivated. The attitude with which students approach the problem of mastering material has an important bearing upon both the rate and extent of mastery which they achieve. If the material contains no intrinsic interest and they can see no value in it, their work will be without interest. However, if they are working on something which they recognize as important or interesting in itself, they will work with enthusiasm and with concentrated attention, and their work will be correspondingly more effective. Witness, for example, the willingness with which the members of a football squad engage in charging and tackling drills. The activity in and of itself is tiring and sometimes painful, but it is well motivated because the end toward which it is directed is clear and seems desirable. Most students are not lazy. They are willing to work hard at things which interest them, and when they appear to be lazy it is likely that they are only bored. Contests between selected teams, improvement charts, and games involving the materials to be mastered are examples of the numerous devices which have been developed for motivating drill work in mathematics.

Drill exercises should be conducted in such a manner that students can work at differing rates and at different levels according to their abilities. The certainty of individual differences within a group makes it clear that the individuals, even though they may all need drill on the same things, will not perform at the same rate or at the same level of difficulty. It is uneconomical to have those who have attained substantial mastery continue drilling on tasks which no longer challenge them. It is equally wasteful to have them do nothing while waiting for the others to catch up. In order to avoid situations of this sort, drill exercises should contain enough material to keep all the students profitably occupied throughout the drill period and also sufficiently diversified material to provide worthwhile and stimulating practice for students of different attainments and capacities.

Drill periods should generally be rather short. The attention span of children is not great, and long periods of continuous drill become tiresome and ineffective. In general it may be said that no drill period should extend for more than 20 minutes and that in most cases drill periods of not more than half that length are preferable. This does not mean that a given skill can be mastered to a desired point of proficiency in 5, or 10, or even 20 minutes. Rather, it means that more time, if it is required, should be distributed in relatively small amounts at recurring intervals which should become more widely spaced as time goes on. This principle of spaced learning, as contrasted with the idea of complete immediate mastery, is exceedingly important and is coming to be widely recognized in the organization of textbooks and instructional materials.

In order to be most effective, drill must be specific. By this is meant that it should be concentrated upon particular skills or even on particular details of operation. The students should, of course, be aware of the relation of any detail to the whole situation of which it is a part. But for purposes of fixation, which is the object of all drill, the particular detail or skill should for the moment be dissociated from its setting and context and drilled upon per se. When the desired proficiency in them has been attained, the details should be progressively reintegrated into the entire process or situation of which they are components.

When drill is begun on any process or skill, correctness should be insisted upon as the prime consideration, and for the time being speed should be regarded as of secondary importance. Every effort should be made to detect mistakes in students' work and eliminate them at the outset. Failure to do so will inevitably have unfortunate consequences, because a wrong habit is fixed as readily as a right one, and it is much harder to eliminate a wrong habit that has become established and replace it by a correct one than it is to establish the correct one in the first place. Thus it is of extreme importance to supervise *closely* the initial work of the students on any new process. The insistence upon *right practice* from the start cannot be too greatly emphasized. Teachers often overlook this important principle when they assign homework involving procedures which have not been previously mastered in class. When they do so, the students are likely to make mistakes that could have been avoided by a small amount of carefully supervised drill.

There are few things which cause students to take a keener interest in their work or apply themselves with more verve and intensity than the satisfaction of knowing immediately whether their work is right or not. In much of the work of secondary mathematics it is desirable to have students apply mathematical tests or checks to ascertain the correctness of their own work. The checking of work in this manner is a real educational exercise, in many cases fully as valuable as the original work itself. This method of applying mathematical checks can be used in connection with drill work just as it can with problem work. It has, however, the disadvantage of slowing up the drill and diverting time and attention to procedures other than those for which the drill was originally planned.

Some teachers dislike to provide students with answers to verbal problems or materials assigned for home study on the theory that the students may easily misuse the answers. It is quite conceivable that this argument may have some justification as regards the kind of work mentioned, but in drill work conducted in the classroom the situation is different. It is, in fact, a definite stimulus to the student to know *immediately* whether his responses are correct or not. If they are, he secures an immediate satisfaction; if they are not, he is challenged to correct his work before his attention has shifted to other things. For these reasons answers should be provided for selected problems and exercises, and when answers are not provided, specific and efficient checking techniques should have been developed previously. Students should be required to check all results with care. When answers are provided, mere agreement is a sufficient check. Otherwise, independent work must be carried out and results must agree. There are times when variety of experience is the major desideratum of the drill and time is at a premium. On such occasions answers should be provided for all exercises. The question of dishonesty is minimized. The fact that the student realizes that he is being trusted to play fair operates as a definite incentive to him to do just that. Experience has shown that it actually works out in this way and that it affords a real training in honesty and self-responsibility, besides adding zest to the work itself.

Whenever possible, drill materials should also be provided with some means whereby the student can *score* his own work and compare his performance not only with that of the other members of the class but also with established standards and with his own performance on previous occasions. Here again, experience has shown that students are greatly interested in noting their own progress, and no finer incentive than this could be devised. The most valuable of the published drill materials are those for which standards of comparison are available and which are provided with record sheets or charts on which each student can keep a continuous running record of his own achievement.

Finally, the students should be kept aware that drill work is only part of their mathematical training, but that without it they would be handicapped in their pursuit of understandings, appreciations, and generalizations. Without speed and correctness in the fundamental skills they would be under a handicap similar to that of a student of a foreign language whose vocabulary is deficient, or a person trying to play a Liszt rhapsody without having acquired a good technique of fingering the piano keyboard. The student who lacks mastery of the mechanical skills of mathematics will find it difficult to free his mind of those skills so that he can give full attention to interpretation and analysis of mathematical theorems or problems. Nobody can read Shakespeare or Tennyson or even a contemporary short story with much appreciation if he has to stop and spell out the words.

The following summary of principles of drill is taken from an excellent article by Sueltz.[4] It is given here for convenient reference.

1. The learner should both understand what he is practicing and appreciate its significance to him as an individual.
2. The learner should have sufficient propaedeutic experience so that the *newness* in what he is practicing does not create a mental block for him.
3. The learner should be an active participant both in setting his goals and in the thinking-striving aspects of learning. He should not merely repeat "parrot-fashion" from a teacher or textbook.
4. Drill should follow the developmental and discovery stages of learning and be used to reinforce and extend basic learning.
5. Drill should be varied so that procedures do not become monotonous and so that different pupils have types of drill perhaps better suited to them.
6. Drill should be spaced so that (*a*) time is not wasted in excessive overlearning in initial stages and (*b*) previous learnings are kept fresh and useful.
7. Drill should be an integral part of various phases of learning but should not be used to hasten the achievement of results at the sacrifice of meaning and understanding.
8. Drill policy should recognize different rates and modes of learning with different pupils and not try to fit all into a common mold.
9. In general, it is better to provide for drill upon whole processes rather than parts thereof, unless some particular part, such as, for example, subtraction in a long division exercise, causes trouble and needs teaching and practice for reinforcing.
10. Drill should be done with correct processes lest a child practice errors which need to be remedied later.
11. Drill should be based upon or involve thinking and insight so that it never becomes a mere mechanical repetition.

[4]Ben A. Sueltz, Drill—Practice—Recurring Experience, *Twenty-first Yearbook* (Washington, D.C.: National Council of Teachers of Mathematics, 1953), pp. 192–204.

12. Drill should be used when and where needed. It should not be used as a punishment nor should things already well learned be assigned for more practice.
13. There should be some sense of organization of drill so that (*a*) pupils see the sense and relationships of what they are doing and (*b*) important elements are not overlooked.
14. It seems that pupils of lower mental abilities require more drill than the more able, but this may be due to other related factors such as attention, insight, and other such causes.

Review

Review is sometimes identified with drill because they are both characterized by repetition and because they both aim at the fixation of reactions, concepts, or relationships. As the terms are used in this book, however, a distinction is made between drill and review. Drill is aimed mainly at the automatization of relatively detailed processes and reactions. Review, on the other hand, aims not only at the fixation and retention of details but also at the thoughtful organization of the important things in a chapter or unit into a coherent whole in order that the relationship of the various parts to each other and to the whole unit may be clearly understood.

Review should usually be concerned with more or less comprehensive units of subject matter. One of its functions is indeed to make recall more certain and more effective, but it aims to achieve this through the deliberate processes of organizing, systematizing, and relating elements to each other through giving, indeed, a "re-view," or a new look, at the unit which has been studied, rather than through reducing reactions to the plane of automatic responses. It emphasizes thought and meaning rather than habit formation. Thus while drill and review have some things in common, they also have certain differences. Each has its proper function, and each is highly important in the study of mathematics.

Review work may be incidental in the sense that it may be integrated with the other work of the course, or it may be specialized by making it the primary feature and objective of particular assignments. Both of these types of review are necessary to the most effective teaching. Review of the incidental type is especially valuable for the gradual building up and clarification of concepts through repeated reference and through continual reapplication in those situations in which they play component parts. Concepts and principles are generalized through being met with in many situations which vary in other particulars and from which the concepts and principles are gradually dissociated and abstracted. Perhaps this process may not be recognized as review at all if it is systematically made an integral part of the regular work, but it is review in a very real and important sense. One of the strong arguments for a continuous program of integrated mathematics is that this sort of incidental or integrated review would necessarily run systematically throughout the entire program, giving strength and coherence to the entire structure through continual interassociation of the components.

At the same time there is need of special review work to supplement the incidental review which has been described. The functions of the special review are to help the student organize more or less comprehensive bodies of material with reference to their logical relationships, to assist him in classifying their important ideas, and to give him a sense of the unity of the whole which might otherwise be lacking. The review lesson, which should be planned with this idea dominant, will generally follow the assimilative study of a unit. In preparing for a review lesson, the student should be expected to summarize the outstanding ideas which have been considered in the unit and to make an outline from which he can give a brief but coherent and systematic discussion of the material in the unit or division. The preparation of such an outline will make it necessary for the student to review the unit in the fullest sense of the term. Through making the necessary association of the ideas in the unit, he will be aided not only in remembering them but in understanding them and appreciating their interrelations.

On the whole, most teachers do a better job of conducting drill work than they do of conducting review work of this type. This is probably due in part to their failure to recognize the main function of review as different from that of drill. Students need to be taught how to review material just as they need to be taught how to study. They cannot review effectively without definite instructions. Yet all too commonly the only instructions they receive are something like, Review chapters seven and eight for tomorrow. The task of helping students plan their review work is a responsibility which every teacher should take seriously.

Maintenance A planned program of cumulative drill and review work is aptly designated a maintenance program. The importance of such a program is implied in the discussion in the foregoing paragraphs. The fundamental requirement of a satisfactory maintenance program is that it shall operate to prevent the forgetting of facts, concepts, and relationships and forestall the disintegration of skills. To this end it must provide for systematic application of the important elements of the instructional program and for appropriate or needed practice on these elements even after current attention and emphasis have passed on to other matters. Therefore the planning of a really adequate maintenance program must be built upon the following principles:

1. The materials to be included should be selected from the point of

view of relative values. The program should not be cluttered up with trivial things. Only significant skills, concepts, relationships, principles, and problem situations should be included.

2. In accordance with established principles of drill and review, the items should be distributed throughout the program in such a way that practice upon any particular element will not be too greatly concentrated but will recur at increasing intervals and in decreasing amounts.

3. The maintenance program should be diagnostic, preferably self-diagnostic, so that each student may be able to discover his own weaknesses. To this end some means should be provided whereby each student may systematically keep and study his own achievements in detail.

4. There should be provided supplementary practice material for remedial work on the various particular elements included in the maintenance program. This supplementary material can be used most effectively if it is keyed with the diagnostic record. In this way each student will be able not only to determine those things upon which he most needs practice but to carry on his own remedial work with a minimum of direction.

5. The different sets of exercises in the maintenance program should be comparable in terms of some uniform scoring or rating schedule so that each student may keep a record of his general achievement and his progress. This will be of great value in stimulating pride, effort, and genuine interest in maintaining skills and principles after the original interest due to their newness has worn off.

Numerous textbooks published in recent years recognize the need for systematic maintenance work and make provision for it through sets of drill exercises, diagnostic inventory tests, cumulative reviews, and the like placed at strategic points in the texts. In some cases these exercises have evidently been prepared hastily and with little attention to their validity or suitability. In other cases their organization and arrangement have been based upon extensive and painstaking study and upon well-established principles of the psychology of learning. These same comments are equally applicable to the multitude of drill books and workbooks and sets of practice exercises which are now commerically available to supplement textbooks. They are not all equally good, but the better ones are valuable aids to the teacher in carrying on an adequate maintenance program. Many teachers lack both the experience and the time needed to prepare thoroughly suitable materials for regular maintenance work. Prepared materials which are scientifically planned and for which standards of attainment are available serve at least three useful purposes: (1) they make for economy of time and labor and therefore for efficiency in instruction; (2) they provide a strong motive to achievement, since they foster the students' continued study of their own performances, and (3) they provide the best possible insurance against forgetting and against the deterioration of skills and understandings.

Teaching for transfer

The transfer of training When people speak about "transfer of training," it is not always clear just what they have in mind. The idea and the term stem from the old theory of formal discipline, which held that the mind is made up of several "faculties," such as memory and reasoning, and that these can be strengthened in a general sense by exercise, much as a muscle can. Thus it once was held that, since mathematics is largely concerned with reasoning, the study of mathematics would automatically strengthen the "logical faculty" as a whole, and that this faculty would then inevitably operate more effectively than before in every kind of situation. This was a comfortable theory, but the early studies of William James, Thorndike, Woodworth, and others cast grave doubt upon its validity as a theory of learning, and it has long been discredited. That is to say, with respect to the teaching of mathematics, reputable psychologists no longer hold that the study of mathematics will guarantee improved reasoning in other fields, such as religion or politics or the affairs of daily life.

This is not to say, however, that the learning of mathematics has no effect on the learner beyond the immediate things learned. On the contrary, evidence indicates that considerable carry-over, or transfer, is possible and in fact is often attained. In other words, the effects produced upon one in learning mathematics may materially influence his reactions to situations other than the immediate one. This is transfer in a more limited and less definite sense, since usually it is incomplete and may take any of a large variety of forms. Although a few people still identify the term "transfer" with the old concept and doctrine of mental discipline, most people now use the term in this more restricted sense. It is usually taken to denote the functioning, in a second or new situation, of certain aspects or structures or relations which were learned in an original situation.

Much remains to be done in ascertaining the manner in which transfer takes place and the circumstances upon which it is conditioned, but competent psychologists are now agreed that under favorable conditions transfer can and does occur. On the other hand, there is abundant evidence that it is neither automatic nor inevitable. Various theories have been proposed to account for the fact and the nature of its occurrence and to determine ways of bringing it about.[5] It is evidently a very

[5]Myron F. Rosskopf, Transfer of Training, *Twenty-first Yearbook* (Washington, D.C.: National Council of Teachers of Mathematics, 1953), pp. 203–227.

complex phenomenon. Probably each of the theories (except the doctrine of formal discipline) explains certain aspects of it and has some implications for teaching, and probably none of the theories gives the complete explanation. But while there may not be complete agreement on just how transfer takes place, the most competent observers do agree that, to achieve the transfer values for any subject, it is important to teach the subject with that end in view. As Rosskopf says,[6]

> To secure maximum transfer, in the sense of applying "an integrated knowledge [a whole principle] . . . to all tasks involving the same principle," teachers of mathematics must teach in such a way that demonstration exercises (or tasks) serve as examples of the application of that principle.

Teaching or directing learning in mathematics in such a way as to achieve the transfer values of the subject must therefore be recognized as a major objective. The problem of how to attain that objective gives rise at once to the following questions:

1. What are those elements of mathematical training the transfer of which to other situations is desirable?
2. By what methods of teaching can the transfer of these elements be fostered and promoted most effectively?

The objects of transfer The first of these two questions can be answered with definiteness. In the first place, it is desirable that all those elements of mathematical training which most people have occasion to *use* shall be taught in such a manner that they *can* be used whenever occasion demands. This category includes such things as the fundamental properties, combinations, skills, operations, and concepts of arithmetic; the laws and formulas involved in mensuration of the common geometrical figures; the interpretation of commonly used statistical conventions and devices; some understanding of what is meant by the structure of a number system; the construction and interpretation of straight-line, circle, and bar graphs; the ability to read pictographs intelligently; the fundamental meaning of a formula; the ability to evaluate formulas; in a word, practically all the understandings and abilities, other than those of formal algebra, which are commonly included in the mathematics of the junior high school. These things are fairly specific and are needed by practically everybody. Since they cannot be directly taught in all the specific situations to which they have potential application, it is desirable that the generality of their application be emphasized so that the student will not be at a loss when occasion requires their use in new situations.

In the second place, the fundamental concepts, formulas, and skills of elementary algebra are desirable objects of transfer. Too often these are taught with specific reference only to the immediate algebraic

[6] *Ibid.*, p. 217.

situations in which they occur in the textbook and with little or no reference to the generality of their meanings or applications. To this group of algebraic understandings and skills should be added the knowledge and understanding of certain of the more important facts and relationships that are developed in plane and solid geometry. Of course, every proposition constitutes a link in the immediate chain of development, and to this extent the very consciousness of its relation to the preceding and subsequent parts of the development involves a measure of transfer. Also, some of the propositions constitute extremely important generalizations which have wide application not only in the field of demonstrative geometry itself but also in subsequent mathematical courses and in other fields of study, such as engineering and certain parts of the physical sciences. Substantially the same observation may be made with reference to the concepts, skills, and relationships of numerical trigonometry. Such important and pervasive generalizations as the Pythagorean theorem, the angle-sum relationship, the proportionality of line lengths in similar figures, the sine and cosine laws, the metric properties of circles, and various area formulas are cases in point.

The foregoing list of objects of transfer may be grouped for convenience into two categories, viz., things to know and understand and things to be able to do. The detailed items which would be included under either of these lists are reasonably specific.

A second type of objects of transfer is represented by more general and abstract concepts of mathematics, with their associated technical nomenclature, vocabulary, and notation. These are well illustrated by such concepts as number and numeration, place value, symbolism, properties of equality and of inequalities, measurement and approximation, set, subset, variable, operation, mapping, relation and function, inverse relation and inverse function, probability, the meaning of deductive reasoning and the nature of proof, and the concept of the structure of a mathematical system. The study of mathematics should bring about an understanding of such concepts and an awareness of how they provide a framework and structure under which the more detailed and specific things can be subsumed. To the extent to which this objective is attained, genuine transfer will have taken place.

Finally there is a third object of transfer which has probably received more emphasis in writings on mathematical education than in actual teaching. This is the acquisition of a mathematical manner of thinking. It was implied in the statement of the "disciplinary aims" listed in the 1923 report of the National Committee on Mathematical Requirements: "the acquisition of mental habits and attitudes which will make [mathematical] training effective in the life of the individual."[7]

[7]National Committee on Mathematical Requirements, "The Reorganization of Mathematics in Secondary Education" (Boston: Houghton Mifflin Company, 1923), p. 12.

It was essentially reaffirmed thirty-six years later in the *Twenty-fourth Yearbook* of the National Council of Teachers of Mathematics, Chapter 9 of that book being titled Mathematical Modes of Thought.[8] It is a thing which all mathematics teachers hope for but which, for lack of a methodology, has usually been hopefully anticipated as a by-product of mathematical instruction rather than a definite outcome to be worked for through indefinite procedures.

Under this broad interpretation the desirable transfer values of mathematical study may be thought of as involving potentially such values as awareness of and insistence upon precision; facility and confidence in the use of fundamental skills; the establishment of self-reliance and the self-imposition of responsibility for information, procedure, and results; perseverance in the face of difficulty; habitual insistence upon the precise use of language and upon clarity and precision in definition and statement; the ability to discriminate between a mere assertion and an inference; the habitual testing of inferences for consistency with known or given conditions; the ability to discriminate between sound and specious argument and between valid inferences and unwarranted inferences; awareness of the nature of postulational reasoning, the arbitrary nature of hypothesis and definition, and the inevitable but contingent nature of conclusion; the ability to build a consistent argument; the ability to generalize relationships and apply generalizations; and the ability to eliminate emotional or prejudicial factors from an argument.

In particular, the ability to generalize meanings, symbols, relationships, and processes and apply such generalizations to new situations represents transfer of the most genuine and vital sort. In fact, this is precisely what is implied by the expression "functional" mathematics, which has come into use to express the dominant idea for the courses in general mathematics as well as for the more formal sequential courses. Indeed, this aspect of transfer would seem to lie at the very root of all really functional education. It is implied in every application and every interpretation of any concept or circumstance; for correct interpretation must form the basis for any intelligent application, whether to a problem in physics or geometry or to a business or social situation.

How shall we teach to secure transfer? As has already been pointed out, students of modern educational psychology are agreed that transfer is possible but is neither automatic nor inevitable in its desirable forms. Furthermore, the theories on how it takes place seem to be drawing somewhat closer together. There seems to be some agreement

[8]National Council of Teachers of Mathematics, The Growth of Mathematical Ideas, Grades K–12, *Twenty-fourth Yearbook* (Washington, D.C.: National Council of Teachers of Mathematics, 1959), pp. 370–404.

now that meaning plays a most important role in the process and that the theories of generalization and the structuring of knowledge probably represent substantially the avenues through which positive transfer of higher mental functions takes place. Generalization does not deny the importance of the identical or similar "elements" which formed the basis of one of the early theories of transfer. Indeed it implies their necessity but denies their sufficiency to account for the phenomenon. It says, in effect, that if a principle is to transfer to (or be applied intelligently in) a particular situation, the situation must of course contain elements or relationships analogous to those found in the principle, but this is not enough. These similarities must not only exist but also *be recognized by the learner* before significant positive transfer can take place. It is this act of recognition of similar elements which really constitutes transfer at the higher levels and which, indeed, alone characterizes all functional and relational thinking and sets it apart from mere specific identification and mechanical rule-of-thumb procedure.

The problem of teaching for transfer would seem to resolve itself, then, into the problem of teaching children not only to recognize similarities between new situations and other situations with which they are already familiar but also to form the habit of consciously being on the lookout for these similarities. When confronted by a new and unfamiliar situation, the student must learn to ask himself, in effect, "Does this situation fit into the pattern of any other experiences or situations with which I am already familiar? What elements of similarity are there, and how can I use these elements that are familiar to me in interpreting this new situation and in bringing it under my control?"

A typical illustration of lack of transfer is found in the inability of many students to apply the principles and operations of algebra to problems in physics. The physics teachers usually complain that the students have not mastered the mathematical principles involved, but in most cases it is more likely that they simply fail to recognize in the concrete physical problem relationships which are perhaps quite familiar to them when seen in the abstract or symbolic mathematical setting in which they have been encountered previously. Innumerable examples illustrating this point could be given; they occur many times even within a particular branch of mathematics itself. Thus students who will readily factor $a^2 - b^2$ may fail to recognize such expressions as $t^2 - 36$ or $x^2 - 2xy + y^2 - 9z^4$ as being of precisely the same type and so may be unable to factor the latter expressions. Similarly, in connection with verbal problems, which bear the reputation of being the hardest part of elementary algebra, the difficulty is almost never in solving the equations to which the problems give rise but rather in translating the verbal problems into symbolic form. This is mainly due to failure to recognize the essential identity of the abstract and generalized symbols, formulas, and equations of formalized algebra with the concrete and specific conditions and relationships set forth in the verbal statements of the problems.

In some cases, of course, the similarities or identities in different situations are simple and obvious, and in such cases transfer is fairly well assured, especially among students of superior intelligence. In many cases, however, the similarities are obscured by other, more prominent elements and, in such cases, it is often necessary to make careful analyses in order to disclose them. Children will not learn to make these analyses unless they are systematically trained to do so. They need to be shown how to make them, and they must have much practice under carefully supervised conditions in order to master the technique. But even this is not enough. If this practice is to become really functional in their mathematical training, the students should become impressed with the advantage of *habitually* making this approach to any problem. They should form the habit of deliberately instituting a search for elements of relationships in the problem in hand which are similar to corresponding elements or relationships in other situations with which they have already had experience, whenever such similarities are not apparent at the outset. To the extent that such a procedure is consistently followed, the transfer of mathematical processes and techniques will be facilitated and this essentially mathematical mode of thought will become a really functional contributor to the effectiveness of rational thinking in general.

Some nontraditional patterns of mathematical instruction

The customary arrangement for organized instruction in mathematics, as in most other subjects, is one in which each teacher works with one moderate-size class at a time and in which the teaching procedures are largely those of explaining, discussing, questioning, directing the classroom study of the students, and testing to determine the results of the instruction. Since we shall want to mention in the present section some devices or procedures which present certain points of contrast with the usual arrangement described above, we may speak of that as the *traditional* pattern of instruction. Then, for purposes of contrast, we can apply the term "nontraditional" to instructional patterns or devices which deviate susbtantially from the traditional pattern.

In the past decade, and particularly since about 1960, certain unconventional or nontraditional patterns of instruction in mathematics have attained some prominence. Among these can be mentioned the use of such audio-visual devices as films and filmstrips, team teaching, honors courses and individual projects for superior students, the use of open- or closed-circuit television, and the use of so-called teaching machines or programmed instruction. These devices have come into being partly in response to the unprecedented and increasing numbers of students taking mathematics, with the consequent shortage of qualified teachers, partly to provide feasible ways of improving or expanding existing instructional facilities, and partly because of advances in the psychology of learning.

Undoubtedly there are plausible arguments that can be advanced with respect to the potential effectiveness and advantages of all these instructional media. It is equally certain that each of them lacks some of the advantages which are widely thought to accrue to the traditional instructional pattern as described above. Some teachers welcome these newer avenues of instruction with enthusiasm; others view them with skepticism. But regardless of one's personal feelings about them, they must be taken into account. In the present section we shall speak about three of them.

Films and filmstrips. The use of mathematical films and filmstrips, of course, is not new. Some films were available as early as 1935 and perhaps even earlier, and the number has increased significantly since that time. Reviews which have been published indicate that some have been superior to others in conception, treatment, and technical excellence. Invariably they have been topical, and they have been intended for use as supplementary material.

Opinion as to their usefulness has been divided. Many classrooms are not well adapted to the use of projection equipment, and many teachers are not skilled in the use of such equipment. Also, difficulties of scheduling films at appropriate times and of getting prompt delivery are important practical considerations which have to be taken into account. On the other hand these limiting factors will probably diminish as time goes on. More and better films are certain to become increasingly accessible. Many new classrooms are being equipped for the use of projection equipment, and this equipment itself is being improved all the time. Moreover, as the number and range of selection of available films and filmstrips increase, the problems of scheduling and delivery should become less acute. All things considered, these devices will probably play a larger and more important role in mathematical instruction in the future than they have in the past.

Instruction by television. The use of television presents another nontraditional avenue for instruction in mathematics which, although it is still in the experimental stage, may come to have important possibilities. Closed-circuit television has been and is being used with apparent success in a number of institutions of higher education for instruction in some subjects, and in a few instances it has been used for instruction in mathematics. On a much broader scale two half-year television courses on contemporary mathematics, which were a part of the program entitled "Continental Classroom," were presented over a nationwide (NBC) hookup of television stations in the 1960–1961 season. Probably nobody knows just how many people took these courses, but the number was evidently large. College credit was offered for these courses in 256 colleges and universities in 44 states.

Another variant of the use of this medium in presenting courses is found in airborne television instruction. This is accomplished by having the television programs or lessons broadcast from a high-flying airplane and beamed downward to cover an area perhaps as large as several counties. An experimental program in airborne television instruction in school subjects was begun in 1961 under the sponsorship of the Ford Foundation. With headquarters at Purdue University, the project included in 1961–1962 (its first full year of operation) courses in five subjects for elementary schools and five subjects for high schools. The latter included a course in geometry. The program also included the telecasting of suggestions and material for the assistance of teachers whose classes were using the television lessons. Source units describing the objectives and content of each lesson and suggestions for preparatory and follow-up activities were made available through the Midwest Airborne Television Headquarters at Purdue University.[9]

Programmed instruction. A third nontraditional device or plan for instruction in mathematics is the use of "teaching machines" or programmed instruction. A teaching machine is, in essence, some device which directs a learner step by step and detail by detail through a planned sequence of steps or activities which, it is hoped, will bring the learner to a point of understanding or mastery of that which was to be learned. In effect, it involves a preplanned sequential program of detailed learning steps and a device which in some manner automatically directs the learner's thoughts and reactions along the channel which has been prepared. It is a sort of automatic self-teacher, containing within itself both the substance of what is to be learned and the sequential directions for learning it. Advocates of the use of programmed learning claim a number of advantages for it, among which are the following:

1. It encourages and helps students to discover the desired concepts and relationships for themselves by providing them with sound sequences of developmental exercises.

[9]The Midwest Program on Airborne Television and Instruction, *American Mathematical Monthly*, **69** (1962), 310–311.

2. It permits each student to proceed at his own optimum pace. It can be used in situations where the number of students desiring to take a subject is too large to be handled effectively in regular classes by the available staff.
3. It can be used in small schools, where the number of students desiring to take a subject is too small to justify the organization of a class in that subject.
4. It can be used to advantage as a supplementary instructional device in classes organized along conventional lines.

On the other hand, there are some who feel that such potential advantages as may accrue to the use of programmed instruction are partially or wholly offset by other considerations. Among these adverse criticisms the following have been mentioned.

1. Once a course is programmed, it is inflexible. It cannot be modified either in content or emphasis without making a new program for it.
2. Some courses in mathematics which have been programmed have been very traditional in content and organization and do not reflect the spirit of modern mathematical thought.
3. Among the important values claimed for the usual teacher-class instructional pattern are the ability to communicate understanding to others and the feedback and interaction between teacher and students and between students and students. Teaching machines and programmed instruction make no provision for these valuable interactions and make little demand upon the ability to communicate ideas.

Thus programmed instruction has its advocates and its critics. It lacks certain advantages commonly attributed to the usual mode of instruction, but it appears also to have significant possibilities. In any case it seems clear that it cannot be dismissed lightly as a fad. There is substantial evidence that it is receiving serious attention in important circles, quite apart from mere commercial enterprises. Three articles on the subject were carried in volume 69 (1962) of the *American Mathematical Monthly*. In New York City the Center for Progammed Instruction (a nonprofit organization incorporated under the laws of the State of New York) has completed the programming of a number of courses in school mathematics, among others. A number of courses in mathematics have also been programmed and made available commerically by business organizations. It is especially significant that both the UICSM and the SMSG programs have established special projects for programming experimental mathematics courses for secondary schools.

It seems clear that significant experimental and commercial work on programmed instruction in mathematics is proceeding on an expanding scope and at an accelerating pace. Mathematics teachers will want to watch carefully the further developments in this field and be prepared to take advantage of such benefits as it may seem to offer for making their instruction more fruitful.

EXERCISES

1. What is meant by "developmental teaching"? Why should it be regarded as a phase or aspect of teaching rather than as a method of teaching?

2. Make a clear, concise statement of the fundamental objective in each of the following: (*a*) developmental teaching, (*b*) teaching for assimilation, (*c*) teaching for permanence, and (*d*) teaching for transfer.

3. Explain why all the aspects or phases of teaching listed in exercise 2 are complementary and necessary parts of the whole process of instruction in mathematics.

4. Point out the effects that would result from neglecting any of the aspects of teaching listed in exercise 2. Illustrate from your own experience if you can.

5. In your opinion, which of the phases of the teaching-learning process listed in exercise 2 is most neglected? Give reasons for your answer.

6. Compare the function of laboratory or field work in mathematics with the function of laboratory or field work in the sciences. What is the principal contribution which laboratory or field work can make to the learning of mathematics?

7. In view of the contribution which laboratory or field work could make to the study of mathematics, why has it played such a limited role in mathematical education?

8. In what grades or in what mathematics courses is field work likely to be most effective? Give reasons for your answer.

9. Describe several activities or projects which could be carried on profitably as laboratory work in mathematics. For each one, tell quite specifically the understandings or skills you would expect the students to gain from carrying out the project or activity.

10. List a number of items of equipment and supplies which you think would be helpful for laboratory work in mathematics.

11. In this chapter a distinction is made between demonstration activities and experimental activities in connection with laboratory work in mathematics. Explain the distinction, and make clear the principal aim and method in each type of activity.

12. Give some examples of items of equipment for laboratory-type work in mathematics which could be made by students at little expense. Make and demonstrate one such item of equipment, explaining how it could be used and why you think it would be helpful.

13. Why is laboratory work in mathematics properly considered to be a form or part of developmental teaching? Can it contribute to other phases or aspects of teaching and learning? Discuss this, giving illustrations if you can.

14. When you were in junior high school did you have, in your mathematics classes, any work that could be regarded as laboratory-type work? If so, describe some of the things you did.

15. Discuss at some length the need for careful planning of laboratory or field work in mathematics to prevent it from becoming desultory and aimless.

16. Enumerate some advantages claimed for directed study as an integral part of the teaching-learning program in secondary school mathematics.

17. Mention and discuss some dangers which must be guarded against in connection with directed study in mathematics.

18. What is the main function of drill, and why is drill necessary in mathematics? Defend your statement.

19. Enumerate some important principles of drill procedure. Illustrate each.

20. In what respects are drill and review, as discussed in this book, alike? In what respects do they differ?

21. Why is review an important phase or aspect of learning?

22. What is meant by a "maintenance program," as the term is used in this chapter? Explain how you would set up such a program, for example, in ninth-grade algebra.

23. Compare several textbooks in ninth-

grade algebra to see what provision they make for systematic maintenance work.

24. Examine several textbooks in geometry, and try to decide which would be the most helpful for the kind of maintenance program you would like to use.

25. Teachers commonly use examples to illustrate mathematical principles and relationships. In what sense can this be considered as teaching for transfer?

26. One of the important objectives of a course in demonstrative geometry is to get students to understand and appreciate the meaning of a deductive proof. When teachers strive for this, it can be said that they are teaching for transfer. Explain.

27. Discuss the proposition that instruction in mathematics can be fruitful only to the extent to which transfer takes place.

28. What are some advantages that have been claimed for the use of teaching machines or programmed instruction in mathematics. Comment on these.

29. Discuss some advantages which you feel the traditional teacher-class pattern of instruction in mathematics has over the use of programmed instruction.

30. Discuss some circumstances in which programmed instruction could be used to advantage, even though the traditional pattern of class instruction might not be feasible.

31. Describe some mathematical concept which you had not mastered well when you finished high school. Try to account for this lack of mastery, and discuss what your teacher could have done to remedy this deficiency.

BIBLIOGRAPHY

Anderson, Frank: A Mathematics Seminar, *Mathematics Teacher*, **54** (1961), 109–110.

Andrews, John D.: High School Algebra via Television, *Mathematics Teacher*, **53** (1960), 376–380.

Archer, Allene: "How to Use Your Library in Mathematics" (Washington, D.C.: National Council of Teachers of Mathematics, 1958).

Beatley, Ralph: Reason and Rule in Arithmetic and Algebra, *Mathematics Teacher*, **47** (1954), 234–244.

Brannon, M. J.: Individual Mathematics Study Plan, *Mathematics Teacher*, **55** (1962), 52–56.

Bruner, Jerome S.: On Learning Mathematics, *Mathematics Teacher*, **53** (1960), 610–619.

Clark, J. F.: Programmed Learning: My First Six Months, *Mathematics Teacher*, **55** (1962), 579–581.

Crosby, Gwladys, and Herbert Fremont: Individualized Algebra, *Mathematics Teacher*, **53** (1960), 109–112.

Dadourian, H. M.: How to Make Mathematics More Attractive, *Mathematics Teacher*, **53** (1960), 548–551.

Dickie, Paul: A Supplementary Program in Junior High School Mathematics, *Mathematics Teacher*, **55** (1962), 56–60.

Dodes, Irving Allen: The Science of Teaching Mathematics, *Mathematics Teacher*, **46** (1953), 157–166.

Dunn-Rankin, Peter, and Raymond Sweet: Enrichment: A Geometry Laboratory, *Mathematics Teacher*, **56** (1963), 134–140.

Fehr, Howard F.: The Role of Insight in the Learning of Mathematics, *Mathematics Teacher*, **47** (1954), 393–400.

"Free and Inexpensive Materials," 11th ed. (Nashville, Tenn.: George Peabody College for Teachers, 1962).

Hansen, Viggo P.: New Uses for the Overhead Projector, *Mathematics Teacher*, **53** (1960), 467–469.

Hayden, Dunstan: Finding Illustrative Examples and Exercises, *Mathematics Teacher*, **54** (1961), 373–377.

Henderson, Kenneth B.: Anent the Discovery Method, *Mathematics Teacher*, **50** (1957), 287–291.

Hendrix, Gertrude: Learning by Discovery, *Mathematics Teacher*, **54** (1961), 290–299.

Johnson, Donovan A.: Attitudes in the Mathematics Classroom, *School Science and Mathematics*, **57** (1957), 113–120.

———: Enriching Mathematics Instruction with Creative Activities, *Mathematics Teacher,* **55** (1962), 238–242.

Johnson, Larry K.: The Mathematics Laboratory in Today's Schools, *School Science and Mathematics,* **62** (1962), 586–592.

Kluttz, Marguerite: The Mathematics Laboratory: A Meaningful Approach to Mathematics Instruction, *Mathematics Teacher,* **56** (1963), 141–145.

Matchett, Margaret S.: Teaching Machines or What? *Mathematics Teacher,* **55** (1962), 351–355.

May, Kenneth O.: Small versus Large Classes, *American Mathematical Monthly,* **69** (1962), 433–434.

Midwest Program on Airborne Television and Instruction, *American Mathematical Monthly,* **69** (1962), 310–311.

Osborne, Alan R.: Using the Overhead Projector in an Algebra Class, *Mathematics Teacher,* **55** (1962), 135–139.

Pólya, George: On Learning, Teaching, and Learning Teaching, *American Mathematical Monthly,* **70** (1963), 605–619.

Randall, Karl: Improving Study Habits in Mathematics, *Mathematics Teacher,* **55** (1962), 553–555.

Robinson, Edith: Let's Say What We Mean, *Mathematics Teacher,* **54** (1961), 460–461.

Sawyer, W. W.: The Concrete Basis for the Abstract, *Mathematics Teacher,* **52** (1959), 272–277.

Schmidt, Roland L.: Using the Library in Junior High School Mathematics Classes, *Mathematics Teacher,* **56** (1963), 40–42.

Secondary School Curriculum Committee of the NCTM, Report of: *Mathematics Teacher,* **52** (1959), 389–417.

Sister Margaret Cecilia, C.S.J.: Mathematics Projects, *Mathematics Teacher,* **54** (1961), 527–530.

Sister Mary Corona: Seminars: An Integrating Force in a Program of Concentration, *Mathematics Teacher,* **48** (1955), 209–213.

Smith, Robert E.: A Desk, Some Chairs, and a Blackboard, *American Mathematical Monthly,* **69** (1962), 658–666.

Swain, Henry: "How to Study Mathematics" (Washington, D.C.: National Council of Teachers of Mathematics, 1961).

"Teacher Training Film Series" (Minneapolis, Minn.: University of Minnesota, 1962). (Bulletin on SMSG mathematics: a list of titles.)

Teaching Machines and Mathematics Programs, *American Mathematical Monthly,* **69** (1962), 552–565. (Report on a symposium.)

Totten, W. Fred: Words as a Basic Factor in Understanding Algebra, *School Science and Mathematics,* **56** (1956), 230–233.

Unkrich, Harmon: Using the Overhead Projector in Teaching Geometry, *Mathematics Teacher,* **55** (1962), 502–505.

Van Engen, H.: Multitrack Programs, *Mathematics Teacher,* **52** (1959), 205–206.

———: Some Psychological Principles Underlying Mathematics Instruction, *School Science and Mathematics,* **61** (1961), 242–250.

Vaughn, William D.: Some Drill Techniques for Arithmetic, *Mathematics Teacher,* **50** (1957), 436–437.

Vollmar, Robert, and Philip Peak: "How to Use Films and Film-strips in Mathematics Classes" (Washington, D.C.: National Council of Teachers of Mathematics, 1960).

Wallen, Rev. C. J.: Stressing the Creative Aspects of Mathematics in Teaching the Gifted Child, *Mathematics Teacher,* **55** (1962), 243–248.

Webber, G. Cuthbert, and John A. Brown: "Basic Concepts of Mathematics" (Reading, Mass: Addison-Wesley Publishing Company, Inc., 1963).

Williams, Horace E.: A Study of the Effectiveness of Classroom Teaching Techniques Following a Closed-circuit Television Presentation in Mathematics, *Mathematics Teacher,* **56** (1963), 94–96.

Wills, Herbert: The UICSM Programmed Instruction Project, *American Mathematical Monthly,* **69** (1962), 804–806.

SEVEN

Planning for effective teaching and learning

AS IN ANY other undertaking, instruction in mathematics aims at certain outcomes, or objectives; and as in any other undertaking, the likelihood of attaining the objectives will depend in large measure on how well it is planned. The establishment of a sound program of mathematical education involves both general and specific considerations. If the broad, general objectives are to be realized, comprehensive long-range planning must be done. On the other hand, actual instruction takes place in individual classrooms, and this requires specific and detailed planning day by day.

In planning at either level, numerous problems must be faced and decisions must be made. It is the purpose of this chapter to call attention to some of these problems and to point out why they exist, in the hope that through attention to these matters means may be found and plans may be formulated which will make instruction in mathematics as effective as possible.

Long-range planning: the curriculum Actually, planning for the mathematical education of the students begins with the planning of the curriculum. Here decisions are made, at least with respect to the courses which are to be offered, and here policies are established for the counseling and guidance of students with respect to the courses offered. This is generally considered to be an administrative function. Indeed, administrative considerations sometimes must predominate in determining what courses can be offered. This is not a desirable situation, but there are circumstances, especially in very small schools, in which it seems to be inevitable.

But even under such circumstances the mathematics teachers should have a voice in the decisions which are reached at this stage of planning. They should be given the privilege and responsibility of making recommendations, and weight should be given to their recommendations. Certainly this would be true in the larger schools, where restrictions on the kinds of courses that can be offered are not so tight as they may be in the very small schools. By the same token, the mathematics teachers should look upon this not only as an opportunity but as a responsibility which they cannot lightly disregard. They, better than anyone else, can be aware of the educational implications of various programs of mathematics courses, and their well-considered judgments can be influential in the establishment of sound mathematics programs in the schools.

Provision for individual differences as a stage in planning

It is axiomatic that, if instruction is to be really effective, it must reach the individual students and promote their learning as individuals, and individuals differ greatly in their interests and abilities. The problem of adapting instruction to individual differences has existed whenever and wherever the group receiving instruction has consisted of more than one student, but since early in this century it has occupied a much more prominent place in educational thought than it ever occupied before. There are several reasons for this, the most important one being that the problem itself has become much more acute and pressing than it was before. The unprecedented and bewildering growth of the secondary school has been accompanied by a decline in the average intellectual ability of the student population while the spread of the range of abilities has been accentuated. As a result, the always questionable practice of giving identical instruction to all students in an unselected group has become more questionable than ever. If the instruction for the group is geared to a level which will challenge the abilities of the better students, then students of mediocre ability will miss much of it and will tend to lose interest or will resort to memorizing, while the inferior students will soon fall hopelessly behind and become discouraged. On the other hand, if the instruction is adapted to the limited abilities of the slow students, then the superior students will soon lose interest because the work will not challenge their best efforts. It may be noted parenthetically at this point that the importance of really challenging the best efforts of the best students is now receiving belated recognition. In either case the situation not only will result in inefficient instruction but may easily become a fertile breeding ground for discontent, loss of interest, and possible disciplinary difficulties.

School administrators as well as teachers have now become keenly aware of this problem and its implications. It is now recognized that the only way of meeting this educational dilemma efficiently is through differentiation of instruction and requirements, to provide, in some measure at least, learning activities appropriate to the capacities of the students. Recent courses of study, professional books and articles, and the prefaces of nearly all recent textbooks in secondary mathematics bear witness to the urgency of the problem and the effort which is being put forth to provide suitably differentiated materials and methods of instruction, to the end that profitable work may be provided for all students.

Impressive evidence of widespread concern over this matter can be found in the space and attention given to it in the *Twenty-second Yearbook* of the National Council of Teachers of Mathematics. Here are assembled fifteen articles on the subject of differentiated courses and curriculums in mathematics. Twelve of these articles describe courses or programs of courses specially designed from one standpoint or another for the special groups or categories of students they are to serve. The remaining three articles are concerned with the guidance of students with respect to their selection of courses from among those available. The courses and curriculums described exhibit uniformity of general purpose but not of detail. The variety of criteria employed in planning these courses is suggested by the Table of Contents of Part One of this yearbook. The fifteen articles, with indication of the states from which they are reported, are grouped under five main classifications, as follows:

1. Providing a Differentiated Curriculum through a New Organization of Content
   a. An Emerging Mathematics Curriculum (Florida)
   b. A Curriculum Development to Capitalize on the Interrelationships of the Many Areas of Mathematics (California)
   c. The Development of a Differentiated Curriculum (California)
   d. Mathematics for the Consumer (Washington, D.C.)
2. Providing Differentiated Curriculums in Schools Where Homogeneous Grouping is Feasible
   a. A Differentiated Curriculum for Homogeneous Groups (Illinois)
   b. Using Homogeneous Grouping to Lead Pupils to Their Own Highest Levels of Achievement (Wisconsin)
   c. A Mathematics Program for Grade XII (New Hampshire)
3. Providing Differentiated Curriculums in Schools Where Homogeneous Grouping is Not Feasible

   a. Adjusting Work within the Class to the Varying Abilities of its Members (Ohio)
   b. Methods Used to Provide Differentiated Curriculums within the Classroom (New York)
   c. In Small High Schools, Many Purposes—Many Curriculums (Pennsylvania)
4. Differentiated Curriculums Resulting from Pupil, Parent, Teacher, and Community Planning
   a. Geometry Developed through Pupil-Teacher Planning (Illinois)
   b. Working Together in Developing the Mathematics Curriculum (Kansas)
5. Guidance for the Optimum Use of Differentiated Curriculums
   a. The Importance of Early Guidance at the Junior High School Level (Michigan)
   b. Guidance in the Mathematics Program (California)
   c. The Mathematics Teacher's Part in Effective Guidance for Optimum Use of Differentiated Curriculums (Massachusetts)

These classifications and titles clearly indicate a wide diversity of motivations and approaches to the problem, but a common broad purpose is evident throughout. This attempt to provide for individual differences among students through appropriately differentiated courses represents a phase of planning. Indeed, it touches all stages of planning. It finds its broadest manifestation in the long-range considerations that guide curriculum planning. In particular, the double-track or multiple-track plan which was discussed in Chapter 4 represents simply a long-range plan to provide appropriate kinds of courses for students of different abilities.

Apart from the matter of separate and different courses per se, this attempt to provide for individual differences has taken a number of forms, prominent among which may be mentioned ability grouping or homogeneous grouping, differentiated assignments, honors courses, directed study, programmed instruction, and even individual instruction.

Ability grouping The plan which most people have come to associate most readily with provision for individual differences is the arrangement generally called "homogeneous grouping," or "ability grouping." As the names imply, it consists essentially in grouping the students in such a way that disparities in the abilities or interests within a given group will be reduced as far as possible. The great objection to the traditional miscellaneous grouping has been that instruction generally becomes geared to some one level of ability, to the consequent disadvantage of all students whose abilities are either above or below that level. The plan of ability grouping, though it would by no means entirely eliminate individual differences within any group, would materially reduce the range of abilities and thus tend to reduce the acuteness of the problem.

Despite differences of opinion as to the effectiveness and the desirability of ability grouping, the plan has come into widespread use in schools large enough to make it feasible to have two or more class sections in the same grade or the same subject.

There have been numerous adaptations of the plan, but the basic principles and *modus operandi* are well defined. The principal variants consist in its use in the following ways:

1. Providing different courses for students who are in the same grade but who differ widely in mathematical interests and potential
2. Providing different sections of the same course so that, of the students who will take that course, those having differing degrees of mathematical potential can be grouped in separate sections

Until comparatively recent years the differentiation of students for homogeneous grouping was based mainly on the results of intelligence tests. More recently it has come to be generally felt that, while such tests are important, they alone are not a wholly satisfactory criterion. Increasing reliance is being placed upon supplementing these indexes of general intelligence by other considerations, such as the expressed desires of the students and their parents, prognostic tests, marks in previous courses in mathematics, reading ability, and teachers' estimates of probable success in subsequent mathematics courses.

Certainly the employment of any pattern of homogeneous grouping would represent a phase of planning and would require a great deal of careful thought. The actual subject matter of each course or of each section of a course would have to be considered and defined with great care. Specific objectives and units of study would have to be agreed upon and set up. Time allotments would have to be established. The criteria that would govern the placement of students in various courses or sections would have to be worked out. Thus preplanning is importantly involved here all along the line, with respect to policy and administrative procedures as well as to the objectives and details of the various courses or sections.

Differentiated assignments The foregoing discussion has centered on long-range or broad-scale plans for providing appropriate learning activities for students of varying interests and abilities. The devices of differentiated curriculums and homogeneous grouping represent means through which, at least in part, the attainment of this objective may be facilitated. But even the most sanguine advocates of these measures will readily concede that they represent only a first stage of progress. Even with a multiple-track program of different courses and with a number of homogeneous sections within a given course, there will still exist substantial differences among the students within any given class or section. Here again, then, we are faced, in a sense, with the same problem as before. Even if the range of abilities has been somewhat diminished, the problem itself is actually accentuated. At this stage it cannot be solved by administrative planning; it is something that has to be both planned and handled by each individual teacher. He cannot delegate sections of the class or parts of the work to his assistants, because normally he will have no assistants. Whatever is to be done must be done by the teacher himself. Thus if he is to give more than casual or incidental attention to the problem, he will have to do a good deal of careful planning as well as a good deal of hard work.

One method of adapting instruction to individual capacities and interests within a class is the use of differentiated assignments for students whose abilities and rates of work are not alike. This plan has met with favor because it can be used even in schools which are too small to permit homogeneous grouping. While it tends to complicate the work of the teacher, it has much to commend it from the standpoint of instructional effectiveness.

Methods of providing differentiated assignments have taken a number of forms and variations. In classes that are not too large, the differentiation can sometimes be made almost on an individual basis, perhaps with little organization and with the assignments planned through liaison between each individual student and the teacher. The theoretical advantages of such a method are clear. Unfortunately, in most cases it has practical limitations which are also manifest and which in effect preclude its general use in large classes. Other methods are needed in such cases, and they must be methods that can be more highly organized so that the work assigned can be given in different categories. Two such methods which are in common use may be called the "contract" type of assignment and the "multiple-level" type of assignment. These have certain similarities, but they should not be regarded as being identical.

The contract type of assignment Under the contract type of assignment, each unit of work is organized in such a way that the accomplishment required for a bare passing grade is specified as the minimum contract which all students are required to execute. Other contracts calling for additional work or work of a more difficult nature are set up as requirements for successively higher marks. As commonly set up, each successive contract presumes or specifies that the requirements for all the lower-level contracts be satisfied and that certain additional requirements also be met. These additional requirements may be qualitative, or quantitative, or some combination of both. The following illustration represents a set of contracts that was used by one teacher to cover a marking period.

D Contract

1. Be able to find the area of any square, rectangle, parallelogram, or triangle, when dimensions are given.
2. Hand in at least half as many problems as the average of the class.
3. Take all required tests.
4. Have an average rating of at least 5 on your workbook.
5. Be able to find the volume of any cube or rectangular prism when the dimensions are given.
6. Be able to estimate the area of an irregularly shaped figure by using graph paper.
7. Have a good attitude and be pleasant and industrious.
8. Meet any other requirements that may be added and posted here.

C Contract

All the *D* Contract plus the following:

9. Be able to find the area of any trapezoid, dimensions being given.
10. Be able to find the circumference and area of any circle if the radius or diameter is known.
11. Solve problems based on areas and volumes of figures mentioned above.
12. Hand in at least four-fifths as many problems as the average of the class.
13. Have an average rating of at least 6 on your workbook.

B Contract

All the *C* Contract plus the following:

14. Be able to explain how we got the formulas for the areas of the triangle, parallelogram, and trapezoid.
15. Hand in more problems than the average of the class.
16. Have an average rating of at least 7 on your workbook.
17. Hand in at least one acceptable out-of-class project.

A Contract

All the *B* Contract plus the following:

18. Hand in 20 per cent more problems than the average of the class.
19. Have an average rating of at least 8 on your workbook.
20. Make an outline of notes covering the important things in the month's work and be prepared to give a 5-minute review discussion of this, using only the notes as your guide.
21. Take a private 10-minute oral examination.
22. Hand in at least three acceptable out-of-class projects.

The contract plan is exceedingly definite in specifying the requirements for each grade or mark, so students can know at any time about where they stand. It has two disadvantages, however. One of these is that superior students are generally required to execute all the details of the minimum contract before passing on to the higher ones, and often much of the work of the minimum contract is rather simple and uninteresting routine which fails to interest or challenge the more capable students. The other disadvantage is that the preparation of the various contracts in suitable form, and the large amount of record keeping which is necessary, place a severe burden of extra work on the teacher. Unless these details are carefully planned and systematically carried out, this might even become so burdensome as to impair his effectiveness in the actual instructional work. This problem becomes particularly acute when facilities for duplicating assignment sheets and other instructional materials are inadequate.

The multiple-level type of assignment The contract plan is but one method of providing for individual differences within a class. Another method which is somewhat less stereotyped, but which is probably used more widely, is the multiple-level type of assignment. This approach emphasizes quality and caliber of achievement rather than mere quantity. Its aim is not so much to provide detailed specifications of requirements for the various marks as it is to provide assignments appropriate in nature and difficulty to the abilities of the individual students. This method of differentiation usually provides assignments at two and sometimes three levels of ability. In most cases it is easier to administer than the contract plan, and it avoids some of the objections to that plan. There is much to be said in favor of this method of differentiating assignments, and most of the recent textbooks in secondary school mathematics recognize its potential value. It is frequently mentioned in the prefaces of textbooks, and many of the current textbooks make some provision for facilitating this type of differentiation, in respect both to large units or chapters and to subtopics within units or chapters. Usually this is done through the sets of exercises provided. Such terms as "optional problems," "starred problems," "investigation problems," and "honor problems" are commonly found in connection with lists of exercises, while on a larger scale, chapter or unit summaries and reviews are often arranged under such headings as "easy exercises," "harder exercises," and "honor work."

Assignments differentiated on this basis can be used equally well whether they are made on a day-to-day basis or on a chapter or unit basis. The following description of a case in which this method was used in a plane geometry class presents a good illustration of how it may be employed to advantage.

A class in plane geometry was to spend between two and three weeks on the study of a unit dealing with certain properties of circles. In the class of about twenty-five students there were five who had demonstrated marked superiority and interest in geometry and who liked to investigate their problems and theorems independently, as if they were puzzles to be solved. For this particular unit the teacher proposed to these five students that they work out the essential parts of the unit entirely independently, without any help from the teacher, the textbook, or each other. They were told that, if they wished to do this, they could copy out the statements of all the theorems (more than a dozen) in the unit, but must then make no further reference to their books. Moreover, they were told that, if they decided to take this assignment, they need not even attend the class meetings, but could work during those periods in the study hall. At the end of the time set for the study of the unit they would be asked to turn in complete written proofs for as many of the theorems as they could manage to develop. They were not compelled to take this assignment, but they were given a choice of taking it or doing the work in the usual manner along with the rest of the class.

Without exception the five elected the plan for independent work. During the 2½ weeks that the class spent on the unit, these five students worked individually and independently at devising proofs for the theorems included in their assignment, without any help, even from the textbook. At the end of the time they turned in their written work. Study of these papers revealed that three of them had succeeded in developing satisfactory proofs for all the theorems. A fourth had made a mistake in reasoning on one theorem, and a fifth had mistakes in two theorems. At least two of these five students had formulated correct statements of a generalized theorem which would include some of the given theorems as special cases. The teacher reported that these students took pride in their work, and he felt the assignment had provided motivation of the best kind for them. In his opinion it had not only increased their interest in developing the necessary proofs but had also served to keep their efforts pitched to the limits of their high abilities.

Other plans for providing for individual differences An interesting variant is reported by Stokes,[1] who in an experimental study provided twenty-five units of enrichment material for superior students in ninth-grade algebra to several classes in different schools. These units were used simply to supplement the regular work of the classes throughout the year. No plan of homogeneous grouping was employed, but the enrichment units were given only to the superior students. These students attended the classes only four days a week. On the fifth day they spent the time in the library working on the enrichment units.

In the investigation the work of a group of the superior students who used these enrichment materials was compared with that of other superior students of comparable ability who were taking the same course but who were not provided with the enrichment units.

[1]William Glenn Stokes, "Enrichment for Superior Ninth Grade Algebra Students," unpublished doctoral dissertation (Nashville, Tenn.: George Peabody College for Teachers, 1957), p. 7.

The summary of the results of this study suggests that use of the enrichment units probably contributed materially toward attainment of the objectives for which they were designed and at the same time did not interfere with mastery of the basic material of the course. On the basis of certain test scores it is pointed out that the group of superior students using the enrichment units showed better achievement in algebra than the group of superior students who did not have the enrichment units. It is also pointed out that even the nonsuperior students showed higher achievement in algebra in the classes where the superior students were given enrichment units than the nonsuperior students did in classes where the enrichment units were not used. Observations of the work of the classes and discussions with participating students and teachers tended to support the belief that this kind of special provision for superior students is administratively feasible and that it can operate to the advantage of all the students.[2]

Somewhat allied to the plans mentioned above, but differing from them in certain respects, is the proposal for so-called honors courses. The underlying idea of the honors course is to relieve particularly brilliant students of unnecessary tedium and waste of time and at the same time challenge their best mathematical efforts. It recognizes the fact that there are occasional students for whom much of the normal work of the class is easy to the point of being boring, and it proposes to afford the opportunity for such students to direct their efforts toward special problems which lie definitely beyond the normal scope of the course. In other words, it proposes to offer the brilliant student the opportunity for original and largely independent study of special mathematical topics not contemplated for general class study. Honors courses have not come into very general use in high school, probably because they are off the beaten track and involve extra work in individual supervision and planning on the part of the teacher. As a means for capitalizing the abilities of the very superior students, however, the plan has much to commend it. When it has been given a fair trial, it has more than justified itself in the mathematical growth and the stimulation of interest which have resulted.[3]

Levels of planning

The considerations which need to be taken into account in endeavoring to make mathematical instruction yield its best dividends are varied in character. The long-range or over-all objectives of the curriculum and of each course call for long-range planning which may often involve cooperative efforts of the administrative, supervisory, and instructional staffs. In military parlance this would

[2]*Ibid.*, p. 86.

[3]For discussion of this topic see Howard F. Fehr, Mathematics for the Gifted, *Bulletin of the National Association of Secondary-School Principals*, **38** (1954), 103–110, and Florence L. Elder, Providing for the Student with High Mathematical Potential, *Mathematics Teacher*, **50** (1957), 502–506.

probably be called "strategic planning." It would be primarily concerned with courses and administrative policies and measures, and it would consider units or major sections of each course mainly from the standpoint of their contributions and their placement. It would hardly go into the detailed objectives and activities.

This latter, however, is very important, and it is wholly a responsibility of the supervisory and instructional staff. It might be called "intermediate-range planning." Examples of this kind of planning are often found in syllabuses or courses of study. At this level of planning the teacher or supervisor must consider not only the units or major subdivisions which are to be included in the course but also the specific objectives of each unit and the learning activities and subject matter which appear to provide the best avenues for attaining them.

On the other hand, it would not ordinarily be feasible to lay out, so far in advance, the detailed sequence and schedule of activities to be carried on in each individual class period from the beginning to the end of the unit or block. Unforeseen interruptions and delays, as well as unexpected opportunites for clarification and enrichment, frequently occur even during the course of a class period, and they often require revision not only of the immediate day's plan but also of the plans for subsequent days. Consequently, the detailed daily lesson plans can hardly be made to advantage for more than one or two days ahead. In military terms this might be called "short-range" or "tactical" planning, in contrast to the strategic, or long-range, planning and the intermediate-range planning discussed above.

Planning a schedule for a course It has been suggested that the layout plan for a course may best begin with a days-and-pages schedule. The main use of such a device is that it does provide a schedule which, if followed, will ensure that no principal part of the proposed coverage will be omitted from the course. In making such a schedule, the course, as represented in the textbook, should first be laid out into the main chapters or units that are to be included. Opposite this will be set the total number of days that are available for the course. Then these two layouts must be fitted or matched to each other so that, at least on paper, all the work to be included in the course can also be included in the number of days available. After the days-and-pages schedule is blocked out for the major units or chapters, it can be refined into a contents schedule by weeks, and even by days if desired. Usually this will require some adjustment of preliminary estimates and perhaps the curtailment of certain units or the omission of certain topics. If this is necessary, it is much better to make the adjustment at the outset than to wait and have to correct the inevitable maladjustment after the course is started.

In laying out a time schedule for a course there is always the likelihood that a few days will be lost, as far as instruction is concerned, during the semester or the year. Actually this likelihood amounts almost to a certainty in many schools. Unscheduled interruptions and delays are almost certain to occur. Football games, illness, special meetings, unexpected holidays, and other things may cause dismissal of classes. When this occurs, the reduction of available days entails a corresponding reduction in the amount of work that can be included in the course. Then, too, even experienced teachers operating under well-planned schedules are likely to encounter some necessary slowdowns during the course. These considerations imply and emphasize the importance of leaving a few buffer days or catch-up days in the time schedule for the course. They imply also the importance of weighing the different units and the different parts of each unit on the scales of relative importance. If some units or parts of units must be omitted from the course, they should be things of lesser importance. Only by careful study and preplanning can the principle of relative values be systematically applied to the different parts and worked into the plan of the course, and only by leaving some leeway in the form of buffer days can there be much assurance of having enough time even for all of the things of prime importance in the course.

The daily lesson plan The day-to-day planning of the details and sequence of each day's work must fall to the lot of each individual teacher. It is a continuing responsibility and it is of the greatest importance, because the daily lesson plan for a class determines just what learning activities will go on in that class during that period. Any teacher who goes before a class without having well in mind an orderly plan for the things he expects to do or to have the students do during the period is running a grave risk of wasting time and dissipating effort. Experienced teachers may not need actually to write out a detailed plan for each lesson, though many do so anyway, but young and inexperienced teachers will find it a great help to do so. Indeed, the very act of writing the plan out forces a crystallization of the plan in the teacher's mind. This in itself is an important step toward a successful consummation of what is planned. It is true that daily lesson plans often do need to be modified to take advantage of unforeseen circumstances or to adapt the work to unavoidable delays. But the teacher who can make such needed modifications against the backdrop of a well-ordered plan will be in a much stronger position than the teacher who does not bother to plan each day's work with care.

Lessons have sometimes been classified according to the aims or the types of activities to be carried on: the developmental lesson, the drill lesson, the review lesson, the testing lesson, etc. Such classifications can be helpful by bringing into focus the main objective of the day's work and the kinds of activity which seem most likely to attain the objective.

There still remains, however, the need to decide upon the details of the period's work and the ordering of these details. Apart from such routine matters as taking the roll, the number of kinds of activity which may be included in the learning-teaching situation is not great. Most of them would be included in the following list:

1. Testing for any of several purposes
2. Explaining or discussing new concepts or procedures
3. Drilling or reviewing
4. Directing the work of students at chalkboard or at seats (directed study or directed learning; may include laboratory activities)
5. Assigning work to be done by the students

Each of these kinds of activity requires detailed planning if it is to serve its purpose. A test designed for diagnostic purposes will probably differ from a quiz set up for a drill exercise not only in the use to which it is to be put but also in the time which is required. Explaining or discussing new concepts in a developmental lesson requires that the teacher clarify in his own mind, and ahead of time, the precise things upon which he wants to focus the discussion. It also requires that he consider well just how the explanation can best be made, what illustrations will best serve his purpose, and how he can secure participation in the discussion by the members of the class. The intelligent assignment of work to be done by the students demands consideration of its aim and of its suitability for the students in respect to length and difficulty.

Not all of the activities listed above will be required in each day's work. Some periods will be devoted entirely to testing or to developmental discussion. On other days, during the assimilation stage, supervised study may well occupy most of the period. A brief discussion for purposes of motivation can often be helpful in such cases. Drill work, review, the making of assignments, and short quizzes should be scheduled in the period's activities at times when it is judged that they will yield the greatest advantage, and this may vary from day to day.

The essence of a good daily lesson plan lies in two things: (1) the careful estimation and selection of those activities which give the most promise of good dividends in terms of the immediate objectives and (2) the arrangement of these activities into a properly ordered schedule, with approximate time allotments, so that the period may be used to best advantage. A short check list of fundamental activities such as that given above can serve as a guide in lesson planning. Such lesson plans are simple and easy to make. They can ensure that the important activities for a given period are carried on in the best order and that within the limitations of the period appropriate time allowances are made for each.

Before making out a daily lesson plan, the teacher should carefully think through the main things he wants to do and the things he wants the students to do during the class period for which the plan is to be made. These should be set down precisely in the order in which he wants them to occur, with estimated time allowances. The lesson plan should be neither perfunctory nor stereotyped but should be adapted to taking full advantage of the educational possibilities of the class situation. Obviously, different activities will receive special emphasis on different days. On some days most of the time will need to be spent on developmental work, while on other days the main activity will be directed study, and still other days will be given over largely to testing. The wise variation of the class-period activities is a major factor in stimulating interest and preventing boredom and disciplinary difficul-

Plane Geometry Topic: Proportion

Order of activities	Minutes
Check quiz on review assignment	10
Discussion of proportion and of meaning of theorems 1–6, with illustrations	25
Drill work	None
Directed study	None
Assignment for tomorrow (see back of card)	10

Algebra Topic: Fractional Equations

Order of activities	Minutes
Test	None
Review briefly principles of solving linear equations	5
Discussion and explanation of fractional equations and how they may be solved. Work out four illustrative cases with the class (see back of card)	20
Send class to blackboard to work on exercises 1–6, page 144	15
Assignment for tomorrow (see back of card)	5

Seventh-grade Mathematics   Topic: Graphs
(Class has worked on this topic for three days already)

Order of activities	Minutes
Review of terms used; kinds of graphs we have studied; what sort of thing each can show best; establishing proper scales; form of notation for labeling and title; importance of neatness and care in making graphs	10
Discussion (brief): interpretation of some statistical graphs provided by company X	10
Assignment of work to be done tomorrow: exercises 8–12, page 186 in textbook. Complete any three of these	5
Directed study: class working at seats on tomorrow's assignment	20

ties. It is possible, however, to use a general outline form which will be objective enough to serve as a useful guide in planning and, at the same time, sufficiently flexible to permit adaptation of the lesson plan to any class situation.

A practical hint on planning Many a young teacher in beginning his first job is obsessed with the fear that he will run out of anything to say before the class period is over and thus leave himself and the class at loose ends. If he is at all competent, a little experience will convince him that the contrary is true: there usually is not enough time for all he wants to do. Well-planned discussions which elicit participation by the class will consume time at an unexpected rate, so that the real danger lies in having to leave untouched some of the work that the teacher has hoped and planned to get done during the period. Yet the tendency to overestimate what can be done during the period is very persistent. Sometimes the shortages can be made up in the next period or two by careful replanning and perhaps curtailing the work of succeeding days. If, on the other hand, these shortages are not compensated in some such way and are allowed to accumulate, they can only result eventually in some major hiatus in the course. Unfortunately, this often does occur. Indeed, it is likely to occur unless the teacher adheres pretty closely to a pre-established days-and-pages time schedule. Some people will object that such a schedule is too mechanical and may compel the class to leave some topics before they are fully mastered. But the alternative is to leave some part of the course, and perhaps some major part, wholly untouched.

To make the daily lesson plans fit a long-range schedule, the teacher will need to give careful attention each day to the relative importance of the ideas presented in the portion of the textbook which is assigned for that day. In planning each day's lesson it is important to highlight only the key concepts or relations and save most of the time for them. Only in this way can the full benefit of the textbook and the teacher's enriching discussion be realized, and only in this way can there be any real assurance of ordered and orderly progress through the course.

With respect to unit or block planning, much the same considerations hold and much the same things may be said. The major difference is in degree and not in kind. It lies in the larger scope of the unit and the fact that it usually covers several days instead of a single day. The same principle of relative importance should govern selection of the elements of the unit to be emphasized, and the danger of overestimating what can be accomplished is just as real here as in planning the daily lesson. Judgment on these matters can mature quickly, and experience can be a great help in this. But even with experienced teachers, hope sometimes overrides judgment, and beginning teachers must face this problem without even the benefit of experience to guide them. It is hoped that observance of the cautions noted above may contribute toward wise planning of units and lessons and thus toward the avoidance of frustration and disappointment.

In conclusion

Nearly everything that a teacher does in connection with his work requires some kind and degree of planning. Even the details of his lesson plans must be thought through, appraised, and decided upon. If he is to give a test, he ought to decide what particular things he wants to test for, and then he ought to plan the test so that it will reveal, in terms of the objectives, the particular information he wants. To conserve his own time, he ought to try to arrange the test so that the papers can be checked without excessive labor, and this takes careful planning. If he is to present new material in the form of discussion with the class, he should identify ahead of time the main things he wants to bring out, and he should so plan his discussion that it will highlight and emphasize them. Illustrative examples should be selected with care, and ahead of time, instead of trusting to the inspiration of the moment to provide suitable ones. If the work is to include a field trip or a laboratory type of exercise, there are many things that need to be carefully planned ahead of time, because it is hard to adapt or change such work after it is started. The things to be done must be decided upon in advance and with definiteness, equipment and supplies made ready, and careful instructions given to the students. Forgetting to provide some important instruction or some piece of needed equipment can nullify the exercise and result in loss of time and disruption of morale. Drill and review tasks need to be very carefully planned lest they be aimless and ineffective, and the same thing may be said of chalkboard work by the students. Providing suitable learning experiences for students of superior ability cannot be done incidentally. Directed study can be effective only to the extent to which a proper background has been established and the learning experiences are planned expressly to consolidate and extend this background. Assignments for homework can bear proper fruit only if they are well designed to produce certain predetermined results and are reasonable in their demands upon the student's ability, understanding, and time. In short, assuming academic and professional competence on the part of the teacher, intelligent planning at all levels provides the key to efficient instruction and effective learning. The key may fit imperfectly or stick a bit at first, but experience and faithful use will smooth and ease its operation. It is a *sine qua non* and must not be neglected.

A final word of caution should be given with reference to the use of lesson plans. In planning the work of a class period the teacher must of necessity work on the assumption that the activities of the period will follow a definite course without interruption or deflection. All experienced teachers know, however, that this assumption is often wrong. Circumstances which cannot be foreseen inevitably arise at times, and often such circumstances make it advisable for the teacher to depart from his prepared plan. If by doing so it is possible to capitalize on some unexpected situation and thereby stimulate the interest of the students in their work or repair some unsuspected weakness, the teacher should not hesitate to divert the activities of the period from their charted course. Normally, of course, the best results will be obtained by following the prepared plans, but the teacher should not feel obligated to follow them with a slavish fidelity which would forbid him to take advantage of such opportunities. Frequently, the most effective teaching may be accomplished through spontaneous teacher reaction to unexpected student problems and unpredicted teaching situations.

EXERCISES

1. Discuss the importance of long-range planning for mathematical instruction as it is exhibited in curriculum construction and the broad character of the various courses to be offered. Why should long-range planning be a concern of the administrative officers as well as the instructional staff?

2. Do you agree with the assertion that for most courses in secondary school mathematics the plan of the course is pretty much determined by the textbook that is used for

the course? If this assertion is true, is it a good thing? Defend your answer.

3. Some textbooks in mathematics contain more topics than can normally be treated adequately and mastered by a class in the time allotted for the course. Thus it often is necessary to omit some chapters or parts of chapters. Deciding on what parts to omit and what parts to retain is a very important part of the long-range planning of the course. Take some textbook in intermediate algebra and list the topics or chapters it contains. Next, decide which of these topics you would hope to include in a one-semester course, using that text. Finally, estimate the time that you would need for each. If the total of your estimates exceeds the time available, revise your time estimates or reduce your list of topics until it fits the usual time allowance of eighteen weeks for the semester's work. Report the list which you decided to retain, tell what topics or chapters you decided to omit (if any), and justify your decisions. This is an important exercise because it is precisely the kind of thing you will have to do with each course you teach and with each of the textbooks you use.

4. Select a standard textbook in plane geometry and assume that you are to use it next year; then make a time schedule to serve as an approximate guide for the year's work. Assume that you will have thirty-six weeks of instructional time, including tests and examinations. For each topic or unit which you will include in the course, estimate the time in weeks which you can safely allot to that topic or unit. Such a schedule can be valuable to you in many ways. Make it with care and report it to the class. Present your arguments in support of it, but ask for criticisms and suggestions.

5. Do all the things that are called for in exercise 4, but with respect to some standard textbook in ninth-grade algebra instead of plane geometry.

6. Do all the things that are called for in exercise 4, but with respect to some standard textbook for a year's work in seventh- or eighth-grade mathematics instead of plane geometry.

7. Do all the things that are called for in exercise 4, but with respect to a textbook in trigonometry. Assume that you have just eighteen weeks in which to conduct this one-semester course.

8. It is likely that during any semester or year various circumstances may cause unexpected cancellation of classes on a few days. Many teachers feel that it is well to take this into account in making the overall time schedule for the course. Do you? If so, about how many buffer days per semester would you allow in your time schedule to absorb these lost class periods? Enumerate several possible circumstances that might cause such loss of class time.

9. Explain the aim, philosophy, and limitations of homogeneous grouping as a measure for making suitable provision for the mathematical education of students of different abilities. Do you believe homogeneous grouping is a good thing, assuming that circumstances permit it to be used? Justify your answer.

10. One plan for providing for individual differences in mathematics without homogeneous grouping of students in different classes involves the use of differentiated assignments *within* a class. One well-defined form of this plan is referred to in this chapter as the "contract plan," or the contract type of assignment. Explain how this plan is set up and how it works.

11. Take some section or unit of algebra, geometry, trigonometry, or junior high school mathematics and plan a series of contracts for the unit. Assume that the class for which it is intended includes students with a wide range of ability.

12. Explain the difference between the contract type of assignment and the multiple-level type of assignment as they are described in this chapter. Which do you think would be the easier to plan? Why?

13. Is the selection of a textbook for a mathematics course actually a phase of long-range planning? In selecting a textbook from among several in ninth-grade algebra, what are some of the characteristics with respect to which you would want to compare the books?

14. Select some unit, chapter, or section in a standard textbook in algebra, geometry, or general mathematics and make an overall plan for teaching the unit. Include a detailed list of specific objectives in terms of "things to know" and "things to be able to do." Indicate the parts of the text that would receive special emphasis and estimate the number of class periods that would be required. Present your outline to the class for discussion and criticism.

15. Based on the unit plan called for in exercise 14, decide what items you would want to test for in order to judge the extent to which your students had mastered the unit. Then, based on these specific objectives, devise a test designed to accomplish such an appraisal. Present it to the class for discussion and criticism.

16. From the unit outline called for in exercise 14 select a section that you estimate would require about three class periods to cover. Decide what principal things you would aim at on each of the three days and what particular things you would do or have done to attain your objectives most effectively. Then make out a daily lesson plan for each of the three days, similar to the examples shown in this chapter in the section titled The Daily Lesson Plan. Present these lesson plans to the class for discussion and criticism.

Select a topic from high school algebra and, assuming that you are going to teach that topic, do the following things by way of planning for this:

17. List the specific objectives you would want your students to attain through their study of this topic in terms of (*a*) things to know and (*b*) things to be able to do.

18. Tell what particular things you would highlight as the major foci of the work on this topic.

19. Take each of these major foci and, under it, discuss the following points:
a. Do textbooks and teachers usually present this in such a way as to arouse the interest and curiosity of the students, or merely as a job to be done? How important is this?
b. What difficulties can you expect students to have with this topic, and what mistakes can you expect them to make? Try to decide why they have these difficulties and why they make these mistakes.
c. How can you as a teacher help them to overcome these difficulties and avoid these mistakes? Be as specific as you can.

20. Suggest some ways of supplementing this topic with any ideas, terminology, notation, definitions, postulates, or simple theorems embodying concepts of "modern" mathematics (e.g., sets, relations, functions, or inequalities).

21. Suggest any suitable provision that could be made in connection with this topic for students of especially high ability.

22. Comment critically on the treatment of this topic in three representative high school textbooks. Bring out, in connection with each of the books, the things you liked best and the things you did not like.

BIBLIOGRAPHY

Albrecht, Mary E.: A Teacher Plans Her Day, *Arithmetic Teacher*, **3** (1956), 151–152.

Allen, Frank B.: Building a Mathematics Program: An Adventure in Cooperative Planning, *Mathematics Teacher*, **49** (1956), 226–234.

Brannon, M. J.: Individual Mathematics Study Plan, *Mathematics Teacher*, **55** (1962), 52–56.

Brown, Claude H.: "The Teaching of Secondary Mathematics" (New York: Harper & Row, Publishers, Inc. 1953), pp. 314–318.

Buzetti, Beatrice: An Experiment in Teaching, *Mathematics Teacher*, **48** (1955), 360–365.

Commission on Mathematics: "Program for College Preparatory Mathematics" (New York: College Entrance Examination Board, 1959).

Courses of study: Many courses of study and curriculum guides contain detailed analyses of subject matter for the various courses, with suggestions for teaching. These courses of study represent long-range and intermediate-range planning. Few of them contain sample lesson plans, but all of them contain suggestions that would help the teacher in making his own daily lesson plans. Such courses of study, printed or mimeographed, are available from numerous states and cities at a nominal cost.

Douglass, Harl R.: Remedial Work in Junior High School Mathematics, *Mathematics Teacher*, **48** (1955), 344–346.

Elder, Florence L.: Providing for the Student with High Mathematical Potential, *Mathematics Teacher*, **50** (1957), 502–506.

Freese, Frances: Gifted Students in Senior High School Mathematics, *Bulletin of the National Association of Secondary-School Principals*, **43** (1959), 71–74.

Griff, Ernest R.: The Comparative Effectiveness of One-level and Three-level Assignments in Plane Geometry, *Mathematics Teacher*, **50** (1957), 214–216.

Henderson, Kenneth B.: Anent the Discovery Method, *Mathematics Teacher*, **50** (1957), 287–291.

Hirschi, L. Edwin: Encouraging Creativity in the Mathematics Classroom, *Mathematics Teacher*, **56** (1963), 79–83.

Johnson, Donovan A.: Enriching Mathematics Instruction with Creative Activities, *Mathematics Teacher*, **55** (1962), 238–242.

Kidd, Kenneth P.: Improving the Learning of Mathematics, *Mathematics Teacher*, **47** (1954), 393–400.

Kinney, Lucien B., and C. Richard Purdy: "Teaching Mathematics in the Secondary School" (New York: Holt, Rinehart and Winston, Inc., 1952), pp. 304–325.

Klein, Rose: Self-directed Homework, *Mathematics Teacher*, **44** (1951), 463–465.

Larsson, Robert D.: A Mathematics Enrichment Program for High School Students, *American Mathematical Monthly*, **70** (1963), 205–206.

Latino, Joseph J.: An Algebra Program for the Bright Ninth Grader, *Mathematics Teacher*, **49** (1956), 179–184.

Lentz, Donald W.: The High School Principal Looks at the Mathematics Program, *Bulletin of the National Association of Secondary-School Principals*, **38** (1954), 40–47.

Meserve, Bruce E.: New Trends in Algebra and Geometry, *Mathematics Teacher*, **55** (1962), 452–461.

National Council of Teachers of Mathematics: Report of the Secondary School Curriculum Committee, *Mathematics Teacher*, **52** (1959), 389–417.

______: Relevant articles can be found in a number of the yearbooks and other special publications of the National Council. Lists of these publications can be secured from the National Council of Teachers of Mathematics, 1201 Sixteenth St., N.W., Washington, D.C.

Norton, Monte S.: Enrichment as Provision for the Gifted in Mathematics, *School Science and Mathematics*, **57** (1957), 339–345.

Olander, Clarence: The Use of a Readiness Test in Teaching a Unit on Signed Numbers, *School Science and Mathematics*, **57** (1957), 131–138.

Payne, Joseph N.: Self-instructive Enrichment Topics for Bright Pupils in High School Algebra, *Mathematics Teacher*, **51** (1958), 113–117.

Potter, Mary: Mathematics for the Lower Fifty Per Cent, *Bulletin of the National Association of Secondary-School Principals*, **38** (1954), 96–103.

Reeve, William D.: "Mathematics for the Secondary School" (New York: Holt, Rinehart and Winston, Inc., 1954), pp. 124–166.

______: The Problem of Varying Abilities among Students in Mathematics, *Mathematics Teacher*, **49** (1956), 70–78.

Schult, Veryl: Guideposts in Curriculum Planning in Mathematics, *Bulletin of the National Association of Secondary-School Principals*, **38** (1954), 48–53.

Sister Mary Corona: Seminars: An Integrating Force in a Program of Concentration, *Mathematics Teacher*, **48** (1955), 209–213.

Sobel, Max: Providing for the Slow Learner in the Junior High School, *Mathematics Teacher*, **52** (1959), 347–353.

Vaughn, William D.: Some Drill Techniques for Arithmetic, *Mathematics Teacher*, **50** (1957), 436–437.

Wallen, Rev. C. J.: Stressing the Creative Aspects of Mathematics in Teaching the Gifted Child, *Mathematics Teacher*, **55** (1962), 243–248.

Westmeyer, Paul: Just Stand out of the Way, *School Science and Mathematics*, **57** (1957), 643–646.

Wirszup, Izaak: Some Remarks on Enrichment, *Mathematics Teacher*, **49** (1956), 519–527.

EIGHT

Evaluation of instruction

THE EFFECTIVENESS of instruction is usually determined by means of checking accomplished results against objectives undertaken. Measures of achievement have thus long been employed as an integral part of the educational program. An efficient program of evaluation, however, does not consist merely in the effort to check the completed process but rather in the continual appraisal of student progress toward the attainment of pre-established aims. Such a program should be outlined in terms of significant instructional objectives and used for more efficient pupil guidance. There is probably no more accurate barometer of the fundamental philosophy of any curriculum than a careful analysis of its evaluation program; the techniques used; the aims, objectives, and functions implied; and the interpretation and use of obtained results.

Nature and purposes of evaluation The emergence of pupil guidance as a significant responsibility of every educational program has placed new emphasis on the function of evaluation. No longer is this function defined in terms of the mere measurement of achievement of ill-defined goals. Standards of achievement have been more clearly defined, more carefully differentiated, and better adapted to different kinds of capability and individual levels of attainment. Furthermore, the program of evaluation has been extended beyond the mere measurement of proficiency of performance with basic skills; it incorporates efforts to measure the development of interests and appreciations and to discriminate between varying degrees of aptitude in a given subject field. Also, the techniques of evaluation include not only the giving of tests, whether standard or teacher-made, but also interviews, informal observations, anecdotal records, pupil projects, aptitude and inventory tests, and other methods of obtaining evidence relating to pupil development.

Thus, evaluation can perform a very important function in the educative process. It should no longer be considered merely as a separate procedure to be used at convenient intervals for the purpose of determining marks; rather it should be thought of as a continual process closely related to each aspect of the total program of pupil development. The major responsibilities of a truly effective evaluation program may thus be considered to be the following:

1. To provide a basis for more intelligent guidance of teaching and learning through appraisal of aptitudes and diagnosis of errors
2. To evaluate instructional procedures
3. To measure the attainment of instructional objectives and provide an adequate basis for reporting pupil progress
4. To provide guides for the development of more effective educative experiences
5. To take inventory of pupil readiness
6. To secure information for use as an aid in seeking intelligent and effective parent and community cooperation

The teacher of mathematics has the responsibility of determining the contribution that mathematics can make to the educational development of the individual and then designing a program of evaluation sufficiently comprehensive to measure progress toward maximum benefit from all phases of that contribution. In order to measure progress efficiently, the techniques of measurement must be so flexible that ready adaptation may be made to the characteristic differences that exist among individual abilities, in curriculum demands, and in guidance criteria. Such flexibility should in no sense interfere with the comprehensiveness of the program of evaluation. It is also important that the testing techniques be characterized by balance of emphasis between factual and functional objectives, between tangible and intangible outcomes, between the how and the why, between mere recall and integrated thinking, and between measurement as a check on the completed process and as an aid to more effective instruction.

A satisfactory evaluation program should be further characterized by *continuity*. For efficient guidance there must be a continual check on the student's progress, not only from the standpoint of immediate accomplishment but also from the standpoint of retention. Furthermore, the use of this check for prognostic and diagnostic purposes should be emphasized fully as much as its use as a measure of achievement.

If the evaluation program is to be thoroughly comprehensive and balanced, it must neglect no significant aspect of the subject matter covered and it must take into account all the important objectives which have been set up. Since it can command but a limited part of the school time, it must obviously consist of only a sampling of subject matter and problem situations. Thus the real task of such a program is to use data of varied types collected through several different media to shape a composite appraisal picture of each pupil as an individual and as a member of his group. Care must thus be exercised to ensure that the sampling is truly representative of all the important aspects of the total program.

In the preparation of the instructional program the experienced, well-trained teacher should enjoy a certain freedom from curriculum restraint. There should not be too much dictation of the material to be covered in a specified period of time. This also implies freedom in the curricular materials and the testing techniques to be used in the evaluation program. On the other hand, the inexperienced teacher should seek the counsel of the supervisor or administrator in setting up objectives of instruction and in selecting testing techniques and constructing instruments for measuring student progress toward the attainment of the objectives.

The formulation of a sound philosophy of evaluation is but a necessary prerequisite to the construction of a satisfactory program of evaluation. With the above characteristics as guiding criteria the teacher or administrator can proceed more safely with the technical details incident to the selection or construction of valid and reliable instruments of measurement for use in any particular instructional situation.

Whether the problem is to provide an evaluation program from the point of view of the entire curriculum or of a specific subject-matter field, there are at least five steps to be followed in setting up efficient testing techniques, for example:

1. Determination of those significant aims and objectives which are to be the goals of instruction
2. Provision of pertinent behavior situations to guarantee a valid measure of student reactions
3. Securing a reliable record of the student reactions
4. Accurate and systematic tabulation of the record as an aid in the deduction of implied results
5. Intelligent interpretation of the results in terms of student needs and as an aid to more effective instruction

Evaluation has a very definite function in the learning process which takes place in secondary mathematics; the program of evaluation should be designed in terms of the functional aims as well as the factual aims of mathematical instruction. Is the instructional program such that functional learning and factual learning supplement each other? Are the students learning the why as well as the how? Are they building up integrated funds of information rather than stores of segregated bits of factual knowledge? Is the program of instruction such that it will provide the student with the techniques of critical thinking? Will it develop the ability (1) to distinguish between essential and unessential data, (2) to determine the reliability of facts and the reasonableness of results and conclusions, (3) to generalize circumspectly from known facts to unknown situations and new problems, (4) to evaluate arguments, ideas, and conclusions critically? Carefully selected techniques of evaluation should be used in determining to what extent these aims have been realized by pupils, both as individuals and as groups. Furthermore, it should be constantly emphasized that the most significant functions of effective evaluation include not merely use as an aid in determining pupils' marks but use as an aid to the improvement of instruction as well.

The techniques of evaluation The determination and perfection of techniques to be used in the evaluation of mathematical instruction are a definite responsibility of teachers of mathematics. These techniques, in the main, consist of teacher judgments and teacher-made or commercially produced tests. Teachers should be extremely conscientious in their efforts to evaluate student effort, and, in those situations which do not submit themselves very well to measurement scales, appraisals should be based on discriminative and impartial judgments arrived at after careful deliberation. Such judgments may be made through the medium of oral recitations in class, comparative class observations, the personal interview, the anecdotal record, and the prolonged case study.

If prepared tests are to be used, the teacher will at times have to consider the comparative advantages and disadvantages of standardized[1] and teacher-made tests. Each has certain advantages over the other. The standardized test possesses norms which provide for more equitable comparisons between groups than can be made by teacher-made tests. They are usually constructed by individuals of wide ex-

[1]See the following yearbooks prepared by O. K. Buros: *Educational, Psychological, and Personality Tests of 1933, 1934, 1935* (1936), pp. 14–17, 40–41, 53; *Educational, Psychological, and Personality Tests of 1936* (1937), pp. 10–12, 27–28, 35–36; *The Nineteen Thirty-eight Mental Measurements Yearbook* (1938), pp. 14–42, 83–84, 116–119; *The Nineteen Forty Mental Measurements Yearbook* (1940), pp. 268–314; *The Third Mental Measurements Yearbook* (1949), pp. 399–442; *The Fourth Mental Measurements Yearbook* (1953), pp. 483–527; *The Fifth Mental Measurements Yearbook* (1959), pp. 561–615. Also see Sheldon S. Myers, Annotated Bibliography of Mathematics Tests, *Twenty-sixth Yearbook* (Washington, D.C.: National Council of Teachers of Mathematics, 1961), pp. 181–216.

perience and preparation in both subject matter and the techniques of testing. This increases the likelihood of greater reliability and validity. Standardized tests are usually subject to a greater degree of objectivity in administering and in scoring.

On the other hand, it is probable that standard tests which are used year after year may exert some "backward influence" which might partially nullify their validity so far as the content of the work of a particular class is concerned.

A distinct administrative advantage of the standardized test is that it diminishes the time which the teacher needs to devote to the details of a testing program. This, however, in the minds of some is a questionable advantage, the argument being that thoughtful effort on the part of the teacher in the details of test construction might make a distinct contribution in the direction of improved instruction. The use of such extramural tests as those prepared by the College Entrance Examination Board and the Board of Regents of the University of the State of New York, as well as some standardized tests designed primarily as final examinations, should be definitely restricted to the purposes for which they were designed and the situations to which they are related.

One of the major advantages of the teacher-made test over the standard or extramural test is its flexibility and its adaptability to local situations and to repeated evaluations. Tests of subject-matter mastery should include the material which the class has studied and no other material. They should emphasize those things that have been emphasized in the class, and no item should have much place in a test for a particular class unless that class, in its study, has given some attention to that item or topic. It must be recognized that individual differences exist among classes and teachers just as they exist among individual students. Extramural tests can take some account of different levels of difficulty, but they cannot take account of differences in details of subject matter or emphasis or differences in the methods of presentation and the points of view of different teachers. Only the teachers themselves can make tests which will do so. Other advantages of teacher-made tests over standardized tests lie in their relative inexpensiveness and their inexhaustible availability.

When the tests to be used are to be constructed by the individual teacher or by groups of teachers, there are two major problems to be considered, viz., (1) What is to be tested? and (2) What is the most effective method of testing it? The answers to these two questions are to be found in the answers to certain supplementary questions. What are the instructional objectives to be measured? Is the test to be designed primarily for the purpose of measuring the attainment of standards, or is it to serve as a medium of instruction or as an aid in the educational guidance of the individual pupil? What are the distinguishing characteristics of prognostic, diagnostic, and achievement tests? Such questions as these must be settled by the teacher before he will be able to construct an entirely satisfactory test.

Another question of special importance in this connection is whether an essay-type test or a new-type test is better suited to the particular situation. If the teacher is interested in having the test reflect something of the student's ability to organize and integrate information, then the essay-type test probably provides the better medium. There are certain types of mathematical subject matter that seem to limit themselves largely to the essay type or problem type of test, e.g., solving verbal problems, solving geometrical originals, proving theorems, and constructing geometric figures. The objective tests, on the other hand, offer the opportunity of covering a wider range of material as well as very greatly restricting any subjectivity which might affect the results of the evaluation program. Such tests are likely to be more reliable than tests of the essay type, although the latter, if carefully constructed, may have a high degree of reliability and validity. Objective tests certainly give opportunity for a wider range of sampling, and for this reason they have certain advantages over essay-type tests in the matter of prognosis and diagnosis. For the same reason they make possible the inclusion of a more comprehensive range of items in measuring achievement. However, while their objectivity makes them easy to score and reduces the personal element in scoring, the translation of scores into marks or grades may in some measure offset this advantage. Aside from the fact that they are generally not good tests of organizing ability, their chief disadvantage lies in the fact that the construction of really good objective tests requires much time, considerable experience, and great care.

Such tests are made in various forms, and the determination of which of these forms is most suitable for a particular situation is sometimes a real problem. One must know and weigh the functions, advantages, and limitations of the different forms, such as true-false, direct recall, multiple-response, completion, and matching, and decide which one will lend itself most advantageously to the case in hand.

In any case, whether essay-type or objective tests are being constructed, the following criteria should be observed with the utmost care:

1. A test should be as highly objective as possible. The element of personal interpretation should be minimized in the determination of the correctness or incorrectness of student reactions to behavior situations.
2. A test should be reliable. The reliability of a test is determined by the consistency with which it measures that which it does measure. There are many sources of unreliability, not all of which are attributes of the test itself. The behavior of the examiner, the mental and physical condition of the student,

and the conditions under which the test is given have a great deal of influence upon the reliability of the results obtained from any test. Certain other causes of unreliability are inherent within the test itself, e.g., ambiguity in the instructions for taking the test, lack of clearness in statement of problems and questions, inadequate sampling of the items of information to be tested, inefficient methods of scoring, and erroneous interpretations of test results.

3. A test should be valid. A test can be valid only insofar as it accomplishes for a selected group of pupils the specific purpose for which it was designed. Two significant attributes of validity are reliability and objectivity. However, their presence does not guarantee the validity of a test. To be valid the test must be further characterized by that comprehensiveness and discriminative power most pertinent to the particular function for which it is designed. These criteria imply that the teacher must not only be thoroughly familiar with the objectives of instruction for the material to be tested but must also be well versed in the techniques of apt and precise phraseology and efficacious organization.
4. A test should be economical of the teacher's time. The amount of time required for the construction, administration, and interpretation of a test should not be excessive. The time element, however, is a function of the expected returns from the test.
5. A test should be "student-conscious." The elements of the test should be couched in nonambiguous language, and reasonable tasks should be set for reasonable periods of time. In test items designed to measure understanding of a principle or ability to apply a principle, computation should be minimized.
6. A test should motivate the best efforts of the students. The questions should be so worded and presented that they will discourage guessing and bluffing. The use of the "catch question" should be minimized. However, occasional use of such questions might be justified from the point of view of stimulation of accurate thinking. A test should never be used as a means of punishment but should always tend to create in the mind of the student the attitude that it is worthwhile taking.
7. A test designed to discriminate between students' abilities must provide for measurement of the entire range of abilities. If anything like accurate discrimination between students' abilities is to be approximated, there must be questions easy enough that all students can answer them and questions so difficult that perfect scores would be highly improbable, if not impossible. Some questions should be so designed that the student will have the responsibility of distinguishing between essential and nonessential data.

Prognosis and guidance As an aid to more effective pupil guidance, tests have been used to analyze present status of mastery and to predict possible future achievement. Such tests should be provided not only to measure mechanical ability and functional information, but also to make inquiry into students' interests, aptitudes, work habits, and study skills.

The inventory test is used for the purpose of "taking stock" of mathematical information and ability. It should show what a student knows about a certain topic. Under the modern philosophy of mathematical education the student has many opportunities to learn something of elementary algebra and a good deal of intuitive geometry by the time he enters the secondary school. As he proceeds up the instructional ladder, seasonal inventory tests carefully placed and skillfully used will prevent a great deal of unnecessary repetition of experience on the part of the student and waste of effort on the part of the teacher. They will also serve somewhat in the capacity of insurance against the monotony of learning which might result from student familiarity with teacher-selected material. Such tests may also be used effectively to bring to light the background which the students have for the study of new units and thus aid in the guidance program. The construction of an inventory test on a unit of instruction is not essentially different from the construction of a final achievement test on the same unit. The use of two such comparable tests, one before and the other after the teaching of the unit, will serve as a good indicator of the learning that takes place during the unit. Such a test on exponents and radicals is given here with its tabulation chart. There is also given the tabulation chart for a similar test, identical in form, which was given at the end of the unit. A comparative study of the two tables will give information concerning each pupil and the class as a whole on the learning situations recorded in the test.

Test: *Exponents and Radicals*

1. How many square roots does a number have? ________.
2. 5 is a square root of ____ because ____ times ____ is ____.
3. If $x = \sqrt{y}$, then ______ $= y$.
4.

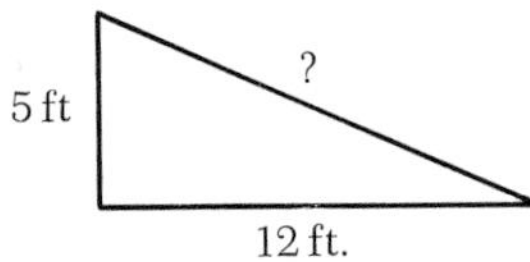

The hypotenuse of this triangle is ____ feet long.

5. Construct geometrically a line segment $\sqrt{3}$ inches long.
6. (*a*) $\sqrt{2} =$ ________; (*b*) $\sqrt{3} =$ ________; (*c*) $\sqrt{5} =$ ________.
7. (*a*) $\sqrt{\frac{a^2}{b^2}} =$ ________; (*b*) $\left(\frac{4}{7}\right)^2 =$ ________.
8. The simplest way to express $\sqrt{x^2y}$ is ________.
9. In the expression $\sqrt[3]{x^2}$ the index is (*a*) ______ and the exponent is (*b*) ______. The sign $\sqrt{\ }$ is called a (*c*) ______ sign.
10. $x^{3/2}$ means the (*a*) ______ root of the (*b*) ______ power of (*c*) ______.
11. (*a*) $\frac{x^5}{x^3} =$ ______; (*b*) $x^{3/4} \div x^{1/2} =$ ______; (*c*) $a^{3/2} \cdot a^{1/4} =$ ______.
12. (*a*) $x^5 \div x^5 = x^{(\ \ )}$ (Supply the exponent in the answer.) (*b*) To what *number* is the above answer equal? ______.

13. (*a*) $a^5 \div a^7 =$ ______. (*b*) Does a^{-3} equal $\frac{1}{a^3}$? ______.

14. $\sqrt{73}$ is between ______ and ______. (Fill blanks with two consecutive whole numbers.)

An examination of Table 8-1 reveals the fact that, as a whole, this unit constituted new material for the entire class. The meaning of square root, item 2 of the test, was generally understood, so no time needed to be spent on its development. Furthermore, the teacher was able to determine those pupils, B, E, F, and H, who would probably need special attention.

TABLE 8-1
Pupil responses before studying the unit

Questions:	1	2	3	4	5	6			7		8	9			10			11			12		13		14	Pupil standing
						a	*b*	*c*	*a*	*b*		*a*	*b*	*c*	*a*	*b*	*c*	*a*	*b*	*c*	*a*	*b*	*a*	*b*		
Pupil:																										
A	x	x					x					x	x		x	x	x									8
B																										0
C		x				x	x					x	x					x						x	x	8
D		x										x	x		x										x	5
E	x	x																								2
F		x										x			x											3
G		x								x								x			x		x			5
H		x											x													2
Class standing	2	7	0	0	0	1	2	0	0	1	0	4	4	0	3	1	1	2	0	0	1	0	1	1	2	
Familiar material		x																								

Table 8-2 gives the record of responses after the period of instruction on the unit. It reveals that pupils A, E, F, and G needed further individual attention on certain specific items and that, from the point of view of the entire class, items 3, 8, 11*b*, 11*c*, 13*a*, and 14 should be retaught.

In the prediction of mathematical achievement some of the most important factors seem to be comprehension of general mathematical techniques, classroom attentiveness, originality, habits of study, and general intelligence. The most efficient prediction seems to be accomplished through a combined use of prognostic tests, intelligence tests, and teachers' marks.

As a corollary to their use as an aid in prediction of achievement, prognostic tests can be used to reduce the number of failures either by

TABLE 8-2
Pupil responses after studying the unit

Questions:	1	2	3	4	5	6			7		8	9			10			11			12		13		14	Pupil standing
						a	*b*	*c*	*a*	*b*		*a*	*b*	*c*	*a*	*b*	*c*	*a*	*b*	*c*	*a*	*b*	*a*	*b*		
Pupil:																										
A	x	x	x	x	x	x	x	x	x		x	x	x	x	x	x	x							x		17
B	x	x		x	x	x	x	x	x	x		x	x	x	x		x	x			x	x	x	x	x	20
C	x	x		x		x	x	x	x	x		x	x	x	x	x	x	x	x		x	x	x	x	x	21
D	x	x		x	x	x	x	x	x	x	x	x	x	x	x			x	x	x	x	x	x	x	x	22
E	x	x		x	x	x	x	x	x	x		x	x	x	x	x	x	x	x							17
F	x	x		x		x	x	x	x	x		x	x	x	x	x	x	x								15
G	x	x		x	x	x	x	x	x	x		x	x	x	x		x	x		x	x	x		x		19
H		x		x	x	x	x	x	x	x	x	x	x	x	x	x	x	x			x	x	x	x	x	21
Class standing	7	8	1	8	6	8	8	8	8	7	3	8	8	8	8	5	7	7	3	2	5	5	4	6	4	
Need to reteach			x								x								x	x			x		x	

eliminating those who are unprepared, or unable for any cause, to proceed further with mathematical study or by providing a basis for the construction of a differentiated mathematical curriculum. Such tests should also serve as an aid in the vocational and educational guidance of pupils and in the better classification of pupils. The discovery of superior ability and unusual aptitude in mathematics is just as important a function of prognosis as is the discovery of the inferior or average.[2]

For the construction of efficient prognostic tests in mathematics the teacher should be familiar with those abilities and interests essential to further progress. Mathematical tests which are to be used as an aid in vocational guidance should be based on a knowledge of those mathematical skills, concepts, and principles incident to success in any chosen vocation. The general characteristcs of comprehensiveness, discriminative power, reliability, validity, balance, and flexibility must then be carefully observed in the framing and organization of the test items.

Diagnosis and remedial teaching Probably one of the most significant steps toward improved instruction that has been taken in recent years is that of incorporating into the instructional program plans for discovering learning difficulties and detecting needs for remedial teach-

[2]An important program of this type is the Advanced Placement Program of the College Entrance Examination Board.

ing. Such plans call for the intelligent use of inventory and diagnostic tests along with personal interviews to discover and analyze pupil difficulties with a view to setting up specific remedial measures to correct errors and remove difficulties. The characteristics of an efficient program of diagnosis may be summarized as follows:[3]

1. Such diagnosis must be made in connection with worthy objectives of a good educational program.
2. It must be objective, reliable, and valid.
3. It should be as specific as the desired outcomes permit and as the possibility of localization of symptoms allows within the limitations of practicality.
4. It should yield results that would be comparable over a period of time and between groups of students.
5. It should be sufficiently precise to note progress during small units of time.
6. It should be comprehensive.
7. It should be appropriate to the educational program.
8. The person making the diagnosis must understand the educational program and be familiar with the fundamental problems of children.

Such a program should be keyed to bring to light distinct weaknesses in learning which call for specifically planned remedial action. An important by-product of any diagnostic program which is carefully constructed will be the discovery of latent interests and abilities which need to be challenged. A second important by-product of the diagnostic program can be the evaluation of instructional procedures. Have they been relatively effective or ineffective? Answers to such questions must be sought in a carefully structured composite picture of individual or group reaction to a specific diagnostic testing pattern. This is particularly true if the tests have been designed for diagnosis of basic understandings, insights into problem solving, and intelligent interpretation of results as well as proficiency in fundamental skills.

The intelligent use of such a program of diagnosis is an important aspect of effective teaching. Its real value, however, definitely will be dependent upon a carefully planned follow-up remedial program and a careful check on, and interpretation of, attained results.

Self-diagnosis by students One of the most important functions of tests as an aid to the improvement of instruction is student use of tests to secure evidence concerning individual development. Such tests, called "practice tests," may be either oral or written, and they can play a very important role in the assimilative period of instruction. They can aid the student in self-diagnosis, but they should never be used by the teacher in any other capacity than to help the student discover for

[3]Ralph W. Tyler, Characteristics of Satisfactory Diagnosis, *Thirty-fourth Yearbook of the National Society for the Study of Education* (Bloomington, Ill.: Public School Publishing Company, 1935), part II, chap. 6, pp. 95–111. Quoted by permission of the society.

himself information concerning his status of achievement in intelligent understanding of subject matter, the speed and accuracy with which he can perform the prescribed operations, and his relative progress as a member of his class group. Such tests must be shaped to reflect individual efficiency in the perspective of group activity.

Oral tests may be used with material that calls for responses which can be readily obtained and simply stated. They may be administered through pointed questions promiscuously, yet evenly, distributed over the entire class or through the medium of team contests. The two principal keynotes of successful oral practice are speed and accuracy of response.

Written tests may be used for both the simple-response and the difficult-response type of practice. As in the case of the oral tests, written tests may be shaped to emphasize speed and accuracy. It should be re-emphasized at this point, however, that understanding is a major responsibility of instruction in secondary mathematics, and some of the practice tests should be designed to that end.

Some of the different ways of administering written practice tests are (1) all students at board, (2) some at the board and others in their seats, (3) all students in their seats. In any of the above cases all students may be working on the same assigned problems, or separate groups may be working on separate problems. These problems may be dictated by the teacher or printed, mimeographed, or otherwise reproduced. Timed tests frequently serve to stimulate interest and attention through competition with other students or competition with one's own previous time record or similar material. Precautions which the teacher must observe are as follows: (1) Do not overemphasize speed at the expense of accuracy; (2) provide for check-up and practice on understanding as well as on speed and accuracy; (3) vary the type of practice material to prevent monotony of effort; and (4) do not continue practice to the point of fatigue.

Achievement In the measure of achievement the teacher is not merely interested in testing mechanical proficiency in certain fundamental processes and factual information. He is also interested in the measure of reasoned understanding of concepts, techniques, and principles.[4] Such a testing program should be so designed that it will compare and discriminate between relative abilities as well as measure retention

[4]For a basic philosophy of such testing and for representative test items see Maurice L. Hartung and Harold P. Fawcett, The Measurement of Understanding in Secondary Mathematics, *The Forty-fifth Yearbook of the National Society for the Study of Education* (Chicago: University of Chicago Press, 1946), part I, pp. 157–174. Also see *Twenty-second Yearbook* (1954), pp. 339–409, and *Twenty-sixth Yearbook* (1961) (Washington, D.C.: National Council of Teachers of Mathematics).

and understanding of learning. The selection of test items must be in terms of an authoritative list of ultimate objectives which in turn have been carefully analyzed into immediate aims of instruction in the light of the significant implications and limitations of the local situation. Although comprehensiveness is one of the important characteristics of an efficient achievement test, it is quite obvious that no such test can be sufficiently comprehensive to include all items of specific information into which an instructional unit may be analyzed. The test is thus a function of the different items used. They must therefore represent an adequate sampling of the entire unit, and each item must make a significant contribution to the composite power of the test to discriminate between pupils of high and low levels of general achievement. The validity of any achievement test is largely a function of the success with which each individual test item performs the function for which it was designed.

Just as in the case of prognosis and diagnosis, there are several different evaluation procedures that can be used for measuring achievement: the standardized tests, the informal teacher-made tests, observations, interviews, anecdotal records, and pupil reports and projects. While standardized tests are available for many different purposes, there are cautions that should be observed in their use. The content of such a test may not conform closely enough to the local program of instruction, and it can vary widely, from author to author, in tests designed, theoretically, for the same general purpose. A comparison of local scores with published norms can thus be inaccurate and misleading. Furthermore, such tests are valid only in the context of the objectives for which they were designed. Interpretations of results should keep these limitations in mind.

Teacher-made tests have the advantage of being constructed entirely in the context of the local teaching situation. The objectivity of such tests, however, usually is not so well defined as in the case of standardized tests. Also, the question structure of teacher-made tests frequently fails to reflect as high a level of expertness as does that of the standardized tests. In the construction of an achievement test for a specific instructional unit and for a given group of pupils the teacher should use the following criteria as guides in selecting the content and shaping the questions:

1. The different levels of achievement potential within the group should be recognized.
2. For each level the test should provide an approximately equal number of items.
3. The items should hold the pupils responsible for concepts, principles, and understandings as well as for basic skills.

4. The items should be selected and worded in the context of reasonable expectations of individual and group performance for the specific instructional unit.
5. The items should be so constructed that they discriminate between different levels of ability.
6. The items should be such that they lend themselves to reliability in scoring.

Both standardized tests and teacher-made tests have their advantages and limitations. Each type of test can make significant contributions toward effective evaluation of achievement. But whether the two types of test are used separately or combined to secure the benefits of both, there remain gaps to be filled in before the true picture of either individual or group achievement can be composed. The observation of performance, the personal interview, the analysis of anecdotal records, and the studious appraisal of projects and reports, each and all can make significant contributions to the intelligent evaluation of pupil progress.

Interpretation and use of results The significance of any program of evaluation is very definitely dependent upon the interpretation and use of the results obtained. It is highly important that the results of a given test be interpreted and used in the context of the function for which the test was constructed and administered. For example, the results from a test designed solely for diagnostic purposes should never be used for the purpose of measuring achievement and then assigning grades. There are sometimes fundamental differences in the construction of such tests, to say nothing of the moral obligation of the teacher to play fair with the student.

In many cases it is necessary that the teacher be familiar with certain simple but fundamental statistical procedures in order to derive maximum benefit from a testing program. The techniques of classifying and tabulating data; grouping into significant class intervals; determining range of distribution; computing measures of central tendency, variability, and relationship; and ranking scores are the more important statistical measures with which the teacher should be familiar in order to summarize efficiently the results of a testing program.

Not only must the teacher have a certain amount of mechanical proficiency in the techniques for tabulating and analyzing test data but also he must be able to make logical inferences from such findings. He must know the appropriateness of various measures and the extent and limitations of their implications. The conclusions drawn must be consistent with the fundamental assumptions underlying the tests and the statistical measures used.

In the measure of achievement the teacher must know the difference between a test score and a grade. Futhermore, he must know when test scores should be translated into grades and be familiar with the recommended techniques for careful conversion. He must know how to detect a typical class error from a diagnosis test, and he must be able to determine whether particular detected errors imply the need for group or individual remedial measures.

Teachers should be familiar with the various purposes and limitations of each aspect of a functional testing program. For maximum value the results should be used within the domain they are designed to serve, in the effort to construct from all sources of relevant information a composite, yet comprehensive, picture of the individual student.

EXERCISES

1. Distinguish among diagnostic, prognostic, and achievement tests as to characteristics and function.

2. Name different ways in which each type of test may be used in the improvement of instruction in mathematics.

3. How specific should one be in the formulation of the objectives for testing?

4. What are some of the recommended measures for improvement of essay-type examinations?

5. Contrast the relative effectiveness of different kinds of new-type tests (true-false, multiple-choice, completion, etc.).

6. Discuss the relative merits of factual and functional testing in secondary mathematics.

7. What are some recommended procedures for measuring mathematical aptitude?

8. What is validity in a test?

9. What is reliability in a test?

10. Give examples of material from secondary mathematics which you consider not well adapted to objective tests.

11. In test construction how much importance should be given to "range of difficulty" and "distribution of item difficulty"?

12. Briefly evaluate the advantages and disadvantages of extramural tests.

13. What are some of the common errors in secondary mathematics that call for remedial work?

14. What are some of the more important techniques for discovering pupil errors?

15. What are some of the recommended techniques for determining the degree of difficulty of test items?

16. What are some of the recommended procedures for transforming test scores into grades?

17. Compare the relative merits of the per cent and ranking techniques of determining grades.

18. What are some of the recommended techniques for testing appreciation and understanding in secondary mathematics?

19. What are some of the more significant recommendations for improving the program of evaluation in secondary mathematics?

20. Take some topic in algebra and enumerate five specific objectives which you would hope to have your students attain through their study of this topic.

21. Make five test items, each designed to test for one of these specific objectives. Make a marking key to be used in grading the test papers.

22. Make an analysis sheet for tabulating the responses of each student for each of the five test items.

23. Explain what uses you would make of this analysis sheet.

BIBLIOGRAPHY

Begle, E. G.: A Study of Mathematical Abilities, *Mathematics Teacher*, **55** (1962), 648, 659.

Bowers, N. D.: Meaningful Learning and Retention, *Educational Research*, **31** (1961), 527.

Callicutt, W.: Problems of Predicting Success in Algebra, *Bulletin of the National Association of Secondary-School Principals*, **45** (1961), 107–111.

Cliffe, Marion C.: The Place of Evaluation in the Secondary School Program, *Mathematics Teacher*, **49** (1956), 270–273.

_____: Mathematics Evaluation in a Large City, *Bulletin of the National Association of Secondary-School Principals*, **43** (1959), 161–165.

Ennis, R. H.: Concept of Critical Thinking, *Harvard Educational Review*, **32** (1962), 81–111.

Gordon, I. J.: Testing and Evaluation, *Educational Leadership*, **20** (1962), 73–76.

Greenspan, P.: Predicting Success in Algebra, *High Points*, **35** (1953), 19–22.

Hartung, M. L.: Evaluating Instruction in Mathematics, *Bulletin of the National Association of Secondary-School Principals*, **38** (1954), 138–143.

Hawthorne, Frank S.: Evaluation in a Large State: The New York Regents Examinations, *Bulletin of the National Association of Secondary-School Principals*, **43** (1959), 165–168.

Johnson, Donovan A.: What Can the Classroom Teacher Do about Evaluation? *Bulletin of the National Association of Secondary-School Principals*, **43** (1959), 154–161.

Kinney, Lucien Blair, and C. Richard Purdy: "Teaching Mathematics in the Secondary School" (New York: Holt, Rinehart and Winston, Inc., 1952), pp. 326–351.

Kinsella, John J.: Evaluation of Student Learning in Secondary School, *Bulletin of the National Association of Secondary-School Principals*, **43** (1959), 125–128.

Koenker, R. H.: Measuring the Meanings in Airthmetic, *Arithmetic Teacher*, **7** (1960), 93–96.

Lankford, F. G., Jr.: What Are Your Pupils Learning? Some Suggestions on Evaluation, *Mathematics Teacher*, **47** (1954), 208–210.

Lehnoff, A. K.: Self-evaluation: One Approach, *Educational Leadership*, **20** (1962), 34–37.

Lindquist, E. F. (Editor): "Educational Measurement" (Washington, D.C.: American Council on Education, 1951).

Morgan, H. G.: What Is Effective Evaluation? *Journal of the National Educational Association*, **48** (1959), 15–17.

Myers, Sheldon S.: "Mathematics Tests Available in the United States" (Washington, D.C.: National Council of Teachers of Mathematics, 1959). (Pamphlet.)

_____: A New Approach to Evaluation of Competence, *Bulletin of the National Association of Secondary-School Principals*, **43** (1959), 150–154.

_____: Cooperative Mathematics Tests: A Progress Report, *American Mathematical Monthly*, **69** (1962), 223–225, 917.

_____: The College Board and Mathematics Reform, *Mathematics Teacher*, **56** (1963), 147.

_____, and Marion G. Epstein: Mathematical Reform and the College Board Mathematics Examinations,` *American Mathematical Monthly*, **70** (1963), 665–667.

National Council of Teachers of Mathematics: The Evaluation of Mathematical Learning, *Twenty-second Yearbook* (Washington, D.C.: National Council of Teachers of Mathematics, 1954), pp. 339–409, 432–434.

_____: Evaluation in Mathematics, *Twenty-sixth Yearbook* (Washington, D.C.: National Council of Teachers of Mathematics, 1962).

Place of Testing and Evaluation in Learning, *California Journal of Secondary Education*, **35** (1960), 40–65.

Rosskopf, Myron F.: The Present Status of Evaluation of Critical Thinking in Algebra and Geometry, *Mathematics Teacher*, **43** (1950), 143–148.

Sampson, Tom: Tests in Algebra, *Mathematics Teacher*, **55** (1962), 117–119.

Shaw, Glenadine Sax: Prediction of Success

in Elementary Algebra, *Mathematics Teacher*, **49** (1956), 173–178.

Shimberg, Benjamin: New Cooperative Mathematics Tests, *American Mathematical Monthly*, **67** (1960), 1027.

Taba, H., and E. I. Swain: Proposed Model in Evaluation, *Educational Leadership*, **20** (1962), 57–59.

Ullsvik, Bjarne R.: An attempt to Measure Critical Judgment, *School Science and Mathematics*, **49** (1949), 445–452.

Weir, E. C.: Some Thoughts on Evaluation, *Bulletin of the National Association of Secondary-School Principals*, **41** (1962), 23–29.

Weitzmann, Ellis, and W. J. McNamara: "Constructing Classroom Examinations" (Chicago: Science Research Associates, Occupational Information Division, 1949).

Wilson, V. W.: Techniques of Evaluating Pupil Progress, *School and Community*, **48** (1961), 18.

Wrightstone, J. W.: Teacher-made Tests and Techniques, *Educational Leadership*, **19** (1961), 170–172.

———, J. Justman, and I. Robbins: "Evaluation in Modern Education" (New York: American Book Company, 1956).

———, and J. I. Krugman: A Guide to the Use of Anecdotal Records, *Educational Research Bulletin* 11 (New York: Board of Education of the City of New York, 1949).

NINE

Supervision of instruction

IN NEARLY every enterprise which engages the services of any considerable number of individuals, the supervision of the work of these individuals is regarded as an important function that is essential to the economical and efficient operation of the enterprise. Engineering and construction crews have their foremen, large stores their departmental managers, restaurants their headwaiters, large offices their chief clerks, governmental bureaus and departments their supervisors, and so on through an endless list. It can be taken for granted that those in charge of the operation of business enterprises would not engage the services of these individuals unless they felt that the returns justified the expense.

Mathematical instruction is a large and important segment of secondary education. Although it is not to be regarded primarily as a business, those responsible for it have an obligation to make sure that it will yield as great a return as possible. There is every reason to believe that good supervision can contribute a good deal toward this end. The purposes of this chapter are to outline certain principles and functions of supervision and to consider ways in which good supervision can help to make instruction in mathematics more effective than it might otherwise be.

Functions of departmental supervision Any means through which the mathematical instruction in a school may be improved is a legitimate and proper function of departmental supervision. It may be taken as axiomatic that the training and competence of the teacher, together with his attitude toward his work and his students, are more influential than any other considerations in determining the effectiveness of instruction. Therefore the most obvious and direct, and perhaps the most important, service which departmental supervision can perform lies in giving that direct counsel, guidance, stimulation, and assistance which will encourage the various teachers in the department to continue their professional development through the study of pertinent subject matter and professional literature.

There are, however, other ways in which the proper supervision of the department may contribute appreciably, if less directly, to the improvement of instruction. These consist mainly in the provision and maintenance of adequate instructional facilities, the maintenance of cordial and cooperative professional relations with the administrative offices of the school, and the prosecution of research and the dissemination of professional information bearing upon the instructional problems of the department. As illustrative of these other functions of supervision, such matters as the following may be mentioned:

1. Selecting and organizing suitable teaching materials for the several classes
2. Preparing courses of study and coordinating the work of the department
3. Comparing the suitability of different textbooks, workbooks, and other published materials for use in instruction
4. Comparing the efficacy and suitability of different methods of instruction, including new or nontraditional devices and methods
5. Establishing and defining suitable standards of attainment for the various courses in the department
6. Planning, inaugurating, and carrying on a systematic program of evaluation of student attainment
7. Maintaining a suitable, convenient, and facile system of departmental records
8. Holding departmental meetings for the consideration of matters of common concern
9. Keeping the members of the department informed with reference to the objectives and activities of the supervisory program
10. Conducting research designed to secure data which may provide sound bases for the improvement of materials or methods of instruction
11. Locating and abstracting worthwhile pertinent articles, research studies, etc., and making the substance of these available in condensed and understandable form to the members of the departmental staff
12. Promoting and maintaining good morale, close rapport, high interest, and friendly cooperation among the members of the department in all possible ways
13. Making special efforts to be helpful to the young and inexperienced teachers through visitation, conferences, and perhaps demonstration
14. Keeping the administrative officers of the school properly informed about any specially meritorious work of individual teachers
15. Cooperating with those responsible for student guidance

16. Keeping the administrative officers of the school informed with respect to the work of the department and maintaining with them reciprocally co-operative relations
17. Keeping the administrative officers of the school informed with reference to departmental needs and making suitable recommendations concerning provision for those needs
18. Evaluating the effectiveness of instruction and submitting the results of such evaluation, together with appropriate recommendations, to the administrative officers of the school

The functions of departmental supervision have been variously classified by different writers. Some of them are mainly of an administrative nature, while others emphasize the coordination of interdepartmental effort, the conducting and reviewing of research work, the organization of instructional materials, the rating of teaching efficiency, the consideration of special problems, and the in-service training of teachers. They all bear either directly or indirectly upon the general problem of improving the quality of instruction.

The need for personal supervision in secondary mathematics

Although departmental supervision can make many important contributions toward improved instruction, there is also need for more direct personal supervision of the work of mathematics teachers in the secondary school. Large numbers of these teachers come into the schools each year fresh from college, with high enthusiasm for their work but with little or no experience in teaching and without much firsthand knowledge of the problems connected with teaching secondary school students. These problems cannot be mastered adequately in the course of one or two years, even under favorable circumstances. Most young teachers can be greatly helped by the guiding advice and counsel of a sympathetic and experienced supervisor for a period of several years after they enter upon their work, and, since the annual turnover in the teaching staffs of secondary schools is relatively high, this period may in many cases include the entire professional career of the teacher.

The need for this kind of supervision is accentuated by the fact that many secondary school teachers are required to teach one or more subjects outside their fields of special preparation. This is especially true of young teachers in the early years of their work, and these are the years when their need for wise counsel and assistance is greatest. A sympathetic supervisor can do much to help young teachers organize and plan their work effectively and to give them poise and self-confidence.

Long experience is a great asset, but sometimes such experience is not without its pitfalls. Unless one guards against it, there is a potential danger of allowing oneself to get into a rut and to become complacent about his work, oblivious or insensitive to possibilities of further improvement. Moreover, the very subject matter of contemporary secondary school mathematics includes concepts, terminology, notation, and emphases with which older teachers may be unfamiliar and which they must learn. Thus even teachers of long experience and substantial backgrounds in classical mathematics may benefit from appropriate supervisory contacts through being stimulated to professional alertness and scholarly advancement.

If supervision is to result in improved instruction, it must be a cooperative effort. Teachers and their supervisors must have a mutual and sympathetic understanding of supervision: the reasons for it, its aims and functions, and the advantages which can be expected to result from it. Such a feeling provides the only sound basis for thorough cooperation in the enterprise, and it is only through such cooperation that lasting and helpful results can be expected.

Improvement of instruction through proper organization and articulation of courses Much of the criticism which has been directed at mathematical instruction in the secondary schools has emphasized the view that the courses have been separated into "watertight compartments" and that the program as a whole has lacked unity and continuity. This charge has not been without foundation. The lack of flow and continuity of ideas from course to course has represented a weakness in the traditional program. Most concepts and understandings do not occur in all their fullness at any one time, but rather they emerge and are clarified and enriched by being met and recognized many times in varying contexts. The growth of mathematical ideas, understanding, and insight is a continuing process. Concepts and processes which are of central importance in algebra will already have been encountered in earlier work in arithmetic, and they may also play important roles in geometry and subsequent courses. But as they are met in different situations, with perhaps different terminology and notation, their similarities and their analogous roles need to be brought to the attention of the students. Only if they come to see the connections will the concepts themselves be enriched and the continuity of the program in mathematics become apparent to the students.[1]

This expansion of one's understandings and insights develops as one perceives similarities, analogies, and relationships between new concepts and ones which have been met earlier. This growth takes place, then, as one meets old principles

[1]Phillip S. Jones, The Importance of Articulation, *Bulletin of the National Association of Secondary-School Principals*, **43** (1959), 107–108.

and processes in new situations, sees new applications for old ideas, observes old ideas as special cases of new, or finds that a new and apparently distinct concept has connections with ones learned earlier.

The implications of this for teachers and curriculum planners seem clear. In lesson planning teachers need continually to look both forward and backward. They need to look for those threads of continuity begun in earlier years to which they may attach the ideas which they are helping youngsters to develop. Further, they must look at concepts which are to be developed in later years and search out ways to prepare youngsters to understand them by directing their attention to elementary special cases and introducing, even though briefly and simply, ideas which will grow in importance later.

It is unfortunate for students to feel that the mathematics of the junior high school is unrelated to that of the senior high school and the junior college or to feel that algebra and demonstrative geometry have no points of contact with the earlier work of the seventh and eighth grades. The importance of continuity and articulation in mathematical instruction cannot be too greatly emphasized, and nobody is in a more strategic position to provide leadership in this direction than the mathematics supervisor.

Improving instruction through a program of testing and associated activities

Tests have been used for the evaluation of student achievement as long as formal education has existed, but they have been used largely as a means of assigning marks. It is coming to be recognized, however, that tests can be used not only to measure the results of instruction but also to provide information which can lead to the improvement of instruction, and there is a widespread and growing feeling that this is the most important service that they can render.

Tests provide the most objective basis we have for knowing how well the goals of instruction are being attained and for revealing places in which they are not being attained satisfactorily, whether at individual level, class level, or on a broader scale. Standardized achievement, or survey, tests with broad-based norms can give valuable information on which to form objective and comparative judgments about the effectiveness of instruction. Prognostic tests provide information that may be helpful in counseling students. Practice or drill tests are useful devices for the organization and fixation of details and processes and for the perfection of skills. Tests designed and used for diagnostic purposes can be helpful in revealing weaknesses and helping to chart appropriate remedial teaching.

Thus a comprehensive and well-planned testing program would seem to be important in the scheme of mathematical education. Since the improvement of instruction is the primary function of supervision, it must follow that the planning of such a program of testing, and the advising and guiding of teachers in carrying out such a program, is an important part of supervisory work.

Many teachers have not had the technical training and the experience which are necessary for mapping out a comprehensive testing program wisely, carrying it out systematically, interpreting results, and translating the findings and their implications into appropriate instructional procedures. It is an important function of the departmental supervisior to familiarize the teachers with ways in which they can make tests contribute to the improvement of their teaching and to offer them constructive practical suggestions with regard to the selection or construction of appropriate tests and the interpretation and constructive use of the results.

The place of research in supervision Research has a dual role to play in supervision. Some of the practical instructional problems which face the teacher may find their solutions or partial solutions in the published results of research that has been carried on elsewhere. On the other hand, such problems may legitimately give rise to research in connection with the work within the department itself. In the one case supervision goes to outside sources for help in answering its questions; in the other, it endeavors to answer them for itself.

Much experimental work has been done in the field of teaching of mathematics. However, the published reports of these investigations are for two reasons often of little direct benefit to teachers in service. In the first place, many of them are not readily accessible except in the libraries of colleges and universities. In the second place, many of them are so replete with technicalities and detail that most teachers have neither the time nor the technical background needed to evaluate the validity of the procedures employed and to isolate and interpret the significant findings so that they can be translated into practice. Teachers in active service need to have the results from such studies made available in concise, understandable, and usable form. Therefore, it is a function of the departmental supervisor to familiarize himself with the published researches which are really significant, to digest them, and to abstract and summarize the important findings of these investigations and make them available to the teachers with suggestions for translating them into practice and incorporating them in their instructional procedures.[2]

Many instructional problems, however, can be investigated by the

[2]Beginning in 1953, annual summaries and digests of research studies in the field of mathematics education have been published. These are available through the U.S. Office of Education.

teachers themselves, and such investigations often turn out to be not only useful in themselves but extremely stimulating to the teachers who conduct them. As a rule they will necessarily be limited in scope, and the findings may be of local, rather than general, importance. In some quarters they might not even be dignified by the title of research. This, however, is beside the point. The important thing is that they represent efforts on the part of the teachers to apply scientific procedures to the solution of instructional problems, and in this way they serve to make the teachers acutely aware of the problems and to lead them to make careful analyses pointing toward practical solutions. The following list represents a number of random suggestions of such problems. It could be indefinitely expanded, since every teacher who trains himself to be "problem conscious" will find many other instructional problems arising in connection with his own work. Perhaps, however, these suggestions may help teachers to become more sensitive to the presence of such problems and to the possibilities for investigating them systematically.

1. Compiling a list of specific formulas for interpretation, solution, or evaluation
2. Compiling a list of specific uses of mathematics in industry or in everyday-life situations
3. Studying the effect of various devices for motivation
4. Analysis of errors in algebra
5. Comparing the treatment of selected topics in algebra as presented in different textbooks
6. Comparing the treatment of selected parts of plane geometry as presented in different textbooks
7. Experimenting with the use of enrichment materials in algebra
8. Comparing different ways of teaching verbal problems
9. Experimenting with the use of programmed learning
10. Devising and using diagnostic tests for parts of algebra, geometry, or trigonometry
11. Devising appropriate supplementary activities for superior students in algebra, geometry, or trigonometry
12. Making careful case studies of rapid learners in algebra
13. Making careful case studies of slow learners in geometry
14. Introducing experimentally some of the concepts, terminology, and notation of modern mathematics in traditional courses

Sometimes the efforts of several teachers or of the entire departmental staff may be enlisted in cooperative studies of this sort. Such an arrangement tends to give added interest to the work and to increase the reliability of the results. It is quite possible for investigations conducted by the teachers themselves to yield objective results that will be practically helpful to them in their own work. However, an even greater benefit is derived from the stimulation of professional interest which almost invariably comes about as a result of participation in such investigations.

It is a function of supervision to envisage significant instructional problems, propose them to the teachers for study, and cooperate with the teachers in the formulation of methods for their investigation. The departmental supervisor should take the lead in this. He should have the most comprehensive view of the problems which should be studied and the most discriminating judgment as to which ones are suitable for investigation by the teachers. The administrative officers of the school are not likely to be sufficiently informed about instructional matters within the department, while the teachers are likely to be too greatly preoccupied with the details of their immediate duties to give much attention to the matter of initiating research. The departmental supervisor alone stands in an altogether favorable position to sense fully the need for these activities, enlist the cooperation of the staff members and, if need be, of the administrative officers, and give the greatest measure of encouragement, guidance, and assistance to the teachers in the prosecution of the investigations.

Improvement of instruction through on-the-job supervision of teachers There are two main aspects of in-service training of teachers. One of these is the improvement of teacher competence in the things which they need to do in teaching their classes. The other is the improvement of teacher competence in the subject matter of mathematics itself. This latter aspect will be discussed in the next section.

Things which teachers need to do in conducting the work of their classes include, in broad outline, the following:

1. Planning units of instruction and daily class-period activities
2. Selecting and organizing the materials of instruction
3. Direct expository teaching
4. Making assignments
5. Directing study and training students in effective methods of study
6. Preparing and supervising appropriate drill, review, and maintenance work
7. Appraising the achievement of students
8. Diagnosing difficulties and applying appropriate remedial procedures
9. Adapting instruction to individual differences
10. Providing motivation of effort
11. Attending to routine matters of class management

There are also other activities and considerations which have definite bearing upon the effectiveness of the teacher's classroom work. Among these may be mentioned the comparison and evaluation of textbooks and other instructional materials, the study of aptitudes of individual students, cooperation with the administrative officers of the school, continuance of interest in professional and academic self-improvement, and the maintenance of personal characteristics which will command the respect and cooperative good will of students and colleagues.

The need for the supervision of teachers in service is evident. Even if it might be assumed that all teachers are sufficiently well grounded in the subject matter of mathematics, some of them lack the experience necessary to give them poise and self-assurance and to enable them to plan and conduct the work of their classes with discriminating judgment. Others, more mature in point of experience, will have developed more or less fixed patterns of thought and work which with the passage of time tend to become more rigid and less adaptable to circumstances.

Some tend to become radically enthusiastic over each new technique, device, or point of view, regardless of whether or not its validity and practicability have been established and confirmed. Others, by contrast, tend to be ultraconservative, skeptical of departures from traditional practice, and reluctant to try out new ideas and procedures. Some are too easygoing and do not maintain proper order and system in their classes. In such cases interruptions occur, attention is dissipated, time is wasted, and little is accomplished. Others tend to be "hard-boiled" and lack sympathetic understanding of the motives and reactions of their students.

The foregoing are only examples of situations which might be improved through the counsel of wise and sympathetic supervision. Others could be given: the planning of work, the construction of tests, the keeping of records, various details of class management, clarification of the teacher's relations with his colleagues and with the administrative officers of the school. All these present problems upon which teachers need suggestions from time to time. Most teachers welcome such suggestions if they are given in a tactful manner and in a helpful spirit. Through such service to the teachers the departmental supervisor can contribute materially to the improvement of instruction.

Improvement of instruction through the encouragement of teachers to seek advanced academic study Another major contribution which supervision can make to the improvement of instruction lies in stimulating in teachers a desire to improve their own mathematical backgrounds. That many teachers in the secondary schools are inadequately prepared for their work has been noted by many observers. In spite of increasingly rigorous requirements for certification and assignment, the fact remains that many teachers must teach courses which are not in their fields of specialization and for which in many cases they have little academic preparation. Moreover, the heavy teaching loads which are common in the secondary schools, and the many special duties and activities which teachers are expected to assume, leave little time for study and reflection. Continual attention to the urgent demands of the moment tends to become a habit which may easily obscure the longer view of the job.

This is unfortunate because instruction cannot be at its maximum potential effectiveness unless those who give it continue to strengthen their scholarship in the subject-matter fields in which their teaching lies. The best teaching is that which is intellectually stimulating to both the students and the teacher, and really stimulating teaching is seldom done by a teacher whose perspective embraces no more than the immediate details of the subject matter which he is to teach.

Moreover, mathematics today is not static, even at the high school level. To teach contemporary courses in high school mathematics the teacher simply must have broader and deeper insights into mathematics than would have been the case at the middle of this century. The impact of the "new mathematics" on secondary school courses has been radical and it has been sudden. Many teachers of long experience who have felt thoroughly at home in the traditional courses but who have had no formal study of mathematics since, say, 1950, find themselves on unfamiliar ground and unprepared to cope with the new concepts, terminology, and notation that they are finding in contemporary high school textbooks. The only remedy lies in strengthening their own backgrounds by further study of the subject.

Opportunities for self-improvement in this direction are not lacking. Many colleges and universities offer in summer sessions and in night schools or extension classes courses in contemporary mathematics which would be helpful to teachers. Summer institutes, supported both by industry and by the government, offering mathematics courses especially designed for teachers are becoming increasingly accessible. The same is true of in-service institutes in which the courses are given either on Saturdays or in evening classes. Teachers who for one reason or another find it impossible to pursue any of these organized courses can still plan and carry on systematic programs of study, either as individuals or in organized study groups.

One of the main objectives of the supervisor should be to encourage his teachers continually to extend their mathematical study and to help them find ways of doing so. Mathematics is a growing subject, and at present it is growing with almost explosive rapidity. Experimental work with modern concepts, terminology, notation, and emphases in the grades of the secondary school has progressed to the point where this new material is now rapidly being incorporated in commercially published textbooks. The implication for teachers is clear. Either they must make themselves academically competent to teach the new mathematics with ease and assurance or they will soon find themselves out of date.

Making supervision effective The success of any program of supervision ultimately depends upon the characteristics and the activities of the supervisor. It has been emphasized that if supervision is to eventuate in any thoroughgoing improvement of instruction, it must be a cooperative enterprise in which the cordial participation of the teacher is an indispensable element. It follows that the first major objective of the supervisor must be to gain the confidence of the teachers and acquaint them with the real purposes of the program. This means in effect that the teachers should be made partners in the enterprise and that they should enjoy the full confidence of the supervisor. This will beget mutual understanding and freedom in the interchange of ideas and suggestions and will tend to prevent or dissipate the distrust and suspicion which unfortunately sometimes mark the attitude of teachers toward supervisory activities.

In order to develop this cooperative attitude successfully, the supervisor must be a person of culture, insight, academic and professional ability, and vision. He should have had extensive experience in teaching mathematics in order that he may know and appreciate the many problems which the teachers actually must face in their work and that he may appraise with sympathetic understanding their methods of handling these problems. He must be tactful in his efforts to assist them. He should have a breadth of knowledge and a degree of mastery of the branches and applications of mathematics which will command the respect of the teachers and out of which he may help them to broaden and enrich their academic perspective. He must be familiar with educational movements and developments, both in general and in the field of mathematics in particular. He must know how to appraise educational movements, and he should make their implications clear to his staff.

He should be a master teacher, because there will be times when it will be desirable for him to teach demonstration lessons. The teachers in the department almost certainly will look with skepticism upon the suggestions of one who is unable to incorporate in his own practice those things which he suggests to others. On the other hand, he should manifest at all times a willingness to learn from the teachers, and he should readily acknowledge his appreciation of any helpful suggestions which they are able to give him.

Finally, he must have organizing and executive ability, initiative, and professional vision, because it is he who must take the lead in initiating and guiding the activities directed toward the improvement of instruction within the department and in coordinating and harmonizing the work of the department with the whole educational program of the school. The supervisor who is equipped with these qualifications should have little difficulty in building up a wholesome atmosphere of interest, respect, cooperation, and good will toward the supervisory program, both among the members of the department and among the administrative officers of the school.

EXERCISES

1. Discuss the need for supervision of mathematical instruction in American secondary schools.
2. Discuss some ways in which a supervisor of mathematics could be helpful to teachers through direct individual conferences.
3. Discuss some ways in which a supervisor of mathematics could be helpful to teachers through departmental meetings.
4. Discuss some ways in which a supervisor of mathematics can contribute to the effectiveness of the mathematics program other than through direct personal conferences with teachers and departmental meetings.
5. Enumerate matters which would be especially suitable for discussion at the first departmental meeting of the school year.
6. Make a list of topics which could profitably be discussed at subsequent departmental meetings.
7. Explain how the proper organization and articulation of the courses in mathematics can contribute to the effectiveness of instruction.
8. Why is it a good thing for the teachers and the supervisor to work together on the problem of articulating courses and planning the course of study?
9. Why should both the teachers and the supervisor have a hand in the selection of textbooks and equipment?
10. Describe explicitly some ways in which the supervisor can help the teachers in planning their work for the school year.
11. Discuss the reasons why the in-service training of teachers should be regarded as perhaps the most important function of supervision.
12. Describe clearly the ways in which prognostic testing can contribute to the improvement of instruction in mathematics. What are the limitations and potential dangers of the use of prognostic tests?
13. Give a detailed discussion of the ways in which diagnostic testing can contribute to the improvement of instruction in mathematics. Illustrate if you wish.
14. Discuss ways in which research may contribute toward making supervision effective. What are the supervisor's responsibilities with respect to research in the supervisory program?
15. Discuss the responsibility of the departmental supervisor for keeping his teachers currently informed about significant books, committee reports, articles, and experimental studies which have bearing on the teaching of mathematics.
16. Select one instructional problem which might be investigated by a departmental staff, state its implications, and outline the procedure which you would recommend for conducting the study.
17. Discuss the supervisor's responsibilities in the matter of encouraging teachers to seek academic self-improve-

ment, and point out possible avenues to the achievement of this aim.

18. Enumerate and discuss the ways in which an adequate and convenient system of departmental records can contribute to the effectiveness of supervision.

19. Explain clearly the particular ways in which the supervisor can contribute to the effectiveness of instruction through his status as a liaison officer between the department and the administrative officers of the school.

20. Explain why it is an important function of supervision to see that adequate facilities and favorable working conditions are provided for the teachers.

21. If you were a supervisor of a mathematics department and were required to submit ratings of your teachers to the administrative officers, upon what bases would you feel it proper to rate them?

22. Enumerate characteristics or traits which the supervisor should have in order to carry on his supervisory program to best advantage.

23. In the light of an honest appraisal of your own limitations in training and experience, draw up a statement of specific ways in which you think a competent and sympathetic supervisor could be helpful to you in your effort to become a better teacher of mathematics.

BIBLIOGRAPHY

Allen, Frank B.: Building a Mathematics Program: An Adventure in Cooperative Planning, *Mathematics Teacher*, **49** (1956), 226–234.

Barnes, Ward Ewing, and John William Asher: Predicting Students' Success in Ninth Grade Algebra, *Mathematics Teacher*, **55** (1962), 651–654.

Bernstein, Allen L.: Recent Research in Mathematics Teaching, *Michigan Education Journal*, **40** (1962), 262, 273.

Brannon, M. J.: Individual Mathematics Study Plan, *Mathematics Teacher*, **55** (1962), 52–56.

Brown, Claude H.: "The Teaching of Secondary Mathematics" (New York: Harper & Row, Publishers, Incorporated, 1953), pp. 304–320, 355–373.

Brown, Kenneth E.: In-service Education for Teachers of Mathematics, *Twenty-third Yearbook* (Washington, D.C.: National Council of Teachers of Mathematics, 1954), pp. 238–243.

______: Teaching Load and Qualifications of Mathematics Teachers, *Mathematics Teacher*, **53** (1960), 2–11.

______: Improved Programs of Instruction Require In-service Education for Teachers, *Mathematics Teacher*, **54** (1961), 85–89.

______ and Daniel W. Snader: "In-service Education for High School Mathematics Teachers," OE-20922, Bulletin 1961, no. 10, U.S. Department of Health, Education, and Welfare, Office of Education, 1961).

Bruner, Jerome S.: On Learning Mathematics, *Mathematics Teacher*, **53** (1960), 610–619.

Carnahan, Walter H., Mildred Kieffer, and Veryl Schult: "The Supervisor of Mathematics: His Role in the Improvement of Mathematics Instruction" (Washington, D.C.: National Council of Teachers of Mathematics, 1959).

Clark, John R. (Editor): "Emerging Practices in Mathematics Education," *Twenty-second Yearbook* (Washington, D.C.: National Council of Teachers of Mathematics, 1954).

Cliffe, Marian C.: Mathematics Evaluation in a Large City, *Bulletin of the National Association of Secondary-School Principals*, **43** (1959), 161–165.

De Vault, M. Vere, W. Robert Houston, and Claude C. Boyd: Do Consultant Services Make a Difference? *School Science and Mathematics*, **63** (1963), 285–290.

Fehr, Howard F. (Editor): "The Learning of Mathematics: Its Theory and Practice," *Twenty-first Yearbook* (Washington, D.C.: National Council of Teachers of Mathematics, 1953).

______: Psychology of Learning in the Junior High School, *Mathematics Teacher*, **49** (1956), 235–240.

Hawthorne, Frank S.: The Role of the State Supervisor of Mathematics, *Mathematics Teacher*, **53** (1960), 448–450.

Hirschi, L. Edwin: Encouraging Creativity in the Mathematics Classroom, *Mathematics Teacher*, **56** (1963), 79–83.

Hoel, Lesta: A Supervisor Plans a Program through Self-evaluation, *Mathematics Teacher*, **49** (1956), 347–352.

Johnson, Donovan A.: Readability of Mathematics Books, *Mathematics Teacher*, **50** (1957), 105–110.

———: Enriching Mathematics Instruction with Creative Activities, *Mathematics Teacher*, **55** (1962), 238–242.

Jorgensen, Paul: In-service Institutes for Mathematics Teachers, *Mathematics Teacher*, **51** (1958), 613–614.

Kidd, Kenneth P.: Improving the Learning of Mathematics, *Mathematics Teacher*, **47** (1954), 393–400.

Kieffer, Mildred, and Anna Marie Evans: "How to Develop a Teaching Guide in Mathematics" (Washington, D.C.: National Council of Teachers of Mathematics, 1955).

Kimball, Roland B.: Improvement of Mathematics and Science Instruction in New Hampshire, *School Science and Mathematics*, **57** (1957), 529–535.

Kinney, Lucien Blair, and C. Richard Purdy: "Teaching Mathematics in the Secondary School" (New York: Holt, Rinehart and Winston, Inc., 1952), pp. 290–368.

Kinsella, John J.: Is Research in Mathematics Education Really Necessary? *Mathematics Teacher*, **50** (1957), 300–301.

Levy, Norton: A Community of Consultants, *Mathematics Teacher*, **55** (1962), 643–648.

Mayor, John R.: Some Thoughts on Teacher Education, *Mathematics Teacher*, **49** (1956), 143–144.

Mueller, Francis J.: Five Recommendations to School Systems for Improving Secondary School Mathematics Instruction, *Mathematics Teacher*, **55** (1962), 637–642.

Reeve, William D.: "Mathematics for the Secondary School" (New York: Holt, Rinehart and Winston, Inc., 1954), pp. 96–122.

Secondary School Curriculum Committee of the National Council of Teachers of Mathematics, Report of: The Secondary Mathematics Curriculum, *Mathematics Teacher*, **52** (1959), 389–417.

Simpson, Ray H.: Mathematics Teachers and Self-evaluation Procedures, *Mathematics Teacher*, **56** (1963), 238–244.

Swain, Henry: "How to Study Mathematics" (Washington, D.C.: National Council of Teachers of Mathematics, 1961).

"Teacher Training Film Series" (bulletin on SMSG mathematics—list of titles) (Minneapolis: University of Minnesota, 1962).

"The Growth of Mathematical Ideas: Grades K–12," *Twenty-fourth Yearbook* (Washington, D.C.: National Council of Teachers of Mathematics, 1959), pp. 461–498.

Wallen, Rev. C. J.: Stressing the Creative Aspects of Mathematics in Teaching the Gifted Child, *Mathematics Teacher*, **55** (1962), 243–248.

West, Jeff, and Agnes Y. Rickey: Miami Area In-service Programs for Mathematics Teachers, *Mathematics Teacher*, **54** (1961), 89–90.

Wolfe, Raphael W.: Organizing the Mathematics Department in the Montebello Junior High School, *Mathematics Teacher*, **51** (1958), 287–291.

Zlot, William: Report of the Textbook Evaluation Project at Yeshiva University, *American Mathematical Monthly*, **69** (1962), 428–430.

TEN

The professionally prepared teacher of mathematics

POSSIBLY THE MOST critical single element in the composite structure of an effective mathematics program in the secondary school is the teacher. A poorly prepared teacher can destroy the effectiveness of any carefully selected and well-organized curriculum with inadequate and unenthusiastic instruction, inaccurate and uninformed interpretation, and indifferent and negative attitudes. On the other hand, a professionally prepared teacher can use even an inadequately structured curriculum to build an instructional program of significant merit. What then constitutes an adequate program for the professional preparation of teachers of secondary mathematics?

The professional preparation of teachers of secondary mathematics There are two equally important aspects of any true profession, viz., significant knowledge and effective technique. One cannot be efficiently professional if there is any distinct weakness in either aspect. A truly functional program of professional preparation must therefore place emphasis on the acquiring of knowledge significant to the chosen profession and also on the acquaintance with and use of the more efficient techniques of that profession.

The Mathematical Association of America, Inc., and the National

Council of Teachers of Mathematics, as well as certain more localized groups, have made notable efforts through their committees and publications to improve the situation as far as mathematics is concerned. The interest of these groups has been directed to the better preparation of teachers as well as to the improvement of the curriculum. The fact remains, however, that the teaching of secondary mathematics in the United States is hardly an established profession. There are individuals teaching secondary mathematics whose academic preparation includes neither a major nor a minor in mathematics. They have no great interest in the subject and, in their teaching, can do no more than treat it in a superficial and fragmentary way. They have little appreciation of the values of mathematics, of the role it has played in the evolution of our civilization, or of its possibilities for integrated development. Likewise, there are those who are deficient in their preparation for teaching because of failure to keep informed in the newer developments in mathematics. Some of this failure to keep abreast of the times is due, unfortunately, to inadequate opportunity but, regrettably, much of it is due to indifferent attitude. There are many teachers, however, whose preparation has been adequate in the field of mathematics itself, but who are unhappy and inefficient in their work because they are required to teach one or more classes in other subjects. Their programs of preparation should have been broad enough to enable them to teach in at least one additional field. There are still other teachers who know their subject well but who, because of their lack of patience with student difficulties and their unwillingness to adjust their teaching to the varying abilities of different students, actually destroy the interest of many students in mathematics when, under more favorable conditions, it might have been made to flourish. Such teachers lack that professional attitude which should impel them to discard any sense of intellectual superiority and view the subject through the eyes of the immature student so that they might patiently guide and encourage him in his efforts and stimulate his interest in further exploration of the field of mathematics.

Masterful scholarship in a body of relevant knowledge is an absolute essential for effective teaching, but it must be supplemented by a proficiency in the use of efficient techniques of instruction. Neither should be emphasized to the exclusion of the other, but a proper balance should be maintained throughout the preparation program.[1] We do not want teachers of mathematics to be "teachers who have nothing to teach," nor do we want them to be "mere purveyors of knowledge and promoters of skill."

[1]"Report of the Commission on Mathematics" (New York: College Entrance Examination Board, 1959), pp. 50–58.

Report of the Secondary School Curriculum Committee, *Mathematics Teacher*, **52** (1959), 389–417.

Significant knowledge There is a trichotomy of knowledge significant to the teacher of mathematics which might be classified under the headings of general knowledge, professional knowledge, and specialized knowledge. We are living in an age in which events take place very rapidly. This rapidity of development and its implications for future change tend not only to stagger the imagination but also to encourage a satisfaction in superficiality of information. Things happen too fast for any individual to be able to attempt a very thorough and systematic acquaintance with the fundamentals of all lines of development. We have to be satisfied with a type of superficial information along some lines. It is for such reasons as this that the teacher of mathematics should have a broad educational background against which to project his thinking and in which to orient his appreciation of values. Such an informational background should be related to the major areas of human experience and designed to build up a more intelligent understanding of the part mathematics has played in the evolution of modern civilization and a deeper appreciation of its relation to social progress.

A professional attitude should be a *sine qua non* for every teacher of mathematics. The term "professional attitude" is interpreted here to mean an enthusiastic interest in mathematics as a chosen field of study and service, an inspired concept of the value of mathematics in the structure of civilization, and an eager readiness to interpret carefully and thoughtfully those fundamental laws, mechanical processes, generalizing procedures, and possibilities of practical applications which so definitely characterize mathematics as a field of study and endeavor. In addition to providing a general education for cultural background, the program for the professional preparation of teachers of mathematics should equip such a teacher with an integrated philosophy of education, a devotion to teaching as a profession, and a sense of responsibility for the contributions he will be expected to make in his chosen field of work. This body of professional knowledge should be provided through courses designed to acquaint the individual with the place and function of education in our social order, with the interrelationships that exist between the various professions, and with the manifold opportunities for service which present themselves to teachers; to build up a psychological foundation for sympathetic understanding of the mental, physical, and social characteristics of those to be taught; to help the individual become informed concerning the advantages and disadvantages in the use of various forms of teaching media, such as models, films, filmstrips, tape recorders, scrambled textbooks, teaching machines, and television; and to provide opportunities for acquiring a safe minimum of teaching skill through observation of good teaching techniques and actual classroom practice under sympathetic but critical supervision.

Although the cultural background and the body of professional knowledge are essential elements to the program of professional preparation of teachers of mathematics, such a program must not overlook the fact that sound scholarship is a fundamental qualification of the teacher. This scholarship, however, should be *relevant* to the problem of teaching. From the point of view of the teacher of mathematics, what materials provide opportunity for development of *relevant* scholarship? The scholarship that is of service in the advancement of mathematical thought and research is not, in every case, the same as that which can be of service in the education of adolescents and immature thinkers. It is almost proverbial to state that "he who learns that he may know and he that learns that he may teach are standing in quite different mental attitudes."[2]

The specialist in mathematics has need of a synthetic type of scholarship in which he seeks mastery not only of the fundamentals of mathematical thought but also of a closely interwoven chain of logic and of methods of making deductions and implications. His only need for the analytic type of scholarship is as a tool to be used in the aid of mathematical research. He is not primarily concerned with the questions of the place of mathematics in the educational program or of the practical value of mathematics to the average man. He is concerned with mathematical implications rather than with educational implications or practical applications of mathematics except, possibly, by the actuary, engineer, or other professional users of applied mathematics. He is the producer of mathematics.

On the other hand, the teacher of mathematics is the seller of mathematics. It is he who must convince the consumer of the value of his subject and, through the medium of efficient service, secure and retain consumers. He is constantly confronted with questions of the value of mathematics as an asset to the individual and a significant element in the program of general education. His interest in mathematics must embrace its educational implications and practical applications as well as its intrinsic subject appeal. Thus the preparation of the teacher of mathematics should emphasize that type of scholarship which seeks to integrate the subject with broad fields of learning and relate it to general human activity and interest. The teacher must learn to evaluate mathematics in the light of its role in the history of civilization, its contribution to the present social order, and its relation to future progress.

Furthermore, since it is to be his responsibility to assist immature learners in the mastery of mathematics, the prospective teacher of

[2]H. S. Tarbell, Report of the Sub-committee on the Training of Teachers, *Proceedings of the National Education Association* (Washington, D.C.: National Education Association, 1895), p. 240.

mathematics should not only strive for proficient mastery of the subject but also make every effort to be conscious of the processes by which he arrives at that mastery. He should pause at significant points for moments of reflection in which he should attempt to analyze the learning processes involved and evaluate the materials studied. Competent scholarship, which emphasizes understanding and mastery of fundamentals, must be constantly emphasized. These fundamentals will vary somewhat, according to whether the prospective teacher expects to teach in the elementary school, junior high school, senior high school, or junior college. To supplement this body of minimum essentials every teacher of mathematics should be encouraged to acquire a certain synthetic proficiency in some chosen line of mathematical endeavor to serve as a reserve of information which he might frequently use as an aid to individual exploration in the unknown realms of mathematical knowledge or in the expanding domain of significant applications of mathematical principles and techniques.

Relevant scholarship for the teacher of secondary mathematics The teacher of secondary mathematics should have some appreciation of the part that mathematics has played throughout the centuries of progress. Furthermore, he should have those contacts with the subject matter and history of mathematics that would enable him to formulate an intelligent notion of the meanings of mathematics. In 1901 Bertrand Russell defined mathematics in words that are superficially facetious but fundamentally significant when he said: "Mathematics may be defined as the subject in which we never know what we are talking about, nor whether what we are saying is true."[3] In discussing this definition Bell says that it has four great merits: (1) it shocks the self-conceit out of common sense, (2) it emphasizes the entirely abstract character of mathematics, (3) it reduces all mathematics and the more mature sciences to postulational forms, and (4) it administers a resounding parting salute to the doddering tradition that mathematics is the science of number, quantity, and measurement.[4] Mario Pieri is responsible for the statement that "mathematics is an hypothetico-deductive system," which merely means that mathematics is a system of logical processes whereby conclusions are deduced from whatever fundamental assumptions and definitions there may be hypothesized. To Benjamin Peirce goes the credit for expressing these thoughts in the

[3]Bertrand Russell, Recent Work on the Principles of Mathematics, *International Monthly*, **4** (1901), 84.

[4]E. T. Bell, "The Queen of the Sciences" (Baltimore: The Williams & Wilkins Company, 1931), pp. 16–17.

more explicit form: "Mathematics is the science which draws necessary conclusions."[5] To think mathematically is to free oneself by abstraction from any peculiarity of subject matter and to make inferences and deductions justified by fundamental premises.

According to Shaw,[6] there are four significant methods of mathematics which might be stated as follows:

1. Scientific, leading to generalizations of widening scope
2. Intuitive, leading to an insight into subtler depths
3. Deductive, leading to a permanent statement and rigorous form
4. Inventive, leading to the ideal element, and creation of new realms

The competent teacher of mathematics should realize that in any system of constructive thought the validity of the conclusions rests entirely upon the validity and consistency of the assumptions and definitions upon which the conclusions are based. It is important that students should have this point of view, and the teacher should make every reasonable effort to assist them in acquiring it. From a logical point of view the basic characteristics of a set of fundamental assumptions are: (1) *consistency*—no two statements should contradict each other; (2) *independence*—no one statement should follow as a logical consequence from any or all of the remaining statements; (3) *completeness*—it should not be possible, without further extensions of the set of primitive elements, to add another postulate which is both independent of, and consistent with, the given set of postulates; and (4) *categoricalness*—any two models of the set are isomorphic: that is, there exists a one-to-one correspondence between the two respective interpretations of the primitive elements of the set which preserves the basic relations among, and operations upon, these elements. Since definitions must be free from circularity, they cannot all be stated explicitly. This means, of course, that there must be a basic set of undefined terms and concepts. The intuitive acceptance of their implicit meanings forms the foundation for the construction of all explicit definitions of the system. An appreciation of this dependence upon fundamental assumptions and definitions and also upon previously established theorems should help to develop an if-then mental attitude which should function in a more intelligent interpretation of human events. A student in the secondary school is by no means to be taught the philosophical and logical aspects of non-Euclidean geometry, but the teacher should be familiar with the high points in the history of Euclid's famous fifth postulate. He should know of the efforts of mathe-

[5]Benjamin Peirce, "Linear Associative Algebra," sec. 1, lithographed, 1870. Reprinted in *American Journal of Mathematics*, **4** (1881), 97.

[6]J. B. Shaw, "Lectures on the Philosophy of Mathematics" (La Salle, Ill.: The Open Court Publishing Company, 1918), p. 11.

maticians to demonstrate the dependence of this parallel postulate upon the remaining postulates of Euclid's fundamental set. He should appreciate the fact that Lobachevskian and Riemannian geometries are logically just as sound as the commonly accepted Euclidean geometry; that, although the Euclidean postulates are accepted because they seem to conform more nearly to the everyday experiences of the world in which we live, in Poincaré's world of changing temperatures the parallel postulate would be absurd.[7] The teacher so informed would have a significant appreciation of geometry as a form of postulational thinking and thus be better equipped to enhance his teaching by a more harmonious and effective coordination of sensible pedagogy and sound logic.

Geometry was used in both Egypt and Babylonia as an art of measuring in connection with agriculture, irrigation, and architecture; thus it was entirely empirical and intuitive without any idea of logical demonstration. Thales (ca. 640–546 B.C.), of Miletus, was the first to conceive of the idea of establishing truths through formal demonstration and, in his Ionian school, geometry was studied not for its own sake but as a general preparation for the study of philosophy. It was Pythagoras (ca. 572–501 B.C.), a disciple of Thales, and his followers who achieved the arithmetization of geometry in the famous Pythagorean theorem. Plato (429–348 B.C.) introduced to geometricians that powerful tool of the logicians, the analytical method of proof, and one of his most brilliant pupils, Eudoxus (ca. 408–355 B.C.), introduced the form of demonstration known as the "indirect method of proof."

In about 300 B.C. Euclid wrote his famous "Elements," in which he made an effort to present a systematic collection of the then-current mathematical knowledge. Though mathematicians, in recent years, have been able to point clearly to inaccuracies and inadequacies of Euclid's effort,[8] it still remains true that possibly his greatest contribution to mathematics was the coordination of all known propositions in a simple but logical sequence. This gave to geometry its characterization as a pattern for postulational thinking. Under the influence of Euclid the center of interest in mathematics shifted from Athens to Alexandria. The first Alexandrian school, of which Euclid, Archimedes, and Apollonius were members, lasted until the beginning of the Christian era, during which time mathematics was studied primarily for the

[7]J. W. Young, "Fundamental Concepts of Algebra and Geometry" (New York: The Macmillan Company, 1911), pp. 15–25.

[8]Felix Klein, "Elementary Mathematics from an Advanced Standpoint," II (New York: The Macmillan Company, 1939), pp. 188–208.

Albert E. Meder, Jr., What's Wrong with Euclid? *Mathematics Teacher*, **51** (1958), 578–584.

Bertrand Russell, "Principles of Mathematics," 2d ed. (New York: W. W. Norton & Company, Inc., 1938), p. 161.

interest in the subject itself. The second Alexandrian school, to which belonged such men as Serenus, Menelaus, Ptolemy, Pappus, and Proclus, flourished during the first six centuries of the Christian era. During this period, when utility was the chief objective for the study of geometry, the ideals of education sank to a very low level and there set in an intellectual stagnation that continued to prevent any significant mathematical progress until the Renaissance period.

In order to appreciate the magnificent structure of geometry, one not only must be familiar with this period of synthetic development but must realize that there are three other important periods of geometrical history, viz., (1) the period of analytic geometry, foreshadowed by the work of Archimedes (ca. 225 B.C.), but in reality exerting a significant influence only after the publication of the researches of Descartes (1596–1650) and Fermat (1601–1665), (2) the period of application of calculus to geometry, and (3) the renaissance of pure geometry which began with the nineteenth century.[9] The teacher of secondary mathematics should have firsthand information concerning these epochs of geometrical history as well as direct contact with the outstanding elements of each. He should know something of the systematized use of algebra that characterizes Cartesian geometry as well as the applications of the techniques of infinitesimal analysis to perfect the study of the relationships existing between the points and lines that generate geometrical configurations. He should know something of the theory of projectivity first enunciated by Poncelet (1788–1867) in 1822 and of Gergonne's (1771–1859) principle of duality, which so definitely enriches the theory of the united position of point and line. Such names as Desargues (1593–1662), Pascal (1623–1662), Ceva (1647–1736), Simson (1687–1768), Euler (1707–1873), Malfatti (1731–1807), Legendre (1752–1833), Monge (1746–1818), Brianchon (1785–1864), von Staudt (1798–1867), and Steiner (1796–1863) should carry significant connotations for him because they represent progressive development in the field of modern synthetic geometry.

Any modern treatment of geometry at the secondary level of instruction will be couched in the language of sets. Point is the basic undefined element. Space, plane, and line are treated as sets of points. The line segment $\overline{AB}$ is the set of points consisting of the two points A and B and all points between them. The ray $\overrightarrow{AB}$ is the union of the line segment $\overline{AB}$ and all points P of the line $\overleftrightarrow{AB}$ such that B is between A and P. An angle is the union of two distinct rays with a common endpoint. A line contained in a plane separates the plane into two disjoint sets of points, each of which is called a "half-plane." A dihedral angle is the union of a line and two half-planes. These concepts are merely illustrative of the

[9] D. E. Smith, "History of Mathematics" (Boston: Ginn and Company, 1925), vol. II, p. 331.

need for a clear understanding of the concept of set and of the basic vocabulary of the language of sets in the study of geometry. Similar illustrations can be exhibited as characteristic of all other areas of secondary mathematics.

Historically, arithmetic developed out of a need for a system of counting, just as geometry found its origin in the necessity for systematic methods of measurement. The teacher of mathematics should know something of the history and nature of number, the foundation of all arithmetic. The beginnings of the concept of number are hidden in the obscurity of time, but there seems to be evidence that some idea of number and patterns for its use preceded written history by thousands of years.[10] The evolution of our numeral system has been a real "survival of the fittest" struggle among various scales and systems of notation and is more or less an anatomical accident. Had the gods decreed that man should have 6 fingers on each hand and 6 toes on each foot, the human race would probably do all of its counting and calculating on the basis of 12 instead of 10. Some argue that this would have worked to the advantage of the practical man, since 12 has more possibilities of factorization than has 10. If, however, the mathematician should decree the base of the number system, he would probably choose a prime, for it is claimed that then there would be economy in symbols, simplification in operations, and eradication of ambiguities.

The definition of abstract number and its elaborate theory possibly form no part of the necessary preparation of the teacher of secondary mathematics. The teacher should, however, have his thinking about the system of natural numbers oriented within the context of Peano's postulates[11] or an equivalent system.[12] He needs to have a basic understanding of how the process of counting and the concept of the number of objects in a collection give rise to the system of natural numbers. This concept of natural number creates an abstract symbol for the number of elements in a nonempty set of distinct elements which, in turn, becomes the designation of a characteristic property of sets of objects between which the correspondence is one-to-one. Furthermore, he should have at his ready command the basic laws of operation and should understand how these laws and the principle of permanence rationalize the extension of the number system first to integers, then to rational numbers, real numbers, and complex numbers. He should recognize the teaching responsibilities accompanying

[10]Tobias Dantzig, "Number: The Language of Science" (New York: The Macmillan Company, 1930), p. 11.

[11]Howard Eves and Carroll V. Newsom: "An Introduction to the Foundations and Fundamental Concepts of Mathematics" (New York: Holt, Rinehart and Winston, Inc., 1958), p. 203.

[12]*Ibid.*, p. 195.

each basic extension. Also, he should be able to transmit to his students some comprehension of the cultural significance of the evolution of this extension, along with the concomitant introduction of place value and the concept of a symbol for the empty set.

Etymologically, algebra means the theory of restitution (or transposition) and adjustment—in other words, a theory of equations.[13] In its modern garb it loses none of this significance but, through its laws of operations upon symbolic forms, expands further into a systematic method for the expression and examination of existing relationships. According to Nesselmann,[14] the history of algebra divides itself into three periods: (1) the rhetorical, (2) the syncopated, and (3) the symbolic. The rhetorical period was characterized by the fact that words were written out in full and no symbols were used. The oldest Egyptian, Babylonian, Arabian, Persian, and Italian algebraists represent this period. In the syncopated period the presentation was similar in literary type to that of the rhetorical period, but abbreviations were used. This period began with Diophantus (ca. 275) and extended up to the middle of the seventeenth century. In the symbolic period abbreviations gave way to signs and symbols.

The following examples show this transition from pure rhetorical algebra to that of modern compact symbolism; they show how the same equation would have been written by:[15]

Regiomontanus, A.D. 1464:

3 Census et 6 demptis 5 rebus aequatur zero

Pacioli, A.D. 1494:

3 Census p. 6 de 5 rebus ae 0

Vieta, A.D. 1591:

3 in *A* quad − 5 in *A* plano + 6 aequatur 0

Stevinus, A.D. 1585:

3② − 5① + 6⊙ = 0

Descartes, A.D. 1637:

$$3x^2 - 5x + 6 = 0$$

There are, of course, no clear-cut lines of demarcation between the three periods. Diophantus, in fact, used certain features of all three.[16]

The teacher of secondary mathematics should be acquainted with the extended domain of algebra under the freedom of symbolic abstraction. Under such freedom it is possible to define many different algebras[17] and their companion arithmetics. The concept of a basic algebraic

[13]Smith, *op. cit.*, pp. 388–390.

[14]G. H. F. Nesselmann, "*Die Algebra der Griechen*" (Berlin: G. Reimer, 1842), pp. 301–305.

[15]L. Hogben, "Mathematics for the Million" (New York: W. W. Norton & Company, 1937), p. 303.

[16]Smith, *op. cit.*, p. 379.

[17]Bell, *op. cit.*, p. 37.

structure arises from the recognition of the fact that, with the ordinary definition of addition and multiplication, the properties of associativity, commutativity, and distributivity characterize these operations not only with natural numbers, rational numbers, real numbers, irrational numbers, and complex numbers but also with polynomials and even more general types of functions as well as with many other sets of elements. Even with slight modifications in the definitions of the basic operations these properties continue to be the basic laws as the operations are applied to more general sets of elements. Thus the concept of algebra is extended beyond a mere symbolization of arithmetic. It assumes individual stature as a definitive structure with specified elements, defined operations, and basic postulates. Such abstractions identify algebra as a truly hypothetico-deductive system, and there come into existence algebras of many different types, such as the algebra of matrices, the algebra of symmetry, the algebra of transformations, and the algebra of sets. The concepts of group, ring, integral domain, and field are basic to the study of algebraic structure. Furthermore, more careful and detailed attention to some of the fundamental properties and techniques of the algebra of inequalities is one of the important innovations of the revolution in mathematics that is effecting such great change in the high school curriculum. It has been recognized that a basic understanding of inequalities and a facility in their use are desirable goals of instruction in mathematics. Students whose programs have been so fortified will be not only stronger students of algebra but also better able to cope with problems from geometry, analysis, approximation procedures, linear programming, and many other areas of mathematical endeavor.

The algebra of the secondary school is the algebra of real and complex numbers. If we restrict this algebra to one of the real numbers, we shall have one that is abstractly identical with the metric geometry of three dimensions. This identity is accomplished through the correlation of points on a line with real numbers, a concept that was suggested to the mathematical world by Descartes. Among an infinitude of significant achievements this equivalence has enabled modern mathematicians to set up the criterion of constructibility and thus through the algebraic analysis of geometrical relations to prove definitely that it is impossible to trisect an arbitrary angle, duplicate a cube, or "square a circle" by using *only* the compass and the unmarked straightedge.

From the secondary school point of view the graph, equation, and concept of function are extremely important. The preparation of the teacher of secondary mathematics should be such that these will be intelligently correlated and understood. The part that coefficients of a function play in determining the shape of its graph, the techniques of construction and proper interpretation of the graph and its application to the solution of numerical equations, and the significance of the graph in the discussion of simultaneous equations consitute some of the contributions that advanced training should make to the professional equipment of the secondary school teacher. He should know the implications of the fundamental theorems of algebra and arithmetic and some of the more important theorems concerning the relation existing between roots of equations and the coefficients, as well as the application of the elementary theory of determinants and eliminants to the systematic study of equations.

In the words of Prof. E. H. Moore, "functionality is the relation or (mathematical) law of connection between two or more quantities or numbers subject to simultaneous and interdependent continuous variation."[18] This concept of the interdependence of magnitudes was recognized by the early Greeks and Egyptians. Two of the most primitive forms in which we find functional dependence expressed are in area formulas and formulas for the relation between arcs and chords. From these crude beginnings the development was slow, and it was not until the latter part of the seventeenth century that the word "function" was associated with the concept of dependence.

Descartes furnished the crystallizing influence in his discovery and development of coordinate geometry. In 1637 he published his "Geometry,"[19] in which he systematized the method of applying algebra to geometry, introduced the notion of variables and constants into the study of geometrical relations, conceived of curves as generated by a moving point, referred these curves to two intersecting lines, and represented them by equations involving two variables, the relation of these variables being determined by the distances from the two lines of reference. It was this notion of expressing curves by algebraic equations that made possible the step from geometry to analysis and thus paved the way for calculus. A few years later Leibniz introduced the word "function" to designate magnitudes involved in Descartes's idea of curves generated by a moving point. The researches of Newton and Leibniz made extensive use of this new concept of the locus of a moving point and by application of the techniques of infinitesimal analysis gave new significance to the implications of functional dependence.

It is interesting to note that Cartesianism also provided the basis for the modern refinement of the concept of function which subdues or

[18]E. H. Moore, Cross Section Paper as a Mathematical Instrument, *School Review*, **14** (May, 1906), p. 318.

[19]This work, which appeared as an appendix to the *Discours de la méthode*, was divided into three books. The first dealt with the products of lines; the second defined two types of curves, geometric and mechanic, and treated of tangents and normals; and the third discussed roots and transformations of equations.

subordinates the idea of dependence to the more fundamental idea of relation. The Cartesian frame of reference composed of two intersecting number lines provides the machinery, and the language of sets provides the terminology, for more precise descriptions of many fundamental mathematical concepts. While relation and function are not necessarily restricted to dealing with numbers, the associations expressed through the Cartesian pairing of numbers in graphs provides a basis for a more precise description of the correspondence existing between different sets of elements. This is accomplished through the mechanism of *ordered pairs* such as (x,y), where x is the first element and y the second element of the ordered pair. A *relation* then is merely a set of ordered pairs, and a *function* is a relation in which there is associated with each first element one and only one second element. Thus the set (1,−1), (1,1), (4,−2), (4,2), (9,−3), (9,3) would be a relation, while the set (−1,1), (1,1), (−2,4), (2,4), (−3,9), (3,9) would be a function.[20] The teacher should have a clear comprehension of these more modern ideas and be prepared to give an informal interpretation of them to his students.

Along with the study of analytic geometry the study of trigonometry and differential and integral calculus affords unlimited opportunities for coming into contact with the fundamental principles that are essential to an appreciative and intelligent comprehension of the basic interrelationships which give significant structure to mathematics as a field of thought. The teacher of secondary mathematics should be not only familiar with the numerical aspects of trigonometry as an effective tool in making indirect measurements but also thoroughly informed concerning the fundamental analytic properties of trigonometric functions and the tremendous import of their applicative value. Also he should know how the method of exhaustions, used by Antiphon (ca. 430 B.C.), Archimedes (ca. 225 B.C.), and others in their efforts to effect the quadrature of the circle, evolved through the method of indivisibles of Cavalieri (1598–1647) and Roberval (1602–1675) into the infinitesimal analysis of Newton (1642–1727) and Leibniz (1646–1716). Finally, familiarity with the power of calculus as a generalizing technique and its importance as a research instrument in pure and applied mathematics should be considered as a significant part of the subject-matter preparation of the teacher of secondary mathematics.[21]

[20]For a good presentation of the more modern concept of function see Kenneth D. May and Henry Van Engen, Relations and Functions, *Twenty-fourth Yearbook* (Washington, D.C.: National Council of Teachers of Mathematics, 1959), pp. 65–110.

[21]For the individual who is interested in pursuing the discussion of this section still further the bibliographies of this chapter and Chapter 3 provide supplementary readings.

Significant professional techniques The demands made on the teacher of secondary mathematics in the modern program of education make it absolutely essential that he know the orientation of his field of work in the entire secondary program; that he be familiar with significant objectives and problems in secondary mathematics; that he know the techniques of selection of textbooks, workbooks, and other teaching equipment; that he be familiar with the fundamental philosophy of significant evaluation of instruction; that he be skilled in the construction, use, and interpretation of tests—factual and functional, standardized and nonstandardized, objective and essay; that he be acquainted with various instructional techniques and know when and how to use them for maximum efficiency; and that he be prepared to assume his share of the responsibility in the pupil-guidance program.

The teacher of secondary mathematics must be thoroughly familiar with the complementary problems of transfer of training and individual differences. He must know the major sources of student difficulties and how to diagnose these difficulties and plan programs of remedial teaching; he must know how to plan an instructional program and how to adapt this program to different ability groups; he must be enthusiastically interested in mathematics and know the fundamental principles of the psychology of motivation; and he should know how to detect and remedy inefficient study habits and techniques. Finally, the teacher of secondary mathematics should be well versed in the fundamentals of the psychology of learning and their application to materials and methods for better instruction in mathematics of the secondary school.

We might list the above as the necessary technical equipment of the efficient teacher. As a highly desirable, but not absolutely necessary, part of the program of professional education of the prospective teacher we should list skill in the use and interpretation of the techniques of educational research and experimentation. The teacher should be equipped to read, interpret, and evaluate the published results of experimental investigation and make use of significant findings in the improvement of his own teaching procedures. It is also very desirable that he be equipped to pursue scientific investigations in connection with his own program and interpret intelligently his findings for the benefit of others.

The well-prepared teacher of mathematics The foregoing discussion presents what might be called a minimum ideal for the preparation of mathematics teachers. It represents a program which the prospective teacher should at least approximate as nearly as possible. Most beginning teachers, however, must teach in small schools, and in small schools practical considerations generally make it necessary for teachers to teach one or more courses outside their fields of major interest and specialization. Consequently the prospective teacher of mathematics is virtually obliged by circumstances to prepare himself in at least one other field, and this may compel him to forego some of the advanced work in mathematics which would constitute a desirable part of his preparation.

Recognizing such varieties of demand and keeping in mind the ideal of effective instruction by an enthusiastic teacher with an adequate background of preparation, the Secondary School Curriculum Committee has presented what it recommends as an appropriate guide for the training of teachers of secondary mathematics.[22]

In view of current curriculum demands teachers of mathematics in grades seven through twelve will need to have competence in (1) analysis – trigonometry, plane and solid analytic geometry, and calculus; (2) foundations of mathematics – theory of sets, mathematical or symbolic logic, postulational systems, real and complex number systems; (3) algebra – matrices and determinants, theory of numbers, theory of equations, and structure of algebra; (4) geometry – Euclidean and non-Euclidean, metric and projective, synthetic and analytic; (5) statistics – probability and statistical inference; (6) applications – mechanics, theory of games, linear programming, and operations research.

Ideally every teacher of secondary mathematics should have completed successfully a five-year program, emphasizing the above areas and culminating in the master's degree. As a minimum, teachers of mathematics at the seventh- and eighth-grade levels should have completed successfully a program of at least eighteen semester hours, including six semester hours of calculus, in courses selected from the above areas. Also as a minimum, teachers of mathematics in grades nine through twelve should have completed successfully a program of at least twenty-four semester hours, including a full-year program in calculus, in courses selected from the above areas. Both programs should contain fundamental treatments of relevant topics from the foundations of mathematics and probability and statistics. These programs in mathematics should be supplemented by a basic program in education and psychology. As a minimum, a teacher should have completed successfully eighteen semester hours, including student teaching in mathematics, in such courses as: a methods course in the teaching of mathematics, psychology of learning (with particular reference to adolescents), psychology of adjustment (mental hygiene), and tests and measurements. This total program of specialization should be based on a strong program of general education.

The Sub-committee on Teacher Certification of the Cooperative Committee on the Teaching of Science and Mathematics of the

[22]Report of the Secondary School Curriculum Committee, *Mathematics Teacher*, **52** (1959), 414–415.

American Association for the Advancement of Science has made the following recommendations in its report:[23]

Part 5. Suggested Courses in Mathematics and Science for High School Teachers of Mathematics (given in semester hours)

Suggested courses	A	B	C	D	E	F	4-year total		5th year		5-year total	
							Math	Supporting Science	Math	Supporting Science	Math	Supporting Science
Teachers of math only (senior high school)	12	6	3	3	3	3	30	18	12	6	42	24
Teachers of math only (junior high school)	9	3	3	3	3	3	24	12	9	3	33	15
Teachers with math minor (junior or senior high school)	9	3	3			3	18					

Notes on Part 5:

1. *Teaching Area:* There are three teaching areas distinguished in this report:
   1. Mathematics in the senior high school.
   2. Mathematics in the junior high school.
   3. Mathematics combined with some other field such as a science, history, or some other field at the junior or senior high level. Even though teaching assignments are not as desirable as those with only mathematics, such combinations must be recognized.
2. *Mathematics Courses:* On the undergraduate level minimum requirements in each section of mathematics are specified. On the graduate level, only the total additional number of hours in mathematics is specified.
   A. *Analysis:* Trigonometry, plane analytic geometry, calculus (at least six semester hours required), solid analytic geometry, advanced calculus, differential equations, infinite series.
   B. *Applications:* Mechanics (statics and dynamics), mathematical physics, astronomy (mathematical), actuarial mathematics (finite differences, interpolation, numerical analysis), uses in behavioral science (theory of games, linear programming, operations research).
   C. *Probability and Statistics:* Emphasizing probability and statistical inference.
   D. *Algebra:* Abstract algebra (fields, rings, groups, linear algebra, vector spaces), matrices, theory of numbers, theory of equations.
   E. *Geometry:* Metric and other geometries (projective, affine, inversive), non-Euclidean geometries, differential geometry, topology.

[23]Alfred B. Garrett, Recommendation for the Preparation of High School Teachers of Science and Mathematics, *School Science and Mathematics*, **59** (1959), 281–289.

F. *Foundations of Mathematics:* Theory of sets, mathematical or symbolic logic, postulates for geometry, postulates for algebra, postulates for arithmetic, the real and complex number systems.

3. *Supporting Science Courses:* Each undergraduate requirement should include a course in physics. The other hours should be chosen from the following: chemistry, biology, astronomy, geology, and meteorology.

After a detailed discussion of what it feels is "an adequate structure for a teacher-education program" the Commission on Mathematics summarizes its recommendations for a preservice training program for teachers of secondary mathematics in these words:[24]

Secondary teachers should include in their preservice preparation courses in modern algebra, probability and statistical inference, elementary and advanced calculus, and geometry. The latter course should stress the foundations of geometry, and the study of geometries other than traditional Euclidean geometry, and should not deal exclusively or even primarily with so-called "advanced" Euclidean geometry.

The Panel on Teacher Training of the Committee on the Undergraduate Program in Mathematics was charged by its parent committee to prepare "a set of recommendations of minimum standards for the training of teachers on all levels" of instruction and also to implement their recommendations. In the preparation of their report they recognized four distinct levels of mathematics instruction and so patterned their recommended program for teacher preparation.[25] In their efforts to implement their recommendations they have conducted several state and regional meetings and issued several supplementary reports in the hope that these meetings and reports would help in the attempt to "make these minimum standards a reality." The original report made the following recommendations:

1. *Recommendations for Level I* (Teachers of elementary school mathematics)

As a prerequisite for the college training of elementary school teachers, we recommend at least two years of college preparatory mathematics, consisting of a year of algebra and a year of geometry, or the same material in integrated courses. It must also be assured that these teachers are competent in the basic techniques of arithmetic. The exact length of the training program will depend on the strength of their preparation. For their college training, we recommend the equivalent of the following courses:

(A) A two-course sequence devoted to the structure of the real number system and its subsystems.

[24] "Report of the Commission on Mathematics" (New York: College Entrance Examination Board, 1959), p. 58.

[25] Committee on the Undergraduate Program in Mathematics: Recommendations of the Mathematical Association of America for the Training of Teachers of Mathematics, *American Mathematical Monthly,* **67** (1960), 982–991; *Mathematics Teacher,* **53** (1960), 632–638, 643.

(B) A course devoted to the basic concepts of algebra.

(C) A course in informal geometry.

The material in these courses might, in a sense, duplicate material studied in high school by the prospective teacher, but we urge that this material be covered again, this time from a more sophisticated, college-level point of view.

Whether the material suggested in (A) above can be covered in one or two courses will clearly depend upon the previous preparation of the student.

We strongly recommend that at least 20 per cent of the Level I teachers in each school have stronger preparation in mathematics, comparable to Level II preparation but not necessarily including calculus. Such teachers would clearly strengthen the elementary program by their very presence within the school faculty. This additional preparation is certainly required for elementary teachers who are called upon to teach an introduction to algebra or geometry.

2. *Recommendations for Level II* (Teachers of the elements of algebra and geometry)

Prospective teachers should enter this program ready for a mathematics course at the level of a beginning course in analytic geometry and calculus (requiring a minimum of three years in college preparatory mathematics). It is recognized that many students will need to correct high school deficiencies in college. However, such courses as trigonometry and college algebra should not count toward the fulfillment of minimum requirements at the college level. Their college mathematics training should then include:

(A) Three courses in elementary analysis (including or presupposing the fundamentals of analytic geometry). This introduction to analysis should stress basic concepts. However, prospective teachers should be qualified to take more advanced mathematics courses requiring a year of calculus, and hence calculus courses especially designed for teachers are normally not desirable.

(B) Four other courses: a course in abstract algebra, a course in geometry, a course in probability from a set-theoretic point of view, and one elective. One of these courses should contain an introduction to the language of logic and sets.

3. *Recommendations for Level III* (Teachers of high school mathematics)

Prospective teachers of mathematics beyond the elements of algebra and geometry should complete a major in mathematics and a minor in some field in which a substantial amount of mathematics is used. The latter should be selected from areas in the physical sciences, biological sciences, and from the social studies, but the minor should in each case be pursued to the extent that the student will have encountered substantial applications of mathematics.

The major in mathematics should include, in addition to the work listed under Level II, at least an additional course in each of algebra, geometry, and probability-statistics, and one more elective.

Thus, the minimum requirements for high school mathematics teachers should consist of the following:*

(A) Three courses in analysis.

(B) Two courses in abstract algebra.

(C) Two courses in geometry beyond analytic geometry.

*The requirements for Level II preparation have been included in this list.

(D) Two courses in probability-statistics.

(E) Two upper-class elective courses, e.g., introduction to real variables, number theory, topology, history of mathematics, or numerical analysis (including use of high speed computing machines).

One of these courses should contain an introduction to the language of logic and sets, which can be used in a variety of courses.

4. *Recommendations for Level IV* (Teachers of the elements of calculus, linear algebra, probability, etc.)

On this level we recommend a Master's degree with at least two-thirds of the courses being in mathematics, and for which an undergraduate program at least as strong as Level III training is a prerequisite. A teacher who has completed the recommendations for Level III should use the additional mathematics courses to acquire greater mathematical breadth.

Since these teachers will be called upon to teach calculus, we recommend that the program include the equivalent of at least two courses of theoretical analysis in the spirit of the theory of functions of real and complex variables.

It is important that the universities have graduate programs available which can be entered with Level III preparation, recognizing that these students substitute greater breadth for lack of depth in analysis as compared with an ordinary B.A. with a major in mathematics. In other respects, graduate schools should maintain great freedom in designing the M.A. program for teachers.

The preceding recommendations have dealt in detail with the subject matter training of mathematics teachers. There are many other facets to the education of the scholarly, vigorous, and enthusiastic persons to whom we wish to entrust the education of our youth. One of these merits special mention by us. Effective mathematics teachers must be familiar with such items as:

(A) The objectives and content of the many proposals for change in our curriculum and texts.

(B) The techniques, relative merits, and roles of such teaching procedures as the inductive and deductive approaches to new ideas.

(C) The literature of mathematics and its teaching.

(D) The underlying ideas of elementary mathematics and the manner in which they may provide a rational basis for teaching.

(E) The chief applications which have given rise to various mathematical subjects. These applications will depend upon the level of mathematics to be taught, and are an essential part of the equipment of all mathematics teachers.

Such topics are properly taught in so-called "methods" courses. We would like to stress that adequate teaching of such courses can be done only by persons who are well informed *both* as to the basic mathematical concepts and as to the nature of American public schools—and as to the concepts, problems, and literature of mathematics education. In particular, we do not feel that this can be done effectively at either the elementary level in the context of "general" methods courses, or by persons who have not had at least the training of Level IV.

The strength of the mathematics program in the secondary schools is primarily the responsibility of the teacher of mathematics in those schools. Its status will depend largely upon his ability to present and interpret his subject as a worthwhile educational venture. The professional preparation of this teacher should equip him with the scholarship and techniques essential to the satisfactory fulfillment of his professional obligation. He must be able to organize and present mathematics in such a way that adolescent boys and girls will be brought not only to a realization of the intrinsic nature and value of mathematics itself but also to an equally clear realization of its role in enabling man to relate, understand, and control his environmental factors and direct his social and economic advancement.

If these ends are to be attained, the training of the teacher must be an organic and continuous process. It should make the teacher unwilling to permit himself to stagnate under a comfortable self-complacency. It should inspire him to incessant effort both in the expanding of his mathematical horizons and in educational experimentation directed toward the improvement of his instructional techniques. The teacher so prepared will not restrict his attention and his instruction to the confines of mere operational mechanics. He will lead his students with contagious enthusiasm into realms of mathematical thought and endeavor which will be both stimulating to their curiosity and intellectual interest and broadly significant to their insights, appreciations, and general cultural development.

EXERCISES

1. Contrast the implications of the following two statements: (*a*) Mathematics is a tool subject. (*b*) Mathematics is a fundamental mode of thinking. Give three illustrations of each of these concepts of mathematics.

2. In the teaching of secondary mathematics what emphasis should be placed on mathematics as a tool subject? What emphasis should be placed on mathematics as a fundamental mode of thinking?

3. What have been some of the major influences that have brought about the employment of so many poorly prepared teachers?

4. Why should the teacher of secondary mathematics be thoroughly familiar with the mathematics programs of all lower grades?

5. What contribution can the history of mathematics make to the better preparation of teachers of secondary mathematics?

6. Do you think there should be a differentiation between programs designed to train the teacher of junior high school mathematics, the teacher of senior high school mathematics, and the teacher of junior college mathematics? Defend your answer.

7. What types of courses could be used to provide for such differentiation?

8. What subjects seem to be most frequently combined with mathematics in teaching combinations?

9. In the light of existing studies, how many subjects should a prospective teaching candidate be prepared to teach?

10. What do you think should be considered minimum mathematics preparation for the teacher of secondary mathematics?

11. In the light of existing studies, from what subjects do you think a major in mathematics should choose a minor?

12. What are the "major areas of human experience" out of which a program of general education should be developed? What contribution can mathematics make to such a program?

13. What would be some of the principal distinctions in treatment in a course in plane analytic geometry planned for prospective teachers and one planned for the prospective research worker in pure or applied mathematics?

14. Answer the question of exercise 13 for a course in algebra.

15. Answer the question of exercise 13 for a course in plane synthetic geometry.

16. Answer the question of exercise 13 for a course in differential and integral calculus.

17. What are the basic similarities and differences between the teacher education programs recommended by the Cooperative Committee of the American Association for the Advancement of Science and the Committee on the Undergraduate Program in Mathematics (CUPM) of the Mathematical Association of America?

18. Check your mathematical background against the recommendations of each committee and determine what further training, if any, you need to meet the standards of each program.

19. Check your professional background against the criteria listed by CUPM under Curriculum-study Courses and determine what further training and experience, if any, you need to meet these standards.

BIBLIOGRAPHY

"An Analysis of New Mathematical Programs," *Bulletin* (Washington, D.C.: National Council of Teachers of Mathematics, 1963).

Beberman, Max: Old Mathematics in the New Curriculum, *Educational Leadership,* **19** (1962), 373–375.

Beckman, Milton W.: NDEA Support for Improved Mathematics Instruction, *Mathematics Teacher,* **53** (1960), 445–447.

Bell, Clifford: What Every Teacher Should Know about the Uses of Mathematics, *Mathematics Teacher,* **56** (1963), 302–306.

Bell, E. T.: "Men of Mathematics" (New York: Simon and Schuster, Inc., 1937).

_____: "The Development of Mathematics," 2d ed. (New York: McGraw-Hill Book Company, 1945).

Boyer, Carl B.: "History of Analytic Geometry" (New York: *Scripta Mathematica,* 1956).

_____: "The Concepts of Calculus" (New York: Columbia University Press, 1939).

Breuer, Joseph: "Introduction to the Theory of Sets," translated by Howard F. Fehr (Englewood Cliffs, N.J.: Prentice-Hall, Inc., 1958).

Brown, Kenneth E.: Teaching Load and Qualifications of Mathematics Teachers, *Mathematics Teacher,* **53** (1960), 2–11.

_____ and Daniel W. Snader: "In-service Education of High School Mathematics Teachers" (U.S. Department of Health, Education, and Welfare, 1961).

Commission on Mathematics, Report of: "Program for College Preparatory Mathematics" (New York: College Entrance Examination Board, 1959).

Committee on the Undergraduate Program in Mathematics (CUPM): Recommendations of the Mathematical Association of America for the Training of Mathematics Teachers, *American Mathematical Monthly,* **67** (1960), 982–991; *Mathematics Teacher,* **53** (1960), 632–638, 643.

Courant, Richard, and Herbert Robbins: "What Is Mathematics?" (Fair Lawn, N.J.: Oxford University Press, 1941).

Eves, Howard: "An Introduction to the History of Mathematics" (New York: Holt, Rinehart and Winston, Inc., 1953).

_____: "A Survey of Geometry," vol. 1 Englewood Cliffs, N.J.: Allyn and Bacon, Inc., 1963).

_____ and Carroll V. Newsom: "Introduction to the Foundations and Fundamental Concepts of Mathematics" (New York: Holt, Rinehart and Winston, Inc., 1958).

Fawcett, Harold P.: Guidelines in Mathematics Education, *Mathematics Teacher*, **53** (1960), 418–423.

Fehr, Howard F.: "Secondary Mathematics: A Functional Approach for Teachers" (Boston: D.C. Heath and Company, 1951).

———: Breakthroughs in Mathematical Thought, *Mathematics Teacher*, **52** (1959), 15–19.

———: How Much Mathematics Should Teachers Know? *Mathematics Teacher*, **52** (1959), 299–300.

———: New Thinking in Mathematical Education, *Mathematics Teacher*, **53** (1960), 424–429.

Garrett, A. B.: Recommendation for the Preparation of High School Teachers of Science and Mathematics, *School Science and Mathematics*, **59** (1959), 281–289.

"Guidelines for Preparation Programs of Teachers of Secondary School Science and Mathematics" (Washington, D.C.: National Association of State Directors of Teacher Education and Certification, 1963), pp. 23–26.

Henkin, Leon, W. Norman Smith, Verne J. Varineau, and Michael J. Walsh: "Retracing Elementary Mathematics" (New York: The Macmillan Company, 1962).

Jones, Phillip S.: New Curriculum Patterns for Mathematics Teachers, *American Association of Colleges for Teacher Education Yearbook* (1962), pp. 90–93.

Kemeny, John G.: Report to the International Congress of Mathematicians, *Mathematics Teacher*, **56** (1963), 66–78.

Kinsella, John J.: Preparation in Mathematics of Mathematics Teachers, *Mathematics Teacher*, **53** (1960), 27–32.

Kline, Morris: "Mathematics and Western Culture" (Fair Lawn, N.J.: Oxford University Press, 1953).

Landin, Joseph: The New Secondary Mathematics Curriculum and the New Teacher, *School Science and Mathematics*, **63** (1963), 367–376.

Mayor, John R.: Mathematics in the Junior High School, *Educational Leadership*, **18** (1960), 165–167.

——— and others: Professional Education of Science and Mathematics Teachers, *Journal of Teacher Education*, **13** (1962), 125–139.

Meder, A. E., Jr., E. R. Lorch, A. W. Tucker, Bruce E. Meserve, R. M. Walter, and F. G. Fender (Panel): The Education of Mathematics Teachers, *American Mathematical Monthly*, **66** (1959), 805–809, 909–914.

Meserve, Bruce E.: The Evolution of Geometry, *Mathematics Teacher*, **49** (1956), 372–382.

———: Modern Geometry for Teachers, *School Science and Mathematics*, **58** (1958), 437–441.

Moise, E. E.: New Mathematics Programs, *School Review*, **70** (1962), 82–101.

Nagel, Ernest, and James R. Newman: "Gödel's Proof" (New York: New York University Press, 1960).

National Council of Teachers of Mathematics: "Insights into Modern Mathematics," *Twenty-third Yearbook* (Washington, D.C.: National Council of Teachers of Mathematics, 1957).

———: "The Growth of Mathematical Ideas, Grades K–12," *Twenty-fourth Yearbook* (Washington, D.C.: National Council of Teachers of Mathematics, 1959).

———: "Instruction in Arithmetic," *Twenty-fifth Yearbook* (Washington, D.C.: National Council of Teachers of Mathematics, 1960).

———: "Enrichment Mathematics for the Grades," *Twenty-seventh Yearbook* (Washington, D.C.: National Council of Teachers of Mathematics, 1962).

———: "Enrichment Mathematics for High School," *Twenty-eighth Yearbook* (Washington, D.C.: National Council of Teachers of Mathematics, 1963).

New Developments in Secondary School Mathematics, *Bulletin of the National Association of Secondary-School Principals*, **43** (1959), 1–203.

Northrop, E. R.: Modern Mathematics and the Secondary School Curriculum, *Mathematics Teacher*, **48** (1955), 386–393.

Pólya, G.: "Mathematical Discovery," vol. I (New York: John Wiley & Sons, Inc., 1962).

———: On Learning, Teaching, and Learning Teaching, *American Mathematical Monthly*, **70** (1963), 605–619.

Rourke, Robert E. K.: Some Implications of

Twentieth Century Mathematics for High Schools, *Mathematics Teacher,* **51** (1958), 74–86.

Secondary School Curriculum Committee, Report of: *Mathematics Teacher,* **52** (1959), 389–417.

Sister Maria Concepta: Retraining of Teachers of Mathematics, *Catholic School Journal,* **62** (1962), 27–28.

Stone, M. H.: Some Crucial Problems of Mathematical Instruction in the United States, *School Review,* **65** (1957), 64–77.

_____: Revolution in Mathematics, *American Mathematical Monthly,* **68** (1961), 715–734; *Liberal Education,* **47** (1961), 304–327.

Van Engen, Henry, J. Landin, P. D. Edwards, and L. E. Bush: Teacher Education in Mathematics, *School Science and Mathematics,* **58** (1958), 27–34.

Willerding, Margaret F.: Teaching Machines: An Annotated Bibliography, *School Science and Mathematics,* **61** (1961), 579–591.

Wren, F. Lynwood: Mathematics in Focus, *Mathematics Teacher,* **48** (1955), 514–524.

_____: Curiosity and Culture, *Mathematics Teacher,* **50** (1957), 361–371.

Zant, James H.: The Mathematics and Science Teacher of Tomorrow, *Mathematics Teacher,* **50** (1957), 426–431.

Part II

THE TEACHING OF THE SPECIAL SUBJECT MATTER OF SECONDARY MATHEMATICS

THE JOB OF THE MATHEMATICS TEACHER

THE TEACHER of mathematics, like all other teachers in the secondary school, is a person of whom many things are expected. His obligations are not confined to the classroom but extend along many avenues to the promotion of the effective functioning of the school and the maintenance of harmonious relations and constructive understanding between the school and the community. The sponsoring of extracurricular activities, cooperation in maintaining a smoothly operating physical organization, participation in counseling and guidance, keeping careful records, making necessary reports promptly, and participation in worthy community interests are but illustrative of the range of demands upon the teacher. It must not be forgotten, however, that his first and foremost obligation is to teach effectively.

Teaching mathematics in the secondary schools is a task which, if seriously undertaken, will challenge the best efforts of the best teachers. It requires more than a thorough knowledge of the subject matter to be taught, though that, of course, is a *sine qua non*. It requires more, even, than a broad perspective of the field of mathematics itself and an understanding of the place and importance of mathematics in any valid scheme of general education. It demands skill in the techniques of teaching each particular topic or aspect of the subject, in developing generalized concepts, in coordinating generalizations with applications, in discriminating between essential and unimportant matters within the subject, in knowing where to place emphasis and where to anticipate difficulties, in detecting difficulties when they do occur, in sensing their precise nature, and in knowing how to help the students avoid or overcome them.

The first task of the teacher in connection with the teaching of any division, unit, topic, or aspect of mathematical subject matter is to decide just what the immediate and definite objectives are, viz., which concepts or items of information the students are to gain from their study of that topic, which skills are to be mastered, and which techniques and materials will be most effective in producing the desired results. Economy and clarity of learning will come only insofar as the multitude of details related to the unit are subordinated to the main issues and are organized and integrated around the few really major concepts and skills so that these will stand out in bold relief against the background of contributory detail. Having decided what important things are to be emphasized in a particular unit, the teacher is in a position to view the whole problem in its proper perspective and to organize and present the material of the unit in a more effective manner.

The teacher of mathematics must remain alert at all times to the major objectives of mathematical instruction. If these are to be attained in an effective and economical manner, the teacher must plan his work with at least five things in mind:

1. He must decide what exercises and activities will contribute most effectively to produce the desired understandings and skills. This teaching material should be selected with great care.
2. He must analyze these teaching materials carefully to anticipate the specific difficulties which the pupils are likely to encounter in attaining the objectives of the unit.
3. In order to help the pupils avoid or overcome these difficulties, the teacher must become expert in sensing the procedures and devices that promise to be specifically helpful and must learn to be adept in adjusting his procedure to the requirements of each immediate situation. Explanations and developmental discussion should be pointedly and skillfully organized. Devices and illustrations should be selected with great care.
4. A careful selection and arrangement of motivating materials must be made. The teacher must keep in mind that it is his responsibility to create, stimulate, and maintain interest in mathematics as well as strive for proficiency in skills and the amassing of information.
5. He must give careful thought to evaluation techniques and remedial procedures.

No teacher can do a thoroughly good job of teaching mathematics unless he is willing to make a careful analysis of his job and be guided by that analysis in making his preparations and in conducting the work of the class. The analysis of the instructional problems involved in the teaching of any topic in secondary mathematics seems to divide itself rather logically into six considerations, as follows:

1. What background of experience and understanding may the student be expected to have when he begins the study of the topic?
2. What are the particular understandings or abilities which the student should acquire or strengthen through the study of the topic?
3. What activities or procedures on the part of the teacher and student will enable the student to gain the desired understandings and abilities most effectively?
4. What specific difficulties may the student be expected to encounter in his effort to acquire the desired understandings and abilities?
5. What specific suggestions, devices, and procedures will most effectively help the student to avoid or overcome the specific difficulties of (4)?
6. What materials and procedures related to the particular topic will best stimulate and maintain the student's interest?

It is the purpose of Part II to consider some of the more important instructional units of secondary mathematics in the perspective of the above questions.

ELEVEN

The teaching of arithmetic

CURRENT CURRICULUM revision in both elementary and secondary school mathematics continues to place emphasis on the fundamental structure of mathematics, the understanding of notational patterns, the clarification of definitions, and the refinement of basic terminology. To meet the demands of such a program teachers of arithmetic, whether at the elementary or secondary level of instruction, must keep themselves alert to the threefold nature of their responsibility. They must place due emphasis upon the meanings, relationships, and properties which cement the fundamental structure of the number systems of arithmetic. Furthermore, they must orient their instruction in a program designed to maintain and strengthen facility in the basic skills. Finally, no teacher of arithmetic has met his full responsibility to his students until he has provided them with a sound basis for the appreciation of the social and cultural significance of number from the point of view both of historical fact and of contemporary potential.

The arithmetical responsibility of the secondary school It is the responsibility of the elementary school to lay the fundamental groundwork of basic concepts, principles, and skills upon which the arithmetical structure must be built. In constructing its curriculum and formulating its instructional program the secondary school is justified in assuming that the elementary school has met this educational obligation. But even if this assumption is valid, the secondary school still has a responsibility for continuing the enrichment of this background and preventing its atrophy through disuse. The broader mathematical obligations of the junior and senior high schools, however, are to strengthen and increase the working vocabulary of arithmetical terms; to effect a clearer understanding of basic concepts, relationships, and principles; to develop further facility in the fundamental skills; to shape a more mature concept of the basic structure of the number system of arithmetic; and to emphasize the abstraction of arithmetical processes to problem situations.

One of the major responsibilities of the junior high school is that of careful, though elementary, consideration of the evolution of the field of real numbers as the significant number system of arithmetic. Careful attention should be given to the fact that a need for greater computational freedom and a desire for a closed number system combine to project the pattern of development from the basic structure of the natural number system through the domain of integers and the field of rational numbers to the field of real numbers. This should be accomplished in the framework of the accompanying modifications of the basic postulates of the natural number system into the field postulates of the real number system. As each new number system is created to accommodate each newly defined operation the teacher has the definite responsibility of acquainting the students with what new computational patterns are possible. Furthermore, it is absolutely essential that care be taken to emphasize the fact that the new definitions and the remodeling of old definitions do not introduce any inconsistencies with previous definitions or procedures. Rather, they serve as extensions which make possible the greater computational freedom desired.

The later study of algebra introduces a need for a further extension of the number system to the field of complex numbers. This extension arises from the desire to find the solution of any given quadratic equation. As we shall see later, this extension calls for further definitions of the four fundamental operations. Here again the definitions must take care not to introduce inconsistencies with previous practice. Once this extension has been accomplished, the number field of elementary mathematics has been structured in the framework of the diagram of Table 11–1.

The measurement problems of geometry and trigonometry offer still further opportunities for emphasis on the fundamental skills and basic understandings of arithmetic. The field of real numbers is sufficient to take care of all the computational needs, and no new extensions of the number system are needed. However, certain new adaptations and guides for computation and interpretation become necessary. This is due to the approximate nature of measurement and the controls that are necessary to guarantee justified results when computing with approximate data. Basic and informed instruction in the exercise of such controls of computation and interpretation is a definite instructional responsibility of all teachers of secondary mathematics.

TABLE 11-1
The number systems of elementary mathematics

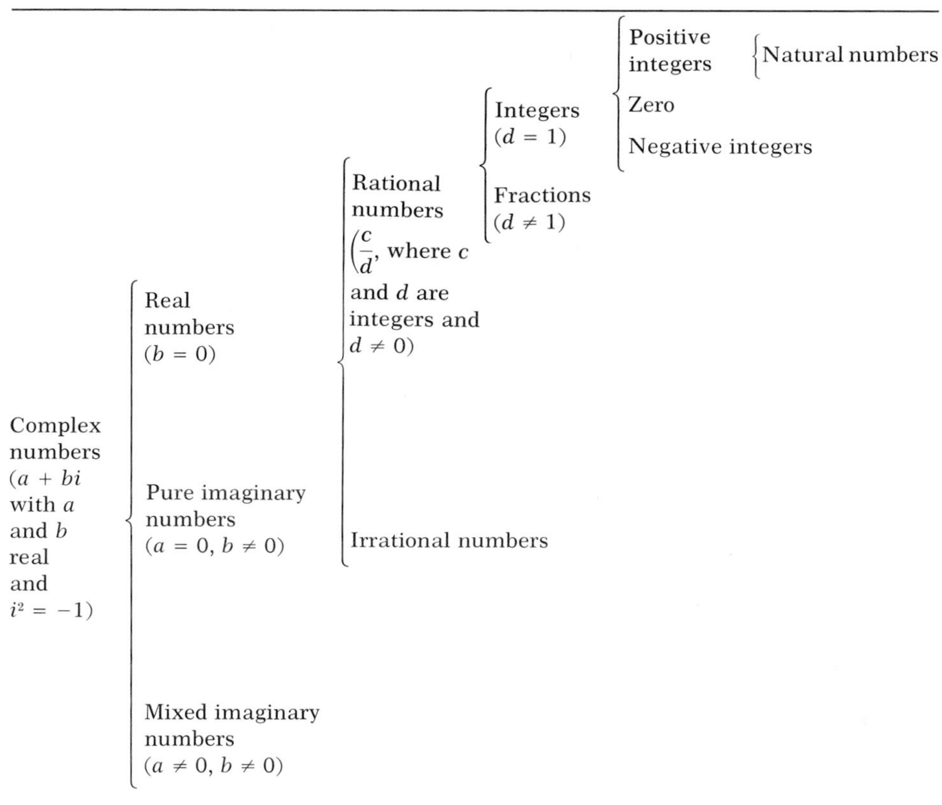

Although the instructional material of the junior and senior high schools offers a greater abundance of situations which are more nearly numerical in nature, the responsibility for increasing accuracy and facility in numerical computation does not end here, since the student passes on to higher levels of instruction. This responsibility, as does that of building up a progressive increase in the student's understanding of the basic structure of arithmetic and appreciation for the power and significance of applications of arithmetical techniques to environmental problem situations, extends even into the junior college.

The structure of arithmetic A number system consists of a set of elements, at least one well-defined operation upon these elements, a set of postulated properties, and all the theorems which are derivable as consequences of the implications of the basic set of postulates. The first such system with which the study of arithmetic brings us into contact is the natural number system, whose postulates ($N1$ to $N10$)

are listed on page 64. The set of elements is the set of natural numbers $N = \{1,2,3,4, \ldots\}$, and there are two well-defined binary operations of addition and multiplication. The fact that each operation is well defined means that when any two elements are combined by either operation there is no ambiguity in determining what the result is and furthermore that this unique result is a natural number. The closure property assures us that addition and multiplication can be used freely and with no restrictions, for there exist natural numbers which are the respective sums or products for any such combinations of natural numbers. In spite of this fact there are certain restrictions of operation incident to the closure property which become the motivation for desirable extensions of the number system to the domain of integers and the field of rational numbers.

If a, b, and c are natural numbers such that $a + b = d$ and $a \times c = e$, then we know that d and e are also natural numbers. But if a, d, and e are natural numbers, does it follow that there exist natural numbers b and c such that the equalities are satisfied? It is a simple matter to supply examples which show that the answer to this question may be either yes or no. For example, if $a = 3$, $d = 7$, and $e = 15$, then $b = 4$ and $c = 5$ are natural numbers such that $a + b = d$ and $a \times c = e$. If, on the other hand, $a = 16$, $d = 7$, and $e = 5$, then there exist no natural numbers b and c such that the equalities are satisfied.

The restrictions on addition, illustrated in the previous paragraph, lead to the extension of the number system to include zero and the negative integers. In this extension the new operation of *subtraction* is defined as the inverse operation to addition in the sense that $a - b = c$ when a, b, and c are natural numbers, if and only if $b + c = a$. Zero is introduced as the *additive identity,* namely, the element 0 such that $a + 0 = 0 + a = a$ for every element a in the new system. A negative integer, $-a$, is defined as the *additive inverse* of a, or an integer such that $a + (-a) = (-a) + a = 0$. This new number system is the *domain of integers* in which the set of elements is the set of all integers $J = \{0, \pm 1, \pm 2, \pm 3, \pm 4, \ldots\}$ and for which the basic postulates are listed as $I1$ to $I9$ on pages 65–66. The definitions of addition and multiplication in the new system are such that the closure, commutative, associative, and distributive properties are retained and the subset of positive integers is *isomorphic* with the set of natural numbers in the sense of this definition: If a one-to-one correspondence exists between the elements of set $S = \{a,b, \ldots\}$ and set $S' = \{a',b', \ldots\}$ such that if $a \leftrightarrow a'$ and $b \leftrightarrow b'$ then $a + b \leftrightarrow a' + b'$ and $a \times b$ corresponds to $a' \times b'$, then the two sets are said to be *isomorphic* with respect to addition and multiplication.

In the context of these extensions of the two operations, the question arises as to how the operations apply to zero and the negative integers.

The answers to these questions are to be found in the following theorems, which are derivable as implied consequences of the basic postulates of the system. In the statements of these theorems, a and b are to be considered as representing any integers.

Theorem 1. $a \times 0 = 0 \times a = 0$.

Theorem 2. $a + (-b) = a - b$ if $a > b$. (This is in accordance with the definition of subtraction and the concept that $a > b$ if and only if there exists a positive integer c such that $a = b + c$.)

Theorem 3. If $b > a$, then $a + (-b) = -(b - a)$, the additive inverse of $b - a$.

Theorems 2 and 3 make it possible to extend the definition of subtraction to apply to a, b, and c as integers. Also, in the light of these two theorems further significance can be given to the inverse relation existing between the operations of addition and subtraction. It is not difficult to prove:

Theorem 4. $(a + b) - b = (a - b) + b = a$. (Thus each of the operations, addition and subtraction, is seen to destroy, or cancel, the effect of the other.)

Theorem 5. $a \times (-b) = -(a \times b)$, the additive inverse of $a \times b$.

Theorem 6. $(-a) \times (-b) = a \times b$.

The restrictions on multiplication, illustrated previously for natural numbers, can be shown to prevail in the domain of integers. These restrictions lead to another extension of the number system of arithmetic, this time to include numbers of the form a/b, where a and b are integers and b is different from zero. Such numbers are called "rational numbers," or, on occasion, "fractions." In this extension the new operation of *division* is defined as the inverse operation to multiplication in the sense that $a \div b = c$, when a, b, and c are integers, if and only if $b \times c = a$. Division by zero is, of course, excluded, since by definition $a \div 0 = c$ if and only if $c \times 0 = a$. Since c is an integer, theorem 1 (above) states that a must be zero; then the equality holds for any integer c, whence the quotient of $a \div 0$ is seen to be undefined. An accepted equivalent form of the symbol for division is a/b. Thus the definition of a rational number may be more formally stated: A rational number is a number which may be expressed as the quotient of two integers.

The set of elements of this new system is the set R of all rational numbers, and the definitions of equality, addition, and multiplication are:

Equality: $\frac{a}{b} = \frac{c}{d}$ if and only if $ad = bc$.

Addition: $\frac{a}{b} + \frac{c}{d} = \frac{ad + bc}{bd}$.

Multiplication: $\frac{a}{b} \times \frac{c}{d} = \frac{ac}{bd}$.

With these definitions the operations of addition and multiplication retain the closure, commutative, associative, and distributive properties. The subset of rational numbers $a/1$, where a is any integer, and the set J of all integers can be shown to be isomorphic with respect to addition and multiplication. The number 1 serves as the multiplicative identity in the sense that $1 \times r = r \times 1 = r$ for any rational number r, and the reciprocal of any nonzero rational number r serves as the multiplication inverse of r in the sense that $r \times 1/r = 1/r \times r = 1$.

The set R with the operations of addition and multiplication form an *ordered number field* for which the basic postulates are as follows. For a, b, c rational numbers:

F1. *Closure.* If $a + b = r$ and $a \times b = s$, then r and s are rational numbers.
F2. *Commutative.* $a + b = b + a$ and $a \times b = b \times a$.
F3. *Associative.* $(a + b) + c = a + (b + c)$ and $(a \times b) \times c = a \times (b \times c)$.
F4. *Distributive.* $a \times (b + c) = (a \times b) + (a \times c)$.
F5. *Additive identity.* The rational number 0 is such that $a + 0 = 0 + a = a$ for every rational number a.
F6. *Additive inverse.* For each rational number a there exists a rational number $(-a)$, called the *additive inverse* of a, such that $a + (-a) = (-a) + a = 0$.
F7. *Multiplicative identity.* The rational number 1 is such that $a \times 1 = 1 \times a = a$ for every rational number a.
F8. *Multiplicative inverse.* For each nonzero rational number a there exists a rational number $1/a$, called the *multiplicative inverse* of a, such that $a \times 1/a = 1/a \times a = 1$. (The symbol a^{-1} is also used to represent the multiplicative inverse of a.)
F9. There exists a proper subset P of R such that for each nonzero element a of R one and only one of a or $-a$ is in P.
F10. If a and b are elements of the subset P, then $a + b$ and $a \times b$ are also in P.

At this point attention should be called to a very important fact. The symbol a/b, where a and b are integers and $b \neq 0$, rather than being a numeral which represents one and only one rational number, represents an entire class of such numbers. It thus becomes what is called the *representative of an equivalence class.* For example, the symbol $^3/_4$ represents the equivalence class which is the infinite set of equivalent rational numbers $\{^3/_4, ^6/_8, ^9/_{12}, ^{12}/_{16} \ldots\}$. It is in this sense that the symbols a/b and c/d are used in the definitions of the rational operations. If we wish to find the sum $^3/_4 + ^5/_{12}$, the definition states that this is the rational number $(3 \cdot 12 + 4 \cdot 5)/(4 \cdot 12) = ^{56}/_{48} = ^7/_6$. Here the symbol = has been used for the purpose of stating that $(3 \cdot 12 + 4 \cdot 5)/(4 \cdot 12)$, $^{56}/_{48}$, and $^7/_6$ are symbols for the same equivalence class. It is not used in the same sense as when finding the sum of two integers. For example, in the expressed sum $8 + 5 = 13$ the symbol = means "is the same number as."

Similarly, in the definition of multiplication of rational numbers, the symbol = carries the connotation of "representative of the same equivalence class" rather than that of "is the same number as." ($\frac{3}{4} \cdot \frac{10}{9} = \frac{30}{36} = \frac{5}{6}$.)

Since both addition and multiplication, as defined, can be proved to be independent of the representatives of the respective classes, the operations are said to be "well defined" in the sense that the class of the sum or of the product is uniquely determined.

If, in any expressed product, the factors are all equal, the process used to find the product is called *involution*, or the process of raising to indicated powers. The inversely related operation is *evolution*, or the process of extracting indicated roots. For example, $(a^{1/2})^2 = (a^2)^{1/2} = |a|$. Just as the inverse relations of subtraction and division made it necessary to extend the number system to accommodate the demands of closure, so does evolution call for extensions. One extension is to the set R^* of real numbers. This is accomplished by the definition of *irrational numbers*, numbers such as $\sqrt{2}$, π, and e, which cannot be expressed as the quotient of two integers. A second extension is to the set C of complex numbers in which the elements are of the form $a + bi$, where a and b are real numbers and $i^2 = -1$.

Addition and multiplication as defined for rational numbers, supplemented by the laws of exponents, need no further definition to accommodate to the set R^*. Subtraction, division, and evolution thus become the related inverse operations. The set R^*, with addition and multiplication, forms an ordered field, since the operations satisfy the ten field postulates $F1$ to $F10$.

For the set C of complex numbers new definitions of equality, addition, and multiplication become necessary.

Equality: Two complex numbers $a + bi$ and $c + di$ are equal if and only if $a = c$ and $b = d$.

Addition: $(a + bi) + (c + di) = (a + c) + (b + d)i$.

Multiplication: $(a + bi)(c + di) = (ac - bd) + (ad + bc)i$.

With these definitions the complex number $0 + 0i$ is seen to serve as the additive identity, since $(a + bi) + (0 + 0i) = (a + 0) + (b + 0)i = a + bi$, and $1 + 0i$ as the multiplicative identity, since $(a + bi)(1 + 0i) = (a \cdot 1 - b \cdot 0) + (a \cdot 0 + b \cdot 1) = a + bi$. Furthermore, addition and multiplication satisfy postulates $F1$ to $F8$, so this system also forms a field. It is not an ordered field, however, since there do not exist elements in C for which $F9$ and $F10$ are true. As a direct consequence of these definitions, the subset of C whose elements are $a + 0i$ and the set R^* can be shown to be isomorphic with respect to addition and multiplication.

The set R is a proper subset of R^*, which, in turn, is a proper subset of C. (See Table 11–1.) From this fact it follows that the field of rational numbers is a *subfield* of the field of real numbers, which, in turn, is a subfield of the field of complex numbers.

The complete formalization of the concept of field is possibly beyond normal instructional responsibility at the level of the junior high school. However, students should emerge from this program with a clear understanding of the basic properties of each significant number system and how they control and give authority for the computational procedures used. The groundwork must be laid for later formalization in the senior high school of the field postulates and informed orientation in the language and procedures of the field of complex numbers, the number field of elementary mathematics.

Because of the fact that the four operations of addition, subtraction, multiplication, and division satisfy the field properties, independent of whether the set of elements is R, R^*, or C, they are frequently called the "four field operations." Since the field of rational numbers is a subfield of both the field of real numbers and the field of complex numbers, the four field operations are also, at times, referred to as the "four rational operations."

Among the theorems which are derivable as implied consequences from these field postulates for rational numbers, there are two which clearly define the inverse relation that exists between multiplication and division. They are:

Theorem 7. If a and b are rational numbers and b $\neq 0$, then $a \times 1/b = a \div b$.
Theorem 8. If a and b are rational numbers and $b \neq 0$, then $(a \times b) \div b = (a \div b) \times b = a$.

Theorem 7 should be recognized as a formalized statement of the rule frequently stated as follows: In division you can invert the divisor and multiply. This theorem, while stated here for rational numbers, can be shown to apply both to real numbers and to complex numbers. Likewise, theorem 2, stated for integers on page 247, can be shown to hold for rational numbers, real numbers, or complex numbers. Furthermore, theorems 4 and 8 also can be shown to apply to the extended systems, thus pairing addition with subtraction and multiplication with division as inversely related field operations.

In this more general context theorems 2 and 7 lend authority to what might be regarded as a fundamental property of field operations, namely: Any computation involving any one or all of the four field operations may be transformed into an equivalent computation involving the respective inverse operations. For example, theorem 7 states not only that division can be accomplished by inverting the divisor and multiplying but also that multiplication can be accomplished by inverting one of the factors and dividing. Similarly, theorem 2 states that addition may be accomplished by inverting one of the addends and subtracting or that subtraction can be accomplished by inverting the subtrahend and adding.

The decimal numeral system Concomitant with the need for clear comprehension of the basic structure of each of the number systems of arithmetic there is the essential necessity for informed understanding of our decimal system of numerals. The concept of place value is possibly the greatest single simplification and efficiency device in our notational system. It would be difficult to overemphasize its nature and importance. Other number systems have been decimal in nature, and some of them have used place value, but in a rather restricted form. For example, in the Roman system of numeration, which is decimal, a symbol for a small number preceding a symbol for a larger number indicates a subtraction of values, and a symbol for a small number following a symbol for a larger number indicates an addition of values. Thus, IX means 10 − 1, or 9, and XI means 10 + 1, or 11.

Our more efficient use of place value makes it possible to use only ten individual symbols in the construction of number symbols, no matter how large or how small the value of the number to be represented. Thus each digital symbol (0, 1, 2, 3, 4, 5, 6, 7, 8, 9) in the symbol for a number might be said to have ascribed to it two values, a *place value* and a *face value*. In the symbol 1302 the digital symbols have certain values because of the position they have in the symbol: the 1 indicates the number of thousands, the 3 indicates the number of hundreds, the 0 indicates the number of tens, and the 2 indicates the number of ones. The concept of one-to-one correspondence enables us to determine the face value of each of these digital symbols, i.e., to tell *how many* each symbol represents. For example, compare the number symbol 1302 with the word "seeded." There are just as many thousands in the number symbol as there are letters *s* in the word; we call it "one" and use the symbol 1 to indicate the number. There are the same number of hundreds as there are letters *e*; we call it "three" and write it 3. There are just as many tens as there are letters *b*; we call it "zero" and write it 0. There are just as many ones as there are letters *d*; we call it "two" and write it 2. Thus, in such numbers, each digital symbol performs two functions; it is both a numeral and a place holder. In any numeral, each digital symbol performs two functions: (1) It serves as a place holder, since it holds a place, or position, in the numeral, and by virtue of this function it acquires place, or positional, value; (2) it serves as a cardinal number, since it tells the count of the units of a specific positional value present in a given number.

Convention has made of 0, the symbol for zero, a much more flexible symbol than any of the nonzero numerals. As indicated in the previous paragraph and in the field properties, it has the full stature of a cardinal number, integer, rational number, or real number. On the other hand convention has decreed that it is proper to use this same symbol in the capacity of a mere place holder. For example, the distance from the earth to the sun is 93 million miles. This is a satisfactory measure stated in terms of a large unit, 1 million miles. There are occasions when it is desirable to write this as a numeral. Since convention has decreed that it is not necessary to use a decimal point in writing a numeral unless it is necessary to indicate the ones position, some scheme for distinguishing the ones position becomes necessary when writing symbols for such numbers as 93 million. By common agreement and use the symbol has become 93,000,000 rather than some such symbol as 93,xxx,xxx. The same situation holds for small numbers. For example, to write 4 thousandths as a decimal, three places are required to the right of the decimal. Since 4 occupies only one place, some symbol must be used to fill the other two. While .xx4 is quite satisfactory as far as filling the basic need is concerned, convention has established .004 as the proper symbol.

In spite of the great notational and computational convenience intrinsic to the conventional flexibility ascribed to the symbol for zero, there are some situations in which it is absolutely incorrect to use the symbol in the sense of a mere place holder. For example, consider this box score of a baseball game played in Chicago between New York and Chicago.

New York	000	100	002	3
Chicago	001	000	04x	5

The 1, 2, 4, and each 0 are numerals which tell *how many* runs were scored during each team's respective efforts to score. The x in the position of the last half of the ninth inning is a mere place holder which convention has established as a proper method for filling out the box score when the home team has already won the game and makes no effort to score any more runs. The symbol 0 would be entirely incorrect in this position because it has numerical significance in such a box score and therefore cannot be used in the capacity of a mere place holder.

Proper instructional emphasis on place value can remove computation from the status of mere rote performance. For example, in finding the sum of 54 and 28, the addends are aligned according to the posi-

$$\begin{array}{r} 54 \\ +28 \\ \hline 82 \end{array} \qquad \begin{array}{r} 54 \\ -28 \\ \hline 26 \end{array}$$

tional value of the digits. 4 + 8 = 12, with the 2 recorded in the ones column and the 1 ten added with the other tens to secure a total of 8 tens. Similarly, in finding the differences, the digits are properly aligned according to place value. In subtraction, one of the 5 tens must be converted to 10 ones and combined with the 4 ones; then 14 ones less 8 ones is 6 ones, and 4 tens less 2 tens is 2 tens. Notice nothing is said about "carry" or "borrow." They are merely convenient words which can be used *if the process is understood, but not until then.* In multiplication, place value is the key to the proper placement of the partial products in order that they may be added correctly, and, in division, it can be used with ease and effectiveness as an aid in estimating and placing trial quotients, as well as in the attendant multiplication and subtraction.

Bases other than ten A study of systems of numeration using bases other than ten can be a distinct aid to the teacher and to the students in attaining a clearer understanding of the significance of place value in number symbolism. In the examples of this section we shall agree to use the concept of place value along with addition in the structure of any numeral. For example, in base ten 2345 is to be interpreted as meaning $2(1000) + 3(100) + 4(10) + 5(1)$ or, in either of two equivalent forms, $2(10^3) + 3(10^2) + 4(10^1) + 5(10^0)$ or $2(10^3) + 3(10^2) + 4(10) + 5(1)$. In this example 10 is used to represent ten. In other words, in base ten the numeral 10 represents *one of the base*. Similarly, this symbol can be used to represent the base in any numeral system which employs the concept of place value. As a result of this fact, in this section, where we are discussing numeral systems with different bases, we can neither interpret nor read 10 as "ten." We shall interpret it *only* as meaning "one of the base," whatever the base might be, and read it as "one-oh."

A numeral system, with base b and using the concept of place value along with the principle of addition, requires a symbol for zero as well as $b - 1$ nonzero symbols. In this section we shall use the familiar symbols 0, 1, 2, 3, 4, 5, 6, 7, 8, 9 of the decimal system insofar as we can. In the duodecimal system (base twelve) it becomes necessary to introduce two new symbols, one for ten (t) and one for eleven (e). Since we are not inventing number names we shall adopt the policy of reading each number digit by digit. Thus 1743 will be read "one-seven-four-three" whatever the base might be, realizing that only in base ten does it carry the specific meaning of "one thousand seven hundred forty-three." With such a convention the symbols t and e will be read by using their customary letter names. Table 11-2 shows the base symbols in each of four different bases with their equivalent numerals in the remaining three bases. Also the numerals equivalent to 995-ten are shown in the other three bases.

There are two basic techniques, multiplication and division, which may be used in converting from a given numeral in one base to an equivalent numeral in another base. This, of course, implies the necessity for computing in the context of the respective bases. A good exercise here is the construction of the tables of basic computation facts in each of several different bases.

TABLE 11-2
Comparing numeral systems using different bases

	Base two (binary)	Base eight (octal)	Base ten (decimal)	Base twelve (duodecimal)
Digital symbols	0, 1	0, 1, 2, 3, 4, 5, 6, 7	0, 1, 2, 3, 4, 5, 6, 7, 8, 9	0, 1, 2, 3, 4, 5, 6, 7, 8, 9, *t*, *e*
Base symbols and their equivalents	10	2	2	2
	1000	10	8	8
	1010	12	10	*t*
	1100	14	12	10
Equivalent numerals	1, 111, 100, 011	1743	995	6*te*

Table 11-3 shows such tables for base eight. In the addition table the sum of 5 + 7 may be found by looking for the square which is at the intersection of the row headed by 5 on the left and the column headed by 7 above. Here the sum is found to be 14 (5 + 7 = 14 in base eight). Of course, this same sum is to be found in the row headed by 7 and the column headed by 5 (7 + 5 = 5 + 7). Furthermore, it should be obvious that this table also serves as a subtraction table, since the differences 14 − 7 = 5 and 14 − 5 = 7 can be found. Similarly, the multiplication table shows 6 × 5 = 5 × 6 = 36-eight, since 36 is found either in the square at the intersection of the row headed by 6 and the column headed by 5 or in the row headed by 5 and the column headed by 6. Just as the addition table can be used to render the inversely related subtraction facts, so can the multiplication table be used to render the inversely related division facts. It must be kept in mind in this connection, however, that division by 0 is undefined.

The techniques for converting from a given numeral in one base to equivalent numerals in other bases will be illustrated by using the equivalent numerals of the last line of Table 11-2.

Example: Consider the numeral 1743-eight.

(1) Use multiplication to convert to an equivalent numeral in base two.
(2) Use division to convert to an equivalent numeral in base two.

(1) The numeral 1743 means $1(10^3) + 7(10^2) + 4(10) + 3(1)$, where each 10 carries the meaning of eight. From Table 11-2 we find 10-eight→1000-two. (The arrow → will be used to mean "converts into.")

TABLE 11-3
Basic computation facts for base eight

Addition

+	0	1	2	3	4	5	6	7
0	0	1	2	3	4	5	6	7
1	1	2	3	4	5	6	7	10
2	2	3	4	5	6	7	10	11
3	3	4	5	6	7	10	11	12
4	4	5	6	7	10	11	12	13
5	5	6	7	10	11	12	13	14
6	6	7	10	11	12	13	14	15
7	7	10	11	12	13	14	15	16

Multiplication

×	0	1	2	3	4	5	6	7
0	0	0	0	0	0	0	0	0
1	0	1	2	3	4	5	6	7
2	0	2	4	6	10	12	14	16
3	0	3	6	11	14	17	22	25
4	0	4	10	14	20	24	30	34
5	0	5	12	17	24	31	36	43
6	0	6	14	22	30	36	44	52
7	0	7	16	25	34	43	52	61

Also 4-eight (= 2 + 2) → 10 + 10 = 100-two
3-eight (= 2 + 1) → 10 + 1 = 11-two
7-eight (= 4 + 2 + 1) → 100 + 10 + 1 = 111-two

We thus have

Base eight	*Base two*	
$1743 = 1(10^3) + 7(10^2) + 4(10) + 3(1)$	$1(1000^{11}) + 111(1000^{10}) + 100(1000) + 11(1)$	
	$11(1) =$	11
	$100(1000) =$	100000
	$^*111(1000^{10}) =$	111000000
	$^*1(1000^{11}) =$	1000000000
1743 ———————	———————	→1111100011
	$^*1000^{10} = 1000 \times 1000$	
	$1000^{11} = 1000 \times 1000 \times 1000$	

(2) Since division is essentially a technique for finding how many groups of a smaller number are contained in a larger number, it may be used as a means for converting from one base to another. The problem of finding the numeral in base twelve which is equivalent to 1743-eight is merely that of regrouping in terms of twelve rather than eight. Since 14 is the numeral for twelve in base eight, the problem of conversion becomes one of dividing, in the context of eight as a base, 1743-eight by 14-eight and recording the remainders as they would be written as numerals in base twelve. The remainder from the first division will be the digit in the ones position; the remainder from the second division will be the digit in the base (10) position; that from the third division will be the digit in the base-squared (10^2) position; and so on until the final quotient is zero.

Eight	*Twelve*
$14 \overline{)1743}$ = 122	
14	
34	
30	
43	
30	
13 ———————	→ $1(8) + 3 = e$
$14 \overline{)122}$ = 6	
110	
12 ———————	→ $1(8) + 2 = t$
$14 \overline{)6}$ = 0	
0	
6 ———————	→ 6
1743 ———————	→ 6*te*

The reader might check these conversions by converting 1,111,100,-011-two and 6*te*-twelve to base ten. Use multiplication for one conversion and division for the other. The results from each conversion should be the same. According to the table it should be 995-ten.

The conversion from base eight to base two in the previous example provides the basis for an interesting deduction which provides an effective simple technique for conversion between these two bases. Table 11-4 shows a basic list of equivalent numeral relations which

TABLE 11-4
Basic numeral equivalents, bases eight and two

Eight	Two	Eight	Two
1	1	6	110
2	10	7	111
3	11	10	1000
4	100	10^2	1000^{10}
5	101	10^3	1000^{11}

exist between the two systems. Note that each period of three in base two can be converted into an equivalent digital numeral in base eight. Each period in the numeral 1,111,100,011-two converts respectively into the digital symbols 1-eight, 7-eight, 4-eight, and 3-eight. These are seen to be the digital symbols in the equivalent numeral 1743-eight. Conversely in converting from base eight to base two all that is required is to transform each digital numeral in base eight into its equivalent numeral in base two and then write the numeral in base two with these numerals in their respective period positions to accord with the given numeral in base eight.

Example: (1) Convert 11,101,001,111-two to base eight.
(2) Convert 62041-eight to base two.

(1) 11-two→3-eight; 101-two→5-eight; 1-two→1-eight; and 111-two→7-eight. Therefore 11,101,001,111-two→3517-eight.
(2) 6-eight→110-two; 2-eight→10-two; 0-eight→0-two; 4-eight→100-two; and 1-eight→1-two. Therefore 62041-eight→110,010,000,100,001-two.

These relations are used effectively in various forms of electronic computers. Since the computations are accomplished by means of electric circuits and a connection is either made (symbol is 1) or not made (symbol is 0), numbers must be programmed in base two for the machines. The ready transformation to base eight provides simpler notation than base two for recording the results as they are taken from the machines.

The four field operations with decimal fractions By the time they reach the junior high school grades, most children should have acquired a fair command of the number combinations and the mechanical rudiments of simple computation using the four field operations with rational numbers, whether they be integers or fractions. This does not imply that they will have acquired any great facility in computing, that they will have a complete understanding of the number system itself, or even that they will fully understand the mathematical justification of all the procedures they use. It seems certain that many do not. Some, of course, will still have difficulty even in performing the operations, especially division, but most of them can be expected to have attained at least a modicum of skill and some understanding of the principle of place value in the structure of numerals.

Unfortunately, it is too frequently true that students, even upon graduation from high school, either have failed to take advantage of the opportunity or have not had the opportunity to learn the full significance of place value in the structure of our numeral system. It not only binds together the thought processes which constitute the rationale of the fundamental operations but also simplifies the mechanics of the several algorisms. It is the keystone of our numeral system, and thus should receive emphasis throughout the elementary and secondary schools. Indeed, since the junior high school is the grade level at which the concepts and skills of arithmetic should be treated with a fair degree of maturity, these are the grades in which special emphasis should be given to place value and its significance to basic understanding in the effective use of numbers. In these grades pupils are expected to strengthen the skills and understandings of arithmetic and extend them to include less mechanical computation techniques with decimal fractions and common fractions. These extensions involve certain difficulties. It is important that teachers be aware of them so that steps can be taken to anticipate them and prevent them from becoming serious impediments to the students' genuine mastery of the subject.

The student who has really mastered the fundamental operations with whole numbers should have little difficulty in extending them to numbers involving decimal fractions. The procedures themselves are identical in the two cases. There is one new element, however, in cases where decimal fractions are involved, and that is the proper placement of the decimal point in the answer. This usually causes no difficulty in finding sums or differences, because when the numbers are written carefully columnwise, the decimal point in the sum or difference falls naturally into place in line with the others.

Mistakes are more likely to occur in placing the decimal point in products or quotients than in sums or differences. As a rule such mistakes are due to haste and carelessness, because the decimal point is too often placed by rote rule alone and without any checking to see whether the result is reasonable or not. It is also true that a good many students seem not to be impressed by the seriousness of the error which is introduced by a misplaced decimal point. The comment "But it's all right except the decimal point" is neither uncommon nor insincere on the part of the students, yet it implies unawareness of how serious the error is. Students need to be made and kept sensitive to the fact that even if an answer is numerically correct so far as the sequence of digits is concerned, misplacement of the decimal point represents one of the most serious mistakes that could be made because such a mistake can make the answer unreasonably large or small. As children learn arithmetic they need to be kept aware that the formal procedures are not divorced from common sense and that the results they get by using these procedures will not be right unless they can be confirmed by common sense.

This suggests a quick, easy, powerful, and in most cases a foolproof method of checking on the placement of the decimal point in a product or a quotient, namely, checking by mental estimate. Consider the product 27.43×12.08, which upon multiplication yields the digits 3313544 and requires that the decimal point be properly placed to give the true value of the product. Since 27.43 is a little less than 30 and 12.08 is a little more than 10, the required product *must* be in the neighborhood of 30×10, which is immediately seen to be 300. Hence the product *must* be somewhere near 300, and this requires that the decimal point be placed after the third digit; that is, the product must be 331.3544. This is readily confirmed by the usual rule, but more significantly, it is confirmed by the student's common sense. From such considerations even young students can readily learn to detect and correct careless misplacements of the decimal point and verify the correct position.

Placement of the decimal point in quotients can be determined and checked through similar considerations. For example, when 87.01646 is divided by 1.06, the sequence of digits 82091 appears in the quotient. The question of placing the decimal point can be resolved immediately by considering that, since the dividend is a little less than 90 and the divisor is just a little greater than 1, the quotient *must* be somewhere in the neighborhood of 90 and must also be less than 90, so it will probably be between 80 and 90. Hence, in order to yield such a quotient, the decimal point *must* be placed after the second digit. That is, the quotient must be 82.091.

Another effective method for placing the decimal point in the quotient is the following one. It is easily observed that $10 \times 1.06 = 10.6$, which is smaller than the dividend, and that $100 \times 1.06 = 106$, which is larger than the dividend. It follows, therefore, that the integral part of the quotient must be a two-digit number, since it lies between 10 and 100. The decimal point is thus to be placed immediately following the second quotient figure. Continued trial of successive powers of 10 is not a difficult procedure for establishing limits between which the quotient must lie. Practice will improve the estimate and reduce the number of trials necessary. Here again confirmation is easily made by applying the customary rule, but it is equally important to have the rule confirmed by the estimate. Indeed, the student's feeling of power and assurance is enhanced by encouraging him to make his preliminary estimate of the answer even before performing the computation. To this end such exercises as the following can be used to great advantage. They can be constructed easily and are unlimited in scope and variety.

Exercise: In the following products or quotients the digits are correct and in the right order. Place the decimal point where it should go, placing zeros if necessary before or after the digits given, and read the correct answer.

$38.501 \times 6.93 = 26681193$	$202.9372 \div 28.03 = 724$
$81.072 \times 39.6 = 32104512$	$129.10072 \div 19.88 = 6494$
$512.47 \times 2.53 = 12965491$	$4693.4705 \div 0.965 = 48637$
$70.386 \times 0.945 = 66514770$	$4.654728 \div 89.514 = 52$

The importance of inculcating in students the habit of checking their work by such estimates can hardly be overemphasized. Of course, it does not provide any check on the numerical work, but it does provide a powerful and easy and almost certain way of avoiding blunders through misplacement of the decimal point, and it injects a rationale into the work with decimal fractions which can hardly be attained in any other way. Actually, students almost always enjoy it, and the assurance and confidence which can result may often be of extreme importance with respect not only to the correctness of the work itself but also to the student's attitude toward it.

Of course, when dealing with decimal fractions, the point should always be made that these numbers are fractions. All the principles and techniques used with fractions still apply. The only differences at all are due to a possible simplification in notation due to the fact that the fractions to be used are now restricted to those whose denominators are powers of ten, the base of our number system. In particular the rules for finding the product and quotient of two fractions still apply. For example, the product 27.43×12.08 can be found as the product of the two common fractions $2{,}743/100 \times 1{,}208/100 = 3{,}313{,}544/10{,}000$, which may, in turn, be written as the decimal fraction 331.3544. Such procedure displays the reason why there are as many digits in the fraction part of the product of two decimal fractions as there are in the sum of the digits in the multiplier and the multiplicand. Similarly, the quotient $87.01646 \div 1.06$ can be found as

$$\frac{8{,}701{,}646}{100{,}000} \div \frac{106}{100} = \frac{8{,}701{,}646}{100{,}000} \times \frac{100}{106} = \frac{82{,}091}{1{,}000}$$

which can be written as the decimal fraction 82.091.

Such demonstration provides the rationale of the inverse rule used to find the number of digits in the fraction part of a quotient. Incidentally, once the rule for multiplication is established, the inverse relationship of division to multiplication could be used to obtain the corresponding rule for division.

Probably the most immediately direct and systematic physical application used to explain and illustrate decimals in arithmetic is the money system of the United States. Built as it is directly on the decimal system of notation, it forms a practically perfect physical illustration of that system, and it has the advantage of being familiar to everyone. Excellent as it is, however, it offers but a single means of illustration. Another, intrinsically just as good though less familiar to most people, is found in the metric system of weights and measures, which, of course, is an important element of the mathematics program in its own right. However, because it is not the system of weights and measures in most common use in this country, few people learn anything about it through informal everyday experience in the way they learn about money. As a rule, if it is learned at all, it is learned in school as a part of the work in mathematics, and its introduction generally occurs after the study of decimal fractions is begun. This, of course, imposes a drastic limitation on its use in *developing* the concept of decimal fractions but does not impair its later usefulness as a means of illustrating and strengthening this concept. Indeed, if the simple elements of the metric system could be taught concurrently with the subject of decimal notation and decimal fractions, it would seem to afford an excellent opportunity for strengthening and enriching both.

Percentage Of all the special topics or centers of attention in arithmetic none has more widespread utility and direct application than the subject of percentage. It is involved in the numerical record and analysis of all kinds of activities from the very simple to the very complex, and to those who understand its language it provides a concise and efficient means of interpreting, comparing, and communicating many kinds of quantitative information. Since it is so closely allied to the subject of decimal notation and fractions, one might conclude that its application would involve no difficulties that are not involved in the study or application of decimals as such. Unfortunately, however, experience indicates that this is not the case. Percentage has been and continues to be one of the most troublesome parts of arithmetic. In spite of its importance as an instrument for analysis and a vehicle for communication, many students fail to attain an assured mastery of it.

Various studies have been made from time to time to determine why students have so much difficulty with percentage, and these have usually taken the form of listing mistakes which students have made on percentage problems. But teachers ought to be concerned not only with what mistakes are made but with why they are made. To point out merely that students do not understand the principle of percentage does not provide much indication of just why they don't understand, or of what could be done to help them understand better. The computational skills involved in the mechanics of percentage are merely those involved in computing with decimal fractions, but they do not suffice for the interpretation and analysis of percentage problems stated in words or drawn from original situations. The latter require an exact understanding of the technical vocabulary and symbolism which has come to be associated with percentage, the ability to interchange different but equivalent forms with assurance, and the habit of meticulously careful analytical reading. The student who thoroughly understands a problem in percentage and who understands the language and symbolism usually will have little difficulty in solving it.

There seem to be several things that contribute to the confusion that is so prevalent with respect to percentage. The terminology that has come to be universally employed is itself confusing and unfortunate. In the identification of "per cent" with "hundredths" the base number often is not mentioned, though neither of these concepts has meaning except as referred to some base. The further representation of, say, "37 per cent" or "37%" by the decimal fraction "0.37" fails to emphasize the clarifying idea that 0.37 itself means 37×0.01 and that the % symbol merely stands for the decimal fraction 0.01. These alternative representations of the same thing thus tend to add to the student's confusion, especially when such expressions as "0.37%" are encountered. Experienced teachers will verify that students often fail to make any distinction in their minds between "37%" and "0.37%." When the subject is taught by "cases" three explicit rules can indeed be developed for the three explicit relations among the three elements involved, but these tend to become confused in the students' minds, and students often have trouble determining "which case this is." Even the single over-all rule or formula *base* × *rate* = *percentage* (or $b \cdot r = p$) requires that the rate must be represented by the decimal or common fraction only, not by use of the % symbol; yet even this is seldom emphasized in the textbooks.

What, then, can be done to make the teaching of percentage more productive of worthwhile results? The terminology and symbolism associated with percentage without doubt present certain ambiguities and difficulties. It seems reasonable, however, to believe that more can be done than usually has been done to make percentage intelligible to students and enable them to think about it with clarity.

Nearly all textbooks that treat the subject of percentage stress the solution of problems by use of the rule or formula: base × rate = percentage. This gives the fundamental relationship of the three elements and provides a pattern for explicit determination of percentage when the base and rate are known. Many textbooks go further and give explicit formulas for each of the three "cases." This may, of course, give quicker results when the students have the three formulas before them and the cases of all their problems identified. But, by the same token, it obviates the need for thinking about the problem and in effect avoids, rather than promotes, training in problem analysis. Moreover, students often get the formulas confused with each other unless they have them all written out before them. Failure to identify correctly the given data is a further major source of mistakes. Also, students frequently fail to check their results by first making rough estimates. Thus they are at times led through mechanical reaction to a rule to accept results which common-sense estimates would show to be ridiculous.

The only apparent reason for teaching percentage by cases with their accompanying three formulas is the belief that with typed problems this method will produce answers more quickly than other methods. But actually, even if that is true, the advantage is more apparent than real, because the same results can be attained about as quickly and with less chance of confusion if all three cases are fed into the one basic formula or rule and the resulting equation solved, when necessary, by a single step which students can learn to use easily and with understanding. As an example, consider this problem: At a school district election, 1,400 people voted. If this was 35 per cent of all the eligible voters, how many eligible voters were there in all? Steps in the solution would be as follows.

$$\text{Base} \times \text{rate} = \text{percentage}$$
$$\text{Base} \times (0.35) = (1{,}400)$$
$$\frac{\text{Base} \times (0.35)}{(0.35)} = \frac{1{,}400}{(0.35)}$$

Since the *base* (total number of eligible voters) is to be determined, it can be done immediately by dividing each member of the equation by the coefficient 0.35, giving the result indicated in the third line of the solution. If the objection be raised that this requires a little bit of algebra, one must reflect that the special formula for this case is itself derived by precisely this method.

Furthermore, this difficulty, if difficulty it is, can be greatly reduced by the realization that such emphasis on this fundamental relationship in percentage problems points out that there are always three numbers involved, and that one of them (*percentage*) is the product of the other two (*base* and *rate*). If the product number (percentage) is not known, then the operation called for is multiplication; if it is known, then the operation called for is division.

As in the multiplication of any two numbers, so in percentage are there four associated relations: $p = r \times b$, $p = b \times r$, $b = p \div r$, and $r = p \div b$. Furthermore, the rate, if it is a known number, usually is labeled with the per cent sign. This means that in percentage the problem situation is reduced to being able to distinguish between the number upon which all computation is based (the base) and the number which is derived through multiplication (the percentage).

As either an alternative or a supplementary device the "one per cent method" or "method of unitary analysis" can be used, often to great advantage in clarifying students' thinking. In this method primary attention is focused at the outset on the concept of one single per cent of the base as an entity—a whole "little" number or quantity in itself. If this is done, then such an expression as "63 per cent of the distance" comes to be thought of not just as some part of the required distance but actually as 63 parts, all equal and each being 1 hundredth of the required distance. This obviates the need for translating from per cents to decimal equivalents and so avoids the mistakes which so often accompany attempts to make this translation. Now 63 per cent becomes not 0.63 (a decimal fraction of the whole) but 63 "little wholes." It brings the thinking from the realm of fractions into the realm of whole numbers; from a field of possible uncertainty or confusion into a realm of familiarity. Then if one of these per cents can be found, any number of them can be found by a turn of the hand. It requires only the kind of reasoning one uses in determining the cost of 4½ gallons of gasoline at 35 cents a gallon or the cost of 115 postage stamps at 5 cents each. And no matter which case a percentage problem represents, 1 per cent of the base can always be found. As an example, consider again the problem about the voters, discussed above. Here our problem is clearly to determine the base number, which is the total number of eligible voters. It is given that 35 per cent of this total is 1,400 people. Think of this as 35 little groups of people, each group containing 1 per cent of the total number of eligible voters, with the total number of people in the 35 groups being 1,400. Now that is exactly equivalent, arithmetically, to such a question as this: If 35 notebooks cost $14.00, or 1,400 cents, how much does each cost? Very few students will not know how to find the cost of one notebook under these conditions, so it is not very hard to lead them to see how to determine the number representing 1 per cent of the required base. Then, having determined that 1 per cent of the total number of eligible voters is 40 (that is, 1/35 of 1,400), it follows that the total number must be 100 times as much, or 4,000.

Now it is easy also to answer at once such questions as the following ones: If 47½ per cent of the eligible voters are men, how many men are eligible to vote? If 3.7 per cent of the eligible voters are at least 80 years old, how many of the voters are not yet 80 years of age? If the number of eligible voters increases by 18 per cent in the next 5 years, how many will there be then?

There are, of course, some drawbacks to this method of analysis. It certainly requires careful and exact reading and interpretation of the problems, and the students will learn to handle the method only through honest, painstaking, and protracted effort on their part and on the part of their teachers. Some old mental associations and fixed habits will probably have to be broken down in order that the primary concept of a single per cent of the base number may come to occupy the focus of attention. This method requires superior teaching, and usually it will not produce answers as quickly as the use of the formula will. For these and perhaps other reasons it has not come into widespread use either in textbooks or by teachers. But it does aim at the fundamental objectives of clear thinking about percentage relationships, and if it is systematically and persistently used with good teaching and adequate supervision, it can do much to help students clarify their thoughts on this important aspect of arithmetic.

There are other considerations which teachers should take into account as means of clarifying and highlighting the main concepts associated with per cents and for providing conditions favorable to effective mastery of this subject. Space limitations preclude detailed discussion of them here, but one or two should at least be mentioned.

The concepts of *base*, *rate*, and *percentage* and the relations among them can be clarified and made vivid by the extensive use of graphs, and teachers should capitalize on this means of strengthening and enriching the concepts. Most textbooks do employ this device to a limited extent, but they need to be supplemented. Fortunately, it is easy to find many examples of graphic illustrations of situations that involve percentage. Newspapers, magazines, financial reports, business articles, brochures, and advertising material are rich sources of such examples. Bar, circle, and line graphs lend themselves readily to use in such illustrations. A great variety of good illustrations is readily available for study, and it can be supplemented at will by having the students make graphic illustrations of their own problems. The systematic use of graphs to illustrate problems and principles of percentage can do much to clarify and fix the concepts and principles that are involved.

Teachers need to be sensitive to the fact that problems which involve more than 100 per cent of the base number are especially troublesome to many students. The trouble may often be traced to failure to read carefully or to interpret relations or notation correctly. This, in turn, may result from the habit of expecting the percentage to be less than the base, since this is almost always the case in the early problems used to introduce the subject. Similarly, students often have trouble in cases that involve numbers less than 1 per cent of the base. The trouble in this case usually arises from failure either to interpret correctly or to write correctly the notation representing the fraction of a per cent. These two trouble spots are serious enough to merit the teacher's special attention in planning the work in percentage. In both of these cases the use of graphs can be very helpful for illustrating such problems, and the use of the 1 per cent method described above can make a real contribution to the analysis of such problems.

As a final suggestion, teachers should be warned that poorly graded sets of problems can be a major source of difficulty and frustration to students. In general the authors of textbooks make sincere efforts to provide well-ordered lists of exercises leading gradually from very simple ones to more difficult or complicated ones, but sometimes they do not succeed very well. Yet nothing is more frustrating to students than to be expected to solve problems for which they have not had adequate preparation. A hard problem placed inappropriately early in a list where the students are not ready for it is not only nonproductive but actually destructive of confidence and morale. In planning assignments for classwork or homework the teacher will be well advised to go through in detail any lists of problems that are to be assigned, to be sure that this situation does not arise. Problem lists should always be regarded as self-administering exercises designed to lead the student step by step to increased mastery and insight and self-reliance. Exercises which are out of place in a problem list do not contribute to this objective and should be either eliminated or properly relocated in the list.

Common fractions

Along with percentage and verbal problems, the fundamental operations with common fractions share the dubious distinction of being the most troublesome parts of arithmetic. The difficulties encountered in the solution of verbal problems will be discussed later in a separate section; this section will deal with some learning and teaching problems associated with common fractions.

The very real and very serious difficulties which many students encounter in working with common fractions may stem from any one or more of several causes. One of them is failure to have a clear concept of what a fraction represents numerically. Another is an apparent reluctance to concede that in operations with fractions the numerators and denominators must be given attention separately; that frequently it is not sufficient to think of fractions merely as single numbers as one would think of integers, but rather, as ratios each consisting of two separate parts or as the expressed quotients of two numbers. This is tantamount to nonrecognition of the real meaning of the numerator and denominator and of the role each has in expressing the value of the fraction. Such recognition requires reflective thought, and thinking is hard, and often slow, work. A third source of difficulty lies in the characteristic impatience of youth—the desire to be done with a problem quickly, and preferably in a single step. This, coupled with fuzzy concepts, uncertain thinking, disregard of definitions, and a tendency to speed things up by uncritical use of analogy, can and often does combine to produce in students a state of mind altogether unfavorable to clear thinking. Such a state of mind leads to a willingness to use any device that will produce a quick answer.

Teachers, of course, cannot disregard these things. Failing to get acceptable progress through the necessarily slow process of insisting on clear thinking about fractions and faced with limited time, teachers often have recourse to the only apparent alternative: that of providing the students with ready-made rules. Students usually like to have them, because the rules provide them with patterns that are easy to follow and which do enable them to get quick results. Rules per se are not bad; indeed, they are very necessary for generalizing and crystallizing procedures and for economizing time and effort. But such rules without accompanying insight are merely arithmetical tools. They may promote computational proficiency but they do not represent genuine mathematical understanding, which alone can lead to intelligent use of any acquired mathematical tools.

While this is recognized by practically all teachers, there are two extreme schools of thought about rules in mathematics. One holds that students should *never* be taught a process until it has been rationalized. The other holds that rationalization will always be easier to understand if students are first given the rule and shown how it works and that the use of the rule or procedure should *always* precede the justification. It is almost certain that neither of these extreme positions is tenable. But without rationalization, whether first or last, genuine growth in mathematical insight cannot take place. The danger in the "rule first, rationalization later" theory is that of time pressure. Inevitably, and perhaps before getting around to the rationalization, comes the need to move on to other things, and to teachers under this pressure the temptation to compromise on reasonable mechanical proficiency in the use of the rules can become very strong.

Too frequently the technique of simplifying fractions, or "reducing fractions to lower terms," is taught as a mechanical process of cancellation. Such a procedure leads to a confused concept of the significance of cancellation and very often reduces it to a mere crossing out of numbers. Such a performance as

$$\frac{\not{4} + 2}{\not{4} + 9} = \frac{2}{9} \qquad \text{or} \qquad \frac{\not{7} + 3}{\not{7} \times 3} = \frac{3}{3} = 1$$

then may, and not infrequently does, result. In instruction which leads to this sort of performance, no basic understanding of the interrelationship among the fundamental operations or of the structure of fractions is developed. It needs to be pointed out to students that the horizontal bar of a fraction indicates a division; that, for example, $\frac{8}{18}$ indicates the division of 8 by 18. Stress should also be laid upon the principle that division and multiplication are inverse processes, just as addition and subtraction are inverse processes. Thus, in the multiplication and division of any number by the same number (other than zero) one operation nullifies, destroys, or cancels the effect of the other. This means simply that the net effect is multiplication, or division, of the given number by 1. Thus

$$\frac{8}{18} = \frac{2 \times 4}{2 \times 9} = \frac{4}{9} \times \frac{2}{2} = \frac{4}{9} \times 1 = \frac{4}{9}$$

We simplify all of this detail by using the convenient device of cancellation:

$$\frac{8}{18} = \frac{{}^{1}\not{2} \times 4}{{}^{1}\not{2} \times 9} = \frac{1 \times 4}{1 \times 9} = \frac{4}{9}$$

The small 1's should be written in to give emphasis to what has actually taken place. Similarly, the net effect of adding the same number to and subtracting it from a given number is equivalent to the addition, or subtraction, of zero. Thus $7 + 2 - 2 = 7 + 0$ (or $7 - 0) = 7$. Cancellation can be used to indicate what has taken place here. There would be no division, however, but merely a neutralizing which can be indicated by simply crossing out the numbers which neutralize each other: $7 + \not{2} - \not{2} = 7$. In the fraction $\frac{4 + 2}{4 + 9}$ the student should be taught that he must think of the operations involved as if the division were expressed in the form $(4 + 2) \div (4 + 9)$. In such situations he can recognize that the additions must be performed before the division and that, since addition and division are not inverse processes, no cancellation is possible.

The principles of the previous paragraph are recognized as based on the inverse properties of the field of rational numbers ($F6$ and $F8$, page 248). Furthermore the principles of cancellation are simply those of theorem 4 (page 247) and theorem 8 (page 250). If the instructional program in arithmetic has given the correct emphasis to the basic structure of the number systems of arithmetic, the bases for answers to many of the "why questions" of the type indicated here will have been constructed before the questions arise. If the student cannot ferret out his own answers to such questions, the teacher can direct the student to this informational background as an aid in his search for the desired answers.

Multiplication of fractions usually presents little difficulty. In the first place the definition is rather simple: $a/b \times c/d = ac/bd$. Second, it can be made to seem reasonable by giving various concrete illustrations and by identifying such notation as $1/3 \times 6/7$ with the corresponding verbal expression one-third of six-sevenths. Graphic or geometric illustrations are effective and are easy to devise. Although the procedure actually represents a definition of the product, it is well to give illustrations to show that the results which it gives are in accord with actual experience and common sense.

Products of fractions can often be simplified by cancellation. As a precautionary measure against mistakes it is well to have students form the habit of expressing the product as a single fraction before doing the cancellation. For example, instead of writing

$$\frac{1}{{}^{1}\not{3}} \times \frac{\not{6}^{2}}{7}$$

it is better for them to write

$$\frac{1}{3} \times \frac{6}{7} = \frac{1 \times {}^{1}\not{3} \times 2}{{}^{1}\not{3} \times 7} = \frac{1 \times 1 \times 2}{1 \times 7} = \frac{2}{7}$$

because it systematizes the form and may prevent mistakes due to careless writing. Of course after a student thoroughly understands the full significance of what is taking place, he no longer needs to bother with so much minuteness of detail.

The procedure for dividing by a fraction is familiar to most students who know how to multiply fractions, for the reason that, after a single simple adjustment, the division problem actually becomes a problem in multiplication. Few, however, of those who know *how* to divide by a fraction understand *why* the inversion of the fractional divisor and the consequent multiplication actually give the required value. In a recent poll of 75 college students taking business arithmetic it was found that 73 of the 75 knew how to divide by a fraction but only 2 knew how to justify the procedure. Here again is a case of a rather familiar process which for the most part is used quite empirically. Where used correctly it gives correct results. Unfortunately, however, the word "invert" seems to stand out as the only important thing in the minds of the students, with the result that sometimes they invert the dividend instead of the divisor and then wonder why the result they get is incorrect or perhaps even ridiculous. The only sure safeguard against such a situation is to get the students to understand the rationale of the procedure. This need not be a long or tedious matter, for a few rather simple illustrations will usually suffice.

While there are several elementary avenues to satisfactory rationalization, it must be kept in mind that the foundation upon which any approach must be based consists in the facts that *(a)* multiplication and division are inverse processes and *(b)* 1 is the identity element for multiplication and division. Thus it follows, for example, that

$$16 \div 4 = \frac{16}{4} = \frac{16 \times 1/4}{4 \times 1/4} = \frac{16 \times 1/4}{1} = 16 \times \frac{1}{4}$$

and that

$$9 \div \frac{1}{3} = (9 \times 3) \div \left(\frac{1}{3} \times 3\right) = (9 \times 3) \div 1 = 9 \times 3$$

Unless some effective measures are taken to have the students understand what is actually taking place and see why the process must give the required result, there will always be some danger of mistakes occurring, and at best the students would have attained only a mechanical proficiency without corresponding mathematical insight. The best teachers will never be content with this.

The greatest source of trouble in this area, however, is the addition and subtraction of fractions, particularly when the fractions have different denominators. The difficulty stems from the sources that have already been mentioned: the desire of the students for short cuts and quick answers, the time pressure on the teachers and the consequent tendency to give inadequate attention to rationalizing the procedure, the excessive dependence on the mechanical use of rules, and the failure to check results for reasonableness. Furthermore, there is the additional fact that the procedure here is characteristically a bit more involved than is that in the operations discussed previously. This, of course, intensifies the pressure on the teacher and tends to diminish any disposition to insist on rationalization and checking, although they are made even more important by the circumstances.

One of the most effective ways of giving meaning to the addition of fractions is the method of unitary analysis, which has already been mentioned in connection with percentage. Under this method as applied, say, to the fraction $3/7$, it would be emphasized that the fraction is made up of 3 "unit fractions" each of which is $1/7$, or

$$\frac{3}{7} = \frac{1}{7} + \frac{1}{7} + \frac{1}{7} = 3 \times \frac{1}{7} = \frac{1}{7} \times 3$$

This decomposition both establishes an identity as shown and suggests the usefulness of identifying the form $3/7$ with the form $3 \times 1/7$. But it does more. Through this latter identification (which curiously is seldom used and often not even recognized by students, even though teachers always assume that it is so obvious as to require no comment) a reversal of the decomposition suggests the fundamental concept of the combination of fractions with like denominators, out of which the formal rule grows. That is to say,

$$\frac{1}{7}+\frac{1}{7}+\frac{1}{7}=\frac{1}{7}\times 3=\frac{1}{7}\times(1+1+1)=\frac{1+1+1}{7}=\frac{3}{7}$$

This illustrates what goes on in the combination of fractions whose denominators are alike. The effect of such an illustration, however, will usually be negligible unless two things are explicitly and *separately* emphasized about the single fraction which makes up the sum, namely, (1) how its denominator is determined and (2) how its numerator is determined, and preferably in the order mentioned. This may seem a trivial insistence, but it is not. It is justified by both psychological considerations and practical experience. The matter should not be hurried; it should be soundly established in the minds of the students by both discussion and practice before taking them on to the more troublesome case of combining fractions whose denominators are not alike.

Once the handling of fractions with like denominators is thoroughly understood by the students, the way is open for proceeding to the general case of fractions whose denominators are not necessarily alike. Recalling that for any given fraction an equal fraction having any nonzero denominator we like can be written, let us then say to the students, "If the denominators are not alike, make them alike. Then we shall know how to combine them." This will, of course, require determination of the least common denominator, the building up of all denominators to this form by writing in the needed factors, and corresponding adjustment of numerators. This is best understood if all the denominators are first written in full factored form and the L.C.D. is also written in factored form and if all these factored expressions are written out separately for reference. For example, consider the sum of the fractions $5/42 + 7/12 + 1/2$. Now

$$42 = (2)(3)(7) \qquad 12 = (2)(3)(2) \qquad \text{L.C.D.} = (2)(3)(2)(7)$$

$$\begin{aligned}\frac{5}{42}+\frac{7}{12}+\frac{1}{2} &= \frac{5}{(2)(3)(7)}+\frac{7}{(2)(3)(2)}+\frac{1}{2}\\ &= \frac{5(2)}{(2)(3)(2)(7)}+\frac{7(7)}{(2)(3)(2)(7)}+\frac{1(3)(2)(7)}{(2)(3)(2)(7)}\\ &= \frac{10}{84}+\frac{49}{84}+\frac{42}{84}\\ &= \frac{10+49+42}{84}=\frac{101}{84}\end{aligned}$$

In such cases it is simpler and probably better to use parentheses, as shown, to indicate multiplication. The meaning of this notation will have to be explained to students who have not had any experience with algebra, but this should take little time and cause no difficulty.

At the outset, of course, much simpler cases would be used—examples in which the identification of the L.C.D. can be very easily made at sight—and perhaps the work in the seventh grade should be largely limited to such cases. It is believed, however, that even here the routine illustrated above will do much to build fundamental understanding of the rationale underlying the process and thus remove it from the realm of mere mechanical tools. Even in the seventh grade the generality of the procedure can be enhanced by giving some illustrations of cases in which the L.C.D. is not immediately discernible as a single whole number. The advantage of this will become more and more apparent as the students go on to subsequent work in arithmetic and in algebra.

Furthermore, even in its simplest form this procedure tends to rationalize the rote process used in the elementary grades for finding the L.C.D. in such situations. It is possible that there may be some students at the seventh-grade level who are not yet sufficiently mature to be able to comprehend such rationalization, even in its simplest form. For such students the rote method of successive multiplications of the largest denominator by the integers 2, 3, 4, etc., will have to continue to suffice.

Everything which has been said in this section applies with equal validity and in all details to both proper and improper fractions. Indeed, since mixed numbers and integers can be written as improper fractions, it can be said to apply to them as well, after they are written in fraction form. Sometimes multiplication, and always division, by mixed numbers can be accomplished most easily by reducing these numbers to improper fractions and proceeding accordingly. It is well to give students some experience in this, both for the understanding of the specific applications and for strengthening the sense of the generality of the methods.

The entire discussion of addition of fractions has been couched in the language of traditional procedures. This has been deliberate, since these instructional problems will continue to exist. It could have been developed entirely within the context of the definition of the sum of two rational numbers. With this approach an appeal would be made to the definition, to the associative property of addition, and to the concept of equivalent fractions. No use would be made of the concept of common denominator. For example:

$$\frac{1}{7}+\frac{1}{7}+\frac{1}{7}=\left(\frac{1}{7}+\frac{1}{7}\right)+\frac{1}{7}=\frac{1\cdot 7+7\cdot 1}{7\cdot 7}+\frac{1}{7}=$$
$$\frac{7+7}{49}+\frac{1}{7}=\frac{14}{49}+\frac{1}{7}=\frac{2}{7}+\frac{1}{7}=\frac{2\cdot 7+7\cdot 1}{7\cdot 7}=$$
$$\frac{14+7}{49}=\frac{21}{49}=\frac{3}{7}$$

Verbal problems To be able to apply correct computation to the solution of genuine problems can be regarded for most people as the end product of the study of arithmetic, for it is here that arithmetic finds its practical usefulness. It is also, for most people, the most difficult aspect of arithmetic. The reason for this is not hard to find. Computation per se resolves itself through rationalization into patterns of procedure which eventually become habituated and used in much the same way as correct habits of speaking. Furthermore, when a computation is presented, the student faces not the question of what he is to do, but only the requirement of doing it.

Problem situations, on the other hand, require not only that the student be able to do the things that need to be done but also that he decide what things need to be done and in what order. Beyond the classification, sometimes made, of certain elementary problems into types such as time-rate-distance problems and work problems, verbal problems follow no special pattern. Every one of them must be thought through. The student has to determine for himself exactly what is required, what data he has available for use, and what he must do with the data in order to arrive at the information that is required. Moreover, since the main source of verbal problems is usually the textbook, the student has to be able to read and interpret correctly what he reads before he can even begin his analysis of the problem. Thus every problem of this sort presents a double problem to the student: he must first read and analyze the problem and set up his procedure, and he must then perform the computations required for obtaining the numerical answer. Of the two parts of the problem, the first typically gives more trouble than the second. Also, the student must be able to recognize in a problem situation the basic characteristics of the fundamental processes. For example, when a problem situation calls for the combining of two or more groups of like objects into a single group, the student must be able to recognize that either addition or multiplication is the process which will accomplish the desired result and that a careful analysis will tell him which of the two to use.

A good many studies have been made in the attempt to identify the causes of student difficulty with verbal problems. Examination of published material on problem solving in arithmetic indicates that much of the difficulty can be attributed to one or more of the following causes:[1]

1. Computation
2. Lack of reasoning ability
3. Poor procedure or complete absence of systematic attack
4. Difficulty in selecting the processes to be used
5. Failure to comprehend the meaning of the problem
6. Inefficient reading habits
7. Vocabulary difficulties

[1]The order of listing here does not imply relative importance.

8. Short attention span
9. Inability to select essential data
10. Carelessness in transcribing
11. Poor eyesight and other physical defects
12. Lack of interest
13. Guessing because of desire for a quick answer

Such a list can be of some help to teachers in trying to identify causes of difficulty with verbal problems experienced by individuals and perhaps to some extent by classes, but it does not provide specific remedies. The causes listed above are not in themselves simple or specific but are individually highly complex. Furthermore, they will seldom, if ever, occur singly. For the most part they are not mutually exclusive but are interwoven and interdependent. For example, difficulty in selecting the processes to be used might be due to failure to comprehend the meaning of the problem, lack of reasoning ability, absence of systematic attack, or inefficient reading habits. Inefficient reading habits in turn may result from lack of interest, poor eyesight, vocabulary difficulties, or short attention span.

The truth is that the solution of verbal problems requires intellectual activity of a higher order and more complex nature than that involved in sheer computation. It requires conceptual understanding, insight, originality, independence of thought, and self-reliance. Some students are more richly endowed with these characteristics than others are. The characteristics are not specifics but complexes, and they usually can be developed only slowly, with painstaking, patient, and unremitting effort.

Efforts have been made and experiments have been carried out to try to determine a best method for teaching problem solving and reducing it to a system. Some of them have been more or less well defined and even given names.

1. The *restatement method*, in which the students are asked to restate each problem in their own words as a means of clarifying the problem.
2. The *analysis method*, in which effort is made to have the student systematically analyze the problem by requiring him to go through the following sequence of steps: (*a*) What is required? (*b*) What is given? (*c*) What operations are to be used? With what numbers? In what order? (*d*) Estimate the answer. (*e*) Solve the problem. (*f*) Check the answer by an estimate.
3. The *method of analogies*, in which the student is given a simple oral problem similar to but shorter than the more difficult written problem.
4. The *method of dependencies*, in which the student is taught to recognize and focus on fundamental dependence relations existing among elements in the problem under consideration. This is, in fact, the central core of the analysis method mentioned above.
5. The *graphic method*, in which the student is taught to use some graphic or diagrammatic scheme to help him identify the elements of the problem and

formulate an explicit statement of their relations to each other. This method is rather specially helpful because it exhibits the problems visually and thus makes the relations easier to detect and formulate.

Because of space limitation, it is not feasible to give illustrations of all these methods here, but one illustration of the graphic method will be given because of its special helpfulness. Consider the following problem.

Example: A shipment of coats was received, and all but one of the coats were sold before Christmas. On the following January 2 the marked price on this coat was reduced by 20 per cent, and the next day the coat was sold at its reduced price of \$60.00. At this price it still yielded a profit which was equivalent to 25 per cent of the cost of the coat. What did it cost and what was the pre-Christmas marked price?

Figure 11-1

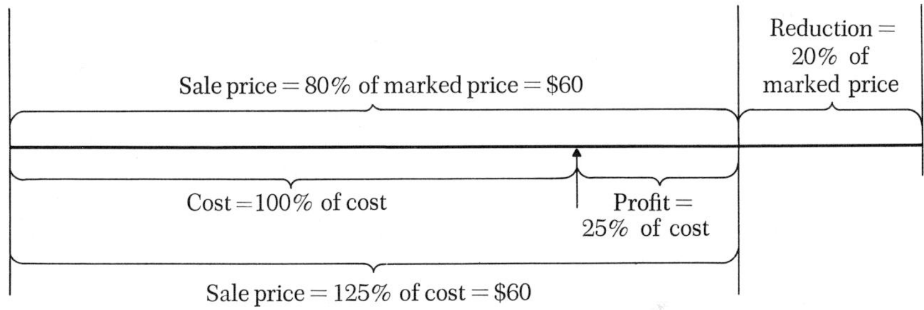

S.P. = cost + profit
= cost + 25 per cent of cost
= 125 per cent of cost
= \$60.00

whence cost can easily be determined as \$48.00.

S.P. = marked price − reduction
= marked price − 20 per cent of marked price
= 80 per cent of marked price
= \$60.00

whence marked price is easily determined to be \$75.00.

No single method stands out as the one best method of teaching verbal problems. Each of those mentioned above has given fair results. Teachers ought to become familiar with all the methods suggested above and make use of those which seem best suited to the requirements of each immediate situation, adapting them as needed and perhaps devising other ways of helping students learn to clarify the elements and relations involved in verbal problems.

At the risk of some repetition it may be worthwhile to list a few statements which can serve both as prerequisites to effective problem solving and as suggested ways in which the teacher can help students improve their abilities in this direction. Some of these ideas will be further amplified in Chapter 14.

1. Since the problems are written problems, the students must be able to read.
2. The students must be able to use the fundamental processes of arithmetic.
3. The students must understand the fundamental characteristics of each of the fundamental operations. They must be able to recognize these characteristics in a problem situation.
4. The students must be able to distinguish between essential and unessential data; hence, some definite instructional program may be necessary to aid them in acquiring this ability.
5. The students must be able to distinguish the known from the unknown. Some specific instruction in this may be needed.
6. The students must be able to sense such relationships as may exist among given data and the required information.
7. The students must be able to translate verbal expressions into mathematical symbols. This is one of the most important of all techniques necessary for an intelligent approach to the solving of verbal problems. The teacher should place a great deal of emphasis upon the translation of the English statements of problem situations into their symbolic statements. Attention should be called to the simplification of operations which results from the use of significant symbolism and diagrams.
8. Independence and confidence are great aids in problem solving. Students should know how to estimate and how to check answers.

EXERCISES

1. What is meant by a well-defined operation upon the numbers of a given number system?

2. State the postulates for the natural number system.

3. State the postulates for an integral domain.

4. State the postulates for a number field.

5. When are two sets of numbers said to be isomorphic with respect to addition and multiplication?

6. Show that the set of complex numbers whose elements are of the form $a + 0i$ and the set R^* of real numbers are isomorphic with respect to addition and multiplication.

Prove each of the following theorems for the real numbers a and b.

7. $a \times 0 = 0 \times a = 0$.
8. $a + (-b) = a - b$.
9. $(a + b) - b = a = (a - b) + b$.
10. $a \times (-b) = -(a \times b)$.
11. $(-a) \times (-b) = a \times b$.
12. If $b \neq 0$, then $a \times 1/b = a \div b$.
13. If $b \neq 0$, then $(a \times b) \div b = a = (a \div b) \times b$.

14. Show that addition and multiplication, as defined for rational numbers on page 247, are both associative and commutative and that multiplication is distributive over addition.

15. Show that the erroneous definition, $a/b + c/d = (a + c)/(b + d)$, for the sum of

two rational numbers cannot hold, since the definition would not be well defined. Recall that a/b and c/d represent equivalence classes and that their sum should represent a unique equivalence class.

16. Given that a and $b \in R^*$ and that the operation # is defined by the relation $a \# b = a + (a \times b)$, where + and × are ordinary addition and multiplication, respectively. Is the system closed under #? Is # commutative over the set? Is # associative over the set?

17. Given the set R of rational numbers with the ordinary operations of subtraction (−) and division (÷). Prove the following:

a. The system is closed under each operation.
b. Neither operation is associative over the set R.
c. Neither operation is commutative over the set R.
d. Division is distributive over subtraction.

18. Given the set of positive integers and the two binary operations # and * defined by $a \# b = a + 3b$ and $a * b = 3ab$, where + and × are ordinary addition and multiplication, respectively:

a. Is the set closed under each operation?
b. Is each operation associative over the set?
c. Is each operation commutative over the set?
d. Is * distributive over #?

19. Explain as you would to a class the details of performing the division 295.6 ÷ 4.73. Justify each step, including placement of the decimal point by the customary rule, and then show that a rough estimate confirms this placement of the decimal point.

20. Without performing any pencil and paper computations, make rough mental estimates of the approximate values of the following products and quotients: 38.47 × 6.24; 253.19 × 19.41; 85.72 × 12.15; 26.06 × 0.486; 0.0945 × 51.54; 281.6 ÷ 71.12; 165.3 ÷ 85.10; 47.364 ÷ 24.336; 19.528 ÷ 0.493; 0.7238 ÷ 0.0352.

21. Give a report to the class in which you explain and illustrate the use in physics and chemistry of the metric system and its counterpart of numbers written in decimal notation.

22. Solve and explain the following problems by using the 1 per cent method and illustrating each with a diagram:

a. 29% of ____ is 145.
b. 72 is ____% of 180.
c. 88 is ____% of 28.
d. 13% of 485 is ____.
e. 0.3% of 220 is ____.
f. 41% of ____ is 1,476.
g. 52 is ____% of 260.
h. 126% of 77 is ____.
i. ____ is 15% more than 80.
j. 44% less than 350 is ____.

23. Solve and explain each of the foregoing problems by direct substitution of given values in the basic formula base × rate = percentage, with solution of the resulting equations.

24. Explain why the quotient $\frac{7}{8} \div \frac{3}{5}$ is correctly given by taking the product $\frac{7}{8} \times \frac{5}{3}$.

25. In teaching the addition or subtraction of mixed numbers some teachers instruct the students to add or subtract the integer parts and the fractional parts of the numbers separately and combine the results. Others have the students change all the mixed numbers to improper fractions, find the sum of these, and then convert this back to a mixed number. Give examples in which you think the first of these methods would be preferable and explain why. Do the same for the second method.

26. Consider the following statement:

$$5\tfrac{2}{7} \times 3\tfrac{3}{4} = 5 \times 3 + 5 \times \tfrac{3}{4} + 3 \times \tfrac{2}{7} + \tfrac{2}{7} \times \tfrac{3}{4}$$

a. If the statement is wrong, criticize it.
b. If the statement is correct, justify it.
c. Present an alternative method of performing the multiplication. Which method do you prefer? Why?

27. Consider the numeral $1{,}451 \equiv 1(10)^3 + 4(10)^2 + 5(10)^1 + 1$ and (*a*) interpret it in base eight and write its equivalent in base ten; (*b*) interpret it in base twelve and write

its equivalent in base ten; and (*c*) interpret it in base ten and write its equivalent in base two, in base eight, and in base twelve.

28. Give illustrations to show the significance of place value in addition, subtraction, multiplication, and division.

29. Consider a symbol a/b as a common fraction with its numerator and denominator written in base ten and reduced to lowest terms. Use the fact that $10 = 2 \times 5$ to explain the following three statements:

a. If b is of the form 2^n, 5^n, or $2^m \cdot 5^n$ $(m < n)$, then a/b will convert into a terminating decimal fraction of n decimal places.

b. If b is a prime number other than 2 or 5, then a/b will convert into a repeating decimal and the repetend will contain no more than $b - 1$ digits. (For example, $2/7 = .\overline{285714}$.)

c. If b is of the form $2^n \cdot c$, $5^n \cdot c$, or $2^m \cdot 5^n \cdot c$, where $m < n$ and c does not contain either 2 or 5 as a factor, then a/b will convert into a repeating decimal. There will be n decimal places preceding the first digit of the repetend. For example,

$$\frac{1}{28} = \frac{1}{2^2 \cdot 7} = 0.03\overline{571428}$$

30. Use only inspection to answer questions (*a*) to (*d*) about the following common fractions: (1) $5/32$, (2) $7/28$, (3) $8/72$, (4) $3/28$, (5) $9/200$, (6) $7/375$.

a. Which fractions will convert into terminating decimals and which into repeating decimals?

b. In each terminating decimal how many decimal places will be required before it terminates?

c. In each repeating decimal how many decimal places will be required before the first digit of the repetend appears?

d. In each repeating decimal what is the maximum number of possible digits in the repetend?

31. Make ten verbal problems involving percentage which you consider suitable for eleventh- or twelfth-grade students.

BIBLIOGRAPHY

Adams, L. J.: "Arithmetic for College Students" (New York: Holt, Rinehart and Winston, Inc., 1961).

Adler, Irving: "Magic House of Numbers" (New York: The John Day Company, Inc., 1960).

———: "Mathematics: The Story of Numbers, Symbols, and Space" (New York: Golden Press, 1958).

——— and Ruth Adler: "Numbers, Old and New" (New York: The John Day Company, Inc., 1960).

Allen, Harold Don: Understanding through Number Systems, *Mathematics Teacher*, **55** (1962), 184–188.

Bakst, Aaron: "Arithmetic for the Modern Age" (Princeton, N.J.: D. Van Nostrand Company, Inc., 1960).

Banks, J. Houston: "Elements of Mathematics," 2d ed. (Englewood Cliffs, N. J.: Allyn and Bacon, Inc., 1961).

Bell, Clifford, Clela D. Hammond, and Robert B. Herrera: "Fundamentals of Arithmetic for Teachers" (New York: John Wiley & Sons, Inc., 1962).

Botts, Truman: Numbers, Sets, and Counting, *Arithmetic Teacher*, **8** (1961), 281–286.

Boyer, Carl B.: Viète's Use of Decimal Fractions, *Mathematics Teacher*, **55** (1962), 123–127.

Brumfiel, Charles F., Robert E. Eicholz, and Merrill E. Shanks: "Fundamental Concepts of Elementary Mathematics" (Reading, Mass.: Addison-Wesley Publishing Company, Inc., 1962).

Dantzig, Tobias: "Number, the Language of Science," 3d ed. (New York: The Macmillan Company, 1945).

Davis, Philip J.: "The Lore of Large Numbers" (New York: Random House, Inc., 1961).

Dubisch, Roy: "The Nature of Number" (New York: The Ronald Press Company, 1952).

Grossnickle, Foster E.: Teaching Arithmetic in the Junior High School, *Mathematics Teacher*, **47** (1954), 520–527.

Hamilton, E. W.: Number Systems: Fad or Foundation, *The Arithmetic Teacher*, **8** (1961), 242–245.

Hamilton, Norman T., and Joseph Landin: "Set Theory, the Structure of Arithmetic" (Englewood Cliffs, N. J.: Allyn and Bacon, Inc., 1961).

Hannon, Herbert: The Role of Meaning in Teaching the Fundamental Processes, *School Science and Mathematics*, **58** (1958), 83–89.

______: A Time to Appraise the New and Reevaluate the Old in Upper Grades and Junior High School Mathematics, *School Science and Mathematics*, **63** (1963), 171–177.

Hohn, Franz E.: Teaching Creativity in Mathematics, *Arithmetic Teacher*, **8** (1961), 102–106.

Hudson, Charles: Some Remarks on Teaching Different Bases, *School Science and Mathematics*, **63** (1963), 649–652.

Jones, Burton W.: "Elementary Concepts of Mathematics" (New York: The Macmillan Company, 1963).

Kingston, J. Maurice: Some Arithmetical Fundamentals of Value to Junior High School Teachers, *Mathematics Teacher*, **48** (1955), 232–236.

Kinney, Lucien B.: Teaching Percentage for Understanding and Use, *Mathematics Teacher*, **51** (1958), 38–41.

Larsen, Harold D., and H. Glenn Ludlow: "Arithmetic for Colleges" (New York: The Macmillan Company, 1963).

Lay, L. Clark: "Arithmetic: An Introduction to Mathematics" (New York: The Macmillan Company, 1961).

Layton, W. I.: "College Arithmetic" (New York: John Wiley & Sons, Inc., 1959).

Marks, John L., James R. Smart, and C. Richard Purdy: "Other Bases in Arithmetic" (Boston: Ginn and Company, 1963).

Morton, R. L.: Decimal and Duodecimal Reciprocals, *Mathematics Teacher*, **56** (1963), 333–339.

Mueller, Francis J.: On the Fraction as a Numeral, *Arithmetic Teacher*, **8** (1961), 234–238.

National Council of Teachers of Mathematics: *Twenty-first* Yearbook (Washington, D.C.: National Council of Teachers of Mathematics, 1953).

______: *Twenty-second Yearbook* (Washington, D.C.: National Council of Teachers of Mathematics, 1954).

______: *Twenty-fourth Yearbook* (Washington, D.C.: National Council of Teachers of Mathematics, 1959).

______: *Twenty-seventh Yearbook* (Washington, D.C.: National Council of Teachers of Mathematics, 1962).

______: *Twenty-eighth Yearbook* (Washington, D.C.: National Council of Teachers of Mathematics, 1963).

Niven, Ivan: "Numbers, Rational and Irrational" (New York: Random House, Inc., 1961).

Osborn, Roger M., and others: "Extending Mathematics Understanding" (Columbus, Ohio: Charles E. Merrill Books, Inc., 1963).

Peterson, John A., and Joseph Hashisaki: "Theory of Arithmetic" (New York: John Wiley & Sons, Inc., 1963).

Rappaport, David: The Meanings of Fractions, *School Science and Mathematics*, **62** (1962), 241–244.

Reckzeh, John K., and Ernest R. Duncan: *E Pluribus Unum*: A Brief Discussion of the "Law of One," *Arithmetic Teacher*, **8** (1961), 413–415.

Ringenberg, Lawrence A.: "A Portrait of 2" (Washington, D.C.: National Council of Teachers of Mathematics, 1960).

______: Infinite Decimals, *Mathematics Teacher*, **55** (1962), 10–19.

Scott, Lloyd: Numeration, Notation, and System: Considerations of Nomenclature, *School Science and Mathematics*, **62** (1962), 551–555.

Shuster, Carl N.: The Advantages of Decimal Notation, *Mathematics Teacher*, **55** (1962), 649–650.

Smart, James R.: "New Understanding in Arithmetic" (Englewood Cliffs, N. J.: Allyn and Bacon, Inc., 1963).

Smith, Shelby D.: A Discussion of Powers of Whole Numbers, *Mathematics Teacher*, **55** (1962), 535–537.

Swain, Robert L.: "Understanding Arithmetic" (New York: Holt, Rinehart and Winston, Inc., 1957).

Sweet, Raymond, and Peter Dunn-Rankin: An Experiment in Team Teaching Seventh Grade Arithmetic, *School Science and Mathematics*, **62** (1962), 341–344.

UICSM Project Staff: Arithmetic with Frames, *Arithmetic Teacher*, **4** (1957), 119–124.

Van Engen, Henry: Rate Pairs, Fractions, and Rational Numbers, *Arithmetic Teacher*, **7** (1960), 389–399.

———: The Reform Movement in Arithmetic and the Verbal Problem, *Arithmetic Teacher*, **10** (1963), 3–6.

Wendt, Arnold: Per Cent without Cases, *Arithmetic Teacher*, **6** (1959), 209–214.

Wiebe, Arthur J. "Foundations of Mathematics" (New York: Holt, Rinehart and Winston, Inc., 1962).

Willerding, Margaret F.: Other Number Systems: Aids to Understanding, *The Arithmetic Teacher*, **8** (1961), 350–356.

———: A Critical Look at the New Mathematics for the Seventh Grade, *School Science and Mathematics*, **62** (1962), 215–220.

Youse, Bevan K.: "Arithmetic: A Modern Approach" (Englewood Cliffs, N.J.: Prentice-Hall, Inc., 1963).

TWELVE

The teaching of further topics in arithmetic

Inequality One of the basic postulates of the natural number system is the law of trichotomy: For any two natural numbers a and b one and only one of the following relations holds: $a = b$, $a + x = b$, or $a = b + y$, where x and y are natural numbers (page 64). Later, the concepts of "less than" and "greater than" are defined to carry the respective meanings: a is less than b ($a < b$) if and only if $a + x = b$, and a is greater than b ($a > b$) if and only if $a = b + y$ in accordance with this law.

In the respective extensions to the domain of integers, the field of rational numbers, and the field of real numbers, 0 is introduced as the additive identity, that is, the number 0 such that $0 + a = a + 0 = a$ for any element a, whether integer, rational number, or real number. In the domain of integers the relation $0 + a = a$ provides for the identification of a positive integer as one greater than 0 and for the setting up of a one-to-one correspondence between the positive integers and the natural numbers. Similarly, any number n, whether integer, rational number, or real number, is identified as *positive* if and only if $n > 0$, and *negative* if and only if $n < 0$. Since natural numbers, integers, and rational numbers are all contained within proper subsets of the set of real numbers, the law of trichotomy may now be restated for all four systems in this form: For any two real numbers n_1 and n_2, one and only one of the following relations holds: $n_1 > n_2$, $n_1 = n_2$, or $n_1 < n_2$. As an immediate corollary of this statement we have: For any real number n, one and only one of the following relations holds: $n > 0$, $n = 0$, or $n < 0$.

The relations of "less than" and "greater than" are *inequality relations*. They satisfy the transitive, additive, and multiplicative properties of equality, but they do not satisfy either the reflexive or the symmetric properties. For this reason one must be very careful in the use of inequalities. One of the important new emphases in the teaching of mathematics focuses attention upon the fact that an understanding of the principles and uses of inequalities is of tremendous significance in mathematics. Because of this fact, early introduction to these principles and continued informed use of them are considered of paramount importance. Some of the more fundamental of these properties are of such a nature that they can be dealt with, at least through concrete examples, in the arithmetic program of the junior high school. Later more abstract patterns can be introduced at the algebra level. These properties are stated here as the following theorems.

For a, b, c, and d real numbers:

Theorem 1. If $a < b$ and $b < c$, then $a < c$. The inequality relation "is less than" is transitive.
Theorem 2. If $a < b$, then $a + c < b + c$.
Theorem 3. If $a < b$ and $c < d$, then $a + c < b + d$.
Theorem 4. If $a = b$ and $c < d$, then $a - c > b - d$.
Theorem 5. If $a < b$ and $c > 0$, then $ac < bc$.
Theorem 6. If $a < b$ and $c > 0$, then $a/c < b/c$.
Theorem 7. If $a < b$ and $c < 0$, then $ac > bc$.
Theorem 8. If $a < b$ and $c < 0$, then $a/c > b/c$.

It should be immediately evident that the corresponding theorems hold for the relation "is greater than (>)."

The real number line affords a ready and effective method for ordering the real numbers. It is an important fact of analysis that a one-to-one correspondence can be established between the set of all real numbers and the points of a line. In order to accomplish this correspondence we mark a point on a line of indefinite extent to be called a "reference point" and give it the label O. (See Figure 12-1.) We then select a fixed line segment such as $\overline{OA}$, whose length will be the unit. It can then be established that, in such a context, the one-to-one correspondence between points on the line and real numbers can be fashioned. Such a line is called a "real number line." The reference

Figure 12-1
The real number line

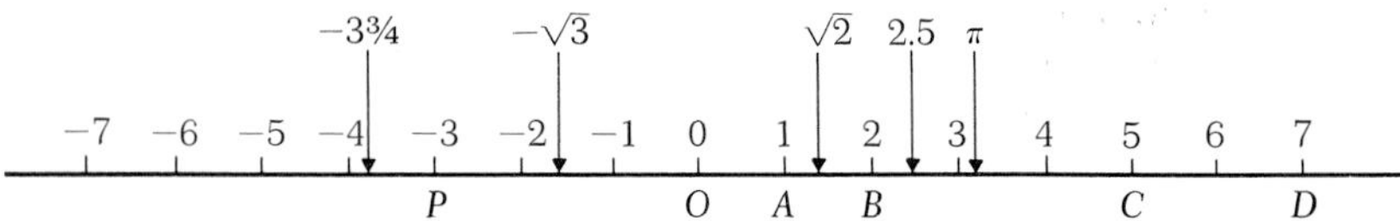

point O is made to correspond to 0, points to the right of O correspond to positive real numbers, and points to the left of O correspond to negative real numbers. In such a context the real number a corresponds to the point on the line whose distance from O is $|a|$, where

$|a| = a$ if $a \geq 0$
$|a| = -a$ if $a < 0$

With the existence of the real number line one can say that the real number $a <$ the real number b if and only if the point on the number line which corresponds to a is *to the left of* the point which corresponds to b. Similarly, the real number $c >$ the real number d if and only if the point on the number line which corresponds to c is *to the right of* the point which corresponds to d.

Example: (*a*) $15 < 20$, since $|15| = 15$ and $|20| = 20$. This means that the point which corresponds to 15 is closer to the reference point than is the point which corresponds to 20. The "15 point" is *to the left of* the "20 point."

(*b*) $-5 < -2$, since $|-5| = 5$ and $|-2| = 2$ and $5 > 2$. This means that the point which corresponds to -5 is farther removed from the reference point than is the point which corresponds to -2. The "(-5) point" is *to the left of* the "(-2) point."

(*c*) $-3 < 0 < 2$, since negative numbers are *to the left of* the reference point and positive numbers are *to the right of* the reference point.

The number line can serve also as an effective aid in laying the foundation for an understanding of the concept of *betweenness*. In Figure 12-1 the point B corresponds to 2, C to 5, and D to 7. The length of the line segment $\overline{BC}$ is $5 - 2 = 3$, the length of $\overline{CD}$ is $7 - 5 = 2$, and the length of $\overline{BD}$ is $7 - 2 = 5$. Since $3 + 2 = 5$, it follows that $BC + CD = BD$. When this condition holds, we say that C is between B and D. What is the corresponding argument to establish that the reference point O is between points P and B?

The very basic concepts of "less than" ($<$) and "greater than" ($>$) not only call for clear identification with the concept of "not equal to" ($\neq$) but also demand careful development as important relations, with intrinsic characteristics of their own, which exist between numbers and certain measurable quantities. The responsibility of instruction at the junior high level in building this significant structure of mathematical understanding is to help shape the foundation through the early introduction and continued pertinent discussion of the more elementary, yet fundamental, aspects of the two relations.

Averages

Averages have such widespread use in everyday affairs and are so much a part of the common experience of everyone that attention should be given to their computation and interpretation in arithmetic. Standings of baseball teams, seasonal temperatures, airplane speeds, weight and height charts, mortality tables, and tax rates are but a few of the many applications of averages with which people are concerned. While the *arithmetic mean* of a set of measures is usually what is meant by the word "average," there are several different types of averages. The junior high school is not the place to attempt to understand the technicalities of computation of averages in complex situations. However, simple illustrations can be used to clarify basic distinctions.

The *mode* is a measure of concentration. In its simplest form it is merely that measure for which there is the greatest frequency. The *median* is the middle score of a distribution, and the *arithmetic mean* is the sum of all the scores divided by the total frequency. The example in Table 12-1 representing lengths of standing broad jumps made in a

TABLE 12-1

Length of jump, in feet	*Number of boys making each jump*
4.0	3
4.2	1
4.5	3
4.8	5
5.0	5
5.2	10
5.5	1
5.8	1

grade school track meet can be used to illustrate these kinds of averages. The *mode* is 5.2 feet, which means that more boys jumped this distance than any other. The *median* jump is 5 feet, which means that, when the lengths of the jumps are listed in order from shortest to longest with the number making each jump, the fifteenth boy, counting from either end, made a jump of 5 feet. Since half of the remaining 28 is 14, there were 14 boys who jumped a distance of 5 feet or less, and there were 14 boys who jumped a distance of 5 feet or more. The average jump, or the arithmetic mean of all the jumps, is 4.9 feet. Although no jump of this length was made, the figure does give a good picture of the lengths of all the jumps. The arithmetic mean can be computed from the measures without making a frequency distribution; the mode and the median cannot.

One of the big disadvantages of the arithmetic mean is that it can be affected very greatly by extreme values. Also, although this measure is usually thought of somewhat vaguely as a sort of middle or "typical" value, it may not be at all typical. The set of numbers 17, 48, 106, 91, and 3 has the same mean, or "average," value as the set 53, 53, 52, 55, and 52. The average value does typify the second set very well, but the five numbers of the first set are so diverse that they simply do not run to type at all.

The average is merely one characteristic of a set of values, and it takes no account of diversity or homogeneity. Therefore, it should not be regarded as giving anything like a complete description of the set. On the other hand, it is very useful to be able to make comparisons of even a single characteristic of sets of values, and the arithmetic mean, or common average, provides probably the most simple, convenient, and useful instrument for doing so. It is a group measure which is easily understood, easily computed, simple to use, and in some sense representative of the set of values from which it is derived, even though it may not actually typify the values very well.

The *weighted average* is seldom mentioned except in textbooks on statistics. As a practical tool the method employed in its computation is probably not very important except when large masses of data are involved, something which is not often true of the problems one finds in school arithmetic. But large masses of data are frequently involved in the practical experience of a good many adults, and the classification of the data and the use of the weighted mean can materially reduce the labor involved in computing the average. Stripped of the formalism in which it is sometimes clothed, neither the concept nor the method of computation involves any difficulty beyond the ability of an intelligent seventh-grader. The fact that such examples as the cost-of-living index appear continually in newspapers and periodicals makes it clear that most adults are at least concerned with averages arrived at in this way, even though they may not have occasion actually to compute them. It would seem desirable that the study of averages, at least in the senior high school, should include some attention to situations in which weighted averages can be used to advantage and to the way in which they actually are determined and used.

In their treatment of averages, textbooks on arithmetic are prone to stress the method of computing averages, but do not, on the whole, give very much attention to discussing the usefulness and the limitations of this measure. Yet these aspects are important, and teachers should not overlook this opportunity to deepen the insights and enrich the appreciations of the students. This is important even in the seventh and eighth grades, but it is even more important when averages are studied or used in the later years of the senior high school. Even adults who are accustomed to the use of the term often attach to it a specific significance which is not wholly justified. Weight charts for persons at various ages are frequently looked upon with a sort of awe, as if the figures had been divinely ordained instead of being merely averages taken from large groups of people, and as if any departure from them should be regarded as cause for serious alarm. Persons who worry because they are 5 pounds "overweight" seldom reflect that the standardizing group itself undoubtedly contained many people whose weights were below the average, as well as many whose weights were above the average, and who perhaps were all equally healthy.

It is for reasons such as the above that a rather strong case is being made these days for the incorporation into the high school program of some of the fundamental techniques and concepts of elementary statistics. The argument is strengthened by the increasing need which, in the normal course of everyday events, the lay public has for informed ways and means of analyzing and interpreting the vast amount of propagandizing, advertising, or even informing data with which it is constantly confronted. Whether or not one agrees that this is a valid argument for the incorporation of statistics into the high school program, the fact remains that we cannot avoid the need for a clear understanding of the concept of averages. It must certainly follow, then, that when averages are studied in the secondary school, the work should not be confined solely to their computation. The concept of dispersion could and should be brought in simply and informally along with the study of averages. In this way emphasis could be given to the limitations as well as the advantages of the average as a working tool.

Another source of misinterpretation and faulty use of averages occurs in the treatment of percentage. One should never average the per cents (rates) unless they are related to the same base or equal bases. For example, let us consider two average daily attendance situations. In school A, Table 12-2, we shall ask for the average per cent of attendance in five different grades on a given school day. In school B we shall ask for the average per cent of attendance in a given grade for a

TABLE 12-2

School A				School B			
Grade	Enrollment	Attendance	Per cent	Day	Enrollment	Attendance	Per cent
7	40	36	90	Monday	80	72	90
8	70	28	40	Tuesday	80	32	40
9	100	70	70	Wednesday	80	56	70
10	90	90	100	Thursday	80	80	100
11	20	10	50	Friday	80	40	50
Total	320	234		Total	400	280	

5-day school week. To get the average per cent of attendance, we shall average the per cents. We shall then analyze the appropriateness of the results thus obtained. Note that the individual per cents are the same in the two cases, thus producing the same average per cent, 70 per cent, for each school. If this were a correct representation of the facts in both cases, then 70 per cent could be used to get the attendance for each grade (school A) or for each day (school B). The totals of these numbers should then give the figure obtained in each case above as the total attendance. As should be expected, and as is shown in Table 12-3, this is the case for school B, where the base is constant. But it is not the case for school A, where the base varies from grade to grade. There is a difference of ten students. True, the enrollment figures, particularly for school A, have been exaggerated. This was done deliberately in order to give stronger emphasis to the point being made. The only way to get the correct figure for school A is to divide the total attendance, 234, by the total enrollment, 320. To the nearest whole per cent this is 73 per cent. The grade attendance figures given by this rate per cent check, as they should.

TABLE 12-3

School A				School B			
Grade	Enroll-ment	Per cent	Attend-ance	Day	Enroll-ment	Per cent	Attend-ance
7	40	70	28	Monday	80	70	56
8	70	70	49	Tuesday	80	70	56
9	100	70	70	Wednesday	80	70	56
10	90	70	63	Thursday	80	70	56
11	20	70	14	Friday	80	70	56
Total	320		224	Total	400		280

Of course, another situation in which per cents can be averaged is the trivial one in which all rates are the same. This is also illustrated by Table 12-3, where in either case the average rate is 70 per cent.

Modular arithmetic The procedure commonly known as "casting out nines" is often used in business as a quick, practical way of checking arithmetical operations, especially multiplication and division. The procedure is easily learned, but many people who use it do so empirically without understanding why it works the way it does. Actually, its validity is established through the algebra of residue classes, but without going into that it is possible to convince students of its plausibility and reasonableness by analysis of suitable examples.

The principle rests on a theorem which asserts that for any non-negative integer, the excess of nines (the remainder left after division by nine) is equal to the excess of nines in the sum of the digits. This would say, for example, that the excess of nines in the number 5,728 is the same as the excess of nines in the sum $(5 + 7 + 2 + 8)$, or 4. This can be verified immediately by direct division, but that alone would carry little conviction that the same principle would apply to other numbers. On the other hand, an analysis such as that given below may well convince students of the generality of the principle.

Let it first be observed that for any integral power of 10 the excess of nines is 1 and that for any single digit 1, 2, 3, 4, 5, 6, 7, or 8 the excess of nines is given by the digit itself. Now consider that

$$\begin{aligned}
5{,}728 &= 5{,}000 && + 700 && + 20 && + 8\\
&= 5(1{,}000) && + 7(100) && + 2(10) && + 8\\
&= 5(999 + 1) && + 7(99 + 1) && + 2(9 + 1) && + 8\\
&= 5(999) + 5(1) && + 7(99) + 7(1) && + 2(9) + 2(1) && + 8\\
&= 5(111)(9) + 5 && + 7(11)(9) + 7 && + 2(1)(9) + 2 && + 8\\
&= 555 \text{ nines} + 5 && + 77 \text{ nines} + 7 && + 2 \text{ nines} + 2 && + 8\\
&= (555 + 77 + 2) \text{ nines} + (5 + 7 + 2 + 8)
\end{aligned}$$

Therefore the excess of nines in the right member of this equation must be $5 + 7 + 2 + 8$, or 22, since that would be the residue if all the nines were cast out from each of the numbers in the sum $(5{,}000 + 700 + 20 + 8)$. The residue from 5,000 is 5; that from 700 is 7; that from 20 is 2; and that from 8 is 8 itself. But since $5{,}000 + 700 + 20 + 8 = 5{,}728$, it follows that the residue after dividing 5,728 by 9 must also be $5 + 7 + 2 + 8$, or 22. Put another way, the excess of nines in 5,728 must be equal to the excess of nines in 22. Furthermore, since the theorem may now be applied again to the number 22, the excess of nines in 22 must be equal to the excess of nines in the sum $(2 + 2)$ of its digits, which is 4. Thus the excess of nines for the number 5,728 can be found without performing any division at all. It is this characteristic of the process which makes it such a quick and easy checking device.

Modular arithmetic affords a more elegant method of presenting the discussion of the previous paragraph. Such a procedure can be used with supplementary exercises as enrichment material for many students in grades 7 and 8.

If a, b, m, and n are integers such that $n = am + b$, then n is said to be *congruent to b modulo m* $[n \equiv b \pmod{m}]$. Of course, if $b = 0$, then n is exactly divisible by m, or $n \equiv 0 \pmod{m}$. The remainder b is called the *residue of n modulo m*, and it may be positive, negative, or zero.

For example, $98 = 14 \cdot 7$, $96 = 13 \cdot 7 + 5$, or $96 = 14 \cdot 7 - 2$; that is, $98 \equiv 0 \pmod 7$, $96 \equiv 5 \pmod 7$, or $96 \equiv -2 \pmod 7$. In modular arithmetic the residue of the smaller numerical value is the one generally used. If

$$n_1 = a_1 m + b_1 \qquad \text{and} \qquad n_2 = a_2 m + b_2$$

then
$$n_1 + n_2 = (a_1 + a_2)m + (b_1 + b_2)$$
and
$$n_1 n_2 = a_1 a_2 m^2 + (a_1 b_2 + a_2 b_1)m + b_1 b_2$$

This theorem therefore follows:

Theorem: If $n_1 \equiv b_1$ and $n_2 \equiv b_2 \pmod m$

then
$$n_1 + n_2 \equiv b_1 + b_2 \pmod m \qquad (1)$$
and
$$n_1 n_2 \equiv b_1 b_2 \pmod m \qquad (2)$$

The number 5,728, which may be written as $5(10^3) + 7(10^2) + 2(10) + 8$, is thus seen to be congruent to $5 + 7 + 2 + 8 \pmod 9$. This sum is 22, and $22 \equiv 4 \pmod 9$.

Equation (1) of the above theorem provides a method for checking sums and equation (2) for checking products by casting out nines. Furthermore, since subtraction and division are inverse processes to addition and multiplication, respectively, the theorem implies checks for these two operations. For example:

Sum	*Excess of Nines*
45,653	5
24,976	1
70,629 (Excess of nines is 6)	6 = Sum of the excesses

Difference

Note in the above sum that just as 70,629 − 24,976 must give 45,653, so 6 − 1 must give 5.

Product		*Excess of Nines*
381		3
29		2
3429		⑥ = Product of the excesses in the two factors
762		↗
11049	Check	
		↘
		⑥ = Excess in the product

In checking division by this method it is necessary to express the result as an integral quotient with a remainder (possibly zero). Next, subtract this remainder from the dividend. Then the product of the excesses for the divisor and the quotient will equal the excess for the modified dividend. Thus:

2,578 ÷ 23 = 112 with a remainder of 2
2,578 − 2 = 2,576, which is the modified dividend

Excess of nines for the divisor = 2 + 3 = 5.
Excess of nines for the quotient = 1 + 1 + 2 = 4.
Product of these excesses = 5 × 4 = 20.
Excess of nines in this product = 2 + 0 = ②.
Excess of nines in the modified dividend =
excess of nines in (2 + 5 + 7 + 6) =
excess of nines in 20 = 2 + 0 = ②. ← Check

Another important application of modular arithmetic is in the development of tests for divisibility. For example, since $10 \equiv 0 \pmod 2$, it follows that $10^n \equiv 0 \pmod 2$. This fact implies the test for divisibility of any number by 2 is that the digit in the ones place be divisible by 2. Similarly, the same test applies for 5. What is a test for divisibility by 4 $(=2^2)$ and 25 $(=5^2)$? By 8 $(=2^3)$ and 125 $(=5^3)$?

Since any composite number can be broken down into relatively prime factors, the tests for divisibility can be extended to take care of composite numbers. For example, since 6 = 2 × 3, the test for divisibility by 6 is the combination of the tests for divisibility by 2 and 3. Such factors must be relatively prime. For example, 18 = 2 × 9 = 3 × 6. The test for divisibility by 18 is a combination of the tests for 2 and 9, *not* a combination of the tests for 3 and 6. This should be evident, for a number which is divisible by 6 is also divisible by 3.

In concluding this discussion, one thing which is not always made clear should be emphasized. The check which this method affords is not an absolutely certain one. In particular, the check for casting out nines will not detect mistakes in which the error is any multiple of 9 nor mistakes resulting from transposition of digits. For example, 381 × 29 = 11,049, and the check would indicate that this is correct. But if the product should be erroneously written as 11,409, this method of checking would not detect the error. Hence it should be used with some caution, since there is a possibility that it might fail to reveal mistakes that had been made. On the other hand, if the check numbers (excesses) obtained in using this method do not agree, then it is certain that some mistake has been made in the work.

Square root The objectives for the study of square root are two: a clear understanding and appreciation of the meaning of the square root of a number and the knowledge of how to determine its exact or approximate numerical value. Children are usually introduced to square roots in the seventh or eighth grade in connection with the inverse process of squaring numbers. Through explanation with relatively small numbers which are perfect squares the concept can be, and usually is, developed without difficulty. High school students may have trouble giving a precise definition of the square root of a number, but they generally understand what the term means.

On the other hand, few of the students see any clear connection between the meaning of a square root and the traditional method by which they have been taught to compute the value. Nor could they be expected to do so. The classic method, still found in most textbooks, is a notable example of an algorism which to the beginner appears to be completely empirical and arbitrary. The fact that it gives correct results will seem to him to justify it, but until he has had opportunity to discover through algebra the algorism for the square of the sum of two numbers, he will have no basis for discovering or reconstructing it for himself. He can use it only as an apparently arbitrary routine, and the only way he can learn it is simply to memorize it. But this is precisely the kind of formalism upon which so much criticism of mathematical instruction has been justly focused in the past. Present-day thinking insists that skill should go hand in hand with understanding. Therefore an alternative method of computing square roots will be advocated here: a method which derives directly from the definition of a square root, which involves only the familiar procedures of division and averaging, which encourages reasonable estimates; and which is such that the student can understand at every step what he must do next, and why.

Let us first define square root of a number as one of two equal factors whose product is the number. For example, $\sqrt{73} \times \sqrt{73} = 73$. Let us next recall that in the process of division the divisor and the quotient are two factors whose product is the dividend.[1] If the divisor and the quotient are equal, each is a square root of the dividend. If they are not equal, the required square root must lie between them. Therefore, if a divisor which is a good approximation to the square root can be estimated, the quotient also will be a good approximation, and the average of the two will be a better approximation than either. If a still closer approximation is required, the process can be repeated with this average, or something near it, as the new divisor.

For example, let it be required to find a good approximation to $\sqrt{73}$. Upon reflecting that $\sqrt{64} = 8$ and $\sqrt{81} = 9$ and that 73 is about halfway between 64 and 81, we may reasonably try 8.5 as a divisor and proceed as indicated above.

$73.00000 \div 8.5 = 8.5882$

The average of 8.5 and 8.5882 is 8.5441, which by trial is seen to be too small to be satisfactory. We therefore repeat the procedure with, say, 8.54 as a divisor.

$73.00000 \div 8.54 = 8.548$

[1]With suitable approximations or remainders, of course, in cases when the division is not exact.

The average of 8.54 and 8.548 is 8.544. By trial, we find

$$(8.544)^2 = 72.999936$$

or almost exactly 73. Hence $\sqrt{73}$ correct to three decimal places is found to be 8.544. Actually, $\sqrt{73}$ correct to four decimal places is 8.5440.

By successive repetitions the square root can be found to any desired degree of accuracy, but often not more than one repetition is needed, and sometimes none. The approximations converge toward the true value amazingly fast with successive repetitions.

This method is now used in the manuals for computing machines, and it is used in programming square root problems for electronic computers. Moreover, it is beginning to find its way into some arithmetic textbooks. Its advantages are obvious, since it involves only familiar processes and students can see at every step not only what they are doing but why they are doing it. It forces students to estimate carefully and to review mentally the simple perfect squares without the usual drill procedure, and it gives results as accurate as desired. In comparison with the traditional rule-of-thumb method this alternative method has much to recommend it.[2]

Since economy of time in the actual use of square roots is important, students should become familiar with the use of tables of squares and square roots and with interpolation in the tables. When possible, they should be made acquainted with the use of the slide rule for obtaining squares and square roots, and advanced students may well be introduced to the use of logarithms for the purpose. Also, students should be made aware that time and labor may sometimes be saved in finding square roots of fractions or of factorable numbers in which one factor is a perfect square. The principle that

$$\sqrt{ab} = \sqrt{a}\sqrt{b}, \text{ or } \sqrt{28} = \sqrt{4}\sqrt{7} = 2\sqrt{7}$$

is probably more important in algebra than in arithmetic, but there are cases when it can be a time saver even in arithmetic. In attempting to find the square root of a fraction such as $\sqrt{3/7}$ many students even in college work out separate, long approximations to $\sqrt{3}$ and $\sqrt{7}$ and then perform the long division $1.7321 \div 2.6458$ instead of rationalizing the denominator and transforming the expression into the equivalent $\sqrt{21/49} = \sqrt{21}/7 = 4.5826/7$, in which the division is less tedious.

Measurement and denominate numbers People seldom realize the extent to which everybody depends on measurement of one kind or another. We go to work by a clock, which measures time. We buy gasoline by the gallon, which is a measure of capacity, and meat by

[2]For an excellent discussion of the use of this method in connection with a slide rule, see Carl N. Shuster, Approximate Square Roots, *Mathematics Teacher*, **45** (1952), 17–18.

the pound, which is a measure of weight. Thermometers measure temperature for us; rulers and tapes measure distance; the speedometers on our cars measure speed; pollsters, the popularity of a radio program; and engineers, the tensile strength of materials. In view of these considerations, systematic instruction in measurement should form an important part of the program in arithmetic. The facts of measurement are exhibited and their various combinations and recombinations are made and recorded through the medium of number.

Among the important concepts which should be, but not always are, made clear to students, the following should be given special emphasis:

1. What a measurement means
2. The arbitrary nature of units of measure
3. The necessity of having standardized units
4. Clear concepts of the most common units of measure
5. Specific relations among some of the common units

These things will require considerable discussion, demonstration, and illustration by the teacher. There are many excellent articles, books, and brochures which provide most interesting and dramatic accounts of the evolution of our units and systems of measurement. The teacher who familiarizes himself with the fascinating story of measurement will be able to present it to his classes in such a way as to stimulate their interest, clarify their concepts, and enlist their enthusiasm in attaining the objectives mentioned above.

Of special interest in this connection is the metric system of measure. While it is not the commonly used system in the English-speaking countries, it is used over much of the world, and it is universally used in scientific circles. Its interesting history, foundation, and structure, and the fact that its units, direct and derived, are based on our common decimal number system, emphasize the importance of having students become familiar with it. Study of the metric system should be directed particularly toward giving the students clear physical concepts of the common units, such as meter, centimeter, millimeter, kilometer, square centimeter, cubic centimeter, gram, and kilogram; proper knowledge and use of the nomenclature; and the ability to make correct interconversions both among units of the metric system itself and between these and units in the English system of weights and measures.

The numbers which are used to express measurements have attached to them such labels as 8 miles, 74 degrees, 5 pounds, and 18 minutes. The label tells the kind of unit in terms of which the measurement has been made, and the number tells how many of these units the given magnitude was found to contain. Such numbers are called *denominate*, or *dimensional*, numbers. Everybody is so familiar with them that nobody stops to think about them. About the only difficulty which can arise in their use is that which might occur in computing with compound denominate numbers such as 3 weeks 4 days and 2 hours 18 minutes 5 seconds. For such computations students need to know the common units and subunits of various kinds of magnitudes and they need to be able to make interconversions of minutes and hours; miles, yards, feet, and inches; pounds and ounces; and the like. Such computations need not be troublesome if the students are taught to look upon them with common sense and not try to clothe them with formalism. Formal rules are unnecessary and probably are actually detrimental to ease of understanding in such cases. The student who multiplies 2 yards 2 feet 10 inches by 8 and gives his result as 16 yards 16 feet 80 inches should not be penalized, for he has correctly done what was required. It should simply be pointed out to him that it is usually preferable to express final results in the largest units possible and that this can now be done easily as follows: The 80 inches make 6 feet 8 inches. The 6 feet can be combined with the 16 feet to give 22 feet, which can be expressed as 7 yards 1 foot. Finally, the 7 yards can be combined with the 16 yards to make 23 yards. Hence, the original answer of 16 yards 16 feet 80 inches can be expressed as 23 yards 1 foot 8 inches. It should be emphasized that this is no more correct than the original answer but is simply a more convenient form for expressing the same thing.

Common sense should predominate in the treatment of denominate numbers. There are only a few common scales of measurement which are national in extent, and even in these some units are generally used only by specialists. But some measures of distance, angular magnitude, weight, area, volume, and time are needed by everybody, and the importance and interrelationships of the common units in these systems should be emphasized. Everybody should know that there are 12 inches in a foot, 5,280 feet in a mile, 60 minutes in an hour, and 90 degrees in a right angle. It is doubtful that everyone needs to know that there are $16\frac{1}{2}$ feet in a rod, but everybody should know what a square foot means and why there are 144 square inches in a square foot. Many details about denominate numbers may well be omitted from the arithmetic of the secondary school, but those parts which are commonly used by many people should not be neglected, and the things that are taught should be taught thoroughly.

The nature of approximate numbers The foregoing discussion of measurement and denominate numbers leads naturally to consideration of approximate numbers. From what sources do they come? How are they to be used? What special considerations must be taken into account in computing with approximate numbers? Until comparatively recent times, such concepts and questions have received no attention in school mathematics except occasional arbitrary instructions for rounding off numbers when so directed. Since about 1930, attempts have been made to get more systematic attention given to approximate numbers in textbooks on arithmetic and general mathematics. This movement, which at first consisted mainly in the efforts of a few dedicated individuals, received support in the second report of the Committee on Post-War Plans and has now begun to bear fruit.

If the teachers of arithmetic had come as far in this direction as the textbooks have, the situation might be regarded with optimism. Unfortunately, however, most teachers have been brought up in the tradition of treating all numbers as exact numbers. Moreover, it is simpler and more satisfying to treat them in this way than to deal with them as approximate numbers. Some time and study are required to learn the necessary concepts and the rationale of computing with approximate numbers. Furthermore, the abandonment of well-fixed ideas is never easy, and the weight of inertia is heavy. There never seems to be enough time for the things that need to be done, and it is argued that students have enough trouble with arithmetic at best, without bringing in additional complications.

All *exact* numbers result from counting and from applying the fundamental processes to counted quantities. When we say that there are 35 children in the sixth grade, that Jane receives $2 each week as her allowance, or that six eggs make ½ dozen eggs, we mean *exactly* what we say. The counting process sets up a one-to-one correspondence that establishes this exactness. On the other hand, numbers which are estimated results—even though they are based on counting, as in the case of the census—or which record the data resulting from measurement are *approximate* numbers. This is true whether we are measuring distance, direction, temperature, or what not. If we say that Jack is 5 feet 6 inches tall, we can only mean that, according to our measuring technique, his height is nearer to this measurement than it is to any other. No measurement can be more precise than the precision of the measuring instrument or more accurate than the relative accuracy of the observation made.

Approximate numbers also may arise from certain mathematical processes which require an infinite number of steps of which only a finite number can be performed. Examples are the extraction of certain roots such as $\sqrt{2}$ and $\sqrt[3]{6}$, the expansion in decimal form of certain nonterminating fractions such as $2/3 = 0.\overline{6}$ and $1/7 = 0.\overline{142857}$, and the evaluation of transcendental numbers such as $\pi = 3.14159 \ldots$ and $e = 2.71828 \ldots$. It should not be inferred from the above remarks that irrational numbers or fractions are necessarily approximate. Whether rational numbers or irrational numbers are exact or approximate depends upon the interpretation of the data involved. If we have a square whose side is exactly 1 unit in length, then $\sqrt{2}$ is the exact length of its diagonal. The actual measurement of this length would, of course, be only approximate.

It should also be stated that exact numbers may be fractional even though the approximation is integral; for example, if lemons are selling at 79 cents a dozen, the 40 cents one pays for 1/2 dozen is an approximation to the 39 1/2 cents which is the exact price. The context in which any given number is used will frequently play an important part in determining whether it is to be regarded as an exact or an approximate number. An individual who states that he purchased 2 pounds of butter is using the number 2 in an exact sense if he means two 1-pound cartons, whereas the actual weight of the butter only approximates 2 pounds. Furthermore, the use of formulas in practical computations frequently gives rise to approximate numbers either because of the approximate nature of the formula itself (as in the case of the formula $A = 3.14r^2$, or $A = \frac{22}{7}r^2$, for the area of a circle and formulas resulting from scientific experimentation) or the use of approximate data in an exact formula (as would result in substituting measurements in the formula $A = lw$ for the area of a rectangle).

Although facility and accuracy in computation with exact numbers is both a desirable and a necessary goal of arithmetical instruction in the elementary school, the secondary school should stress the "exercise of common sense and judgment in computing from approximate data, familiarity with the effect of small errors in measurements, the determination of the number of figures to be used in computing and to be retained in the result, and the like."[3] There is no justification whatsoever, for example, in stating that the circumference of a circle whose radius is given as 3 inches is 2(3.1416)(3) = 18.8496 inches. The measurement of the circumference can be no more precise or accurate than the measurement of the radius used in finding the circumference. It is, then, very important that the teacher and pupil understand certain fundamental criteria for judging approximativeness[4] and rules for computation with approximate data.

Criteria for judging approximativeness The three principal criteria for judging approximativeness are the position of the decimal point, the number of significant digits, and precision and accuracy.

The position of the decimal point. A number may be said to be correct to within a certain unit (e.g., to units, tenths, hundredths, etc.). The distance from the earth to the sun is usually given as 93,000,000 miles. Here the unit of measurement is 1,000,000 miles, and the measurement

[3]National Committee on Mathematical Requirements, "Reorganization of Mathematics in Secondary Education" (Boston: Houghton Mifflin Company, 1923), p. 7.

[4]By "approximativeness" is meant the closeness with which the approximate number approaches the exact number.

is considered correct to this nearest unit. Until recently, the world record for the 100-yard dash was 9.3 seconds. Here either a second or one-tenth second may be taken as the unit of measurement. The observation is said to be correct to tenths of a second. In such cases as these the number of decimal places in the observation proves to be a criterion for judging approximativeness.

The number of significant digits. Our decimal system of numeration is definitely characterized by the fact that the significance of any particular digit in a number is determined by the position it occupies. In the number 333.3 each three denotes a value one-tenth as large as the one on its left and ten times as large as the one on its right. Thus the number 333.3 is given to four significant digits, since each three has a specific relative significance in the make-up of the number. If we consider the numbers 303, 3.03, and 33, it is evident that the presence or absence of the zero affects the relative magnitudes of the threes. In the first two numbers the three on the extreme left is of a magnitude 100 times as great as that of the three on the extreme right, while in the third number the three on the left is only 10 times as great in magnitude as the three on the right. Now consider the numbers 33, 3.3, 0.033, and 330. It is just as evident that the presence or absence of the zero does not affect the relative magnitude of the threes. In each case the magnitude of the three on the left is 10 times that of the three on the right. In the number 330, as in 0.033, the zero serves merely as an aid in placing the decimal point to distinguish 330 from 33, 3.3, 0.033, 33,000, etc., in which case it is not considered a significant digit. Each of the numbers 303 and 3.03 is given to three significant digits, while each of the numbers 33, 3.3, 0.033, and 330, where zero merely helps to place the decimal point, is given to two significant digits. Similarly, both 93,000,000 and 9.3 are given to two significant digits.

The value of π to seven significant digits is $\pi = 3.141593$.

This value is very frequently stated as $\pi = 3.1416$.

In the second sentence, the value of π given in the first sentence has been *rounded off*. The rules usually given for rounding off numbers may be stated as follows:

1. If a whole number, given to a certain number of significant digits, is to be rounded off to a stated number of significant digits, the digits that are to be dropped should be replaced by zeros. When the digits that are to be dropped are located to the right of the decimal point, the use of the zeros is not correct.

2. If the first digit on the left of those that are to be dropped is 5, 6, 7, 8, or 9, then the first digit on the extreme right of the number, which is to be retained, should be increased by unity. This process is known as "forcing the digit." If the first digit on the left of those that are to be dropped is 0, 1, 2, 3, or 4, then no change is made in the digits retained.

A supplementary rule to number 2 that is frequently used, particularly in more mature circles, is as follows:

2*a*. If the portion of the number to be dropped consists only of a 5 in the first left-hand position, either alone or followed by zeros, then the first digit on the extreme right of the number to be retained is rounded to the nearest even number.

3. If, after the forcing, the significant digit on the extreme right is 5, a bar should be placed over it in order to indicate that, if there should be a necessity to drop this 5, the next digit on its left should remain unchanged. For example: 3,464,832 is rounded off to $3{,}46\bar{5}{,}000$. If it should then become necessary to round off the second number, it would be rounded off to 3,460,000.

If we apply the above rules to round off the numbers 296 and 303 to two significant digits, we obtain in each case $3\underline{0}0$. The zero on the left thus becomes a significant digit and is underscored to indicate that fact. Whether the zeros to the right of all nonzero digits of an approximate number are significant or not must be determined from an analysis of the situation which produced the number. In the case of a measurement the significance of such zeros can be determined if the precision of the measurement or the unit of measurement is known. In the case of rounded numbers it can be determined only by reference to the numbers from which the rounded numbers were obtained. If only a number, such as 39,000, is given and nothing is known about what it represents or how it was obtained, then there is no way of deciding whether any of the zeros are significant or not. However, all zeros would be significant in 390.00 meters because the two zeros to the right of the decimal point would be used not as an aid in placing the decimal point but to signify that in the application of the specified unit of measurement *no* quantities were found to occupy the two places to the right of the decimal point. Similarly, the zeros in $390 and $390.50 would be significant, except in the case when the amounts were given as mere estimates. Zero is significant whenever it is used other than as a mere place holder to assist in the proper placement of the decimal point. All nonzero digits are significant.

To illustrate: The following numbers are all correct to five significant digits: 3.2674, 30207, $3126\underline{0}$, 312.67, 3126.0, 0.031267, 0.000031267, 0.00030067, 2400.0, $3000\underline{0}$.

Precision and accuracy. Although precision and accuracy are distinctly different as criteria for the measure of approximativeness, they can be most effectively discussed when contrasted with each other. Measures may be precise to within certain specified units, such as 1,000,000 miles, 1 mile, 1 second, and 1/10 of 1 second. Similarly, numbers may be precise to units, tenths, hundredths, etc. On the other hand, a measure or a number may be accurate within a certain per cent of error or a certain number of significant digits.

The most effective measures of both precision and accuracy are in terms of the errors involved. The maximum error (positive or negative) made in any approximation is defined as follows: "If an approximate number is given as correct to k significant digits, then its error is at the most equal to ± 0.5 of a unit in the kth place, counting from the left to the right."[5]

The *upper* and *lower limits* of the true value of any approximation are obtained by adding this maximum error to, and subtracting it from, the approximate number. The maximum *apparent error* (or *absolute error*) involved in any approximation made to k significant digits is thus seen to be 0.5 of a unit whose magnitude is determined by the kth place of the approximation. For example, the upper and lower limits of the true value of the distance from the earth to the sun are 93,500,000 and 92,500,000 miles, respectively, so the limit of the apparent error is 500,000 miles.

In the measure of time for the foot race the upper and lower limits are respectively 9.35 and 9.25 seconds, and the limit of the apparent error is seen to be 0.05 second. *The precision of a measure or a computation is evaluated in terms of the apparent* (or *absolute*) *error*.

The two measures 93,000,000 miles and 9.3 seconds are both correct to two significant digits. The per cent of accuracy of a measure or a computation is determined by the *relative error* involved, viz., the ratio of the apparent error to the approximate number. The relative errors, to two significant digits, in each of the above cases are respectively

$$\frac{500{,}000 \text{ miles}}{93{,}000{,}000 \text{ miles}} = \frac{0.5}{93} = 0.0054 \qquad \text{and} \qquad \frac{0.05 \text{ second}}{9.3 \text{ seconds}} = \frac{0.5}{93} = 0.0054$$

The *per cent of error* in each case is thus seen to be the same, ½ of 1 per cent. One approximation might be far less precise than another and yet be much more accurate. For example, suppose we have the two measurements 0.000341 inch and 1,256 feet. The first measure is much more precise because its maximum apparent error is 0.5 of a millionth of an inch, while that of the second measure is 0.5 of a foot. The first measure is correct to three significant digits and the second to four; the relative errors are respectively

$$\frac{0.0000005}{0.000341} = \frac{0.5}{341} = 0.0015 \qquad \text{and} \qquad \frac{0.5}{1{,}256} = 0.0004$$

Thus the per cent of error is 0.15 per cent in the first measurement and 0.04 per cent in the second; in other words, the second measure, although far less precise than the first, is about four times as accurate. *The accuracy of a measure or a computation is evaluated in terms of the relative error or per cent of error made.*

[5]Aaron Bakst, Approximate Computation, *Twelfth Yearbook* (Washington, D.C.: National Council of Teachers of Mathematics, 1937), p. 124.

When a common fraction is used in giving approximate data, the denominator of the fraction states the unit of precision used in making the measurement, while the numerator indicates the number of significant digits to which it is read. The unit of precision in each of the following measurements is one-fourth inch: $3/4$ inch, $6\,1/4$ inches, and $34\,3/4$ inches. The number of significant digits in each is $3/4$ inch, one; $6\,1/4$ inches = $25/4$ inches, two; and $34\,3/4$ inches = $139/4$ inches, three. While $6\,1/4$ inches has the same numerical value as $6\,4/16$ inches, there is a great deal of difference in the precision of the two measures. Similarly, there is definite significance to be attached to a measure of $5\,0/8$ inches as contrasted to one of 5 inches. The maximum apparent error in $5\,0/8$ inches is $1/16$ inch, while in 5 inches it is $1/2$ inch.

Computation with approximate data In any computation involving approximate data, the result can never be any more precise or accurate than the least precise or the least accurate of the data used. While the rules for such computation may be stated in several different forms, probably the two most satisfactory rules are:

1. In the addition or subtraction of approximate numbers of the same degree of *precision*, perform the operation and retain the result to the same degree of precision. If one approximate number is of a greater degree of precision than the other, first round the more precise number to within one degree of precision of that of the less precise number. Perform the operation and then round the result to the same degree of precision as that of the less precise number.

2. In the multiplication or division of approximate numbers of the same number of *significant digits*, perform the operation and then round the result to the same number of significant digits. If one approximate number has more significant digits than the other, first round the more accurate number so that it has only one more significant digit than the less accurate number. Perform the operation and then round the result so that it contains the same number of significant digits as the less accurate number.

With some sacrifice in economy of effort but no essential difference in significance of results some writers prefer, for very elementary work with approximate numbers, to simplify these rules to read: In any computation with approximate numbers first perform the required operation with the given numbers just as if they were exact numbers, then round the results: (1) in addition or subtraction, to the same unit of precision as the least precise number used; (2) in multiplication or division, to the smallest number of significant digits that occur in any number used.

The rule for multiplication may, of course, be extended to control the results obtained in raising an approximate number to any given power, and the rule for division extended similarly to the extraction of indicated roots.

The intelligent use of these rules combined with care in the statement of original data will produce results that can be justified as the best possible results to be obtained from the given data.

If instruction in computation with approximate numbers is kept at a level appropriate to the maturity of the students, it need not be confusing to them, and if properly taught and well motivated it can add interest to the course. In Shuster's opinion:[6]

> It is not at all difficult to teach the simple rules for computing with approximate data in the seventh, eighth, and ninth grades. In fact, it is far easier to teach all the student needs to know about the topic in these grades than it is to change the computational habits of graduate students who have always used "exact" computation.

This is not the place to undertake a detailed exposition of the theory of computing with approximate data. Numerous excellent discussions of the subject that are now available[7] deal adequately with both its mathematical and pedagogical aspects and do so in much greater detail than would be possible here. On the other hand, it may be desirable to enumerate the central concepts and principles upon which attention would have to be focused in a systematic study of the subject. The order in which these are listed below represents the order in which they would probably appear in the logical development of the theory of approximations. They are as follows:

1. What a unit of measurement is
2. Why we can be certain that no measurement is exact
3. The approximate nature of the number that is used to record the measurement
4. The apparent (or absolute) error that is always associated with the approximate number and the consequent range of values any of which might be properly represented by the approximate number as written
5. The tolerance (or permissible error) used in industry
6. Estimates as approximate numbers; other ways in which approximate numbers may arise
7. The approximate number as a multiple of the smallest unit in terms of which it is expressed
8. The concept of precision of a measurement or of an approximate number and the consequent implication with respect to the size of the apparent error
9. The inconsistency involved in the use of "ragged decimals" to represent approximate numbers in sums or differences
10. The accepted principle and the rule for rounding off answers in the addition and subtraction of approximate numbers

[6]Carl Shuster, Working with Approximate Data, *Twenty-second Yearbook* (Washington, D.C.: National Council of Teachers of Mathematics, 1954), p. 310.

[7]See Bibliography.

11. Significant digits
12. The concept of the relative error of an approximate number and the meaning of accuracy
13. The relation of accuracy to the number of significant digits used in expressing the approximate number
14. Why high precision of an approximate number does not necessarily imply a high degree of accuracy, and conversely
15. Why the accuracy of a product or quotient involving approximate numbers depends on the number of significant digits in each of the factors rather than upon their precision
16. The accepted principle and the rule for rounding off answers in the multiplication and division of approximate numbers

This is an imposing array, and it is true that some serious study is required in order to attain clear mastery of these concepts and principles. Such mastery ought to be a part of the equipment of every teacher of arithmetic in the secondary school. On the other hand, it is by no means suggested that all these things be taught in a single sequence or even in a single year. Rather, the instruction should be spread over all the grades from 7 to 12, and the concepts and principles introduced in any grade should be only those which students in that grade can be expected to master satisfactorily.

Using numbers expressed in scientific (standard) notation

A very effective method of indicating significant digits, particularly when using very large or very small numbers, is the scientific (or standard) form of notation. A number is said to be written in the scientific or standard form of notation when it is written as the product of a number between 1 and 10 and an integral power of 10. Any significant zeros would be excluded from the power of 10. For example, the volume of the sun is 1,300,000 times the volume of the earth, while Mars is only 0.150 times as large as the earth. If we use S, M, and E to represent the volumes of the sun, Mars, and the earth, respectively, the above statement may be written in scientific notation as

$$S = 1.3 \times 10^6E \qquad \text{and} \qquad M = 1.50 \times 10^{-1}E$$

The advantages of expressing numbers in standard, or scientific, notation are not as apparent in the work of the junior high school as they are in grades 11 and 12. It would be perfectly feasible to introduce this notation even in the seventh grade as an alternative way of expressing numbers which are positive integral powers of 10, and to extend it by the end of the ninth grade to include representation of decimal fractions in this form. However, it is not seriously needed as a tool until the eleventh or twelfth grades, when it can be very helpful to students in physics, chemistry, trigonometry, shop mathematics, or any course in which use is made of logarithms or the slide rule or in which extensive evaluation of formulas is required. The main advantage of its earlier introduction is that a good many junior high school students who do not take physics or mathematics in the senior high school might still get some acquaintance with this notation and the way in which it is used.

The particular usefulness of this notation lies in the fact that it provides a means for writing very large or very small numbers in a convenient compact form that is easy to read and work with, and which lends itself well to quick mental estimates and approximations. Consequently, the objectives to be sought are simply clear understanding of the notation and facility in using it to find products, quotients, or square roots of numbers. It is also useful in checking such operations, particularly the position of the decimal point. The only requirements are an understanding of positive and negative exponents and well-supervised practice to such a point that the students can work with the notation with confidence and facility and interpret their results with assurance.

Most operations with the slide rule consist in finding products, quotients, or some combination of the two, and a major source of trouble is the proper location of the decimal point in the answer. Of course the ordinary rules for placing the decimal point can apply, but they are inconvenient when several factors are involved or when factors are very large or very small. Mistakes can easily be made in such cases, and it is desirable to have an independent method of checking, because misplacing the decimal point is one of the worst mistakes that can be made. The use of standard notation provides such a check, and it is a check based on common sense. Consider such a case as $(73{,}200{,}000 \times 0.0000211)/0.0045$. Direct computation yields a number with the sequence of digits 34323 but provides no easy way for setting the decimal point. But if these numbers are written in standard notation, they are $(7.32 \times 10^7 \times 2.11 \times 10^{-5})/(4.5 \times 10^{-3})$, which can be rewritten as

$$\frac{7.32 \times 2.11}{4.5} \times \frac{10^2}{10^{-3}} \quad \text{or} \quad \frac{7.32 \times 2.11}{4.5} \times 10^5$$

Now $(7.32 \times 2.11)/4.5$ is shown by even a quick rough estimate to have a value somewhere near 3, and this is to be multiplied by 10^5. Thus when the sequence of digits has been determined as shown above, it is clear that the required answer must be 3.4323×10^5, or 343,230. If the original numbers are approximate numbers, the result should be rounded off accordingly. In this case it would be given as 340,000.

In taking square roots of numbers a slight modification is sometimes needed, because the standard form must now contain a factor of the form 10^n, where n is an *even* integer. Such modifications are easily made. For example, $\sqrt{169{,}000}$ is written as $\sqrt{16.9 \times 10^4}$ instead of $\sqrt{1.69 \times 10^5}$, in order that the result will contain a factor which is an integral power of 10. Thus

$$\sqrt{169{,}000} = \sqrt{16.9 \times 10^4} = \sqrt{16.9} \times \sqrt{10^4} \approx 4.11 \times 10^2 \approx 411$$

which is correct to three significant digits as given by the slide rule.

As stated above, the use of scientific notation makes only three demands on the student: an understanding of exponents, knowledge of how to multiply and divide mentally by powers of 10 by moving the decimal point, and the ability to make quick mental estimates of products or quotients of numbers between 1 and 10. The simplicity of the process and the incentive which it could provide probably would justify its introduction on a limited scale in the junior high school. Its usefulness in connection with the slide rule, logarithms, and the evaluation of formulas is undoubted. Students in chemistry, physics, solid geometry, trigonometry, or shop mathematics will find the ability to use this notation an important asset.

Estimating

In view of its importance there is probably no phase of arithmetic which is more neglected than estimating. Everybody gets so involved with the formal processes of computing and with the rationale of analyzing problems that estimation gets overlooked. Yet it is important and it should not be neglected. Indeed, the systematic practice of estimating can be a valuable ally to the student both in the analysis of problems and in checking the reasonableness of solutions. It is indispensable in operating a business or planning any sort of project. Budgets, tax rates, construction bids, merchandising, manufacturing, and a host of other intensely practical things are based on estimates; without intelligent estimates they could not be planned or operated. If students could be kept aware of this, it would help to enrich their arithmetical experience, deepen their insight, and simplify their thinking.

Estimating can be tremendously helpful too in checking the results of computations. It has been mentioned before that students often experience doubt over the proper placement of the decimal point in products, quotients, or square roots of numbers that involve decimal fractions. This is a serious matter, because misplacement of a decimal point is a very bad mistake indeed—much worse than many students seem to realize. But if they become accustomed to making rough estimates of their answers, they are not likely to make this mistake. The estimates do not even have to be very good ones, and they can generally be made mentally with radically rounded-off numbers. For example, 0.327×49.2 yields a product consisting of the sequence of digits 160884 in which the decimal point must be properly placed. If the student reflects that 0.327 is close to $^3/_{10}$ and that 49.2 is about 50, it will be clear to him immediately that the product must be somewhere near 15, which is three-tenths of 50. Therefore the only place where the decimal point can make sense in the answer is after the 6. That is, the answer *must* be 16.0884, since 160.084 is more than ten times as large as the estimated answer, while 1.60884 is only about one-tenth as great as we know the answer must be. If students would consistently use this kind of estimate as a check, or even as a *method*, for placing the decimal point, there would hardly be any need for the formal rules. What is here advocated, however, is not the abandonment of the formal rules for placing the decimal point, but the use of estimates of this kind as a supplementary check—a double insurance against a very bad kind of mistake that occurs far too often.

Other topics in arithmetic Except for limitations of space it would be easy to extend the scope of this chapter to include discussion of numerous other topics. Any extensive survey of courses in arithmetic or courses in which arithmetic has a prominent role would reveal a wide variety of objectives, content, and emphasis. It is doubtful that all the additional topics that could be mentioned would be found in any single course. The orientation of each course will determine at least in part the topics that will receive emphasis in the course, and the degree of such emphasis.

While detailed discussion of these further topics cannot be given here, it may be worthwhile to list some of them. Among those which represent significant parts or aspects of arithmetic at the secondary school level are the following:

- Simplified or abridged computation
- Evaluation of formulas
- Ratio and proportion
- The slide rule
- Teaching arithmetic with calculating machines
- Arithmetic of the shop
- Consumer arithmetic
- Various social applications of arithmetic
- Simple descriptive statistics

Before undertaking the teaching of one of these topics or aspects of arithmetic the teacher will do well to subject it to a deliberate analysis to try to determine the particular objectives toward which the study is to be pointed, what specific difficulties the students may be expected to encounter, and what methods can best be employed. Only in this way can the work be best organized, presented, and studied to minimize the difficulties, highlight the important concepts or skills, and in general bring about the attainment of the objectives so far as this can reasonably be done.

A false dichotomy More than half a century ago a reaction against excessive use of formalized drill in arithmetical instruction had begun to make itself manifest. As time went on, this reaction took on an extreme form with the insistence in some quarters that understanding *rather than* computational proficiency should be the aim, and some people went so far as to insist that understanding should be, in effect, the sole aim in teaching arithmetic. Such catch phrases as "meaning versus drill" have formed the captions of many articles and discussions on objectives, subject matter, and methods.

Nobody will deny that there was good reason for this reaction, for it had become evident that exclusive reliance on drill had not automatically produced adequate understanding either of the processes themselves or of their application to problem situations. On the other hand, it should have been clear, as it has now become clear, that proficiency in computation could not automatically develop as an incidental by-product of understanding any more than understanding could emerge as an incidental by-product of drill. The "meaning versus drill" type of phrase, which has by no means disappeared even yet, implies an "either one or the other but not both" situation which is completely unrealistic and unjustified. Competence in arithmetic does not consist *only* in understanding any more than it consists *only* in skill in computing. The two are complementary parts, and for satisfactory mastery of the subject neither is sufficient without the other. The question of which is the more important is something like asking whether one's right leg or left leg is the more important in walking. The answer is that the question is nonsensical; each leg is as essential as the other, and both are necessary.

Arithmetic must be taught and studied with *both* understanding and computational proficiency as primary objectives, and each of these objectives must be approached through methods appropriate to it. Both are necessary; neither alone is sufficient. To think of the one versus the other is to set up a false and vicious dichotomy which is based on superficial thinking and which is completely unrealistic. Instruction based on such a dichotomy and oriented exclusively toward either of these objectives would inevitably lead at best to one-sided learning having little basis for either present application or further extension.

Provision for the superior student in arithmetic Most of the topics discussed in these chapters are included in textbooks and syllabuses with the hope that all the students will attain some degree of mastery of them. This being the case, the regular content of the courses is necessarily geared to what most of the students can reasonably be expected to accomplish, and often even this modest coverage is cut down to accommodate slow students. But in all classes there will be some students who could easily handle work beyond the normal assignments, and sometimes even students who are exceptionally talented in mathematics. Although it is not always realized, these have commonly been the most neglected students of all. Teachers are not slow to recognize students of outstanding ability, and because they can do the assigned work without help and often in a small fraction of the time required by other students, they are left pretty much on their own. In the absence of really challenging requirements they often become bored and negligent about doing even the work expected of the class as a whole. Yet these superior students, and especially the really talented ones, are the potential from which the future professional scientists and mathematicians must come. Their talent should not be wasted, but conserved and cultivated with special care.

Various suggestions have been made for ways of making suitable provision for gifted students. In large school systems the superior students are sometimes assigned to special sections where they can progress faster and farther than in other sections. In both large and small schools differentiated assignments within the sections have been used with some success. Other suggestions include assignment of supplementary problems, group or individual projects of various kinds, mathematics clubs, and mathematics contests.

Such administrative and instructional devices have been adequately discussed elsewhere, and the discussion need not be elaborated here. They can provide fairly well for the "better" students, but the highly talented student who is capable of original and independent study can be developed to his fullest capacity only by special individual work.

One suggestion[8] that seems promising is that this can perhaps best be done through a *problems course*, in which the individual student will select, with the approval of the teacher, an area of work in which he is interested and on which he will do independent study and eventually make a formal report to the teacher or the class. This area may, but need not, parallel the regular classwork, and the special work should be done in addition to the regular classwork, not instead of it. It should not be just an interesting but trival "recreation," but should represent a

[8]Howard F. Fehr, Mathematics for the Talented, *Bulletin of the National Association of Secondary-School Principals*, **38** (1954), pp. 103 –110.

serious, extended, and sequential study of the chosen area. Successful implementation of such a program would of course imply a highly competent and interested teacher and appropriate library facilities.

At first thought it might appear that such areas for special study would be associated only with the senior high school or with college courses. Upon reflection, however, one can readily identify many topics associated even with arithmetic which could provide avenues for stimulating and worthwhile investigation by highly talented students. The following are examples of such topics:

The history of arithmetic
The metric system
Square root
Tables and interpolation
Magic squares
Computing with approximate numbers
The slide rule
Modular arithmetic
Arithmetic in scales of notation other than ten
Calculating machines
Cross number puzzles

Significant independent investigation of any of these topics would require high intelligence, sound knowledge, insight, intuition, persistence, virtuosity, and insatiable curiosity on the part of the student. These are characteristic of students highly endowed with mathematical talent. Less ambitious projects which might be undertaken by superior but less talented students might include fairly extensive independent work on such things as graphical methods, short cuts in arithmetic, applications of arithmetic in such various areas as banking, insurance, taxation, and sports, and making up lists of original verbal problems. The *Mathematics Student Journal* often publishes interesting problems for investigation.

EXERCISES

1–8. Prove each of the theorems 1 to 8 on page 282.

9. For each of these theorems 1 to 8 write the corresponding theorem for the relation "is greater than" (>).

10. What modifications in the proofs for theorems 1 to 8 are necessary to structure the proofs for the new theorems of exercise 9?

11. For each of the theorems 1 to 8 write the corresponding theorem for the relation "is less than or equal to" (≤).

12. Restate the theorems of exercise 9 for the relation "is greater than or equal to" (≥).

13. What modifications will be necessary in the proofs of the previous theorems in order to develop the arguments for the new theorems of exercises 11 and 12?

14. Construct an illustration to show that the arithmetic mean of a set of scores is affected by extreme scores but that the median and mode are not.

15. Consider the following two sets of integers: $A = \{78, 72, 62, 33, 20\}$ and $B = \{56, 55, 54, 51, 49\}$. (*a*) Find the average (mean) of each set. (*b*) For each set find

the sum of the absolute deviations of the individual numbers in each set from the average of that set. Then for each set find the average of these deviations. (*c*) Compare the averages (means) of the two sets. (*d*) Compare the average deviations in the two cases. (*e*) Discuss the implications of this exercise. Explain why the use of the averages alone to typify the two sets would be misleading and how one can arrive at a more adequate comparison of the two sets by using their average deviations as well as their means.

16. Five kinds of items in a store are priced as shown in the accompanying table, and the number of items of each kind in

Item. . . .	A	B	C	D	E
Price. . . .	\$0.60	\$4.85	\$0.15	\$1.40	\$0.90
Number of items. . .	20	65	100	35	10

stock is given. (*a*) Compute the average of the five prices. (*b*) Compute the weighted average price for all the items. (*c*) Explain why the weighted average gives a better index of the average price of all the items in stock than the mere average of the five prices themselves.

17. Perform the operations indicated in parts (*a*) to (*c*) and check the result in each case by casting out nines. Be prepared to explain your work. (*a*) 5,793 + 8,610 + 2,944 + 877 + 5,555 = , (*b*) 2,184 × 362 = , (*c*) 64,833 ÷ 147 =

18. The casting out of what number in base twelve is equivalent to casting out nines in base ten? What number in base five? In base $b >$ two?

19. Devise tests for divisibility by 4, 5, 7, 8, 9, and 11. [*Hint:* When the positive residue is greater than one-half the modulus, use the equivalent negative residue. For example, $27 \equiv -1 \pmod 7$ rather than 6 (mod 7).]

20. Which of the following numbers are divisible by 12, 15, 18, or 66? (*a*) 280,764, (*b*) 113,445, (*c*) 3,012,180.

21. Devise tests for divisibility by 2, 3, 4, and 5 in a number system in base six.

22. Obtain good approximations to $\sqrt{486}$ by each of the following methods and be prepared to explain your work to the class as you would to a class of high school students: (*a*) the traditional method, (*b*) the method of estimating, dividing, and averaging, (*c*) the slide rule, (*d*) logarithms.

23. Explain as you would to a class (*a*) why "stepping off a distance" is properly regarded as an example of measurement, (*b*) why someone else stepping off the same distance might get a different numerical result, and (*c*) why it is important to have standardized units of measure that are known and accepted by everybody as a basis of common understanding.

24. What error is there in saying that $5/15 = 0.33$?

25. Is 48.6 or 48.7 the closer approximation of $292/6$? How much closer?

26. Give the approximation to $2/3$ which has an error $1/10$ as large as the error in 0.667.

27. If cans of a certain kind of food are priced at three for 35 cents, what is the exact price and what is the approximate price of one can?

28. Which of the fractions $1/8$, $1/7$, and $5/6$ necessarily give rise to approximate numbers when expanded in finite decimal form?

29. Give the number of significant digits in each of the following approximate numbers: 2.5; 2.05; 2.50; 0.25; 250; 2,500; 250.0; 0.0025; 0.2500; 205,000; 205,000.0; and 0.00002050.

30. Which is the more precise measurement and which is the more accurate in each of the following cases: 2.56 inches or 3,216 feet; 52.3 seconds or 15 seconds?

31. If the approximate numbers 47.2; 5.7; 1,238; 0.05; and 265 represent measurements with the same basic unit, (*a*) which is the most precise? (*b*) Which of the numbers is the most accurate? (*c*) Write each in the form (the approximate number) ± (its apparent error). (*d*) Give correctly the sum: 47.2 + 1,238. (*e*) Give correctly the product: 0.05 × 265.

32. Determine the maximum apparent error, the relative error, and the per cent of error in each of the following measurements: (*a*) 6.5 feet, (*b*) 0.000020 inch, (*c*) 5 inches, (*d*) $5^0/_4$ inches, (*e*) 0.005 centimeter, (*f*) 117.200 miles per hour, (*g*) $2^{14}/_{16}$ inches.

33. Determine the relative error and the per cent error in each of the following measurements: 418.0 feet, 4,180 feet, 46.3 seconds, 4 minutes 46.3 seconds, 25,000 miles. Which of these measurements is the most accurate? Which is the most precise?

34. Find the perimeter of each of these quadrilaterals: (*a*) $6^7/_8$ inches, $5^3/_8$ inches, $12^2/_8$ inches, and $8^0/_8$ inches. (*b*) 56.246 inches, 40.300 inches, 35.20 inches, and 27.18 inches.

35. What is the area of the rectangle whose length is measured as 16.72 inches and whose width is measured as 8.46 inches.

36. Give several instances in which approximations or rounded numbers are more directly useful than the original numbers and explain why.

37. Express the following in scientific notation: 3,865; 2,604,000; 79.60; 0.154; 0.000,553; 512.6; cos 5°23′.

38. Express the following in ordinary notation: 2.65×10^5, 5.34×10^{-2}, 7.953×10^{-11}, 4.49×10^{12}, 6.308×10^0.

39. Express the following numbers in standard notation and, without any actual computation, give rough mental estimates of the answers: (*a*) (237 × 5150)/16, (*b*) (729 × 0.035)/9.8, (*c*) (6980 × 0.047)/0.518, (*d*) (44600 × 0.00923 × 1.016)/(0.815 × 254).

40. The star Arcturus is about 223,700,000,000,000 miles from the earth. Find this distance in light years if one light year is approximately 5,870,000,000,000 miles. Express the numbers in scientific notation and explain your work.

BIBLIOGRAPHY

Aiken, D. J., and C. A. Beseman: "Modern Mathematics: Topics and Problems" (New York: McGraw-Hill Book Company, 1959).

Arnold C. J.: An Answer to "Arguments against Universal Adoption of the Metric System," *School Science and Mathematics*, **51** (1951), 310–315.

Bakst, Aaron: Approximate Computation, *Twelfth Yearbook* (Washington, D.C.: National Council of Teachers of Mathematics, 1937).

Banks, J. Houston: "Learning and Teaching Arithmetic" 2d ed., (Englewood Cliffs, N. J.: Allyn and Bacon, Inc., 1963).

Bergamini, David: "Mathematics," Life Science Library (New York: Time Inc. 1963).

Bernstein, Allen: A Study of Remedial Arithmetic Conducted with Ninth Grade Students, *School Science and Mathematics*, **56** (1956), 25–31, 429–437.

Botts, Truman: Linear Measurement and Imagination, *Arithmetic Teacher*, **9** (1962), 376–382.

Bowman, M. E.: "Romance in Arithmetic: Currency, Weights, and Measures" (London: London University Press, 1950).

Boyer, Lee Emerson: Elementary Approximate Computation, *Mathematics Teacher*, **32** (1939), 249–258.

Curtis, Herbert J., and Karl Menger: On the Formulation of Certain Arithmetical Questions, *Mathematics Teacher*, **49** (1956), 528–530.

Dubisch, Roy: Applications of Finite Arithmetic, *Mathematics Teacher*, **53** (1960), 322–324, 430–432; **55** (1962), 162–164.

Evenson, A. B.: "Modern Mathematics" (Chicago: Scott, Foresman and Company, 1962.

Frege, G.: "The Foundations of Arithmetic" (Oxford, England: Basil Blackwell & Mott, Ltd., 1850).

Fujii, John N.: "An Introduction to the Elements of Mathematics" (New York: John Wiley & Sons, Inc., 1961).

Giffel, William J.: Primes and Things, *School Science and Mathematics*, **62** (1962), 684–687.

Goins, William F., Jr.: Putting More Meaning in the Teaching of Measurement, *School Science and Mathematics*, **50** (1950), 745–749.

Greenleaf, Newcomb, and Robert J. Wisner: The Unique Factorization Theorem, *Mathematics Teacher,* **52** (1959), 600–603.

Haines, Margaret: Modular Arithmetic, *Arithmetic Teacher,* **9** (1962), 127–129.

Hamilton, W. W.: Field Work Modifies Our Program in Arithmetic, *School Science and Mathematics,* **51** (1951), 527–531.

Ingham, Carolyn, and Joseph M. Payne: An Eighth-grade Unit on Number Systems, *Mathematics Teacher,* **51** (1958), 392–395.

Johnson, Donovan A.: A Unit on Our Number System, *School Science and Mathematics,* **52** (1952), 556–561.

——— and William H. Glenn: Exploring Mathematics on Your Own (New York: McGraw-Hill Book Company, 1961). (Series of eighteen pamphlets.)

Jones, Burton W.: Miniature Number Systems, *Mathematics Teacher,* **51** (1958), 226–231.

Kinsella, John, J.: The Adolescent and Arithmetic, *School Science and Mathematics,* **50** (1950), 119–124.

Leonard, John L.: A New Method for Finding Square Root, *School Science and Mathematics,* **50** (1950), 40–48.

Miller, Ralph C.: Arithmetic for the Twelfth Year, *Mathematics Teacher,* **40** (1947), 221–224.

Moore, Tabbie Mae: More About Casting Out Nines, *Arithmetic Teacher,* **3** (1956), 204–206.

Paige, Donald D.: Primes and Factoring, *Arithmetic Teacher,* **9** (1962), 449–452.

Parsons, Kenneth B., and Stanley P. Franklin: Divisibility by Two, *Mathematics Teacher,* **53** (1960), 639.

Rassweiler, Merrill, and J. Merle Harris: "Mathematics and Measurement" (New York: Harper & Row, Publishers, Incorporated, 1955).

Read, Cecil B.: Arguments against Universal Adoption of the Metric System, *School Science and Mathematics,* **50** (1950), 297–306.

———: Comments on Computation with Approximate Numbers, *Mathematics Teacher,* **46** (1953), 479–483.

Schaaf, William L.: "Basic Concepts of Elementary Mathematics" (New York: John Wiley & Sons, Inc., 1960).

Scheid, Francis: Clock Arithmetic and Nuclear Energy, *Mathematics Teacher,* **52** (1959), 604–607.

Schiff, Herbert J.: Let Them Measure, *School Science and Mathematics,* **57** (1957), 291–292.

Seeley, Walter J.: The Engineer's Simple Arithmetic, *Mathematics Teacher,* **46** (1953), 565–566.

Seymour, Kenneth A.: A General Test for Divisibility, *Mathematics Teacher,* **56** (1963), 151–154.

Shuster, Carl N.: Teaching Computation with Approximate Data, *Mathematics Teacher,* **42** (1949), 123–132.

———: Approximate Square Roots, *Mathematics Teacher,* **45** (1952), 17–18.

Sister M. Barbara Stastny, O.S.F.: A Test for Divisibility, *Mathematics Teacher,* **53** (1960), 627–631.

Stein, Sherman K.: "Mathematics, the Manmade Universe," (San Francisco: W. H. Freeman and Company, 1963).

Ward, Morgan, and Clarence Ethel Hardgrove: "Modern Elementary Mathematics" (Reading, Mass.: Addison-Wesley Publishing Company, Inc., 1964).

Willerding, Margaret F.: A Teaching Unit in Modular Arithmetic, *School Science and Mathematics,* **60** (1960), 511–518.

Williams, Wendell M.: A Complete Set of Elementary Rules for Testing Divisibility, *Mathematics Teacher,* **56** (1963), 437–442.

Youse, Bevan K.: "Arithmetic: A Modern Approach" (Englewood Cliffs, N.J.: Prentice-Hall, Inc., 1963).

THIRTEEN

The teaching of algebra in the junior high school

A LARGE SHARE of the difficulties which students encounter in their study of algebra may be traced to the fact that it presents them a radically new and different approach to the study of quantitative relationships, characterized by a new symbolism, new concepts, a new language, a much higher degree of generalization and abstraction than they have encountered previously, and an essential dissociation of many of its parts from intuition and concrete experience. Also, in contrast to arithmetic, algebra is more concerned with the conscious examination and study of processes and basic structure than with particular answers to particular problems.

Teachers often fail to take account of the degree and the specific nature of the difficulties which these characteristics involve for beginning students. Unless teachers recognize these difficulties clearly and examine them with sufficient care to formulate specific ways for helping the student avoid or overcome them, the study of algebra is likely to degenerate into an aggregate of mechanical manipulations of symbols largely devoid of meaning.

The fact that teachers often have been too preoccupied, negligent, or uninformed to take proper account of them does not mean that these various difficulties are insuperable. On the contrary, experience has shown that through careful analysis, thoughtful planning, and skillful teaching a great deal can be done to obviate or minimize them. No single topic is free from them. It is the job of the teacher to analyze each topic, to learn to anticipate the particular difficulties that are likely to occur in connection with it, and to plan to teach it in such a way that the difficulties may be avoided or forestalled as far as possible. Such a practice will go far toward enabling the teacher to explain away those difficulties which cannot be avoided altogether.

The first course in algebra In general the content of the first course in algebra should not be very extensive in depth, nor should it be formalized to the extent that the work of later courses will be. Its main objective should be to give the students an introduction to the meaning and use of certain basic algebraic concepts, such as literal symbols, signed numbers, formulas, polynomial functions, graphs, equations, and inequalities. It is not intended that the algebraic work of the junior high school will lead to any large degree of technical skill in algebraic operations, nor is it intended that this work shall be thought of solely in terms of its preparatory values. Rather it should be conceived as serving the double purpose of extending the conceptual background of the student as a sound transitional basis for later work and of providing mathematical experiences interesting in themselves and more general in nature than those encountered in the earlier arithmetic.

Although formulas, equations, etc., have been referred to as algebraic "topics," the reader should not get the impression that they are to be treated once, topically, and then relegated to the limbo of "finished work." On the contrary, they should be studied at recurring intervals and in various contexts throughout the course. Formulas and equations, in particular, are so pervasive and so amenable to gradation and adjustment from the standpoint of difficulty that appropriate applications of them can be made in connection with almost any topic which is likely to be considered in junior high school mathematics. Teachers should be alert to opportunities for making such applications and should become adept at using them to best advantage. At the same time, it is necessary to guard against the tendency to become overly zealous with regard to this part of the course. It should be kept in mind that the aim of the algebraic work in the junior high school is by no means an exhaustive coverage of algebra as such but rather a good and progressively improving mastery of a few of its simpler concepts and processes as they are applied to familiar situations.

For more effective work in such a beginning course in the formal attention to algebra there must be a minimum list of prerequisite expectations of algebraic experience. The Commission on Mathematics gives the following list of such prerequisites for its proposed first course in algebra:[1]

Graphs and Formulas: Use of line segments and areas to represent numbers. Reading and construction of bar graphs, line graphs, pictograms, circle graphs,

[1]Report of the Commission on Mathematics, "Program for College Preparatory Mathematics" (New York: College Entrance Examination Board, 1959), pp. 19–20.

and continuous line graphs. Meaning of scale. Formulas for perimeters, areas, volumes, and percents—introduced as generalizations as these concepts are studied. Use of symbols in formulas as placeholders for numerals arising in measurement. Simple expressions and sentences involving "variables."

Such algebraic work as may be attempted in the earlier grades to meet prerequisites should be informal, and it should be interesting. So far as possible it should be made to seem useful to the students. There should be little or no technical manipulation of symbols. The problem situations that are presented should be so simple that they can be readily associated with familiar arithmetical or geometrical situations, so that by the process of analogy the appropriate procedures may be made to appear reasonable to the students. The main idea should be to give the students an understanding of the meaning of the language and symbolism of algebra as expressed in the formula and the simple equation and an understanding of the simplicity, power, generality, and importance of these mathematical tools.

Most of the work in algebra in these earlier grades should be focused upon the interpretation of graphs and associated concepts, making clear the meaning of literal symbols, their use in setting up formulas and simple equations, and the evaluation of such formulas and the solution of such equations.[2] Many commonplace relationships already familiar to the pupil give rise to formulas. Such relationships may be used to advantage by having the pupils translate their verbal expressions into symbolic language. For example, if pencils cost 5 cents each, the pupil readily states that the cost of 2 pencils will be 2 times 5 cents, the cost of 7 pencils will be 7 times 5 cents, and so on. He can be led without difficulty to generalize this situation to give the cost of any number of pencils at this price; i.e., the total cost will be the number of pencils times 5 cents. It is an easy but important step for him now to pass from this verbal statement to the symbolic statement of the same relation, $C = n \cdot 5$, and eventually to the still more general statement $C = n \cdot p$. The evaluation of C for any given values of n and p thus becomes easy and meaningful.

Many familiar arithmetical problems can be made to yield just as satisfactory formulas and equations. Some examples are given in the following table, which could be extended easily.

In any uniform or average-rate motion, distance equals rate times time.	$d = r \cdot t$
Simple interest equals principal times rate times time.	$i = p \cdot r \cdot t$
Circumference of a circle equals pi times the diameter.	$C = \pi \cdot D$
Perimeter of a rectangle equals 2 times the sum of the length and the width.	$p = 2(l + w)$

[2]See, among others, the following references: Materials for Grade 8 Mathematics, "Mathematics in the Public Schools" (New York: Board of Education of the City of New York, 1955), and the Report of the Commission on Mathematics, *op. cit.*, pp. 18–19.

The annual rent on a home equals 12 times the monthly rent.	$R = 12 \cdot r$
Percentage equals base times rate.	$p = b \cdot r$
Margin equals selling price minus cost.	$m = s - c$
Area of a rectangle equals base times height.	$A = b \cdot h$
The score in a basketball game is the number of free throws plus twice the number of field goals made good.	$S = f + 2g$
The diagonal of a square is equal to the length of one side times the positive square root of 2.	$d = s \cdot \sqrt{2}$
The volume of a rectangular solid is equal to the product of the length, width, and height.	$V = l \cdot w \cdot h$
The length of the hypotenuse of a right triangle is equal to the positive square root of the sum of the squares of the legs.	$h = \sqrt{a^2 + b^2}$
The number of ounces is equal to 16 times the number of pounds.	$n = 16 \cdot p$
The number of gallons in a tank is (about) equal to 7½ times the number of cubic feet.	$g = 7\frac{1}{2} \cdot f$
The number of centimeters is (about) 2.54 times the number of inches.	$c = 2.54 \cdot i$

The equations which are used should be so simple that the pupil will intuitively know how to solve them. So far as possible they, also, should grow out of familiar problem situations, although there can be no objection to setting up short lists of empirical equations for practice. Consider this problem, for example: If John earned $9.60 for 16 hours work, what was his average wage per hour? This gives rise to the equation $16 \cdot w = \$9.60$, and the pupil's task is to solve for w. Intuition furnishes a sufficient guide for this.

Of equal usefulness is this problem; Fred and Joe picked 40 quarts of cherries one day, but Joe picked 8 quarts more than Fred did. How many quarts did each pick? This suggests the equation $F + (F + 8) = 40$, or $2F + 8 = 40$. By subtracting 8 from each side, the equation becomes $2F = 32$, for which, again, the solution is effected intuitively.

Equations of this type provide an easy and natural approach to the more formal methods to be used later. They need not and should not be made difficult. Speed of solution is not a consideration here. The main considerations at this stage should be to ensure understanding of the derivation of the equation, to ensure understanding of the solution, and to develop the habit of using such equations in solving problems.

Such a treatment of formulas and equations, supplemented by frequent use of graphs for visual presentation of information, can provide a strong foundation upon which to build the structure of algebra. It should serve effectively in preparing the way for the student as he enters his first formal course in algebra.

No significant discussion of the subject-matter content of the first course in algebra can fail to call attention to the new emphases on precision and clarity of expression in both definitions and exposition.

Probably the most pervasive single concept used in the efforts to accomplish these desirable goals of instruction is the notion of *sets*. The concepts of set and subset are very simple. A set is defined simply by some consideration whereby one can determine whether a particular object does or does not belong to the set. Innumerable examples can be given: the set of persons in a given algebra class, the set of chairs in a room, the set of all automobile licenses issued in Michigan in a given year, the set of numbers in a telephone directory, the set of points on a line, the set of positive integers less than 13. Indeed, the idea of sets of objects is one of the earliest concepts which children form. They use sets of objects in learning the names of numbers and in learning to count. Even in such simple matters as distinguishing between different kinds of objects, they are implicitly using notions of sets of things having different characteristics.

In view of these considerations one may reasonably ask why children should have any difficulties in studying about sets in connection with algebra. The truth is that there need be very little difficulty at all. In fact, the consideration of sets that is appropriate in connection with the first course in algebra should be largely intuitive and informal, and it should be concerned more with establishing foundations of ideas, terminology, and symbolism than with formal proofs of theorems about sets. At the same time, unless this work is carefully presented and unless enough practice is given both in translating the set symbolism into words and in translating verbal statements into appropriate set symbolism, some difficulties may arise. These would seem to stem mainly from three sources. First, in their early experiences with sets, the attention of the students will usually have been focused either on the individual objects of the set or upon some characteristic that is common to these objects, rather than upon the set itself. Second, the usual operations with sets (union, intersection, complementation, inclusion) are different from the operations of arithmetic and school algebra to which the students have been accustomed. Third, and unquestionably most important, the terminology and symbolism generally associated with sets and operations with sets, and which the students must learn, will be new to them and will seem strange and esoteric at first. Most children will respond readily and correctly to the question, What positive integers are greater than 30 and less than 40? But write on the chalkboard the symbols

Let $P = \{x|x = 1, 2, \ldots, 39\}$
and $Q = \{y|y = 31, 32, 33, \ldots\}$
Then $P \cap Q = \{ \qquad\qquad \}$

and ask them to fill in the last pair of braces, and they are likely to be baffled unless they have previously been taught how to translate these symbols into words.

Venn diagrams are very useful in helping students clarify the notions of union, intersection, complementation, and inclusion. It is also helpful to give illustrations employing finite sets having small numbers of objects. Not a great deal is known yet about how rapidly or how well high school freshmen can master the rules of operation with sets, but this question is probably not a very important one. It should be repeated that no extensive formal study of the algebra of sets is advocated for the first course.

At the same time, an introduction to the concept of sets, explanation of the meanings attached to the terminology and symbolism employed, some simple illustrations and perhaps some simple exercises involving union and intersection of sets can bring several advantages. Most important among these advantages is the fact that students will be learning the language, acquiring a familiarity with the concepts, and building a proficiency in the techniques used so effectively in the study of mathematics. Also, through these avenues students can be made aware that mathematics is not a subject on which the last word has been written but a live and growing field and that there are branches of mathematics other than the traditional algebra and geometry which are new and interesting and of growing importance. They can be given a little glimpse into one of these branches and can become acquainted with some of its technical words and symbols. Few high school students realize that there are algebras other than the conventional school algebra that they study. Some acquaintance with the other algebras can do much to broaden the students' mathematical horizons and give added interest to the work of the regular course in which they are enrolled.[3]

Symbols and formulas The formula, a symbolic statement of relationship between two or more variables, provides an ideal medium for the transition from the earlier work to the more formal and systematic aspects of algebra and a theme about which a great deal of the work of the first course can be organized. It involves or is closely associated with a great many of the concepts of elementary algebra: the symbolic

[3]For illustrations of various types of suggested adaptations to elementary algebra see:

Robert R. Christian, "Introduction to Logic and Sets" (Boston: Ginn and Company, 1958).

Report of the Commission on Mathematics, "Appendices" (New York: College Entrance Examination Board, 1959).

W. R. Krickenberger and Helen R. Pearson, "An Introduction to Sets and the Structure of Algebra" (Boston: Ginn and Company, 1958).

Report of the Secondary School Curriculum Committee, The Secondary Mathematics Curriculum, *Mathematics Teacher*, **52** (1959), 398–402.

James F. Gray, "Sets, Relations, and Functions" (New York: Holt, Rinehart and Winston, Inc., 1962).

Myra McFadden, J. William Moore, and Wendell I. Smith, "Sets, Relations, and Functions" (New York: McGraw-Hill Book Company, 1963).

Bruce E. Meserve and Max A. Sobel, "Mathematics for Secondary School Teachers" (Englewood Cliffs, N.J.: Prentice-Hall, Inc., 1962), pp. 77–176.

language of constants and variables; the concept of dependence and function; graphic representation of relationships; substitution and evaluation; and operations with signed numbers, literal symbols, parentheses, exponents, fractions, radicals, etc. Thus it forms a core which has points of contact not only with the previous experiences of the students but with many of the topics which will be considered subsequently.

The beginning algebra student is not entirely unacquainted with formulas. In his previous work in arithmetic and informal geometry he will doubtless have had some contact with such formulas as those for simple interest and for the mensuration of the simplest and most common geometric forms. If he has had a thoroughly good course in the earlier grades, he should have attained some understanding of the significance and generality of the formula as a shorthand statement of relationships between quantities and as a rule for operation. He will have had some experience in evaluating simple formulas and perhaps will have constructed a few simple formulas from quantitative situations within his experience. He thus brings to his first course in algebra enough background to enable him to use the formula as a point of departure in his work, and his further study of the formula, in turn, serves to familiarize him with, and give him experience in, the progressive mastery of the new language, concepts, symbolism, and operations of algebra.

The main things which the student should get from his more formal study of formulas are these:

1. An understanding and appreciation of the nature and significance of the symbolism of algebra
2. An appreciation of the fact that a formula is merely the translation of an English sentence into symbolic form
3. A clear concept of the meaning of a constant and a variable and the distinction between the two
4. A clear concept and appreciation of dependence and the meaning and relationship of independent and dependent variables
5. The ability to set up simple formulas expressing relationships existing in situations within the student's experience
6. Facility and accuracy in substitution in and evaluation of formulas
7. The ability to represent graphically the relationships indicated by formulas involving two variables
8. The ability to solve formulas, i.e., to transform an implicit relationship into an explicit relationship through application of the laws of algebraic operation

If the teacher will organize the work relating to formulas around these main foci and will consciously plan every exercise and activity so that it will bear upon and contribute to the attainment of one or another of these main objectives, then worthwhile results may be expected. Otherwise, the work is likely to follow a too prevalent piecemeal pattern whose only plan is the order of topics and exercises in the textbook, a pattern in which organization, emphasis, and direction will be lacking and from which any worthwhile outcomes which may occur must be regarded more as welcome accidents than as legitimate expectations.

One of the first of the fundamental tasks which the student faces in the study of formulas and algebra in general is to acquire a good understanding of the real meaning of symbolism. It is customary to introduce students to the notational significance of algebraic symbolism by having them (1) consider common situations in which the relationships between two or more elements are known, (2) state these relationships in words, and (3) abbreviate the verbal statements by substituting letters and symbols of operation and equality for the words. For example, the student may be asked to tell how to find the distance which an automobile traveling at a uniform speed will cover in a given time. His statement will probably be to the effect that the distance is equal to the rate of speed (in miles per hour) multiplied by the time (expressed in hours). He can easily be led to see that, by using letters to represent the verbal expressions, he can write this same relationship more briefly and conveniently as $d = r \cdot t$. That is, in this simple case he has little difficulty in associating the letter d with distance, r with rate of speed, and t with time. He thus gains almost at once the important idea that a letter may stand for a meaning which can be expressed more elaborately in words.

This, however, is not the whole story. Unless the student is made keenly aware not only that the letter is to be associated with a verbal expression (e.g., r for rate) but that it must be identified in any particular instance *with a number,* he is likely to come to the erroneous and meaningless conclusion that "miles per hour times hours equals miles" or that "feet times feet equals square feet." Such statements are not at all uncommon, but they exhibit a lack of clarity with respect to the meaningful use of symbolism. A concept fundamental to the clear and precise use of symbols is that the student be made to understand that they primarily and essentially represent numbers, although they may refer to the enumeration or numerical measurement of some particular kinds of objects or magnitudes. The intelligent use of symbols probably can be developed most effectively through numerous illustrations of the use of letters to represent such things as lengths of line segments, weights, sizes of angles, or unknown quantities in simple verbal problems or equations. Such illustrations should be closely associated with repeated and carefully supervised practice in the actual evaluation of formulas by the direct substitution of specified numbers and the performance of the indicated operations after the substitutions have been made. The teacher should employ illustrations of these procedures freely, because the immature mind responds much more readily to illustration than it does to definition or verbal direction. During this period of development and early practice in the employment of symbols, the work of the student should be under the close supervision of the teacher in order that any misconceptions and mistakes may be detected and corrected at the outset and so prevented from becoming fixed habits.

Constants, variables, and functions Letter symbols are often used to represent *variables*. The two are not synonymous, because letter symbols are also used at times to represent *constants*. While the concept of variable is not to be restricted to the domain of variation, it does provide the language and symbolism for dealing with the principles and problems of variation, and it is indispensable to the complete understanding of formulas, equations, and the nature of dependence.

A *variable* is a symbol that may represent any element from a specified set of elements called its *domain,* or *replacement set*. For example, the letter r is frequently used to represent the radius of a circle. Thus the domain of values for r consists of all the positive real numbers, since, theoretically at least, there exists a circle for any positive real number which might be specified as the radius. This is not true for negative numbers. If the value of r should be specified as -3, there does not exist a circle with such a number as its radius. Note that in this illustration no thought of variation is expressed. The symbol r is simply used to *stand for* any number that might be used as the radius of a circle. On the other hand, the concept of variation might well be in the picture, as, for example, in the use of the symbol t to represent time as it is changing during some specified interval.

A *constant* is a symbol used to represent a fixed value *during a particular discussion*. In other words, a constant is a symbol for which the replacement set contains one and only one element. Such symbols as 2, -3, $\sqrt{2}$, $5/6$, and π are constants. They are fixed in value. They are known as *absolute constants*, in contrast to *arbitrary constants* (or *parameters*) such as the symbol m in the equation of the straight line $y = mx + 3$. For any particular discussion the value of m may be chosen and it will remain fixed for that discussion, but it may change from one discussion to another. The value of the absolute constant 3 remains the same for all discussions. The lines $y = 1/2x + 3$, $y = -4x + 3$, $y = 5x + 3$ are straight lines, all passing through the point (0,3) but with the respective slopes of $1/2$, -4, and 5.

The ordinary experiences of children furnish innumerable illustrations of both variables and constants. The fact that many children come through one or more years of work in algebra without any clear understanding of what is meant by either of the terms "variable" and "variation" can mean only that teachers do not take the trouble to present a sufficient number or variety of these illustrations. Changes in age, height, or weight of individuals, the distance of a moving body from a fixed point, and changes in temperature are but a few examples of many familiar situations which could be used to make the meanings of variation, variable, and constant clear. If these illustrations are to yield the desired results, however, the teacher must see to it that the attention of the students is focused upon the respective characteristics of each concept, and this emphasis must be made repeatedly and specifically. One cannot reasonably expect any clear comprehension of any one of the three concepts to emerge as a mere incidental by-product. They are not difficult to develop, but they must be developed through planned activity if they are to be really understood by any substantial majority of the students.

Just as the concept of variable has suffered through the years because of the inclination of many to restrict it to considerations of variation, so the concept of function has suffered because of similar restrictions to considerations of dependence and dependent variation. It is true that the concept of function furnishes the language and symbolism for effective consideration of the characteristics of dependence, but it is not to be thought of as being restricted merely to such considerations. Mathematicians[4] are inclined to emphasize two basic concepts of "function," namely:

1. A *function* is a set of ordered pairs of elements (a,b) so related that, when the value of a is determined in its set of admissible values, the value of b is determined uniquely in its set. The two sets are not necessarily distinct.

Thus, the ordered pairs (a,a^2), $(a,\sqrt{a})$, $(a, \sin a)$ are possible functions. If the set of values for both variables is specified as the set of all positive real numbers, each ordered pair is a function. To any value of the first variable there corresponds a unique value of the second variable. This is illustrated in Table 13-1 for a few values of a.

TABLE 13-1

a	a^2	$\sqrt{a}$	$\sin a$
1	1	1	$\sin 1$
2	4	$\sqrt{2}$	$\sin 2$
$\frac{1}{4}$	$\frac{1}{16}$	$\frac{1}{2}$	$\sin \frac{1}{4}$

If the set of values for a is specified as the set of all negative real numbers and the set of values for the second variable is specified to be the set of all real numbers, then (a,a^2) and $(a, \sin a)$ are functions, but $(a,\sqrt{a})$ is not. For example, if $a = -4$, then (a,a^2) becomes $(-4,16)$,

[4]For interesting and helpful discussions of constant, variable, and function, see Chaps. III, VIII, and XIII of "Insights into Modern Mathematics," *Twenty-third Yearbook* (Washington, D.C.: National Council of Teachers of Mathematics, 1957).

$(a, \sin a)$ becomes $[-4, \sin(-4)]$, and 16 and $\sin(-4)$ are real numbers. On the other hand, $(a,\sqrt{a})$ becomes $(-4,\sqrt{-4})$, and $\sqrt{-4}$ is not a real number.

2. A *function* is a rule, expression, or table which defines a specific relationship between two sets (not necessarily distinct) of elements, such that when an element from one set is given, an element from the other set is uniquely determined.

The expression is frequently no more than the formula form of the rule. For example, the rule that "the area of a circle is equal to π times the square of the radius" is more conveniently expressed by the formula $A = \pi r^2$. Caution must be exercised here in the interpretation of just what it is that the formula is and is not. It is a convenient device for selecting the numbers that give us the function defined by the set of ordered pairs of numbers (radius of a circle, area of the circle) symbolized by (r,A). The set of values from which r may be selected is the set of all nonnegative real numbers, and after r is selected, a value of A is easily determined. The formula is *not* the function. The values which define the function do, indeed, meet the conditions of the formula, but there are ordered pairs of values which meet the conditions of the formula but do not meet the conditions of the function. For example, the pair of values $(-3,9\pi)$ satisfies the formula but not the function, since there is no circle with radius -3. Thus, if the function F is the above set of ordered pairs (r,A), it is incorrect to say that $F(-3) = 9\pi$. McShane[5] refers to such incorrect usage as this as using a formula "beyond its domain of validity," and emphasizes that it "can lead to absurdities, not only in mathematics but in any science."

> The *domain* of a function F is the set of all objects x for which $F(x)$ has meaning; in other words, an object x is in the domain of F if and only if there exists some y such that (x,y) is in F [that is, $F(x) = y$]. The *range* of the function F is the set of all objects y which are values of the function; that is, y is in the range of F if and only if there is an x for which the equation $F(x) = y$ is true.[6]

Table 13-2 gives another illustration of how a function may be defined. Here the set of ordered pairs of elements is (t,T), where t represents time and T represents temperature. The domain of the function is the set of even hours of the day from 2 A.M. to 2 A.M., and the range is the set of temperatures (54°, 60°, 61°, 62°, 64°, 66°, 69°, 70°, 71°, 73°). Note that the set of ordered pairs (T,t) would not be a function, since for $T = 61°$ or $T = 62°$ there is not a *unique* determination of a value for t. However, the set of ordered pairs (T,t) is a *relation* in accordance with this definition: A *relation* is a set of ordered pairs (x,y) such that to each value for the first element x there corresponds at least one value

[5] E. J. McShane: Operating with Sets, "Insights into Modern Mathematics," *Twenty-third Yearbook* (Washington, D.C.: National Council of Teachers of Mathematics, 1957), p. 57.

[6] *Ibid.*, pp. 57–58.

TABLE 13-2

Time	Temperature	Time	Temperature
2 A.M.	61	4 P.M.	70
4 A.M.	61	6 P.M.	66
6 A.M.	61	8 P.M.	62
8 A.M.	64	10 P.M.	62
10 A.M.	69	Midnight	60
Noon	71	2 A.M.	54
2 P.M.	73		

for the second element y. Thus, a function is a special kind of relation. The formula $y = \pm\sqrt{x}$ affords another example of a relation which is not a function. If the domain of the relation is the set of all positive real numbers, then to each value of x there correspond two values for y.

The first symbol in the ordered pair which defines a relation is the *independent variable*. It is the variable whose value is arbitrary so long as it is chosen from the domain of the relation. The second symbol is the *dependent variable*. It is the variable whose value is determined in the range merely by the assignment of an arbitrarily chosen value to the independent variable.

The more restricted concept of relation, namely, the idea of dependence of one element in a situation upon one or more other elements, is not inherently difficult to develop with children. The reason why it is usually so inadequately developed is that specific attention is so seldom given to it. It seems to be one of those outcomes which many teachers passively hope for as a by-product of instruction but which they erroneously regard as so sure of occurrence that to give direct and specific attention to it would be a waste of time.

As is the case with most elementary concepts, the best method of development lies in illustration. The concept of dependence is best illustrated by taking cases involving related quantities such as the diameter and circumference of a circle and showing that, when one of these is known, the other is uniquely determined and that a change in either of the two will produce a corresponding change in the other. In this connection it is helpful to have the students build tables by computing and tabulating the values of the dependent variable which correspond to arbitrarily assigned values of the independent variable or variables and then make graphs from these tables of variables, as illustrated in Figure 13-2. It is possible, of course, for students to perform the necessary substitutions and computations in a mechanical way and *without any conscious recognition* of the interdependence of the quantities involved. It is largely because teachers have failed to stress this conscious recognition of dependence and keep it continually in the focus of

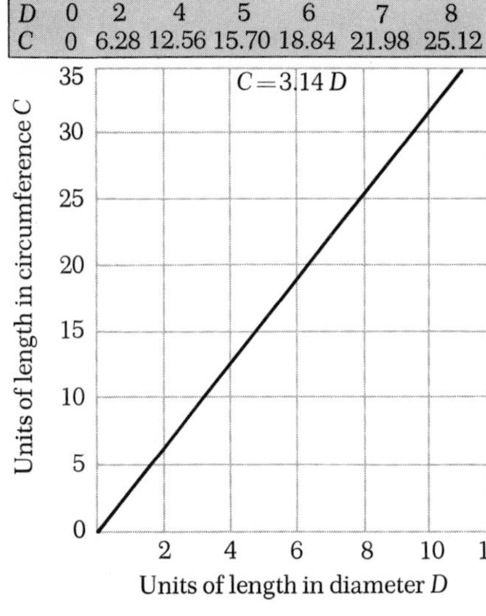

D	0	2	4	5	6	7	8
C	0	6.28	12.56	15.70	18.84	21.98	25.12

Figure 13-1
Relation of the length of circumference of a circle to its length of diameter

attention of the students that the notion of functionality has not played the important part it should play in mathematical education. It is not that it is hard to understand, for it is not. If the concepts of dependence, relation, and function are to be made to play an integral and basic part in the mathematical thinking of students, teachers must continually, deliberately, and specifically bring them to the attention of the student and keep his attention centered upon them by repeated illustrations of their occurrence.

The concepts of *dependent* and *independent variables* are implied in the understanding of dependence. But here again the differential characteristics of these concepts are not likely to emerge and stand out with distinctness in the minds of the students unless the teacher directs special attention to them and shows by repeated illustration just *why* they are called variables and why one of them is designated an *independent* variable while the other is called a *dependent* variable.

Attention has already been called to the practice of having students *translate verbal statements of relationships into formulas* by the use of letter symbols to represent the related elements in the situation. There can be little doubt that such practice in translating statements or laws into formulas is of great value in centering the students' attention upon the fundamental concepts which have been discussed and in clarifying these concepts. Probably the simplest and most effective way to give students an understanding start in this use of symbolism is to show them that it may be regarded as a sort of shorthand method of writing down what would otherwise have to be written in a less convenient verbal form. The contrast between the verbal and the symbolic forms and the advantage of the latter can be emphasized by actually writing down the verbal statements of relationships and then "for the sake of convenience" rewriting the statements by using merely the initial letters of the key words rather than the words themselves. The following examples illustrate this method.

Distance	equals	rate of speed	multiplied by	time
d	$=$	r	$\times$	t

Cost of gasoline	equals	number of gallons	multiplied by	price per gallon
C	$=$	g	$\times$	p

A few such examples will serve to enable most students to get the idea of what is being done and learn to appreciate the significance of the symbolism and the expressed relationships. However, in order to ensure something distinctly beyond a mere threshold understanding of these concepts, the students should be given a substantial amount of practice in this work, and the practice should be spread over a considerable period of time.

Teaching students to solve linear equations One of the most common and important activities of the first course in algebra is the solution of linear equations. Presumably the student will bring to his study of algebra some understanding of what an equation means, since he will have had experience with simple equations in his previous work in arithmetic and informal geometry and perhaps even with certain very simple equations in which the unknown quantity is represented by a literal symbol. In all probability, however, his experience in solving equations will have been barely above the intuitive level. For example, if confronted with the equation $3n = 24$ and required to find the number represented by n, he will probably reason that, if three n's make 24, then "it stands to reason" that one n will have to be one-third of 24, or 8.

These intuitive reactions are generally sufficient and satisfactory so long as the situation is very simple, i.e., so long as it is possible for the student to keep in mind clearly and simultaneously all the pertinent elements and relationships which are involved in the situation. On the other hand, the moment a problem situation becomes so involved that he is unable to keep all the elements and their proper relationships clearly in mind at the same time, intuition breaks down; and when this happens, logic must take its place. In such cases the only recourse is to more formal and powerful tools for the analysis of problem situations. Such a tool is the algebraic equation.

Since the turn of the century much criticism has been directed against formalism in secondary school algebra. It is undoubtedly true that the mechanical aspects of algebra have been heavily stressed and that the emphasis placed upon the formal operations has too often given little or no consideration to underlying meanings. There is a great difference, however, between formalism, conceived in this sense, and the formalization of mathematical procedures. Algebra really consists fundamentally in the generalization and formalization of these procedures, but this formalization need not and should not be divorced from meanings. Rather, it should be conceived as merely an extension of familiar procedures into an environment of number concepts more general and more powerful than those of elementary arithmetic. The student should be taught to look upon the algebraic equation as a device which enables him to investigate easily relationships which would be too complex to be investigated successfully or easily without its aid. It should be explained to him that the solution of formulas or equations operates under certain fixed laws sometimes called *axioms*. He should learn the meaning of these axioms. They should be explained to him and illustrated by the teacher in terms of the familiar quantitative concepts of his past experience. After he has thus been given a feeling of the reasonableness of the axioms, he should be given practice in using them not only with arithmetical numbers but with literal numbers as well.

The fundamental operational axioms involved in the solution of linear equations are as follows:

1. If equals are added to equals, the results are equal.
2. If equals are subtracted from equals, the results are equal.
3. If equals are multiplied by equals, the results are equal.
4. If equals are divided by equals other than zero, the results are equal.

The student should learn to react without hesitancy to these axioms. They should become so much a part of him that he will come to apply them as readily to literal numbers as to ordinary arithmetical numbers in an equation.

Linear equations in one unknown assume a variety of forms, of which the following are illustrative:

$$ax = b \qquad x + a = b \qquad ax + b = c$$

$$\frac{x}{a} = b \qquad a - x = b \qquad x - a = b$$

$$ax + b = cx + d \qquad ax + bx = c$$

While these forms are all variations of a common form, the similarity is usually not immediately apparent to children encountering them for the first time. Moreover, textbooks and teachers are frequently deficient in giving emphasis to this point. As a consequence the different forms are often taught separately, a special technique being developed for each, much as the three cases of percentage are often taught in arithmetic. Such a practice probably makes for quick mastery of the separate techniques but for little else. It is in fact precisely this type of treatment against which the legitimate criticism of algebra has been directed. It does not and cannot make other than an incidental contribution to the development of any real power of generalized understanding and original analysis. It produces little more than the acquisition of certain transitory skills, and so it largely fails in the attainment of its real objective.

A much sounder procedure would be to try to find a single unifying principle which would be applicable to all forms. Such a principle fortunately is available and can be stated in a way which is clearly understandable to beginning algebra students. It can be formulated in three or four key sentences somewhat as follows:

1. In solving *any* linear equation in one unknown for the unknown (we may call it x), the object is to get an equation in which x will stand alone on one side of the equation and will not appear on the other side.
2. In order to do this we must get rid of all the other numerals or symbols which are associated with x on its side of the equation.
3. We get rid of these numerals or symbols by undoing the operations which associate them with x, that is, by applying the processes which are the inverse of those which bind these symbols or numerals to x.
4. If any operation is performed on one side of an equation in order to change its value, the same or an equivalent operation must be performed on the other side of the equation, because if it is not, we shall no longer have an equation in balance.

This principle gives a basis for the solution of linear equations without any recourse whatever to intuition, except the intuitive feeling that the only way to make a number symbol stand alone is to get rid of the other number symbols that are connected with it. It gives emphasis to the character of the equation and lends organization and generality to the solution of linear equations. This, in turn, eliminates any necessity for developing special methods for the different forms. For the student who follows this general plan, the specialized procedures will emerge automatically as he finds need for them, since they are but adaptations of the general plan to particularized forms of the equation.

Example: Let it be required to solve $ax - b = c$ for x. In order to make x stand alone on one side of the equation, it is necessary to get rid of the b and the a from that side of the equation. Since the x appears in only one term, we may first get rid of the other term, b. This is done by adding b to both sides of the equation, since originally b was subtracted from ax and any subtraction can be undone only by the inverse process, addition. This[7] gives $ax = c + b$. It is now necessary to get rid of the a from the left member of the equation. Since the a is a multiplier of x, we can get rid of it only by undoing the multiplication. For this purpose we must employ the inverse process, division; that is, we must divide both sides of the equation by a. This will give the required solution: $x = \dfrac{c + b}{a}$

[7]This is the equivalent of "transposition," which may be used as a convenient short cut if and only if the student understands the full significance of the process.

Sometimes the unknown appears in more than one term. When that occurs, it is first necessary to collect these terms and to factor out the unknown as a common factor. After this has been done, the solution is identical in nature to the one that has just been described.

Example: Let it be required to solve the equation $ax + b + cx = d$ for x.

Solution:

1. Collect the terms in x. — 1. $(ax + cx) + b = d$.
2. Factor out x as a common factor. — 2. $x(a + c) + b = d$.
3. Get rid of the term b from the left member of the equation by subtracting b from both members. — 3. $x(a + c) = d - b$.
4. Get rid of the multiplier $(a + c)$ from the left member by dividing both members by $(a + c)$. — 4. $\dfrac{x(a + c)}{(a + c)} = \dfrac{(d - b)}{(a + c)}$.

or

$$x = \frac{d - b}{a + c}.$$

These two illustrations have been presented in the somewhat casual language frequently found in traditional usage. The careful observer, however, sees that they make significant use of basic properties of a number field and of the relation of equality. (See below and page 64.) The great danger in such casualness is that it leads to mechanical operation in the context of memorized rules. Although the formal study of number fields is no part of the responsibility of the first course in algebra, it is important that students at this level of instruction be made conscious of the field properties as they define the field of real numbers and the subfield of rational numbers. Although the field properties have been stated previously, they are of such great significance to the study of algebra that they are restated here.

Given the set of elements F and two operations, addition $(+)$ and multiplication $(\times)$.[8] The set F is called a *field* if, for every element $(a, b, c, d, \ldots)$ of F, the following postulates hold:

F1. *Closure.* $a + b$ and $a \cdot b$ are elements of F.
F2. *Uniqueness.* If $a = b$ and $c = d$, then $a + c = b + d$ and $a \cdot c = b \cdot d$.
F3. *Commutative.* $a + b = b + a$ and $a \cdot b = b \cdot a$.
F4. *Associative.* $(a + b) + c = a + (b + c)$ and $(a \cdot b) \cdot c = a \cdot (b \cdot c)$.
F5. *Distributive.* $a \cdot (b + c) = (a \cdot b) + (a \cdot c)$.
F6. *Additive identity.* There exists in F an element 0 such that $a + 0 = a$ for every a in F. The element 0 is the *additive identity*

[8]Attention is called to the fact that, although the names and symbols of the two operations are the familiar ones, the nature of each operation is dependent upon its definiton in each specific context. For example, if F is the set of integers, then addition and multiplication are defined in the familiar way, based on counting. If F is the set of rational numbers, then each element can be expressed in the form $a = p/q$ and $b = r/s$, where p, q, r, s are integers with $q \neq 0$ and $s \neq 0$. In this case

$$a + b = \frac{p}{q} + \frac{r}{s} = \frac{(p \cdot s) + (q \cdot r)}{q \cdot s} \quad \text{and} \quad a \cdot b = \frac{p}{q} \cdot \frac{r}{s} = \frac{p \cdot r}{q \cdot s}$$

F7. *Multiplicative identity.* There exists in F an element $1(\neq 0)$ such that $1 \cdot a = a$ for every a in F.

F8. *Additive inverse.* For each a in F there exists an element $-a$ in F such that $(-a) + a = 0$. The element $-a$ is called the *additive inverse* of a.

F9. *Multiplicative inverse.* For each nonzero element a in F there exists an element a^{-1} in F such that $a^{-1} \cdot a = 1$. The element a^{-1} is called the *multiplicative inverse* of a. An equivalent form for writing a^{-1} is $1/a$.

Attention is called to the fact that the operational axioms 1 and 3 of page 326 are now incorporated as the field property $F2$. In actuality, the operational axioms 2 and 4 now become theorems which are rather readily derived from the more fundamental field postulates.

The first of the above two illustrative examples is now repeated in more formal form to illustrate the manner in which the field postulates substantiate the previously stated solution. First it should be stated that a, b, c, and x are all assumed to be elements of a field, and $a \neq 0$.

Steps	*Reasons*
1. $ax - b = c$.	1. *Given.*
2. $ax + (-b) = ax - b$.	2. *A provable theorem based on the field postulates.*
3. $ax + (-b) = c$.	3. *Transitive property of equality (page 64).*
4. $[ax + (-b)] + b = c + b$.	4. *Provable theorem based on the addition property of equality (page 64).*
5. $ax + [(-b) + b] = [ax + (-b)] + b$.	5. *F4.*
6. $ax + 0 = ax + [(-b) + b]$.	6. *F8 and addition property of equality.*
7. $ax = ax + 0$.	7. *F6.*
8. $ax = c + b$.	8. *Steps 4, 5, 6, 7 and transitive property of equality.*
9. $a^{-1} \cdot (ax) = a^{-1} \cdot (c + b)$.	9. *Multiplication property of equality (page 64).*
10. $(a^{-1} \cdot a) \cdot x = a^{-1} \cdot (ax)$.	10. *F4.*
11. $1 \cdot x = (a^{-1} \cdot a) \cdot x$.	11. *F9 and provable theorem based on multiplication property of equality.*
12. $x = 1 \cdot x$.	12. *F7.*
13. $x = a^{-1} \cdot (c + b)$.	13. *Steps 9, 10, 11, 12 and transitive property of equality.*
14. $a^{-1} \cdot (c + b) = (c + b)/a$.	14. *A provable theorem based on the postulates.*
15. $x = (c + b)/a$.	15. *Steps 13, 14 and transitive property of equality.*

This detailed presentation of the illustrative example does not carry any implications that this sort of development should be expected of the students in the first course in algebra. It is quite possible that there will be students of sufficient understanding and ability to pursue solutions in such logical detail. There should be developed in all students a basic understanding of what is taking place in such problem situations, and they should be held accountable for recognition of the fact that there is a basic structure to the algebra they are studying. It is not a mere aggregate of rules to be memorized and executed.

Similar development of the second illustration is left as an exercise for the reader.

Both illustrative examples have attempted to point out the type of reasoning processes involved in the solution of linear equations in one unknown. Nothing has been said about the specific nature of the result. Just what is it that such a process produces? Is it the value of the unknown which, if used to replace the unknown, will produce the desired equality? One does not know until the substitution is made and the equality is tested. In the first example the reasoning is as follows: If $ax - b = c$, then it follows that $ax = c + b$, from which, in turn, it follows that $x = (c + b)/a$. (Note that even this statement does not follow if $a = 0$.) This reasoning simply states that if $ax - b = c$, then it is *necessary* that x have the value $(c + b)/a$. It *does not say* that $x = (c + b)/a$ is *sufficient* to make $ax - b = c$. This must be tested by substitution (we call it checking the work). The test will reveal that $x = (c + b)/a$ is *both a necessary and a sufficient condition* that $ax - b = c$. Similar reasoning is present in the second illustrative example.

Two further examples are given to illustrate this very important point. For the existence of a unique value of x which will satisfy $ax - b = c$ it is *necessary* that a be different from zero. That this is not sufficient can easily be demonstrated by the fact that if $a \neq 0$, then $1/a$ has a value, and $x = 1/a$ gives $a(1/a) - b = 1 - b$, which may or may not be equal to c. Furthermore, substitution will reveal that $x = k(c + b)/ka$, $k \neq 0$, is sufficient to give $ax - b = c$. Only $x = (c + b)/a$ is both necessary and sufficient to give $ax - b = c$.

A more homely illustration may be obtained from consideration of the following sentences:

1. To make a 20-cent purchase, it is necessary that one have x cents.
2. To make a 20-cent purchase, it is sufficient that one have y cents.
3. To make a 20-cent purchase, it is both necessary and sufficient that one have z cents.

Any number of cents less than 20 cents could be used to replace x and statement 1 would be true.

Any number of cents greater than 20 cents could be used to replace y and statement 2 would be true.

Only the number 20 could be used to replace z and make statement 3 true.

No process for obtaining the solution of an equation is complete until the obtained solution is checked in the original equation.

It is hardly necessary to give further illustrations. The single unifying principle of getting rid of the unwanted terms, divisors, and multipliers by the application of inverse processes results automatically in the solution of all forms of the linear equation in one unknown, Approached intuitively in the beginning, its complete reasonableness can be made apparent to children without difficulty. Thereafter they should be led to focus their attention on the process per se and to give less and less attention to its concrete numerical setting. Thus eventually it will stand out as a general, abstract, mechanical principle of operation, not devoid of meaning (because it will have been built upon meanings in the beginning) but no longer dependent upon intuition and therefore more certain and more powerful than the earlier and less formal procedures.

The evaluation and solution of formulas Theoretically the *evaluation of formulas* presents no learning difficulties. Actually, however, students make mistakes in this simple process, and they are not always mistakes in computation. Mistakes in substitution occur with unexpected frequency. These are most often associated with the rewriting or recopying of the formulas with the letters replaced by corresponding numerical values. This type of error can be offset to a considerable degree by having the students make a practice of enclosing in separate parentheses each numerical value which is substituted for a letter. This has a tendency to focus attention upon each quantity as a separate element in the formula and so avoid the confusion of one such element with another. In chalkboard work it is helpful to have the students actually erase one by one the letters in the formula and write in the numerical value of each letter as that letter is erased. This makes the students keenly conscious of the fact that *the letters are actually to be replaced by the numbers* and thus strengthens the appreciation of the real meaning of evaluation. While this practice of erasing and rewriting *in situ* cannot be followed so satisfactorily when the work is being done with pencil and paper, something of the same effect can be attained by having each substituted number enclosed in separate parentheses and written in a place which precisely corresponds to the place occupied in the formula by the letter for which the substitution is being made.

The evaluation of formulas involving only two variables can also be tied up with the graphs representing the relationships. Assuming that the graph has been constructed, any value of the independent variable (lying within the domain covered by the graph) may be selected. When this value is referred to the corresponding point on the graph and that point, in turn, to the axis of the dependent variable, the value of the latter is given (at least approximately) at once. To illustrate, use the relation for the number of pounds to the number of kilograms, $P = 2.2K$. If we let K have the value 2.5, Figure 13-2, we immediately determine P as being (at least approximately) 5.5. Similarly, if K is $5\frac{3}{4}$, the corresponding value of P is found to be about 12.7; for $K = 8$, we get $P =$ 17.6; etc.

The *solution of formulas* often causes students much difficulty. This is because the students are not made consciously and specifically aware of the general principles underlying the solutions. Indeed, teachers themselves often seem to overlook the general principles. The principles do exist, however, and are quite simple and capable of being applied in an understanding manner by junior high school students. They are merely the principles which underlie the solution of all simple equations, whether numerical or literal, integral or fractional, rational or irrational.

The general procedure may be illustrated by considering the formula $A = P + Prt$. Let it be required to solve for t in terms of A, P, and r. Since the letter t occurs in only one term, that term must be retained and all other terms eliminated from that member of the equation. This elimination of elements from one member of the equation (or formula) is always accomplished by *undoing* the operation which binds that element to the rest of the given member of the equation. In this case P is related to Prt by addition. Hence, to eliminate P from that member of the equation we must undo this addition; in other words, we must sub-

K	0	1	2	3	4	5	6	7
P	0	2.2	4.4	6.6	8.8	11.0	13.2	15.4

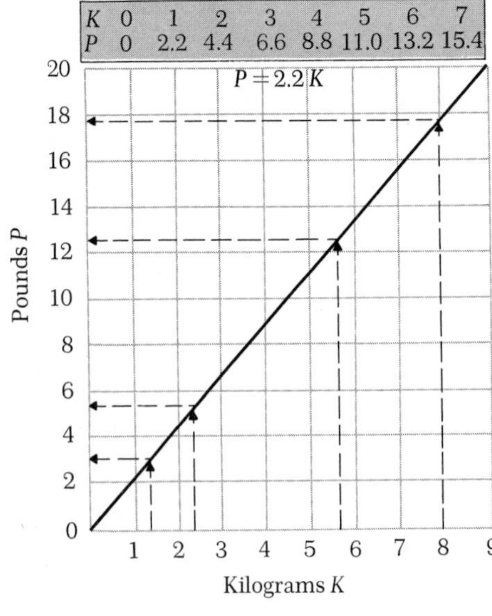

Figure 13-2
Relation of pounds to kilograms

tract P from the right-hand member of the equation. It therefore becomes necessary to subtract P also from the left-hand member of the equation. This (the equivalent of adding the additive inverse of P) gives the equation $A - P = Prt$.

Now, since we wish to solve for t, we must eliminate Pr from the right member. But Pr is bound to t by multiplication. Hence, in order to eliminate Pr and make t stand alone, we must undo the multiplication by using a process which is the inverse of multiplication, viz., division. Therefore, we divide the member Prt by Pr; and if we divide one member of an equation by a given quantity, we must also divide the other member by that same quantity. This is equivalent, of course, to multiplying both members by the multiplicative inverse of Pr. Thus we get

$$\frac{A - P}{Pr} = \frac{(Pr)t}{(Pr)} \quad \text{or} \quad \frac{A - P}{Pr} = t$$

This principle of "elimination by undoing" (or by applying inverse processes) is perfectly general and is not difficult once the students are brought to see it in its essential simplicity. It removes the solution of formulas from the status of a bag of tricks and places it upon a reasonable basis.

Apparent complications are introduced when the student is required to solve for a letter that occurs in two or more terms. In such cases, however, it should be pointed out that it is merely necessary to use the field properties as authority for grouping these terms and remove the required letter as a common factor. The procedure then follows the general pattern indicated above. To illustrate: Let it be required to solve the foregoing formula for P in terms of A, r, and t. The steps are:

$$A = P + Prt$$
$$A = P(1 + rt)$$
$$\frac{A}{(1 + rt)} = \frac{P(1 + rt)}{(1 + rt)}$$
$$\frac{A}{(1 + rt)} = P$$

Note that after using the associative and distributive properties to factor the right member, it remains merely to eliminate the factor $1 + rt$ by undoing the multiplication, i.e., by dividing both members of the equation by that factor or multiplying both members by the multiplicative inverse of $(1 + rt)$.

The teaching of graphs In recent years an increasing amount of importance has been attached to the study of graphs in junior high school mathematics. Among the several reasons for this may be mentioned the interesting character and the practical importance of graphical devices; the simplicity and power of the graph for presenting data in a condensed, understandable, and striking way; and the increasing prominence of graphical devices in newspapers, magazines, and other current publications.

There are two fundamentally distinct types of graphs, the statistical graph and the mathematical graph. The former is a device used to picture the relationship that exists between several different quantities which are comparable but are not necessarily interdependent, while the latter is used to picture the relationship that exists between two or more variables whose values are so related that they are dependent on each other. Of the statistical graph there are four distinct types which are, at times, classified as abstract, geographical, frequency, and historical. The nature of the graph or chart is, of course, a function of the distribution of the data to be represented. Among the more frequently used bases for classifying the mathematical graph there are (1) type of relation, e.g., linear and quadratic; (2) type of curve, e.g., straight line, circle, parabola, ellipse, hyperbola, sine, and tangent; (3) continuity; and (4) multiplicity of values.

From either point of view the graph is an effective means of presenting data, making comparisons, and depicting relations; it offers untold opportunities for free play of the imagination, the application of simple or ingenious constructive abilities, and the development of an enthusiastic interest in mathematical methods and a more intelligent understanding of fundamental procedures on the part of all those becoming proficient in its construction and interpretation. As the minimum contribution it should make to the program of attaining this proficiency, the secondary school should develop the following abilities:

1. To construct and interpret bar, broken-line, curved-line, and circle graphs in the presentation of statistical data and to interpret pictographs
2. To make comparisons between various comparable statistical graphs
3. To recognize the characteristics of data to be represented by each of the five types of statistical graphs, as well as certain fundamental cautions that are to be observed in their construction and interpretation[9]
4. To construct and interpret a mathematical graph as referred to a reference frame of coordinates
5. To use the mathematical graph in solving algebraic equations and to understand the simpler geometric implications
6. To interpret the graph in the light of the relationship shown, including simple maximum and minimum values

Frequently the assumption is made that the complete understanding of graphs is implied and guaranteed by the ability to construct them, but such an assumption is unwarranted. It is entirely possible for a

[9]For a good discussion of graphs with misleading characteristics see Darrell Huff, "How to Lie with Statistics" (New York: W. W. Norton & Company, Inc., 1954).

student to plot a series of points whose coordinates satisfy a particular equation, draw a smooth line through these points, and call this the "graph of the equation" without having any clear realization of the meaning of what he has done. This is not to say that the construction of graphs is unimportant. On the contrary, not only is it extremely important in the development of a full understanding of the meaning of graphs but it also gives valuable review and practice in understanding the meaning of the coordinates of a point and in the solution of equations and the substitution of numbers leading to the evaluation of algebraic expressions. The construction of graphs and the study of their meaning should go hand in hand.

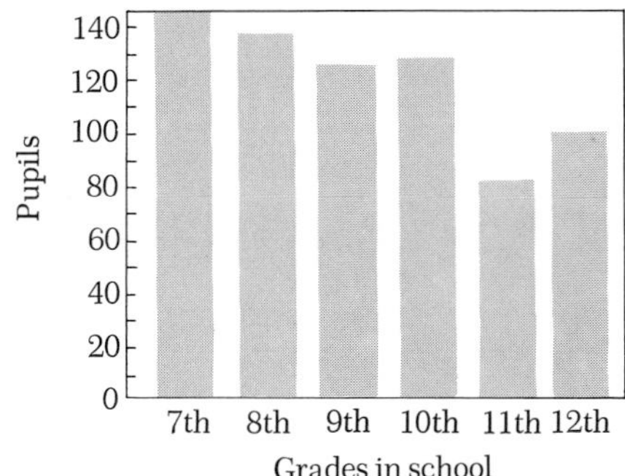

Figure 13-3
Number of pupils enrolled in a city high school

Figure 13-4
Bar graph of a family budget (100 per cent)

Savings	Rent	Food	Clothing	Housekeeping	Miscellaneous	Health
10%	14%	28%	14%	10%	17%	7%

Figure 13-5
Do students in a certain school like the school? (Each figure represents 100 students.)

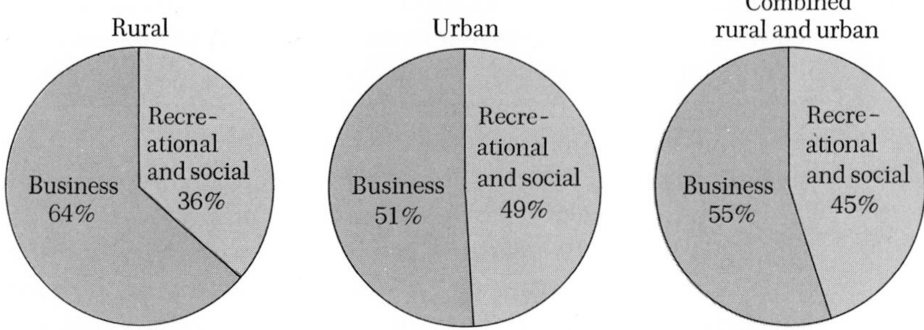

Figure 13-6
Passenger automobile mileage used for business and social purposes in rural and urban areas

Figure 13-7
Men and women licensed to drive

The customary way of teaching students how to construct mathematical graphs is to give them an equation such as $2x + 5y = 9$ and have them build a table of number pairs which satisfy the equation. They are then shown how to locate points by means of the number pairs. After they have located a few points, they are instructed to draw a smooth line through them. Too often the subject is carried no further. Frequently, teachers fail to give adequate instruction even with reference to such fundamental matters as the dependence of one of the variables upon the other, the arbitrary assignment of values to the independent variables, the naming of the axes, and the selection of suitable scales.

The construction of graphs can contribute little toward the development of adequate concepts of variation, continuity, and dependence if it is taught in this purely perfunctory fashion. These concepts are not likely to enter into the students' thinking unless they are specifically pointed out, not once but many times, by the teacher. Many and varied illustrations should be used. The students will find within their own common experiences many situations involving relationships among variable quantities that may be appropriately subjected to graphical treatment and which, because of their familiarity, will help materially in giving meaning to the graphs.

As an illustration, consider the relationship between the amount of gasoline that goes through a pump at a filling station and the total cost of the gasoline at 34 cents a gallon. This provides an excellent situation for emphasizing the *dependence* of one variable, the cost C, upon another variable, the number of gallons N, the price remaining constant. It can be expressed by the formula $C = 0.34N$. This formula can then be used as a basis for constructing the graph, Figure 13-8. After the graph has been made, it should be carefully re-examined with attention directed to the way in which it answers such questions as: What happens to the cost as the number of gallons increases? As the cost increases, does the number of gallons increase in the same ratio? Does a decrease in either of the variables bring about a corresponding decrease in the other? How does the price per gallon affect the direction of the graph? If the price were increased, how would the direction of the graph be changed? Approximately how many gallons of gasoline could be bought for \$1? For \$1.50? For \$2? For \$3? Does the graph show the cost of 8 gallons? For *any* point on the graph should the ordinate C give a number exactly 0.34 times as great as the number given by the abscissa N of that point? Would the same result be given by the formula? If a point were to move along the graph, would its ordinate or its abscissa change the more rapidly? How many times as rapidly? Explain how the graph

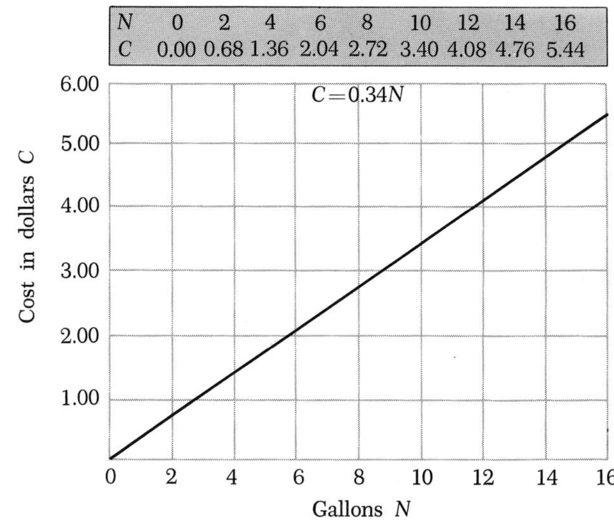

N	0	2	4	6	8	10	12	14	16
C	0.00	0.68	1.36	2.04	2.72	3.40	4.08	4.76	5.44

Figure 13-8
Cost of gasoline at 34 cents a gallon

shows that the cost *depends* on the amount of gasoline bought. Explain how the graph shows that the number of gallons of gasoline one can buy *depends* upon how much money he could spend for gasoline.

By such questions as the foregoing ones the students can be made conscious of the graph as a device which shows in a striking way the fact and the precise nature of the dependence of either of the variables upon the other, the meaning of dependent and independent variables, and the precise way in which a change in either variable inevitably brings about a corresponding change in the other variable. The students become more clearly aware of the meaning of coordinates. They learn to associate the relationships shown by the graph with those indicated by the formula or equation upon which the graph is based. They learn, in short, to understand what a graph means, and this, in turn, enhances their comprehension of dependence and functional relationship as a permeating principle, whether it is expressed graphically or by means of formulas or equations.

An associated problem calling for the graphs of two simultaneous equations could be set up as follows: One filling station sells gasoline at 34 cents a gallon; a competitor advertises 30 cents a gallon plus 30 cents service charge. Make cost graphs for both stations on the same set of axes.

This problem involves writing a second formula, $C = 0.30N + 0.30$, and the construction of another graph along with the one already made and discussed. Questions similar to those heretofore indicated should now be discussed with reference to the new graph, Figure 13-9.

In addition, such questions as the following should be discussed: With what amount of money could one purchase the same amount of gasoline at the second station as at the first? At which station could

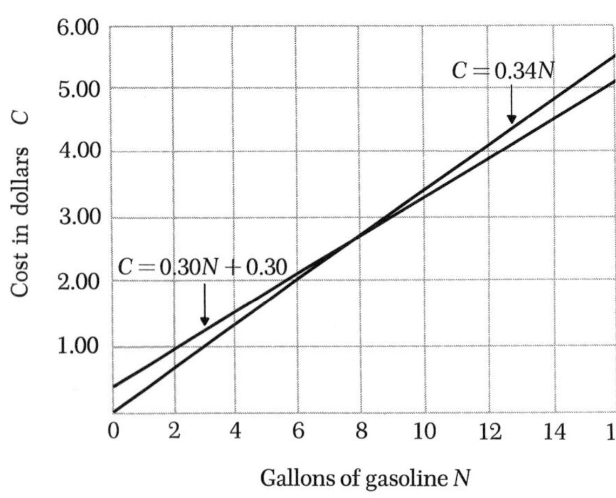

Figure 13-9 *Comparison of the cost of gasoline at two prices*

one get more gasoline for \$1? For 50 cents? For \$2? How much more gasoline could be purchased at one station for \$4.00 than at the other station? At which station could one buy 10 gallons at the lower cost? At which station could one buy 2 gallons at the lower cost? How much could one save by buying 15 gallons at the station that offered the lower price on this amount? Show how to find this out from the graphs. Does the service charge made by the second station affect the direction of the graph? Does it affect its position? Explain. Does the price per gallon affect the direction of the graph? Explain. Would a change in the direction of the graph indicate a change in the price per gallon? Explain.

Consideration of the direction of a graph leads naturally and easily to the concept of *slope*, which is also to be associated with the rates of change of the two variables and with the coefficient of the independent variable in the formula or equation. Similarly, the point where the graph crosses the axis of the dependent variable should be associated with the constant term in the equation, and the effect which any change in this constant term has upon the position of the graph should be studied. The students will be interested in noting that, when the equation is written (rewritten if necessary) in the form of the linear function $y = mx + b$ (or $C = 0.30N + 0.30$), the b always indicates the point at which the graph crosses the axis of the dependent variable and the m always indicates the slope. Thus, by solving any linear equation of the form $ax + by = c$ for y ($b \neq 0$), the student has at his command a method for constructing the graph which is at once less tedious and more meaningful than the method described earlier in this section.

Attention should be called to the fact that the m and b, or the *slope* and the *y intercept*, are two conditions that determine the position of a straight line just as two points determine its position. The method of determining the x intercept and y intercept from the equation of any line and the use of the two intercepts in plotting the graph of the line should then be emphasized. All this discussion of the linear equation and its graph should lead to the summarizing generalization: To determine the position of a straight line in a plane, it is necessary to have two independent conditions.

Emphasis should be given to the fact that there are distinct cases to consider in analyzing the linear equation $ax + by = c$.

Case 1. $a \neq 0$, $b \neq 0$. Under these conditions the equation can be transformed into the formula for the *linear function* $y = mx + b$, where $m \neq 0$. The graph of the linear function is a straight line which intersects both coordinate axes. If $c = 0$ the graph passes through the origin.

Case 2. $a = 0$, $b \neq 0$. Under these conditions the equation can be transformed into the formula for the *constant* function $y = k$. The graph of the constant function is a line parallel to the x axis if $c \neq 0$ or is the x axis if $c = 0$. The constant function is *not* a special case of the linear function, since the slope of the graph of the constant function is zero ($m = 0$) while the slope of the graph of the linear function is different from zero ($m \neq 0$).

Case 3. $a \neq 0$, $b = 0$. Under these conditions the equation can be transformed into the formula for the *linear relation* $x = h$. This equation is that of the relation (h,y) in which there are many values of the dependent variable y which correspond to the one value h for the independent variable. It is not a function. For the linear relation the slope is undefined, and its graph is a line parallel to the y axis if $c \neq 0$ or is the y axis if $c = 0$.

There is no case for consideration if $a = 0$ and $b = 0$. Under these conditions c also is of necessity zero, since, otherwise, $ax + by = c$ is not a true statement. When $a = b = c = 0$ the statement of equality becomes a trivial relation satisfied by any set of values for x and y. Thus the equation $ax + by = c$ is the equation of a straight line if and only if a and b are not both zero.

Specific attention to these considerations not only adds interest and value to the study of graphs but, in an easy, natural, and understandable way, provides the beginnings of a sound technical foundation for a real understanding of later work in analytic geometry and calculus. Obviously, more time is required for this sort of treatment of mathematical graphs than would be required for the mere construction of the graphs themselves. One may feel sure, however, that the thorough discussion of a few instances along the lines which have been indicated will do more to give the students a sense of functional relationships involved than will the mere rule-of-thumb construction of large numbers of the graphs.

The teaching of directed numbers

The study of directed numbers is an integral part of the study of algebra. It is also one of the most difficult topics to develop successfully, and teachers and writers are not altogether agreed upon the most satisfactory methods of teaching it. There is general agreement, however, on the main outcomes which are desired. They may be clearly stated as follows:

1. The student should gain an understanding of the meaning of directed numbers.
2. He should understand that the definition of each operation with directed numbers is structured by the field postulates. In the first course this must be accomplished largely by rationalization through carefully selected examples and by assurance that the procedures are supported by theorems which are derivable from the postulates.
3. He should be led to see that the operations with directed numbers are consistent with the operations of arithmetic and that they constitute a more generalized procedure in which the operations of arithmetic appear as special cases.
4. He should gain considerable facility in performing the fundamental operations with directed numbers.

The fact that students fail to attain adequate mastery of these objectives undoubtedly accounts for a great deal of the difficulty which they experience in the study of algebra.

The student's numerical experience prior to the introduction of the concept of negative numbers will have been confined entirely to dealings with the numbers of arithmetic, i.e., with numbers representing quantities actually greater than zero. Up to this time he has used *zero* in two capacities, either as a number or as a place holder in writing numbers such as 305 and 500. Now, however, it becomes necessary to give to zero a new significance. In addition to its use as a number and as a place holder, *zero* will now be regarded as an arbitrary starting point in the number line from which one may measure in either direction; numbers which correspond to measures made in one direction will be referred to as *positive numbers*, and numbers which correspond to measures made in the opposite direction will be referred to as *negative numbers*. Many illustrations of this new use should be given.

The number line is probably the most satisfactory and helpful of all devices for making clear the nature of positive and negative numbers and for illustrating their characteristics of oppositeness, direction, and position. It should be used, however, in connection with other devices for illustrating the opposite character of positive and negative numbers and the arbitrary selection of the zero, or reference, point. Illustrations of assets and liabilities, north and south latitude, temperatures above and below zero, etc., are helpful in developing the fundamental concepts of oppositeness, direction, and position with reference to an *established* zero, but they present only a partial picture of the nature of positive and negative numbers. They fail to make clear that whether a number is to be regarded as positive, negative, or zero relative to some other number depends not only upon its own position in some number scale but also upon the position of the number to which it is referred and that that number may or may not be the previously established zero. Thus we may speak at 3:00 P.M. of an event which happened, say, at 1:00 P.M. The position of the event in time, using 1 hour as a unit, would be indicated by -2 if reckoned from *now* (3:00 P.M.) but would be indicated by $+1$ if reckoned from noon, or by $+13$ if reckoned from the previous midnight, Figure 13-10.

On referring this illustration to a number scale, it is seen that the event's position in time is positive with reference to *any number* that

Figure 13-10

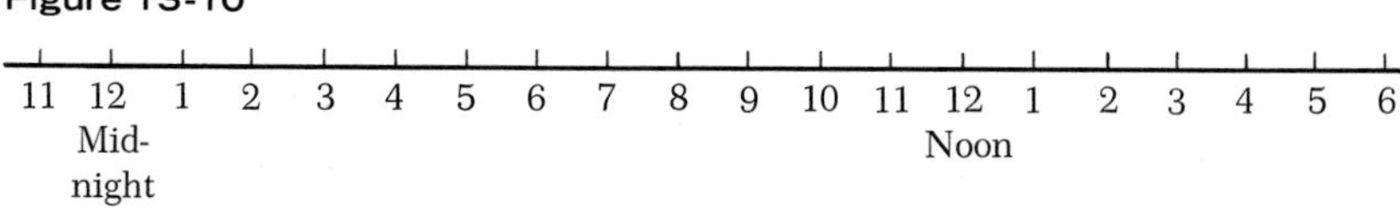

lies to its left on the scale and negative with reference to *any number* that lies to its right on the scale. Thus the statement "all negative numbers are less than zero and all positive numbers are greater than zero" is true only when the pre-established zero is the number to which all other numbers are referred. This is in exact accordance with the ordering of numbers on the real number line. Numbers are positive or negative according as they are to the right or to the left of the chosen zero point. Also, when any two numbers a and b are compared, $a > b$ or $a < b$ according to whether a is to the right or to the left of b on the number line.

There is considerable difference of opinion among writers and teachers over the lengths to which teachers should go in the effort to rationalize the operations with directed numbers and explain them in terms of the familiar operations of arithmetic. It is undoubtedly desirable to have these operations explained in such a way that they will be manifestly consistent with established arithmetical operations. On the other hand, some of the attempts which have been made to rationalize operations with directed numbers more or less defeat their own purpose because, in the attempt to explain the new entirely in terms of the familiar, they so emphasize the illustrative objects that attention is drawn away from the new process rather than being focused upon it. In other words, the thing being illustrated tends to become obscured by the illustration. It must not be forgotten that, after all, we are here *defining* certain operations with a totally new kind of number whose characteristics themselves depend upon arbitrary definition. Therefore, since we are thus extending our number system, obviously the new cannot be explained entirely in terms of the old. Rather, the main concern must be to make clear that the operations with the new (directed) numbers are in the context of the field postulates and that the definitions are such that they are consistent with the old (arithmetical) operations.

It is in this connection that the students should have their attention drawn to the fact that, with these new numbers, it is no longer impossible to subtract one number from a smaller one. Make sure that they understand why it was impossible previously, while henceforth it will be possible. Also, here is the place for discussion of zero as the identity element for addition and of the significance of addition and subtraction as inverse operations. Make sure that there is clear understanding of what is meant by the statement that numbers $+n$ and $-n$ are inversely related. One is the additive inverse of the other just as surely as n and $1/n$ are inversely related through multiplication.

As soon as the student has acquired an understanding of the nature of negative numbers as contrasted with positive numbers, he should be taught how to perform the fundamental operations with signed

numbers. The first of these operations to be undertaken is that of algebraic addition. Here the student is likely to experience some confusion in the beginning, owing to the fact that in arithmetic the sum of two or

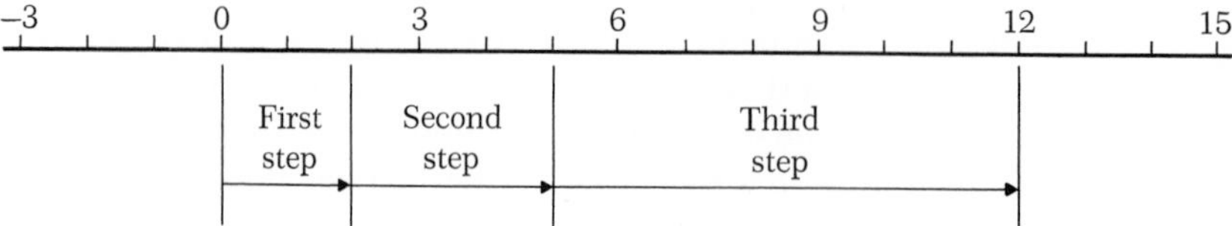

Figure 13-11

more numbers is always greater than either of the addends. Reference to a number scale is useful in clearing up perplexities on this point. It should be carefully re-emphasized that addition is a process of "combining" or "taking together." By reference to a number scale it can be made clear why it is that, when a positive number and a negative number are combined, the result will be less than the positive number alone.

The analysis of the addition (combination) of positive and negative numbers is entirely analogous to that of the addition of two or more positive numbers. For example, in finding the sum $2 + 3 + 7$ we start at the zero point on the number scale (Figure 13-11) and count two units to the right, since to the right is the direction in which we agree to count positive numbers. Then *from there* we count three more units to the right. Then *from there* we count seven more units to the right. The result of these operations leaves us at a point which is 12 units to the right of zero. Hence we say that the sum is $+12$. In a similar manner the sum $4 + (-7) + 8$ may be found. We start at the zero on the number scale and count 4 units to the right (Figure 13-12). Then *from there* we count 7 units to the *left* (since this is the direction in which we agree to count negative numbers). Then *from there* we count 8 units again to the right. The result of these movements leaves us at a point 5 units to the right of the zero point on the number scale. Hence we say that $4 + (-7) + 8 = +5$.

Figure 13-12

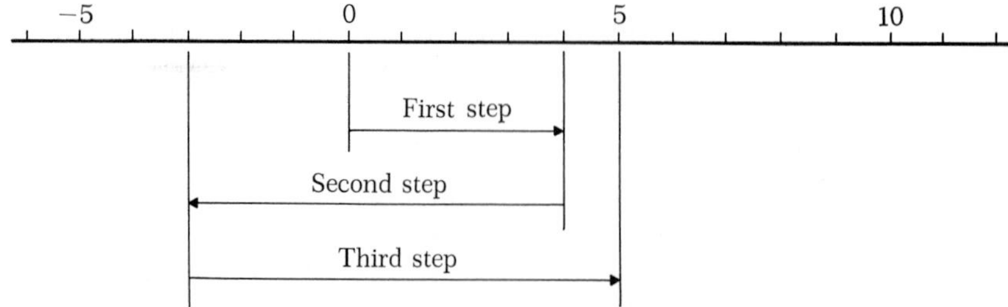

Students will have little difficulty in seeing that the addition of negative units offsets or neutralizes a corresponding number of positive units, or vice versa, so that the sum of any series of signed numbers is determined by seeing whether the series contains more negative units than positive ones or more positive units than negative ones, the absolute (or numerical) value of the sum of the series being given by the excess of the one over the other. From these considerations the student may formulate his own rule or method for determining the absolute value and the sign of the algebraic sum.

Since addition is a binary operation, any such sum will be obtained as a sequence of sums of two numbers. Whatever rationalization process is used, it should lead the student to the formalization of the rule that, for any two real numbers a and b, $a + (-b) = a - b$ if $a > b$ and $a + (-b) = -(b - a)$ if $a < b$. These are theorems which are derivable from the field postulates. For example, if $a = 8$ and $b = 3$, $8 + (-3) = 8 - 3 = 5$; if $a = 3$ and $b = 8$, $3 + (-8) = -(8 - 3) = -5$.

Simple and easy as this may appear, it requires much carefully supervised practice to fix these ideas and procedures firmly in the minds of the students and to give the students assurance and facility in adding signed numbers. It must not be forgotten that, because this is a new and difficult extension of their mathematical experience, the students will require considerable time and experience to adjust themselves completely to it. It is particularly important that training in the addition of signed numbers not be slighted or unduly hurried, for the reason that the concepts and procedures involved therein form the basis for understanding the subsequent processes of subtraction, multiplication, and division of signed numbers.

In the subtraction of one signed number from another, students may be expected to experience initial difficulty because they may need to revise their idea of the meaning of subtraction. In arithmetic, unless they have been taught to use the additive method, they will have come to regard subtraction as taking one number away from another, and since arithmetic always deals with positive, or absolute, values, the result of subtraction as always less than the minuend. Now, however, it becomes necessary to analyze the process more carefully. The analysis should start with familiar arithmetical examples and then be extended to include both positive and negative numbers. For example, just what does it mean to subtract 5 from 8? One basic interpretation is to find what number is left when 5 units are taken away from an aggregate of 8 units. On the other hand, to speak about taking away "minus 5" units from an aggregate of units would have no meaning. Hence we must make a further and more general analysis of the meaning of subtraction. It is not difficult to point out to students that subtraction can be defined, in a more general way, as the process of

finding what number must be added to 5 to give 8 and that, when we find this number, it will be precisely the number which is left when we take 5 away from 8. This definition has meaning when applied to either positive or negative numbers, since the student has already learned

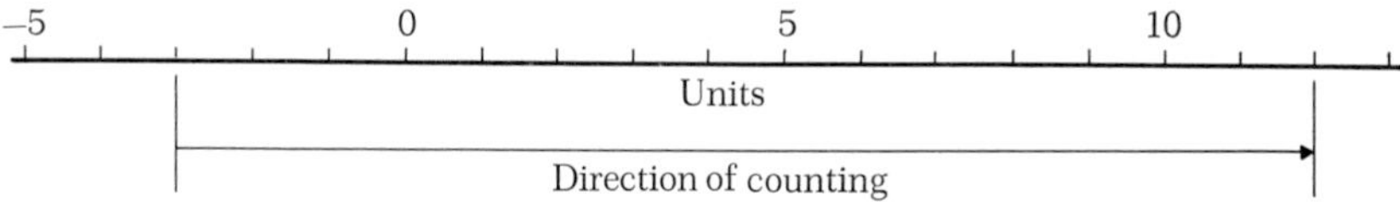

Figure 13-13

that they may be combined by addition. Similarly, the operation indicated by $12 - (-3)$ means that we must find the number which, when added to -3, will give 12. Obviously, this definition of subtraction will involve no new difficulties for students who have learned to use the additive method of subtraction in arithmetic.

This may be further illustrated by use of a number line. Thus, since we are to find what number must be added to -3 to give $+12$, we must start at -3 and count to $+12$. This necessitates moving over 15 units on the scale (Figure 13-13). Since the direction of motion is to the right, the sign of the result is positive and the result is $+15$. In other words, $(-3) + (+15) = (+12)$, and this is merely another way of saying $12 - (-3) = (+15)$.

Again, take the example $5 - 8$. Here we must count from $+8$ to $+5$. That is, we pass over 3 units on the scale, but this time the direction of motion is to the left; hence the result is -3. In other words, we have the result

Subtrahend	+	result of subtraction	=	minuend
(+8)	+	(−3)		(+5)

which is another way of saying that $(+5) - (+8) = (-3)$(Figure 13-14).

Another effective way of illustrating the subtraction, say, of -3 from $+8$ is as follows:

From	+8	+8	+8	+8	+8	+8	+8	+8	+8	+8	+8	etc.
Subtract	+5	+4	+3	+2	+1	0	−1	−2	−3	−4	−5	etc.
Difference	+3	+4	+5	+6	+7	+8	+9	+10	+11	+12	+13	etc.

Attention should be directed to the fact that, when positive numbers alone are involved and the subtrahends are diminished by unity in

Figure 13-14

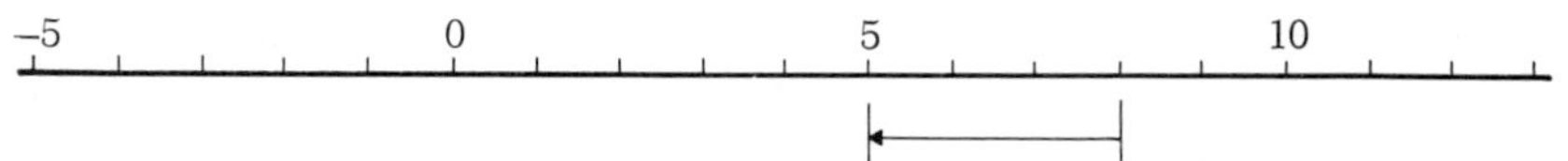

successive cases, the differences increase in corresponding fashion. For consistency in operation it is, therefore, essential that the same pattern be followed when negative numbers are used. It is observed that under these conditions, even when negative subtrahends are used, the necessary principle that the algebraic sum of the subtrahend and the difference must equal the minuend is satisfied. Stated in terms of the foregoing discussion of the number line, it is seen that in every case the difference is obtained by counting from the subtrahend to the minuend, regardless of whether the subtrahend is positive, zero, or negative. The support for the above procedure is found in the definition of subtraction: Subtraction is the process of finding the difference d between two numbers a and b, where $a - b = d$ if and only if $b + d = a$.

Numerous similar examples exhibiting various combinations of positive and negative numbers should be given, some being explained by the teacher and others being worked out by the students, until the students thoroughly understand the process. As soon as the process is thoroughly understood, the examples should be reviewed, or others given. The students should then have their attention specifically directed to the fact that every subtraction, when analyzed in this way, gives a result which is the same as it would be if the sign of the subtrahend were changed and the problem treated as a problem in addition instead of subtraction. When this point has been made clear, it may be formulated into the rule: To subtract one signed number from another, change the sign of the subtrahend and then treat the problem as an addition problem rather than as a subtraction problem. Henceforth the students should be expected to use this method of subtraction. Its advantages are manifest, because it reduces the process of subtraction to the already familiar process of addition. The rationalization of the method is not intended to be used after the method is understood but is solely for the purpose of showing that the method is consistent with the meaning of subtraction. In spite of the apparent simplicity of the method the students should be given much closely supervised practice in its use.

In the multiplication of directed numbers the law of signs is very simply stated, but its rationalization can be rather complicated. Some writers have gone so far as to recommend the omission of any effort at rationalization. They would have the teacher merely state the rule and allow the understanding to come through use. Such procedure does not satisfy the curiosity that develops in the minds of many students as to why the rules are what they are.

One of the most effective methods of rationalization is to explain multiplication as repeated addition if the multiplier is a positive number. Thus (+2)(+3), to be read (+2) *multiplied by* (+3), means (+2) + (+2) + (+2) = +6, and (−2)(+3) means (−2) + (−2) + (−2) = −6. Attention should be called to the fact that (+2)(+3) may also be written (+3)(+2), read (+3) *times* (+2), and still mean to add (+2) three times. Similarly, (−2)(+3) may be written (+3)(−2) to indicate the sum of (−2) + (−2) + (−2). Each of these processes can be demonstrated very simply on the number line.

Since the sign of subtraction is −, (+9) − (+2) means that +2 is subtracted from +9 one time. The result is +7, which is the same result as that obtained from adding −2 to +9, or (+9) + (−2). In a similar way 0 − (+2) is the same as 0 + (−2). Since + (−2) means to add −2 one time, and (+3)(−2) means to add −2 three times, so −(+2) means to subtract +2 one time and (−3)(+2) means to subtract +2 three times. Just as +(−2) = −2 and −(+3) = −3, so (−3)(+2) = −6 and (+3)(−2) = −6.

After it has been established that (+2)(+3) = +6 and (−3)(+2) = (+3)(−2) = −6, attention should be called to the fact that in finding the product of two numbers, *the change of the sign of one of the factors changes the sign of the product*. Opportunity should be provided through practice to become familiar with this fundamental rule of multiplication. The question that should then be raised is what the effect would be if in either of the multiplication examples (−3)(+2) = −6 and (+3)(−2) = −6 the − sign were changed to a + sign. This provides the opportunity for observing that the familiar product (+2)(+3) = +6 is obtained if the rule is applied. After a few practice exercises of this type, the class is ready for this question: What will be the effect if, in either of the multiplication examples (−3)(+2) = −6 and (+3)(−2) = −6, the + sign is changed to a − sign? The application of the rule gives (−3)(−2) = +6. Practice exercises should then be provided for becoming familiar with this last case of multiplication with signed numbers. This entire development is supported by the fact that it can be proved that, for any two real numbers a and b, the product $(-a)(b)$ or $(a)(-b)$ is the additive inverse of ab, namely, $-(ab)$; similarly, the product $(-a)(-b)$ is the additive inverse of $-(ab)$, namely, ab.

As an alternative or supplementary method of rationalizing this process, the following plan has been found to be effective. Exhibit several sets of factors as shown here, using the same multiplicand in every case but with the multipliers diminishing by unity from left to right.

Multiplicand	+5	+5	+5	+5	+5	+5	+5	+5	+5	etc.
Multiplier	+5	+4	+3	+2	+1	0	−1	−2	−3	etc.
Product	+25	+20	+15	+10	+5	0	−5	−10	−15	etc.

By using first only the nonnegative multipliers, attention is given to the fact that, as the multipliers diminish, the products diminish proportionally. If this principle is extended, by analogy and with the control of consistency, to include the cases with negative multipliers, the negative products obtained will be accepted by most students as perfectly reasonable consequences. The fact that this does not constitute a rigorous proof is no indictment of its usefulness as a device for making the principle acceptable to the students. Similar arrangements can subsequently be used in the same way to give a feeling of reasonableness to the proposition that the product of two negative numbers is positive. Thus

Multiplicand	−5	−5	−5	−5	−5	−5	−5	−5	−5	etc.
Multiplier	+5	+4	+3	+2	+1	0	−1	−2	−3	etc.
Product	−25	−20	−15	−10	−5	0	+5	+10	+15	etc.

After suitable rationalization has been made, a few review exercises should then lead to the summarizing of the four cases into the two rules: (1) The product of two numbers which have like signs is positive; (2) the product of two numbers which have unlike signs is negative.

Opportunity should then be given for practice in the application of the rules to the finding of the product of both arithmetical and literal numbers. Emphasis should be given to the fact that the numerical value of the product can be obtained by disregarding the signs, and the proper sign can be given to the product through application of the rules.

Whatever pattern of rationalization might be used, the teacher should have it clearly in mind that no proof of the process has been given. He should also make this fact clear to the students. The actual situation is that the number system has been extended from the natural numbers, which we now identify with the positive integers, to include zero and the negative integers. Ultimately, of course, fractions are also included in the extension.

What does it mean to add, subtract, multiply, and divide these new numbers? In the first course in algebra the answer to this question is arrived at largely through definition. We must define each of the operations with the new numbers, and we must be controlled by the practical desirability of consistency of operation with the old, or natural, numbers. Thus, for example, we define $(+4)(-2) = -8$ because we can interpret this to mean that we subtract 2 four times, which is consistent with the result we should get by subtracting 8. Since the commutative law of multiplication must hold, it follows that, if $(+4)(-2) = -8$, then $(-2)(+4) = -8$. The distributive law must also hold. It states that for any three numbers a, b, and c it is true that $a(b + c) = ab + ac$. For consistency this law must hold for positive and negative integers. Furthermore, we know that for any positive number n there exists its unique additive inverse $-n$ such that $(+n) + (-n) = 0$. Now consider the three numbers -2, $+4$, and -4. By the distributive law

$$(-2)[(+4) + (-4)] = (-2)(+4) + (-2)(-4)$$

Since $(+4) + (-4) = 0$, it follows that

$$(-2)[(+4) + (-4)] = (-2)(0) = 0$$

By the law of substitution we now have

$$0 = (-2)(+4) + (-2)(-4)$$

Since $(-2)(+4) = -8$, it follows that the only definition we can give to $(-2)(-4)$ is $+8$, since $+8$ is the additive inverse of -8, and we have

$$0 = (-8) + (+8)$$

Since the quotient obtained by dividing one number by another is a number whose product with the divisor must give the dividend, it must follow that the law of signs for division is the same as that for multiplication. That is, if the signs of the divisor and the dividend are alike, the quotient will be positive; if they are different, the quotient will be negative. This explanation of the law of signs for division is usually quite satisfactory if illustrated by numerical examples, and ordinarily there is no material value in more elaborate attempts to rationalize it.

EXERCISES

1. Make a formula for determining the score earned in a game of contract bridge by setting one's opponents n tricks if the opponents were not vulnerable and not doubled.

2. Make a formula for determining the score of a team in a football game, in terms of t (number of touchdowns), p (number of points on plays after touchdowns), k (number of points on kicks after touchdowns), f (number of field goals), and s (number of safeties).

3. Let a distance be expressed as x yards y feet z inches. (*a*) Make a formula that will give this distance in inches alone. (*b*) Make a formula that will give this distance in feet alone. (*c*) Make a formula that will give this distance in yards alone.

4. Evaluate the formula $s = \frac{1}{2}n(a + l)$ for each of these sets of values of a, n, and l.

a	7	2.6	$\frac{4}{5}$
n	12	5	10
l	40	7.8	$6\frac{4}{5}$

5. Given the formula $w = dF/s$, what is the effect on w in each of the following circumstances? (*a*) d is doubled and F and s remain unchanged. (*b*) Both d and F are doubled, but s remains unchanged. (*c*) d, F, and s are all doubled. (*d*) d and F remain unchanged, but s is doubled. (*e*) d is halved, s is doubled, and F is tripled.

6. In the two formulas $P = xy$ and $Q = x + y$, compare the effects on P and Q (*a*) of doubling x but leaving y unchanged, (*b*) of doubling y but leaving x unchanged, (*c*) of doubling both x and y.

7. Generalize your results of exercise 6

and state the generalization as a rule of action.

8. For what particular reasons does the formula seem to be the most suitable avenue for introducing students to the study of algebra?

9. How would you make clear to a class the distinction between constants and variables? Between independent and dependent variables?

10. Explain why the solving of an equation is fundamentally incomplete until the obtained values of the unknown have been checked in the original equation.

11. Explain how the checking of solutions of equations gives good training in precisely the same kinds of mathematical activities as those used in the evaluation of formulas. Be specific.

12. In this chapter "formalism" in algebra is deplored, but the *formalization* of algebraic procedures is held to be important. Review the discussion of these two concepts, and make the contrast between the two clear.

13. If the drive shaft of a steel lathe turns through 20 revolutions a minute, a definite relation exists between the number of minutes and the total number of turns. (This simple situation can be utilized as a basis for learning and understanding a good many things about a relationship between two variables and about the formula and graph which exhibit the relationship.) The following questions and instructions refer to the drive shaft. Examine them critically, and decide what particular thing or things each could contribute toward helping students understand and interpret the relationship and the modes of representing it.

a. Make a formula giving the relation between the number of turns N and the time in minutes T.

b. By using this formula, make a table of corresponding values of T and N.

c. Draw, label, and scale a pair of perpendicular reference lines or axes. Then plot a point for each pair of corresponding values in the above table.

d. Will they all lie on a straight line? Explain why.

e. Draw the straight line through these points.

f. If you used other pairs of corresponding values obtained from this formula to plot points, would the latter points lie on the same straight line as the points of *c*?

g. If you should take some other point on the line and use it to get a pair of corresponding values of N and T, would these values satisfy the formula you set up originally? Try one and see.

h. Using the graph and taking $T = 3\frac{1}{2}$, find the corresponding value of N. Explain in words what this means.

i. Using $N = 50$, find by using the graph the corresponding value of T. Explain in words what this means.

j. Why are N and T called *variables*?

k. Which is the *independent* variable? Why? Why is the other called the *dependent* variable?

l. What do we mean when we speak of the *coordinates* of a point? Explain and illustrate.

m. Must each axis be scaled uniformly?

n. Must both axes be scaled the same?

o. If the unit lengths on both axes were doubled, would the graph have the same direction as before? Explain why or why not.

p. If the unit lengths were changed on one axis but not on the other, would the direction of the graph be changed? Explain why or why not.

q. If the speed of the shaft were doubled after 2 minutes, would the graph change direction? Why or why not? Explain.

r. Why is it advisable to scale and label both axes clearly?

s. If one axis were scaled evenly and the other were scaled unevenly, would the graph of this relationship still be a straight line? Explain why or why not.

14. Criticize or support the assertion that the very essence of algebra lies in the gen-

eralization of its concepts and the formalization of its procedures.

15. The transposition of terms is a rule-of-thumb method widely used in lieu of either or both of two axioms of elementary algebra. Cite these axioms. Criticize or justify the teaching of transposition as such in first-year algebra.

16. Which is the more important to the average student from the standpoint of later application, the ability to construct graphs or the ability to interpret graphs readily. Does the one imply the other? Discuss the pedagogical implications of your answers.

17. Do you think drill is needed in learning algebra? Give arguments in support of your viewpoint.

18. State the operational axioms 2 and 4 of page 326 as theorems about real numbers. Use the field postulates to prove each theorem.

19. Show how the field postulates are used in the solution of the exercise in the illustrative example of page 328.

20. State and prove for real numbers the theorems cited as provable and used as reasons in the following steps of the example on page 329: step 2, step 4, step 11, and step 14.

Prove each of the following theorems for real numbers.

21. $a - (-b) = a + b$.

22. $(-a) + (-b) = -(a + b)$.

23. $(-a) \times (b) = (a) \times (-b) = -(a \times b)$.

24. $(-a) \times (-b) = a \times b$.

25. For x an integer, let $s = \{x|0 < x < 30\}$ and $T = \{x|5 \leqq x \leqq 42\}$. What is the set $S \cap T$?

26. If a, b, and c are real numbers and if $a < b$ and $b < c$, is it true that $a < c$? If X, Y, and Z are sets, $X \subset Y$, and $Y \subset Z$, is it necessarily true that $X \subset Z$? (Note that in this case the rule for inclusion among sets is an exact counterpart of the rule for inequalities among real numbers.)

27. If a and b are real numbers and $a \neq b$, then either $a < b$ or $b < a$. If A and B are sets and $A \neq B$, is it necessarily true that either $A \subset B$ or $B \subset A$? (Note that sets are said to be equal if and only if they contain exactly the same elements.)

28. Consider the sets $A = \{7, 8, 9\}$ and $B = \{12, 13\}$. In this case note that the set $A \cap B$ contains no elements at all. Such a set is called the *empty* set, or the *null* set, and is usually designated by the symbol $\emptyset$. Give several examples of such sets, e.g., the set of all numbers each of which is less than 5 but greater than 8, or the set of living men who are more than 500 years old.

29. Let $\{a \ldots b\}$ be the set of points on a scaled line and in the interval extending from a on the left to b on the right. Let $A = \{3 \ldots 7\}$, $B = \{5 \ldots 12\}$, and $C = \{8 \ldots 15\}$. Then express correctly in set notation each of the following: $A \cup B$, $B \cup C$, $A \cup C$, $A \cap B$, $B \cap C$, and $A \cap C$.

BIBLIOGRAPHY

Adkins, Jackson B.: Goals in Algebra, *Mathematics Teacher*, **47** (1954), 368–370.

Barnes, Ward Ewing, and John William Asher: Predicting Students' Success in First-year Algebra, *Mathematics Teacher*, **55** (1962), 651–654.

Beatley, Ralph: Reason and Rule in Arithmetic and Algebra, *Mathematics Teacher*, **47** (1954), 234–244.

Beberman, Max, and Bruce E. Meserve: The Concept of a Literal Number Symbol, *Mathematics Teacher*, **48** (1955), 198–202.

——— and ———: Graphing in Elementary Algebra, *Mathematics Teacher*, **49** (1956), 260–266.

Brumfiel, Charles: An Introduction to Negative Integers, *Mathematics Teacher*, **49** (1956), 531–534.

Clark, J. F.: A Concrete Approach to Elementary Algebra, *Mathematics Teacher*, **53** (1960), 285–287.

Crosby, Gwladys, and Herbert Fremont: Individualized Algebra, *Mathematics Teacher*, **53** (1960), 109–112.

Davis, David R.: "The Teaching of Mathematics" (Reading, Mass.: Addison-Wesley Publishing Company, Inc., 1951), pp. 162–170, 193–212.

Entwhistle, Alice: Subtracting Signed Numbers, *Mathematics Teacher*, **48** (1955), 175–176.

Johnson, Donovan A., and William H. Glenn: "Sets, Sentences, and Operations" (New York: McGraw-Hill Book Company, 1960).

_____ and _____: "Adventures in Graphing" (New York: McGraw-Hill Book Company, 1961).

Kinney, Lucien B., and C. Richard Purdy: "Teaching Mathematics in the Secondary School" (New York: Holt, Rinehart and Winston, Inc., 1952), pp. 59–99.

Klimczak, W. J.: The Solution of Linear Equations and Inequalities, *Mathematics Teacher*, **48** (1955), 460–463.

Koenen, William: Illustrating Simple Transformations, *Mathematics Teacher*, **49** (1956), 467–468.

Lewis, Eunice: The Pupil Discovers Algebra, *Mathematics Teacher*, **47** (1954), 81–85.

McGarvey, Paul: Programmed Instruction in Ninth-grade Algebra, *Mathematics Teacher*, **55** (1962), 576–579.

Meserve, Bruce E.: New Trends in Algebra and Geometry, *Mathematics Teacher*, **55** (1962), 452–461.

Messler, Dorothy L.: A Study of Pupil Age and Achievement in Eighth-grade Algebra, *Mathematics Teacher*, **54** (1961), 561–564.

"Modern Elementary Algebra" (Chicago: Society for Visual Education, Inc., 1963). (Two sets of filmstrips in color.)

Olander, Clarence E.: The Use of a Readiness Test in Teaching a Unit on Signed Numbers, *School Science and Mathematics*, **57** (1957), 131–138.

Perisho, Clarence R.: Curves with Corners, *Mathematics Teacher*, **55** (1962), 326–329.

Reeve, William D.: "Mathematics for the Secondary School" (New York: Holt, Rinehart and Winston, Inc., 1954), pp. 245–275.

Rheins, Joel J., and Gladys B. Rheins: The Additive Inverse in Elementary Algebra, *Mathematics Teacher*, **54** (1961), 538–539.

Robinson, George A.: Useful Generalizations of the Concept of Function, *Mathematics Teacher*, **52** (1959), 444–448.

Rosskopf, Myron F.: What Algebra for the Seventh and Eighth Grades? *Mathematics Teacher*, **51** (1958), 377–379.

Schaaf, Oscar: Student Discovery of Algebraic Principles as a Means of Developing Ability to Generalize, *Mathematics Teacher*, **48** (1955), 324–327.

Schaaf, William L.: "Basic Concepts of Elementary Mathematics" (New York: John Wiley & Sons, Inc., 1960).

School Mathematics Study Group: "Mathematics for Junior High School" (New Haven, Conn.: Yale University Press, 1960).

_____: "First Course in Algebra" (New Haven, Conn.: Yale University Press, 1960).

Sites, V.: Logical Approach to $(-a)(-b)$, *Mathematics Teacher*, **40** (1947), 384.

Sobel, Max: Concept Learning in Algebra, *Mathematics Teacher*, **49** (1956), 425–430.

Stein, Edwin I.: "Supplementary Units in Contemporary Arithmetic and Elementary Algebra" (Princeton, N.J.: D. Van Nostrand Company, Inc., 1960).

Swain, Robert L.: The Equation, *Mathematics Teacher*, **55** (1962), 226–236.

Taylor, Ross: First Course in Algebra—UICSM and SMSG: A Comparison, *Mathematics Teacher*, **55** (1962), 478–481.

Trine, F. Dawson: An Introduction to Algebra with Inequalities, *Mathematics Teacher*, **53** (1960), 42–45.

UICSM Project Staff: Arithmetic with Frames, *Arithmetic Teacher*, **4** (1957), 119–124.

Uth, Carl: Teaching Aid for Developing $(a + b)(a - b)$, *Mathematics Teacher*, **48** (1955), 247–249.

Van Engen, Henry: Logical Approaches to $(-a)(-b) = ab$ and $x^0 = 1$, *Mathematics Teacher*, **40** (1947), 182–185.

Van Waynen, M.: Another Approach to $(-a)(-b)$, *Mathematics Teacher,* **42** (1949), 90.

Volpel, Marvin C.: Solving Percentage Problems by the Equation Method, *Mathematics Teacher,* **47** (1954), 425–427.

Washton, Nathan S., and Ethel B. Friedman: A Teaching Unit on Graphs, *Mathematics Teacher,* **48** (1955), 77–81.

Webber, G. Cuthbert, and John A. Brown: "Basic Concepts of Mathematics" (Reading, Mass.: Addison-Wesley Publishing Company, Inc., 1963).

Williams, Kenneth C.: The Three Faces of (−), *Mathematics Teacher,* **55** (1962), 668–669.

Wollan, G. N.: What Is a Function? *Mathematics Teacher,* **53** (1960), 96–101.

FOURTEEN

The teaching of further topics in elementary algebra

Teaching the solution of pairs of simultaneous linear equations

The systems of simultaneous linear equations of concern in elementary algebra are limited to only two equations in two unknowns. The three commonly used methods for solving such systems are (1) the graphical method, (2) the method of elimination by substitution, and (3) the method of elimination by addition or subtraction.

The graphical method has many advantages, but it should be based on a clear understanding of what it is that the graph of a relation represents. For example, consider the two relations $y > x$ and $y = -x + 8$ under the following specifications:

Example 1: The domain and range of both relations are to be the same, namely, the set of all positive integers < 8. Under these restrictions the complete graph of $y > x$ is the set of points represented by dots in Figure 14-1. The complete graph of $y = -x + 8$ is the set of points represented by the crosses in the figure. The solution set of the two relations considered simultaneously is, therefore, the set of points represented by the crossed-over dots in the figure: namely, the points $\{(1,7), (2,6), (3,5)\}$.

Example 2: The domain and range of both relations are to be the same, namely, the set of all real numbers. Under these restrictions the incomplete graph of $y > x$ is the set of points represented by the shaded portion of Figure 14-2. The incomplete

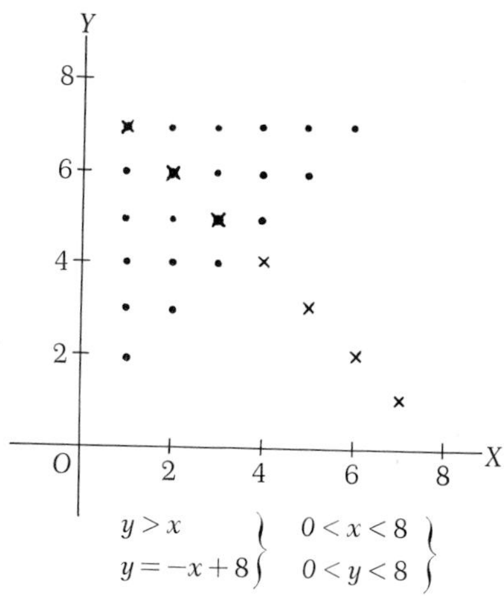

Figure 14-1

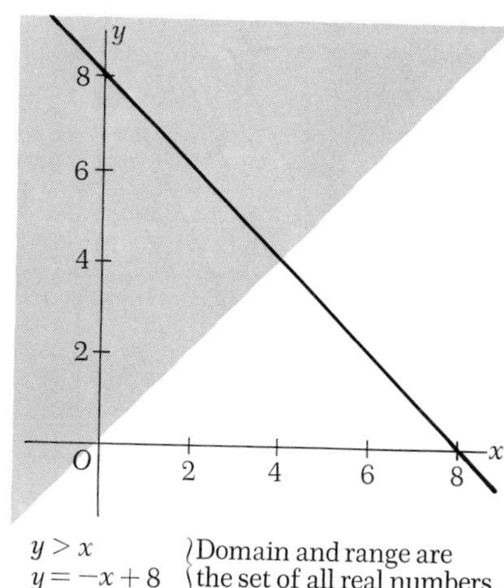

Figure 14-2

graph of $y = -x + 8$ is represented by the straight line. The solution set of the two relations considered simultaneously is the portion of the straight line which crosses the shaded area of the figure.

Furthermore, in consideration of the linear function

$$y = mx + b \qquad m \neq 0$$

it is important that there be a clear understanding of the part the parameters m and b play in determining the graph of the line. Since $(0, b)$ is a point on the line, it is evident that b is the y intercept of the line. In Figure 14-3 the various lines all have the same slope ($m = 2$) but different y intercepts (b varies). The function represented in this graph is $y = 2x + b$. On the other hand, in Figure 14-4 the various lines all have the same y intercept ($b = 2$) but different slopes (m varies). The function represented in this graph is $y = mx + 2$.[1]

In the above discussion the restriction was placed that m be nonzero. When $m = 0$, the expression $y = mx + b$ reduces to $y = b$, the graph of which consists of the x axis ($y = 0$) and all the lines of the plane parallel to the x axis. The condition $m \neq 0$ guarantees that the formula which produces the set of ordered pairs of the linear function will contain the symbol representing the first element. Under this restriction the graph of $y = b$ is thus not a portion of the graph of the linear function $y = mx + b$.

[1]For a more complete discussion of the graphs of such relations see the Report of the Commission on Mathematics, "Appendices" (New York: College Entrance Examination Board, 1959), pp. 8–27, 36–57. The chapters on the pages referenced are respectively Sets, Relations and Functions and The Linear Function and the Quadratic Function.

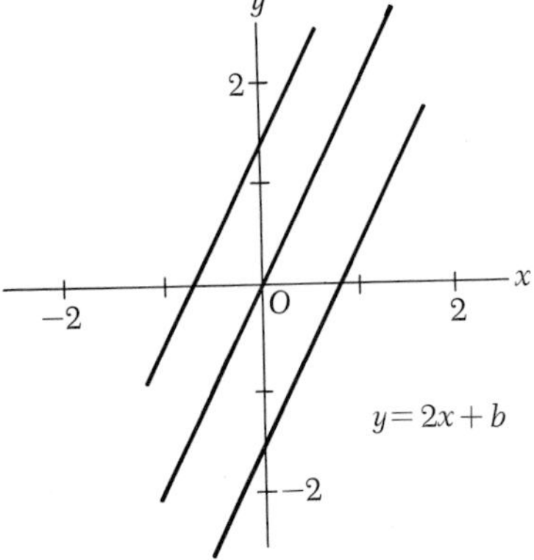

Figure 14-3

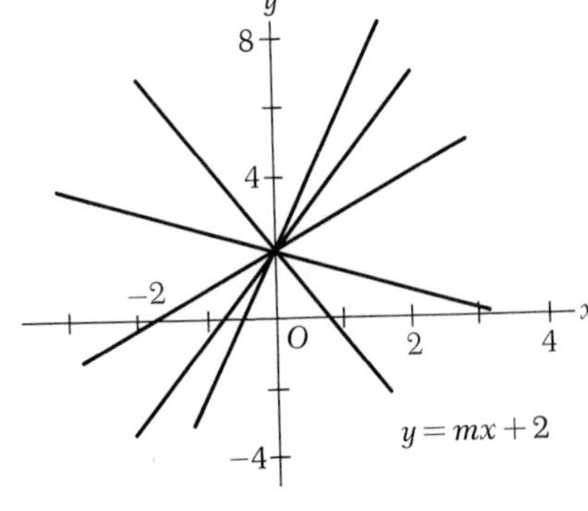

Figure 14-4

The principal advantages of the graphical method lie in the fact that it is interesting and illustrates in a very convincing manner the reason why the solution set of such a system must consist of a pair (or set of pairs) of numbers rather than a single number. It affords a very effective method for demonstrating the significance of the relationships existing when the equations are consistent, inconsistent, indeterminate, dependent, or independent, Figure 14-5. This method also proves valuable in developing a clear understanding of just what is meant by *simultaneous linear equations*. Auxiliary advantages are that it gives an excellent review of graphs of linear functions and the associated concepts and procedures.

Its main disadvantages are two. In the first place it is possible, in general, to get only approximate solutions instead of exact ones. This often introduces apparent discrepancies in checking the solutions and gives the student a consequent feeling of dissatisfaction. Secondly, it is a comparatively slow, tedious, and inefficient method for solving simple linear equations. For this reason, after students have learned the more exact and efficient algebraic methods, they are likely to prefer them to the graphical method.

Aside from any difficulties which the students may experience in the construction of the graphs themselves, the only point of potential difficulty involved in the graphical method is the interpretation of the solution. To assist students in this, the teacher should remind them that any point on any graph has two coordinates (numbers) associated with it, and that these numbers satisfy the equation which was used in making the graph. Therefore, if a point *lies on two graphs at the same time* (say graph A and graph B), its coordinates must satisfy the equation used in making graph A and, at the same time, the equation used in making graph B. Consequently, the coordinates of this point must belong to the solution set of the system. This basic concept is the real crux of this method of solving simultaneous equations, and unless it is strongly emphasized by the teacher, the students may miss the main point of the whole procedure.

If the students have developed a thorough understanding of the meaning of substitution and how to solve and evaluate formulas and literal equations, there is nothing new for them to learn in solving simultaneous equations by the method of substitution. Consider, for example, the system

$$3x - y = -13$$
$$2x + 3y = 17$$

The first step is to solve one of the equations for one of the unknowns in terms of the other. This is merely the solution of a literal equation or formula. The student should select the one which can be solved more easily. In this case he would probably solve the first equation for y and get the result $y = 3x + 13$.

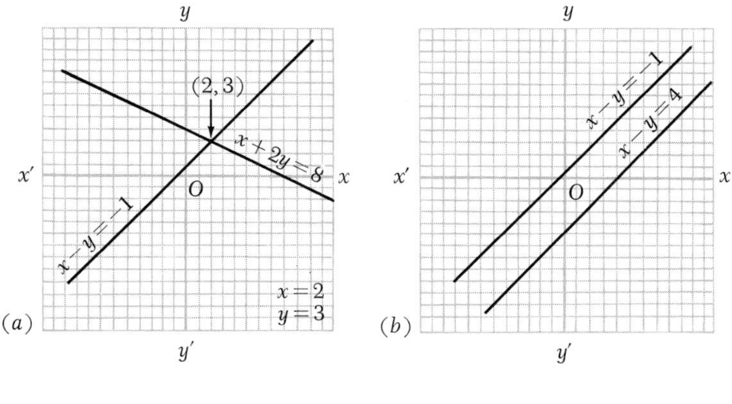

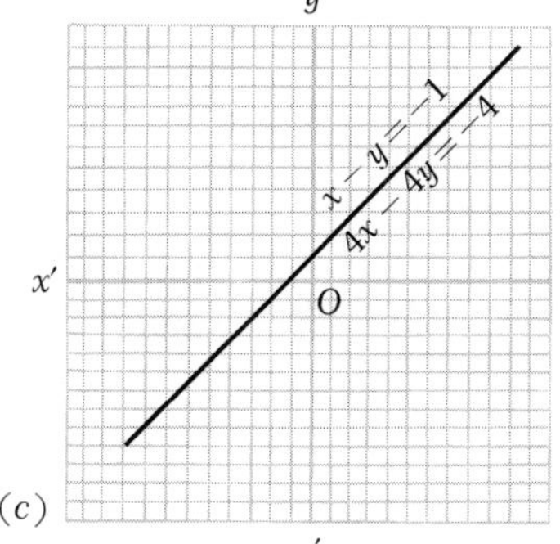

Figure 14-5
The graphical method demonstrates the relationships that exist when equations are consistent (a *and* c), *inconsistent* (b), *indeterminate* (c), *independent* (a *and* b), *and dependent* (c).

He will now substitute this result for y in the second equation and get a resulting equation in which no term in y appears:[2]

$$2x + 3(\quad y \quad) = 17$$
$$2x + 3(3x + 13) = 17$$

Next he will perform the indicated operations and collect terms:

$$2x + 9x + 39 = 17$$
$$11x \qquad + 39 = 17$$

Then he will solve this equation for x:

$$11x \qquad + 39 = 17$$
$$11x \qquad = 17 - 39 = -22$$
$$x \qquad = \frac{-22}{11} = -2$$

Finally he must substitute this value of x back in the first equation (the one which he originally solved for y) to get the numerical value of y:

$$y = 3(\ x\ ) + 13$$
$$y = 3(-2) + 13 = -6 + 13 = +7$$

The solution of the system can now be completed by substituting the values obtained in both of the original equations. The first equation is as follows:

$$3(\ x\ ) - (y) \stackrel{?}{=} -13$$
$$3(-2) - (7) \stackrel{?}{=} -13$$
$$-6 - \ 7 = -13$$

This checks. The second equation will be checked in the same manner.

The detailed steps in the foregoing illustration have been given for the purpose of showing how the principles and procedures discussed in Chapter 13 are applied by the student to this new situation involving a system of simultaneous equations. In particular it is to be noted that the student does not need to learn or to use in this process anything that is new to him. He has merely to learn to use familiar mathematical tools in a new setting. In the process of doing so he receives a most valuable review and a fuller comprehension of the nature of these mathematical tools and, at the same time, gains added proficiency and facility in their use.[3] The student should be made fully aware of how

[2]Note the use of parentheses.

[3]In connection with the detailed steps in the foregoing illustration, the reader may well refer to the sections of Chap. 13 dealing with symbols and formulas and the solution of equations.

the field properties provide the authority for the operations used in passing from one step to the next in finding the solution set of such a system.

It is well to make sure that the students understand the thinking that is back of the process of substitution. In the above discussion

$$y = 3x + 13$$

gives a formula for finding a value of y which will satisfy the first of the two equations. This is true for any value which might be used for x, a fact which can be verified by experimenting with a few arbitrarily selected values of x and the corresponding values of y determined by the formula. When $3x + 13$ is used to replace the y in the second equation, the condition is imposed that whatever value of y satisfies the first equation must also satisfy the second equation. Imposing this condition on y removes the arbitrariness from x, a fact which should be made clear to the student. There is now only one value of x which can be chosen, and it is determined by the equation $2x + 3(3x + 13) = 17$ to be $x = -2$. The formula $y = 3x + 13$ associates one and only one value of y ($y = 7$) with this value of x. Thus the solution set of the system of equations is $(-2,7)$, which can and should be verified by checking in the two equations. Actually, the check in the first equation is no more than a check of the computation of the value of y from the determined value of x. This is due to the fact that $y = 3x + 13$ is but an equivalent form of the original equation $3x - y = -13$. The real check is the substitution in the second equation. The process of solving the two equations establishes that $x = -2$ and $y = 7$ is a necessary condition that the two equations be satisfied. The check establishes it as a sufficient condition.

The method of elimination by addition and subtraction is very effective if the method of substitution leads to the substitution of fractions, a complicated combination of symbols, or a maze of parentheses or signs of aggregation. It is a very simple process, but the simplicity of the technique should not be allowed to camouflage the basic structure of the process. Consider the same two equations

$$\begin{aligned} 3x - y &= -13 \\ 2x + 3y &= 17 \end{aligned}$$

The process of elimination by addition or subtraction would lead to the multiplication of the first equation by 3 and then to the addition of the transformed equation to the second equation. This process would produce $11x = -22$, which would then be solved to obtain $x = -2$, and the value would be used in either of the original equations to produce

$y = 7$. Actually, when analyzed in its finality, the values $x = -2$ and $y = 7$ are produced as the solution set of the two equations

$$\begin{aligned} 11x &= -22 \\ 3x - y &= -13 \end{aligned} \qquad \text{or} \qquad \begin{aligned} 11x &= -22 \\ 2x + 3y &= 17 \end{aligned}$$

By what right can it be said that the solution set of either of these two systems of equations is the solution set of the original system? Of course, the simple answer to this question is that $(-2,7)$ can be verified as the solution set of the original equations merely by substituting these values in the two equations and seeing that the equations are satisfied. Such a check would justify the process used to find a solution set of any system of equations. A more fundamental question is: How can one be assured that the technique used will produce the solution set of a system of linear equations, if such a set exists? Consider the original system of equations written in the equivalent form

$$\begin{aligned} 3x - y + 13 &= 0 \\ 2x + 3y - 17 &= 0 \end{aligned}$$

The process produced the following identity:

$$3(3x - y + 13) + (2x + 3y - 17) \equiv 11x + 22$$

For all values of x the expression on the left is equal to the one on the right. Hence any value of x which will simultaneously satisfy any two of the equations $3x - y + 13 = 0$, $2x + 3y - 17 = 0$, and $11x + 22 = 0$ will also satisfy the third one. Always the process of solving any equation or system of equations establishes the solution set as a necessary condition that the equations be satisfied. The check alone establishes that it is a sufficient condition. Why is this? For this reason one should never be satisfied with a determined solution set of a given equation or system of equations until it has been carefully checked. Again students should be fully conscious of the part the field postulates play in such a solution process.

Operations with fractions The ordinary operations with fractions which find a legitimate place in elementary algebra include reduction and "stepping up," multiplication and division, and addition and subtraction. The student's experience with arithmetical fractions will serve as a point of departure for beginning the work with algebraic fractions. It would be a mistake, however, to assume that familiarity with arithmetical fractions will eliminate all difficulty in working with algebraic fractions. Algebra lacks the familiar, concrete intuitive basis which characterizes a good deal of arithmetic, and the student must learn eventually to work almost entirely upon the basis of established rules or patterns of procedure rather than by intuitive methods. These patterns, of course, are merely generalizations of the methods used in arithmetic and so may be developed and explained largely by means of analogy with arithmetical situations. The chief difference to be emphasized is that in algebra the student will find it necessary to confine his attention more and more specifically to the processes by which he works and pay relatively less attention to the particular numerical values of the quantities involved.

Since the use of fractions in elementary algebra is confined largely to the solution of simple formulas and certain types of verbal problems and to the simplification of algebraic expressions, it is neither necessary nor desirable to include highly complicated fractional expressions in the work of the beginning course.

Many textbooks, both in arithmetic and algebra, introduce the addition and subtraction of fractions before taking up the multiplication and division of fractions. There are those who contend that this plan is psychologically unsound. They argue that multiplication and division are the less difficult of the operations with fractions and hence should be studied first. In accordance with this point of view the plan or organization followed in some texts is to consider first the reduction and stepping up of fractions, then the multiplication and division of fractions, and finally the addition and subtraction of fractions.

The student should acquire through his study of fractions the following abilities and understandings:

Understanding of the different aspects of the meaning of a fraction

Understanding of what it means to reduce a fraction to lower terms or to change a fraction to higher terms

Understanding of the nature of the terms of a fraction and how the increase or decrease of the numerator or denominator affects the value of the fraction

Ability and skill in multiplying fractions together or in dividing one fraction by another

Ability and skill in adding or subtracting fractions

In arithmetic various meanings are attached to the word "fraction." Thus

As a *number* a fraction may express:

One or more of the equal parts of a unit

One of the equal parts of a single quantity consisting of one or more units

The quotient of one number divided by another number

As a *relation* a fraction may express:

The ratio which one number bears to another number

The idea which seems to persist most vividly in the minds of most students is that a fraction, when used as a number, is a part or a number of parts of some quantity. This is doubtless because many arithmetical fractions, and even operations with such fractions, can be most easily and concretely illustrated by reference to tangible objects, visible geometric or graphic diagrams, and denominate numbers. Thus the student acquires a sort of intuitive feeling for such a fraction as a part of something. In algebra, however, the precise numerical relationships are not present in the sense that they are in arithmetic; hence it becomes necessary to construct a less intuitive but more definitive meaning. The student must now learn to think consistently of a fraction, if not expressing a ratio, as merely an indicated quotient or an indicated division of one quantity (the numerator) by another quantity (the denominator). Whether the indicated division can actually be carried out exactly or not is immaterial.

If students are to learn to attach this meaning to a fraction, it will be necessary for the teacher to give specific attention to it and focus the attention of the students upon it repeatedly. It may be illustrated and made to appear reasonable by reference to concrete, numerical, geometric, or physical quantities, but it must not stop with such illustrations. There must also be given illustrations in which the precise numerical relations which provide the intuitive basis for the earlier meaning of a fraction are replaced in part or in their entirety by purely symbolic quantities, and students must be specifically trained to regard such expressions as a/b or $(x - 3)/2y$ as being fractions just as truly as $3/4$ or $8/15$. The meaning itself must be made to have the status of a definition, so that it may persist even when no intuitive basis exists. In this context such expressions become, as it were, symbolic representations of rational numbers. They are known as *rational expressions* and are subject to the same laws of operation as those which govern rational numbers.

The *reduction of fractions*, as well as the inverse operation of changing fractions to higher terms, involves the general problem of changing the form of a fraction without changing its value. Such changes can always be effected by the operation of a single simple principle, viz., that *the value of a fraction remains unchanged if its numerator and denominator are multiplied or divided by the same quantity.*[4] Children generally are able to apply this principle quite successfully when working with arithmetical fractions, but they probably do so intuitively and without much conscious recognition of the principle itself. Evidence of this is found in the fact that, when they come to work with algebraic fractions, they often fail to apply the principle and consequently get such erroneous results as

$$\frac{x + 4}{4} = x \qquad \text{or} \qquad \frac{2n + a}{-3n + a} = \frac{2}{-3}$$

[4]Division by zero is, of course, excepted, and here multiplication by zero must also be excepted, since it would render the value of the fraction indeterminate.

Results of this sort are almost certainly due to the failure of the students to realize that this procedure does not constitute division of numerator and denominator by a common factor. The undefined use of the word "cancellation" and the failure to place proper emphasis on the inverse relations between multiplication and division, and between addition and subtraction, probably are the major reasons for such looseness in thinking.[5]

Students must be kept aware of the fact that the addition or subtraction of like quantities (except zero) to or from the numerator and denominator of a fraction will certainly change not only the form but the value of the fraction, whereas in the reduction of fractions the value of the fraction must be kept intact. They must also be kept aware that in dividing numerator and denominator by a common factor, the factor must be a divisor of the *whole* numerator and of the *whole* denominator. Continued consciousness of this elementary principle will prevent the occurrence of such errors as this:

$$\frac{3a + 5}{a + 2} = \frac{3 + 5}{2} = \frac{8}{2} = 4$$

Most of the mistakes which occur in the reduction of fractions could be avoided by the consistent practice of expressing (rewriting if necessary) the numerator and denominator of the fraction in factored form and enclosing each separate factor, no matter how simple, in its own parentheses. If this is done, the division, or cancellation, of common factors will be effected with real understanding of what is being done. Similarly, in changing fractions to higher terms, it is good practice to have the students immediately enclose the numerator and denominator of the original fraction in parentheses at the outset and then write the common multiplier also in parentheses as a multiplier of the numerator and as a multiplier of the denominator. The consistent use of parentheses in this way serves to keep all factors intact and to prevent students from treating a factor of a part as a factor of the whole.

The *multiplication of fractions* generally causes little difficulty. The principle governing this process is exceedingly simple: The product of two or more fractions is a fraction whose numerator is the product of the numerators of the original fractions and whose denominator is similarly the product of the denominators. It should be illustrated freely by examples drawn from arithmetic, and, by analogy, the application to algebraic expressions can be made without difficulty.

The fractional product can often be reduced to lower terms. Hence it is desirable to have it rewritten as a single fraction, the numerators and denominators of the component fractions being written in factored

[5]See pages 268-269 for similar discussion with respect to arithmetic.

form with every factor enclosed in its own parentheses. It should be stressed that the numerator of every component fraction must be regarded as a factor of the numerator of the product, and similarly for the denominators. The students will be more likely to keep this consciously in mind if they make a habitual practice of enclosing the individual numerators and denominators of the component fractions in parentheses at the outset, before doing anything else. Thus

$$\frac{4 - x^2}{2 + x} \cdot \frac{x}{2 - x}$$

would be rewritten as

$$\frac{(4 - x^2)}{(2 + x)} \cdot \frac{(x)}{(2 - x)} = \frac{(2 - x)(2 + x)(x)}{(2 + x)(2 - x)} = x$$

In the *division of one fraction by another* it is necessary only to see that the students understand that division is always exactly equivalent to multiplication by the reciprocal of the divisor. They will probably be more or less familiar with this principle from their arithmetic, especially as regards division by a fraction. However, the principle should be clearly explained and numerous illustrations should be given. The student should understand that dividing by a fraction means finding the number which, when multiplied by the divisor, gives the dividend. This is always the test of division. For example, if 7 is divided by $^3/_5$, the result must be such that the product of itself and $^3/_5$ will give 7 [or 7(1)]. We must therefore find a number q such that $q(^3/_5) = 7$. Evidently, q must equal $7(^5/_3)$, since $7(^5/_3)(^3/_5)$ equals 7(1), or 7. Thus 7 divided by $^3/_5$ equals 7 times $^5/_3$. Similarly, in the example $a \div (x/y)$, we have $a \div (x/y) = q$. But $q \cdot (x/y) = a$, whence $q = a \cdot (y/x)$. Thus $a \div (x/y) = a \cdot (y/x)$. The rationale of this process, of course, finds its authority in the definition of division and in the property of the multiplicative inverse. The student should be made fully aware of this fact.

As a rule the main difficulties to be anticipated are those incident to the multiplication and simplification of fractions, and these have been discussed in the foregoing paragraphs.

Sometimes students have difficulty in multiplying or dividing fractions by whole numbers. Some writers prefer to treat this as a special case to be covered by the rule: In multiplying or dividing a fraction by a whole number only the numerator of the fraction is to be multiplied or divided by the whole number. Others feel that it is better to have the students regard the whole number as the numerator of a fraction whose denominator is 1, thus bringing the problem under the general procedures for multiplying and dividing fractions. Either of these methods will probably give satisfactory results. The second, however, appears to have certain advantages over the first, in that it gives more unity and generality to the whole matter of multiplying and dividing fractions and obviates the necessity for the special rule. It also has the advantage of applying to the division of a whole number by a fraction, which is not precisely covered by the special rule.

In introducing students to the *addition of fractions* care must be taken to prevent the occurrence of such errors as this:

$$\frac{5x}{a} + \frac{2}{n} = \frac{5x + 2}{a + n}$$

Mistakes of this kind reveal a lack of understanding of the real nature of a fraction and of the real meaning of the numerator (numberer) and the denominator (namer). Furthermore, rational expressions must conform to the definitions and operational properties of rational numbers. Such a result does not conform to the definition, which states that the sum of two rational numbers a/b and c/d is given by $a/b + c/d = (ad + bc)/bd$. This is obviously equivalent to finding the common denominator bd of the two fractions and then adding the numerators. This latter procedure allows for the simplification of finding the least common denominator. The two processes are equivalent, and neither supports the erroneous practice exhibited above. As an added precaution attention should be redirected to the fact that addition is essentially a combining process. There is no occasion for such combination, nor can any sensible interpretation be given to the result unless the sets of objects to be combined are essentially sets of like objects. If students can really get the idea that the denominator of a fraction merely indicates what kind of things are being considered and that the numerator merely indicates how many of these are taken, they will have gone far toward heading off mistakes of the kind described above. Appropriate illustrations of arithmetical fractions are helpful in emphasizing this point because, if sufficiently simple illustrations are taken, the students can immediately check the correctness of their results. For example, they know that $3/4 + 1/4 = 1$, and they can at once see the discrepancy of saying that

$$\frac{3}{4} + \frac{1}{4} = \frac{3 + 1}{4 + 4} = \frac{4}{8} = \frac{1}{2}$$

because $1/2$ is obviously not equal to 1, and they know that the correct answer must be 1. They should be trained to the habit of using some such simple numerical illustration to check up any doubtful operation to see whether or not it is legitimate and correct, and they should learn also to go back to the original meanings of the numerator and denominator to clarify their thinking. To this end it is often helpful to rewrite fractional expressions with the denominators written out in words. Thus $2/7 + 3/7$ can be written as 2 sevenths + 3 sevenths, in which case the expression becomes similar to the expression for the sum of any like denominate quantities, such as 2 dollars and 3 dollars. In other words, this process helps to make clear the idea that fractions are in a sense the same as denominate numbers, the denominator merely telling what kind of thing is being considered and the numerator telling how many are being considered.

The tendency to add numerators and to add denominators is probably a carry-over from the operation of multiplying fractions. It is important that the students get the distinction between these processes clearly in mind so that they will not confuse them.

The first step in teaching students to add fractions is to have them recall the basic principle of addition: Addition should be used only for combining groups of like things. Thus, fractions should not be added until they have been changed to fractions with a common denominator, for then, and then only, are they groups of like things. The denominator of the sum is the common denominator of the addends, and the numerator is the algebraic sum of their numerators. It is not sufficient, however, merely to tell students this. The teacher should give numerous carefully selected illustrations, working them out at the chalkboard and discussing them with the class while he works. The process is not difficult to understand or perform, but it needs to be explained very carefully and deliberately and to be fixed very carefully in the minds of the students.

Such careful and adequate explanation can give the students an understanding of the addition of fractions, but the fixation of the ideas and the procedure requires that the students shall have a substantial amount of practice in doing the thing themselves. The practice exercises should be selected with great care. They should be very easy at first and become more difficult by gradual stages. The increasing complexity will be essentially in the numerators, since in this first stage only fractions having like denominators will be used. There should be no great difficulty if care is taken, because the only real algebraic work will be the algebraic addition of the numerators. Essentially this will be nothing but a review of the algebraic addition of polynomials, with which the students should be expected to have considerable familiarity. The exercises should include fractions whose numerators are of varied types, including simple integers and literal monomials, binomials, and trinomials, some of the binomial and trinomial numerators being given in factored form requiring expansion in order to effect the simplification of the resultant sum.

Too much emphasis cannot be laid upon the principle that the transition to the more complicated forms should be made *gradually*. Teachers often assume that little attention need be given to the addition of fractions with like denominators. No greater mistake could be made;

the assumption is entirely unwarranted. The fact is that when the students *really understand* the addition of fractions with like denominators, they are likely to have little difficulty in mastering the addition of fractions with unlike denominators.

When fractions with unlike denominators are to be added algebraically, the students should be firmly impressed with the guiding principle: *If the denominators are not alike, make them alike*. That is, the students should become clearly aware that the first thing to do is to change the given fractions into new fractions whose values are identical with those of the original fractions but whose forms are changed in such a way that they will all have the same denominator. After this has been done, the problem of the algebraic addition of these fractions becomes the already familiar one which has been described above.

While the statement of this principle sounds simple and clear, there are often intermediate details which will tend to obscure the essential simplicity of the matter. Consider, for example, the following case: $3a/(5n + 2) + 5a/(2n - 3)$. Here it is necessary to determine first what the common denominator will be. Since the denominators have no common factor, the common denominator will have to be taken as the product of all (in this case both) of the separate denominators, viz., $(5n + 2)(2n - 3)$. This should always be expressed in factored form. Now, in order to make the first fraction have this common denominator, it is necessary to multiply its denominator (and consequently also its numerator) by the factor $2n - 3$. Similarly, the denominator and numerator of the second fraction must be multiplied by the factor $5n + 2$. The two fractions now have the form

$$\frac{3a(2n - 3)}{(5n + 2)(2n - 3)} + \frac{5a(5n + 2)}{(2n - 3)(5n + 2)}$$

in which the denominators are alike. The student may proceed to write the sum by writing the product $(5n + 2)(2n - 3)$ as the denominator of the sum $\frac{\qquad}{(5n + 2)(2n - 3)}$, and then writing in the numerator the indicated sum of the numerators of the transformed fractions: $\frac{3a(2n - 3) + 5a(5n + 2)}{\qquad}$. Thus the sum[6] will be written as

$$\frac{3a(2n - 3) + 5a(5n + 2)}{(5n + 2)(2n - 3)}$$

The student should feel that when he has carried the work this far, he has already completed the essential part of the job of adding the fractions, although it may often be desirable to simplify the expression

[6]Note that this is identical with the result obtained directly from the definition of the sum of two rational numbers.

which he has obtained. Generally this simplification will consist merely in expanding the indicated products and collecting like terms. Occasionally it may require a refactoring of the numerator and denominator and the "cancellation" of factors common to both. However, most problems in the addition of fractions in first-year algebra should be comparatively simple. Certainly any types which exceed in difficulty the illustrative example discussed above should be reserved for subsequent courses.

Teaching the solution of equations containing fractions

Students often have difficulty in solving equations containing fractions even though they may readily solve equations without fractions. The difficulty generally can be traced to the complicated appearance which the presence of fractions gives to the equation. Lacking experience with such equations, the student tends to become confused at the outset because he does not know how to start the analysis of this problem.

The student needs to be taught two basic things to help him out of his difficulty. (1) He must come to understand that equations which contain fractions may be changed into equivalent equations which do not contain fractions and that, when so changed, equations in one unknown may be solved readily because they will then be in the same form as the equations to which he is accustomed. (2) He must learn how to change an equation containing fractions into an equivalent equation which does not contain fractions. After he has done this, he has merely to deal with ordinary linear equations concerning which suggestions have been given in the preceding chapter.

A few illustrations should serve both to convince him that it is in general possible to change an equation containing fractions into an equivalent one which does not contain fractions and to make clear to him the method by which this is accomplished. The method of explanation should be substantially as follows:

Let us consider the equation $2/3 + 3/x = 5/6$, in which we are required to solve for x. We know how to solve equations without fractions; hence, we could solve this equation if we could change it into one that would contain no fractions. We could do so if we could get rid of the denominators. But the only way we can get rid of them is to have a factor in the numerator of each term which is exactly equal to the denominator of that term so that we may divide both numerator and denominator of each individual term by the whole denominator of that term.

We can get new factors in the numerators of all the terms if we multiply every term in the whole equation by the same quantity, because multiplying a fraction means multiplying its numerator. We have a right to multiply all the terms in the equation by any common multiplier we wish, because while this changes the value of each individual term, it does not destroy the equation.

We wish, therefore, to find the smallest multiplier which can be exactly divided by the denominator of each fraction in the equation. This multiplier will be, as you know, the least common denominator of all these fractions. In the case of the equation which we are considering in this problem, the L.C.D. will be $6x$, since this is the smallest quantity of which 3, x, and 6 are all exact factors.

Let us therefore multiply each term in the equation by $6x$, whence[7]

$$\frac{6x(2)}{3} + \frac{6x(3)}{x} = \frac{6x(5)}{6}$$

Now, if we reduce each term to its simplest form by dividing its denominator and numerator by whatever factor is common to both, we have a resulting equation $4x + 18 = 5x$, which has no fractions in it. We can easily solve this equation, since we have solved many others like it.

Students often make mistakes in solving equations containing fractions because they are careless in writing their work down. With special frequency they produce crowded and often illegible work when inserting the L.C.D. as a common multiplier of the numerators of the various terms in fractional equations. The following illustration is not exaggerated:

$$\frac{n}{2n - 8} + \frac{16}{n^2 - 16} = \frac{1}{2} \qquad \frac{n}{2(n-4)} + \frac{16}{(n-4)(n+4)} = \frac{1}{2}$$

2(n-4)(n+4)   2(n-4)(n+4)   2(n-4)(n+4)

$$\frac{n}{2(n-4)} + \frac{16}{(n-4)(n+4)} = \frac{1}{2} \quad \text{L.C.D.} = 2(n-4)(n+4)$$

Such carelessly written work can hardly fail to be productive of mistakes. It can be avoided if the students are taught to do a little planning with regard to the details of form. They should learn to recognize that where factors are to be inserted, space will be required for writing the

[7]Attention should be called to the fact that the multiplication of the equality gives

$$6x\left(\frac{2}{3} + \frac{3}{x}\right) = \frac{6x(5)}{6}$$

The authority for this is the multiplicative property of equality (page 64). The distributive property and substitution then provide for the replacement of the left member by

$$\frac{6x(2)}{3} + \frac{6x(3)}{x}$$

factors and that they should provide such space in order that their work will be neat and legible. Thus the foregoing problem might be advantageously written as follows:

$$\frac{n}{2(n-4)} + \frac{16}{(n-4)(n+4)} = \frac{1}{2}$$

$$\frac{n(\not{2})(n-4)(n+4)}{\not{2}(n-4)} + \frac{16(2)(n-4)(n+4)}{(n-4)(n+4)} = \frac{1(\not{2})(n-4)(n+4)}{\not{2}}$$

$$n(n+4) + 32 = (n-4)(n+4)$$

When the need for space in writing is anticipated and provided for in this way, the written work is invariably improved in neatness and legibility, and the likelihood of mistakes is greatly diminished. Although this is a matter of form rather than of mathematics, it is by no means a trivial matter.

Sometimes students confuse the procedures involved in solving equations containing fractions with those involved in the addition of fractions. It is important to point out clearly that the two problems are fundamentally different. In the one case the aim is to find the algebraic sum of certain given fractions. This obviously makes it necessary to preserve the *original value* of each individual fraction, although its form may be altered. On the other hand, in solving an equation, both the form and the value of the individual terms may be altered if necessary, provided the *equality* of the two members of the equation is preserved. For this reason, in adding fractions, we may not multiply either the numerator or denominator of any fraction unless we multiply *both* by the same factor, whereas, in clearing an equation of fractions, the multiplicative property of equality gives us the authority to multiply the numerators of *all* the terms by *the same multiplier* without multiplying the denominators at all. It is important that illustrations of this point be presented to and discussed with the students and that they come to make a clear distinction between the meanings and the implications of these two fundamentally different problems.

The solving of verbal problems The solving of verbal problems is probably the most troublesome part of algebra for most students. This is not surprising, because here the student must analyze and set up the problem before he can solve it and, except for the dubious practice of classifying certain verbal problems by types, there is no definite pattern for this analysis. It is true, of course, that for the most part verbal problems involve relationships which may be cast in the form of one or more equations, and those problems which are found in algebra textbooks ordinarily involve relationships that can be represented by relatively simple equations which can be solved without any difficulty once they are set up. The trouble lies in setting up the equations, i.e., in translating the verbal statements into algebraic language. Therefore the principal effort of both teacher and students in connection with the study of verbal problems should be directed primarily toward developing the ability to translate the problems into equations.

The difficulty which children encounter in making such translation is quite understandable. In the first place, most children are not very careful analytical readers. The recent emphasis in the schools on rapid, cursory reading is doubtless appropriate and valuable for many purposes, but it does not lend itself well to the careful analysis of problems. Analysis is characteristically a slow and tedious process, and the ability to read analytically requires patience as well as concentrated and sustained attention. These characteristics, generally, can be developed to a satisfactory degree only by special training in giving conscious attention to them. The teacher of algebra must assume responsibility for giving this special training in careful analytical reading if he expects to have his students become proficient in solving verbal problems.

One of the material difficulties encountered by children in interpreting the verbal statements of problems lies in the fact that the relationships are not always stated explicitly but are often *implied.* For example, in the familiar distance-rate-time problems relationships between units of measure are implied, such as the number of feet in a mile or the number of seconds in a minute. In the many problems that imply the use of money, the relationships between the various units of monetary value are always assumed as known. Such words as "complementary," "supplementary," and "right triangle" are used to imply pertinent facts or relationships which are not stated explicitly. Hidden implications of this sort may appear so obvious to the teacher that he will perhaps not even be consciously aware of the lack of explicit statement. Often, however, they constitute a real source of confusion to students. The students need to be trained specifically to be on the lookout for these hidden implications, to learn to detect them, and to take them into account in analyzing and setting up the problems.

Closely associated with the difficulties involved in this implicit manner of indicating facts or relationships is the difficulty which sometimes arises from the use of words or expressions whose meanings are not entirely clear to the students. For example, the expression "x less 5" means $x - 5$, while the expression "x less than 5" carries the ambiguous meaning of either $5 - x$ or $x < 5$, and students frequently fail to detect these differences because they do not recognize that the meanings to be attached to the word "less" are not the same in the two expressions.

In the second place, the careful analysis of problems requires much patience, concentrated attention, and the willingness to take the time to write down and organize all relevant data with painstaking care. These are not generally to be regarded as normal characteristics of normal, healthy young children. Children tend to be impatient with problems which they cannot organize intuitively in a moment. They want to get to the answer quickly and are often content to dismiss, with the remark "Too hard," any problem involving relationships that cannot be seen and organized at a glance. Development of the ability to give concentrated and sustained attention is not only desirable as a general trait but absolutely necessary in the successful study of mathematics, and it is especially necessary in setting up verbal problems. The students need to be made and kept specifically conscious of this fact and to be trained in the habits implied.

Finally, and perhaps most important of all, students have difficulty with verbal problems because there is no single general pattern according to which all verbal problems can be set up. Certain "general methods" have been proposed and are doubtless helpful in systematizing the analysis, but there is, and can be, no formula which will obviate the necessity for alertness, care, ingenuity, and resourcefulness on the part of the student. The solution of equations, the addition of fractions, and many other operations with symbolic algebraic expressions can be reduced to mechanical laws which operate invariably. It is not so with the setting up of verbal problems. Every problem presents its own peculiar elements, relationships, and requirements which must be studied, interpreted, and organized strictly and solely in the light of the conditions and data stated or implied in the problem itself.

It is true that many of the problems customarily found in the textbooks tend to fall into certain general groupings or types. It is also true that several of these types have characteristic formulas which express the relationships involved. To this extent verbal problems may be classified and their solutions somewhat standardized, and for this reason some authors both advocate and practice the procedure of presenting verbal problems according to type. On the other hand, the component elements and the mathematical relationships involved in one type of problem may be entirely unlike those involved in other types. Thus, while a student may be able to set up and solve type problems when he knows to what types they belong, he may be completely at a loss when he attempts to classify problems by type. For this reason the advisability of teaching verbal problems by type seems questionable, at best. It does tend to produce specific classroom results more quickly than any other method, but they are results which are more in the nature of specific skills than general powers. Some authors suggest compromising the situation by supplementing the type lists of problems by unclassified lists of miscellaneous problems, holding that this secures the advantages of teaching problems by type and at the same time avoids the disadvantages. It would seem that this might be an effective compromise, provided that appropriate emphasis were given to the study of the unclassified problems.

In general, verbal problems lead to equations. Therefore, somewhere in the problem, it should be possible to find at least one quantitative element for which two different mathematical expressions can be obtained. This element may be a particular distance, a particular volume, or any one of a variety of quantitative elements. The equality may be expressed specifically, or it may be merely implied. The search for such an element and for the two different ways of expressing it constitutes the analysis of the problem.

Example: How much alcohol must be added to a pint of 10 per cent solution of iodine to make an 8 per cent solution?

Here the quantitative elements in the problem are the amounts of alcohol, the amounts of iodine, and the total amounts of the solutions. If each of these is considered under both the initial and final conditions, it is seen that the element which remains quantitatively the same in both cases is the amount of iodine. Thus we get the basic equation:

Original amount of iodine = final amount of iodine

By considering now the composition of each solution and designating by n the number of pints of alcohol to be added to the original solution, we may readily get two different expressions for the amount of iodine. A diagram will be helpful in this case.

It is seen from the diagram, Figure 14-6, that the original amount of iodine is 10/100 of 1 pint and the final amount of iodine is 8/100 of $(1 + n)$ pints. By substituting these expressions in the basic equation given verbally above, we get the equation:

$$\frac{10}{100}(1) = \frac{8}{100}(1 + n) \qquad \text{or} \qquad 10 = 8(1 + n)$$

from which the value of n can be found directly.

Example: Two trains, 350 miles apart, travel toward each other until they meet. Train A travels at an average speed of 55 miles per hour and train B travels at an average speed of 48 miles per hour. How long will it be after they start before they meet?

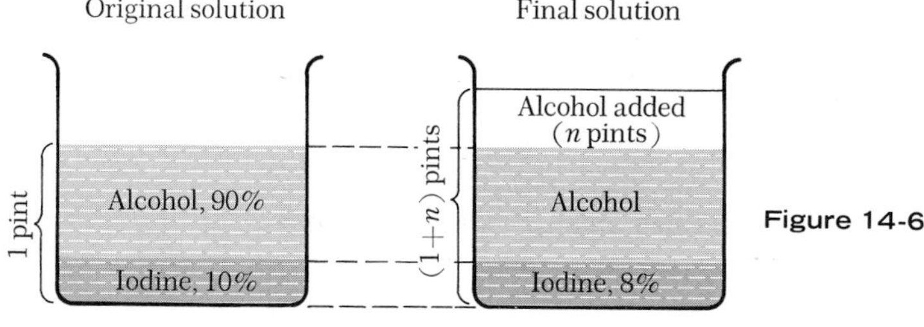

Figure 14-6

Here the elements involved in the two situations are distances, rates, and times. One element, which is the same in the case of both trains, is obviously the time. Thus we may set up our basic equation in words:

Time for train A = time for train B

It remains now merely to get two mathematical expressions representing the time in terms of respective distances and rates of speed. To this end the detailed data should now be tabulated in some such manner as the following:

Elements involved	Train A	Train B
Distance traveled, miles	x	$350 - x$
Rate, miles per hour	55	48
Time (distance/rate)	$\frac{x}{55}$	$\frac{350 - x}{48}$

The substitution of these two expressions for the time in the basic equation given verbally above gives the desired equation in algebraic form:

$$\frac{x}{55} = \frac{350 - x}{48}$$

This may be solved for x, the distance traveled by train A, and since the rate is known, the time can easily be computed.

Another, and perhaps easier, approach to this particular problem may be made by reflecting that the total distance is constant and that two expressions for this distance must be equivalent. One such expression is given explicitly in the problem, viz., $d = 350$ miles. Another may be inferred from the fact that the total distance is the sum of the distances traveled by the two trains. Thus we have a basic equation:

Total distance = total distance
(Miles traveled by train A) + (Miles traveled by train B) = (350 miles)

By again tabulating the data, recalling that the trains travel the same number of hours t, and making use of the relation $d = r \cdot t$, we have

Elements involved	Train A	Train B
Rate, miles per hour	55	48
Time, hours	t	t
Distance traveled, miles	$55t$	$48t$

By substitution in the basic equation, we get the simple equation

$$55t + 48t = 350$$

from which the required length of time can be found directly.

The alternative approaches to the above example make it clear that there is considerable latitude in the analysis of many verbal problems and that success depends largely upon the care and ingenuity of the student. The setup of the problem may involve implied relationships which the student must seek in his background of experiences. The student who in his earlier work in arithmetic and informal geometry has accumulated a rich store of ready information about such relationships will have a great advantage in the analysis of problems. It is often possible to make graphic or diagrammatic sketches which are helpful in making the relationships among the elements seem concrete and tangible.

Intuition, induction, and deduction in problem solving Whether a problem is simple or complex, it is distinctly characterized by three significant attributes: the data, the unknown, and the particular conditions which relate the data to the unknown. Any successful approach to the obtaining of a solution for a given problem, therefore, necessarily calls for a careful analysis of the problem situation in order to discover what the essential data are, what constitutes the unknown, what fundamental relations tie the data and the unknown together, and what operations are pertinent. Thus, the solving of problems in no sense can be regarded as a trial-and-error process of haphazard guessing or unsystematic reasoning. Rather it should be looked upon as a combination of intelligent efforts directed by intuition, induction, and deduction reinforced by analogy, specialization, and generalization.

Following one's intuition is largely a process of attempting to capitalize on significant hunches. Such guesses, however, have some form of authoritative justification rather than being merely chance occurrences. They arise from an implicit perception of the total problem situation and a careful perusal of all of its essential pertinencies. Although they have no basis in any pattern of formal reasoning, truly germane intuitions are ready apprehensions arising from contextual familiarity with the general orientation of the problem. While intuitive reasoning, through its appeal to analogy and specialization, can be very helpful in the discovery of effective leads to be followed in the search for the solution of a given problem, it is by no means a conclusive process. True, it is possible that results arrived at intuitively may, through a careful check in the given problem situation, prove to constitute a valid solution. This, however, is not the likely case. More generally, the intuitive process will yield only ideas to be subjected to more formal and rigorous tests before their real worth can be determined. The use of intuition, though fraught with dangers, is to be encouraged as an important aid to intelligent problem solving. It can lead through analogy to the recognition of special cases which may or may not be helpful. These special cases can vary from those with the same problem structure but simpler data to analogous problem situations with simpler structure. They may take the form of diagrams illustrating the basic relations between the data and the unknown or simpler special cases which are significant components of the more difficult general problem.

Induction is fundamentally a process of reasoning that carries one from the particular to the general. Such a pattern of thinking can lead one to examine the special cases, resulting from intuition, in the quest for a characteristic thread of similarity, regularity, or coherence which might suggest techniques for dealing with the more general situation. Just as is the case with intuition, the most significant techniques of induction are analogy, specialization, and generalization. Through the analogies of special cases generalizations are sought in order that they might be checked against other specializations. Such generalizations lead to the formalization of formulas or rules which summarize and characterize recognized basic relations that exist between data and between data and unknown. Great care must be exercised, however, in drawing conclusions from any inductive process. Such conclusions should never be stated as actualities but only as probabilities that are possibly worthy of further investigation.

Some of the potentialities and limitations of intuitive and inductive reasoning are illustrated in the following example.

Example: Although Euclid (ca. 300 B.C.) was able to prove that the number of prime numbers is infinite, no one has ever been able to construct a formula which would always yield a prime number. The French mathematician Pierre de Fermat (ca. 1640) conjectured that $2^{2^n} + 1$ was such a formula. In other words his conjecture was that this formula would yield a prime if any nonnegative integer is substituted for n. For example:

$n = 0$: $2^{2^0} + 1 = 2^1 + 1 = 2 + 1 = 3$
$n = 1$: $2^{2^1} + 1 = 2^2 + 1 = 4 + 1 = 5$
$n = 2$: $2^{2^2} + 1 = 2^4 + 1 = 16 + 1 = 17$
$n = 3$: $2^{2^3} + 1 = 2^8 + 1 = 256 + 1 = 257$
$n = 4$: $2^{2^4} + 1 = 2^{16} + 1 = 65{,}536 + 1 = 65{,}537$

The numbers 3, 5, 17, 257, and 65,537 are all primes. When $n = 5$, $2^{2^5} + 1$ is a very large number which Fermat thought might be a prime. In 1732, nearly 100 years later, the famous mathematician Euler was able to prove that this number was not a prime by showing that it could be factored in the form $641 \times 6{,}700{,}417$. So Fermat's conjecture based on intuitive and inductive reasoning proved to be false.

Deduction is the process of reasoning by implication. If we use p to represent one statement, or proposition, and q to represent another, we say that p implies q, or symbolically $p \to q$, if it is absolutely impossible for q to be a false statement when p is a true statement.

Example: Let statements p and q be as follows:
$(p)x$ is an integer such that $x + 2 = 5$
$(q)x$ is the integer 3

In this case p implies q $(p \to q)$ because if p is a true statement, then q must be a true statement.

The pattern of deductive reasoning provides a technique of seeking out necessary conclusions which follow from given or derived truths. Two very essential questions which must be resolved in any intelligent effort at problem solving are: (1) What truths are implied by the data? (2) What truths are implied by the relations which exist between the data and the unknown? Once these questions are answered conclusively, the way is usually cleared to a satisfactory solution of the given problem. One should keep clearly in mind, however, that the deductive process leads only to necessary results. In other words, the results obtained from such a process provide the only possibilities for a solution set for the given problem situation. They must be checked with the specifications of the problem to determine whether or not a solution set has been found.

Example: For what values of x is $\sqrt{2x - 1} = x - 2$?
If x is assumed to be a real number, then the field properties allow us to pursue the following chain of implications:

$$\sqrt{2x - 1} = x - 2 \to 2x - 1 = (x - 2)^2$$
$$2x - 1 = (x - 2)^2 \to 2x - 1 = x^2 - 4x + 4$$
$$2x - 1 = x^2 - 4x + 4 \to 0 = x^2 - 6x + 5$$
$$0 = x^2 - 6x + 5 \to 0 = (x - 5)(x - 1)$$
$$0 = (x - 5)(x - 1) \to x = 5 \text{ or } 1$$

The conclusion reached is that if $\sqrt{2x - 1} = x - 2$, then x must equal either 5 or 1. These values substituted in the original equation render these results:

For $x = 5$	For $x = 1$
$\sqrt{2(5) - 1} = 5 - 2$	$\sqrt{2(1) - 1} = 1 - 2$
or	or
$3 = 3$	$1 = -1$

Thus $x = 1$ is seen *not* to be a solution, but $x = 5$ is a solution.

Types of problem-solving difficulties The difficulties which confront an individual attempting to solve a given problem may be grouped into four distinct types: *comprehension, structure, operation,* and *judgment.* Any effective program designed to assist individuals in acquiring facility in problem solving must provide techniques for discovering such difficulties, instructional procedures for removing them, diagnostic measures for determining the effectiveness of the instructional program, and a carefully designed remedial program for those individuals who require more than a normal pattern of developmental instruction.

Comprehension difficulties. Is there clear comprehension of just what the problem is? When the answer to this question is no, the source of the difficulty usually can be traced to inadequate vocabulary, poor reading habits, inability to interpret phrases or sentences, inability to determine what the unknown is, inability to detect suggestions or leads, inability to ferret out implied questions, inability to rephrase or summarize significant statements, or inability to sense pertinent implications.

A good dictionary, encyclopedia, or other source of reliable information can be used to clear up difficulties of understanding and aid in making proper interpretations. Students need to learn to use and rely upon such source materials as well as to develop patterns of individual research. Another means of getting at the clear comprehension of a problem is through the requirement that the essential context of the problem be described in one's own words. Even after there is clear understanding of the language of the problem there remain certain basic questions hidden in, but implied by, the phraseology used. Furthermore, the identification of the unknown element, or elements, can be rather subtle and involved. Experimentation has revealed that this is one of the real trouble spots in problem solving. Along with this difficulty there is the closely allied difficulty of not being able to identify and describe basic relationships. Finally, one of the most stubborn and perplexing of all difficulties which confound efforts at problem solving is that of not being able to detect and comprehend the nature of the implications of the given information. A hidden question which is present at least once, and frequently many times, in any problem situation is: What statements, or relationships, involving data and unknown must be necessarily true if the statements of the problem are accepted as true? There must be constant emphasis on slow, careful, and critical reading. Students must be taught to phrase questions that are pertinent to the thought content of a given problem and then seek their answers. They must have recurring experience in the analysis of various problem patterns and practice in rephrasing a problem in their own words. Finally, the nature and significance of reasoning by implication must be continually analyzed and underscored. The deductive process cannot be overemphasized as an important tool in problem solving.

Structure difficulties. Is there ability to structure the solving process? The instructional path to an affirmative answer to this question is obstructed by many obstacles and complications. The techniques of intuition, induction, and deduction all come into prominent play. The more adept one is in the use of these instruments of critical thinking, the more efficiently he can proceed toward the successful solution of any given problem. The tendency to react in a noncritical fashion to the story told by the words of the problem is accompanied by a failure to distinguish between essential and nonessential data as well as failure to recognize absence of critical information. Furthermore, any such lackadaisical attitude toward the challenge of a problem situation can result only in the failure to recognize basic relationships, hidden questions, and significant implications. Some of the most important attributes of proficient problem solving are: careful and critical reading habits, analytical insight, good study techniques, systematic procedure, and persistent effort.

An instructional program designed to help one overcome troublesome structural difficulties in problem solving must give emphasis to: selection and evaluation of data; detection of basic relationships, pertinent formulas, hidden questions, and significant implications; intuitive and inductive thought processes leading to the use of analogy and specialization as aids in interpreting the problem situation; the characteristic properties and basic functions of the fundamental operations; the significance of symbolism and techniques for translating from the English sentence to appropriate symbols and vice versa; the value of educated guesses as contrasted with the detrimental effect of haphazard guesses; the importance of good study habits, persistent effort, systematic procedure, and neatness in recording or presenting derived results. Some teaching aids which may be effective in implementing such a program are:

1. Direct attention to the selection of appropriate data by such questions as: What is given? What are you required to find? Is any additional information needed? What do you need to know in order to be able to answer the questions raised? Why do you need to use certain data and not use other data?
2. Draw and label pertinent diagrams.
3. Emphasize the function and characteristics of each of the fundamental operations as an aid in determining which need to be used.
4. Supply sets of data and have students construct verbal problems for the class to solve.
5. Use simpler problems of the same basic structure as the given problem.

This is a tremendous assignment, but it must be recognized and accepted as a major instructional responsibility. The ability to determine the basic structure of a problem situation so that its significant elements may be carefully delineated and then formulated into an intelligent solution pattern is one of the major trouble spots in the study of mathematics.

Operation difficulties. Once a problem is structured properly there arises the very natural question: Is there ability to use effectively the fundamental operations necessary to arrive at a solution? Where there is lack of this ability it probably can be traced to inadequate comprehension of fundamental principles, unfamiliarity with the full implications of the basic algorisms and formulas, or just plain carelessness. By the time one is ready to undertake the solving of verbal problems he should have established a ready proficiency in the computational procedures which are to serve as the tools necessary to arrive at the solution. This implies a basic understanding of the significance of place value in the structure of our numerals and a clear comprehension of the implications of the fundamental properties of association, commutation, and distribution as they apply to and govern the operations of addition and multiplication. Furthermore, there should be a clear concept of what is meant when subtraction is referred to as the inverse operation to addition and division as the inverse operation to multiplication. Addition and multiplication must be understood as the operations to be used when sets of objects are to be combined. Subtraction and division, the inverse operations, thus provide the techniques for separating or comparing. It must be recognized that these controls over the operations continue when the operations are extended by definition from the natural numbers to the integers, to the rational numbers, to the real numbers, and finally to the complex numbers. The algorisms, which we use as a means to increase proficiency in the fundamental operations, have a long history of gradual development. Their present forms have evolved out of a struggle to capitalize on the simplifying potential of place value. This should be emphasized in any instructional program directed toward imparting computational facility. The formula, graph, and equation also play a very important role in problem solving in elementary mathematics. They give clear expression to implied relationships, thus enabling one to concentrate on the essential elements of the problem situation. Their importance should be emphasized constantly.

To combat the threat of carelessness there can hardly be an overemphasis on systematic effort and neat production. These are also good study disciplines.

Judgment difficulties. Is there ability to determine whether an obtained solution is correct? Is there ability to interpret an obtained solution? Once a result has been obtained there is, entirely too frequently, the tendency to enjoy a feeling of complacency that a solution has been found and the task has been completed. Unfortunately, this is not necessarily the situation. It is quite possible that the implications of the solving process have merely produced a result that, of necessity, must be the solution *if* the problem has a solution. There is a question which needs to be raised and its answer sought very carefully, namely: Is the obtained result a solution? Unfortunately, it is too often the case that students fail to recognize a clear-cut distinction between necessary and sufficient conditions in a given problem situation. As a consequence there is failure to realize the need for checking any obtained result in the given problem situation to see whether it is sufficient as a solution. This, of course, emphasizes the need for recognizing what constitutes a valid check as well as for knowing effective techniques for establishing a check.

The instructional program should place constant emphasis on the distinction in the significance of necessary and sufficient conditions, the need for careful checks in the original statement of the problem of all obtained results, the importance of making careful estimates, and the nature and significance of physical and operational restrictions implied in the original data.

Example: A concrete walk is to be laid around a circular flower bed whose radius is 9 feet. What is to be the width of the walk if its area will be 63π square feet?

$$\begin{aligned}(9 + x)^2\pi - 81\pi &= 63\pi \\ (9 + x)^2 - 81 &= 63 \\ x^2 + 18x - 63 &= 0 \\ (x + 21)(x - 3) &= 0 \\ x &= 3 \text{ or } -21\end{aligned}$$

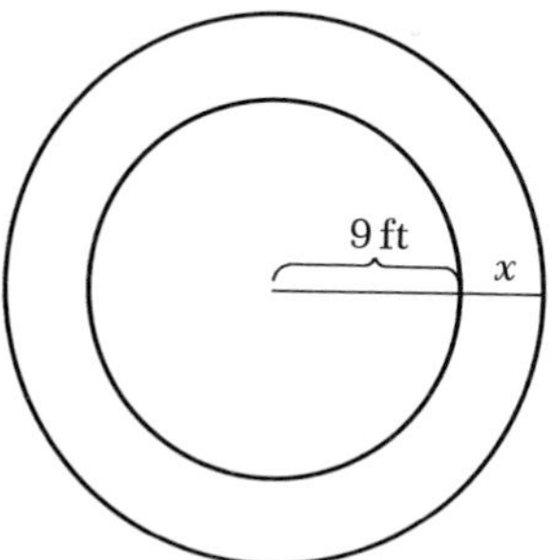

Figure 14-7

The conditions of the equation imply that if there is a value of x which is a solution, then it must be either 3 or -21. Since x represents a measure, the width of the walk, it cannot have a negative value. For this reason -21 is a necessary condition but *not* a sufficient condition for the physical specifications of the problem. On the other hand, 3 is not only a necessary condition, it is a sufficient condition. Therefore, the width of the walk is 3 feet.

The following suggestions, while neither a panacea nor a guarantee of success, will probably be helpful to students as a check list to use as a guide when attacking verbal problems.

1. Read the problem carefully and consider all the elements either expressed or implied. Assign letters or symbols to represent all elements which are unknown.

2. If possible, make a diagrammatic sketch representing the elements and the relationships in the problem.
3. Try to find some element which remains quantitatively unchanged throughout the problem, or for which two separate expressions can be obtained to make the basic equation.
4. Write this basic equation in words.
5. Translate the basic equation into algebraic language, using the data given or implied in the statement of the problem. It will probably be helpful in this connection to tabulate the pertinent data.
6. Solve the equation.
7. Check your solution *in the original problem.*
8. Be patient and painstaking. Do not become discouraged.
9. Use particular care to make your written work neat and orderly.
10. In problem situations that are not too involved, it is frequently desirable to make rough estimates of the answers before attempting to solve the problems.

Selection of verbal problems It is generally felt that one serious limitation to the effectiveness of the work with verbal problems is that so many of the customary problems are outside the range of the students' ordinary experiences and therefore do not seem real to the students. It has often been said, and with entire truth, that many of the problems are artificial; that they lack reality because the students may feel no need for solving such problems by algebraic methods. The familiar clock problems are good examples of this. Why should anybody want to know the time between three and four o'clock when the hands of a clock will be together? And, if one *should* want to know this, could he not find it out more easily by the practical method of actually turning the hands of his watch to the desired position?

Or again, take such a problem as this: Mary is half as old as Susan. In 8 years Mary will be three-fourths as old as Susan. How old is each girl now? Obviously, if this were an actual situation, one would have to know the ages of the two girls before he could set up the problem, and the problem could not conceivably have any personal interest or practical importance to anyone except the acquaintances of the two girls, who probably would already know the ages.

Many teachers and writers are greatly concerned about this admitted lack of reality, genuineness, and practical importance in much of our verbal problem material. There is evidence, however, that this is not the sole criterion of student interest. As a matter of fact, many problems that are of the sheer puzzle type and without any practical importance whatever have been found to be highly interesting to students. On the other hand, some problems which contain elements of reality fail to elicit much student interest.

Teachers should be primarily concerned with developing in their students a right attitude toward solving verbal problems. It is a mistake to try to give the impression that all verbal problems are practical or that the whole benefit to be derived from their study lies in their usefulness. There seems to be little justification for "dressing up" essentially unreal problems to give them a superficial semblance of reality. There is certainly nothing psychologically wrong nor pedagogically unjustified in the frank admission that some problem material is designed primarily for practice in the intricacies of problem solving rather than for practicality of appeal. Such problem material can be used in such a way as to present a real challenge for significant learning to the student. It is in the soil of such challenge that the seeds of motivation to excellent performance can be sown.

Nevertheless, it will be generally conceded that, other things being equal, problems that lie within the experiences of the pupils and exhibit genuine reality and practicality are more desirable than those which lack these characteristics. The criticism of much of the problem material on this score is a valid one. Teachers and textbook writers have not been oblivious to the shortcomings of the textbooks in this respect, and in recent years serious efforts have been made to improve the situation. Some progress has been made. However, problems which are genuinely real and practical, and which at the same time are within the comprehension and experience of young students and which also submit themselves to elementary algebraic analysis, appear to be very scarce. Teachers should be always on the alert to detect, select, or create such problems to supplement those found in the textbooks.

Special products and factoring The amount of time and effort justified for the study of special products and factoring in the beginning algebra course is somewhat limited. The uses of factoring are mainly confined to work with fractions and to the solution of certain equations, and the uses of special products are mainly in the direction of facilitating factoring. The equations and fractions suitable to the first course are relatively simple, and the difficulty of the factoring and the special products studied should be in keeping with the difficulty and the requirements of these applications. The work in factoring should be confined to expressions involving a common factor, the difference of two squares, the square of a binomial, or the quadratic polynomial in the simple form $x^2 + px + q$ and also in the more general form $ax^2 + bx + c$, with $a \neq 1$. Consequently, the work in special products should include the product of a binomial by a monomial, the product of the sum and difference of two terms, the square of the sum or difference of two terms, and the product of two binomials of the form $(x + a)(x + b)$ or, more generally, of the form $(ax + b)(cx + d)$. In all this work positive and concentrated effort should be directed toward having the student become consciously aware of the fundamental role played by the field properties of associativity, commutativity, and distributivity in all problems of multiplication or factorization of polynomials.

So far as the special products themselves are concerned, the aim is to enable one to save time by writing the products down without going through the details of multiplication. So far as their use in factoring is concerned, the aim is to suggest the factors and enable one to write them down without the need of going through the details of trying and checking. The attainment of either of these aims is conditioned primarily upon the following considerations:

1. Knowledge of the type forms of the products to which the various special sets of factors (in type form) give rise
2. Knowledge of the type forms of the factors to which the various sets of special products (in type form) give rise
3. Ability to identify a particular pair of factors as belonging to a particular type and as giving a type product of a particular form
4. Ability to identify a particular product as belonging to a particular type and as having factors of a particular form
5. Ability to identify each element in a special given factor or product with the corresponding element in the type form to which it belongs, and to make the appropriate substitutions

Thus the two fundamental requisites are knowledge of the type forms of the various special kinds of factors and their associated products and ability to recognize, identify, and associate particular cases and particular elements with the general types to which they belong or with the corresponding elements therein. Consequently, the two foremost pedagogical questions are: How can the student most effectively be brought to know these type forms, and how may he best become able to identify expressions in particular problems with the special types to which they belong?

Geometrical and arithmetical illustrations will help to rationalize all these type forms and will provide a basis by which the student can easily reconstruct them. For example, consider the factorization of the difference of two squares:

$$a^2 - b^2 = (a + b)(a - b)$$

The geometric illustration, Figure 14-8, shows clearly why the area represented by the product $(a + b)(a - b)$ is the same area as that represented by $a^2 - b^2$.

Now suppose a is 7 and b is 2. Then $a^2 - b^2 = 49 - 4 = 45$. But $a + b = 9$ and $a - b = 5$, and $(9)(5) = 45$. Thus we may also illustrate arithmetically the fact that $a^2 - b^2 = (a + b)(a - b)$. The other type forms may easily be illustrated in similar fashion.

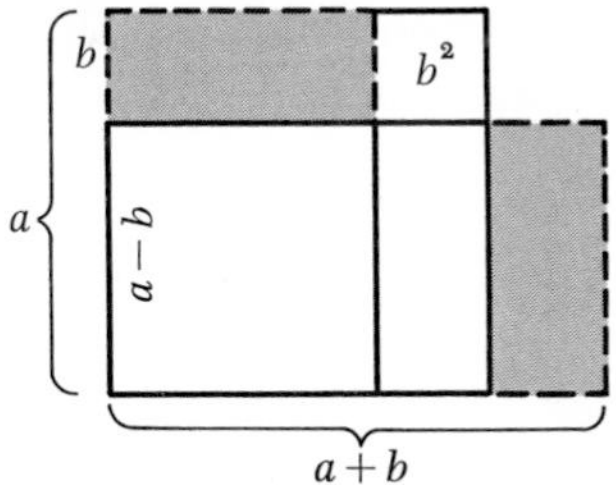

Figure 14-8

To be of much use, the type forms must be learned thoroughly. They must be understood, and they must also be memorized. This means that the students must be shown in the beginning that the type forms either result from or are verified by actual multiplication. But it also means that in addition to this the students must have sufficient practice and drill upon these type forms to make the forms themselves become indelibly fixed in their minds.

This drill, however, should not be mere mechanical repetition. It should be made meaningful through constant illustration and application to specific examples involving both literal and numerical terms. The students should be kept conscious at all times that their principal job in connection with either writing special products or factoring expressions is to *recognize* each problem as being a special case of one or another of the types which they have learned, to *identify* it with the type to which it belongs, and to make the appropriate substitutions of corresponding terms. Incidentally, this matter of identification and substitution of corresponding terms is one whose difficulties sometimes are not recognized by the teacher, although it actually constitutes the very crux of the difficulties which many students encounter. At no point is special attention more needed, and no point seems to be more neglected than this. There is no better way of ensuring real mastery of special products and factors than to give a well-organized special series of practice exercises on term-by-term identification and substitution.[8]

A topical study of special products and factors is a necessary but not a sufficient condition for permanent mastery. The applications which arise normally in connection with subsequent parts of the course are not in themselves sufficient to ensure continuation of satisfactory mastery even after it has been attained. If the skills are to be maintained, there should be a systematic program of subsequent drills spaced at suitable intervals throughout the remaining part of the course.

Exponents, powers, and roots of numbers Students will generally have little difficulty in performing operations involving exponents if they understand clearly the meaning of exponents. That so many students make mistakes in these operations is doubtless due to the fact that the laws which govern the operations are too often developed hurriedly and without adequate care to ensure that the meanings are

[8]The reader may well review at this point the discussion of the solution and evaluation of formulas in Chap. 13.

made clear. Results such as the following make it painfully clear that too often work with exponents comes to be a mere meaningless juggling of symbols:

$$a^3 + a^2 = a^5 \qquad (a^2)^3 = a^5 \qquad a^2(b^2) = (ab)^4$$

Such results would be less likely to occur if the concepts of positive integral exponents were adequately developed at the outset, for the laws of operation are simple and inevitable consequences of these concepts.

The meaning of a positive integral exponent is not hard to make clear. The approach is, in fact, suggested in most textbooks through one or two illustrative examples. It is pointed out, for example, that such a product as $(r)(r)(r)$ is written as r^3 for convenience and that the number symbol ^{3}, which is called the exponent in the expression r^3, merely indicates how many times r is to be used as a factor. Then two or three examples are given to illustrate the use of exponents in multiplication and division, the rules are stated, and exercises are given to afford the student opportunity for applying the rules.

The unfortunate thing is that this all seems so familiar and so obvious to the teacher that he is likely to assume that the one or two illustrations offered in the text are sufficient to make the matter equally obvious to the student, which, of course, is not generally the case. Examples of the foregoing type should be given until the students themselves are able to express the results in exponential form, tabulate them, and derive the rules for themselves. When they can do this, they will have the basis for a real understanding of positive integral exponents and of the laws for operating with such exponents. Also, in case they should ever become confused with regard to these rules, they will understand how to take the matter back to original meanings for their analysis of it and to rebuild the laws for themselves. They should, of course, have plenty of practice and drill in using the laws of exponents as such, after their meaning is understood. Above all, they should be trained to examine every problem carefully and to be sure that they understand precisely what is called for before proceeding with their work on it.

Since a positive integral exponent indicates *the number of times* the base is to be used as a factor, it is evident that special meanings will have to be attached to zero, negative, and fractional exponents. We want the meanings to be such that we may operate with the special kinds of exponents under the same laws as those we use for positive integral exponents so that the results of the operations will be consistent in all respects with the results obtained by using positive integral exponents.

Consider the two laws for operating with positive integral exponents:

Law 1 $\qquad a^m \times a^n = a^{m+n}$
Law 2 $\qquad a^m \div a^n = a^{m-n}$

If the use of 0 as an exponent is to be so defined that these laws hold, then it is evident from law 1 that for $a \neq 0$

$$a^0 \times a^n = a^{0+n} = a^n$$

It immediately follows that $a^0 = 1$ is a justified meaning to give to the use of 0 as an exponent.

If a similar substitution is made in law 2, we have for $a \neq 0$

$$a^0 \div a^n = a^{0-n} = a^{-n}$$

But since $a^0 = 1$, this may be written

$$1 \div a^n = a^{-n}$$

Thus it immediately follows that a justified interpretation of a negative exponent is that it indicates the reciprocal of the same nonzero quantity raised to the corresponding positive exponent.

We cannot give meaning to fractional exponents until we define roots of numbers. The students should have gained from their arithmetic some understanding of the meaning of square roots and cube roots of numbers and of the symbols $\sqrt{\ }$ and $\sqrt[3]{\ }$. It is best, however, not to assume too much on this point. The square root of a number should be explicitly redefined as one of its two equal factors, the cube root as one of its three equal factors, etc., and the appropriate symbols should be carefully reassociated with their respective meanings.

A real problem, which frequently causes trouble at this point, is that of the proper interpretation of the radical symbols. Athough there are two square roots of a number, the symbol $\sqrt{\ }$ represents only the positive square root. For example, $\sqrt{16} = 4$. Only the symbol $\pm\sqrt{16}$ can represent both square roots, ± 4. Similarly, there exist n nth roots of any number, and the symbol $\sqrt[n]{\ }$ refers only to one such root, called the *principal* n*th root* in accordance with the definition.

Definition: For x any real number and n an integer greater than 1 the principal nth root of x^n is $\sqrt[n]{x^n}$, where

1. For n even: $\begin{cases} \sqrt[n]{x^n} = x \text{ if } x \geq 0 \\ \sqrt[n]{x^n} = -x \text{ if } x < 0 \end{cases}$

2. For n odd: $\sqrt[n]{x^n} = x$

Example: $\sqrt{3^2} = 3 \qquad \sqrt{(-3)^2} = -(-3) = 3 \qquad \sqrt[4]{0^4} = 0$

$\sqrt[3]{(-2)^3} = -2 \qquad \sqrt[3]{2^3} = 2$

From the definition of square root, $(\sqrt{y})(\sqrt{y}) = y$. Also if there were a number represented by the symbol $y^{1/2}$ and if it were subject to the laws of multiplication by exponents, then we should have $(y^{1/2})(y^{1/2}) = y^1 = y$. Now since $\sqrt{y}$ is one of two equal positive factors whose product is y, and since $y^{1/2}$ may also represent one of two equal positive factors whose product is y, we may reasonably agree to think of $y^{1/2}$ and $\sqrt{y}$ as representing the same number. In other words, we may reasonably agree that $y^{1/2}$ shall have the same meaning as $\sqrt{y}$. Similarly, the corresponding meanings may be attached to such expressions as $y^{1/3}, y^{1/4}, y^{1/5}$, etc.

In accordance with these definitions $(x^n)^{1/n}$ may be used, synonymously with $\sqrt[n]{x^n}$, to represent the principal nth root of x^n. Thus $(3^2)^{1/2} = 3$, $[(-3)^2]^{1/2} = -(-3) = 3$, $(2^3)^{1/3} = 2$, and $[(-2)^3]^{1/3} = -2$.

Since these meanings have been arrived at by defining these fractional exponents in such a way that they will be subject to the laws of operation formulated for positive integral exponents, we may now apply those laws in such cases as $(y^{1/3})(y^{1/3})$. This obviously gives $y^{(1/3+1/3)}$, or $y^{2/3}$. It is equally clear that we have here $(y^{1/3})^2$. It is also clear that $(y^2)^{1/3}$ would give the same result, since $(y^2)^{1/3} = y^{2(1/3)} = y^{2/3}$.

By using numerous illustrative examples, carefully selected and arranged to bring out these analogies and identities, the students can be brought to understand what fractional exponents represent. It is well to have them tabulate the different forms of writing such expressions as

$y^{2/3}$	$(y^{1/3})^2$	$(\sqrt[3]{y})^2$	$(y^2)^{1/3}$	$\sqrt[3]{y^2}$
$x^{3/4}$	$(x^{1/4})^3$	$(\sqrt[4]{x})^3$	$(x^3)^{1/4}$	$\sqrt[4]{x^3}$
. . . . .	. . . . .	. . . . .	. . . . .	. . . . .
$x^{p/r}$	$(x^{1/r})^p$	$(\sqrt[r]{x})^p$	$(x^p)^{1/r}$	$\sqrt[r]{x^p}$
. . . . .	. . . . .	. . . . .	. . . . .	. . . . .

The careful comparison of the tabulated results of such equivalent forms will lead to a real understanding and generalization of the meaning of fractional exponents. In many cases the students themselves will be able to formulate the general relation that $x^{p/r}$ means the pth power of the principal rth root of x, or the principal rth root of the pth power of x. Numerical examples are helpful in making this meaning clear. A considerable amount of practice of the drill type should be given in order to fix the meanings and the identities of the equivalent forms firmly in the minds of the students.

Having now developed meanings and consistent general laws for exponents which may be either positive, negative, or zero and either integral or fractional, it is clear that these laws may now be extended and made applicable to literal exponents as well, since these represent numbers of one or another of the kinds just mentioned. While the students will have little occasion to use fractional or literal exponents in the first course in algebra, the teacher should have a clear concept of the organic and definitive nature of the progressive generalization of the laws to cover all kinds of exponents.

The use of parentheses In connection with the use of parentheses the principal aims should be to have the students acquire (1) a clear understanding of the meaning of parentheses, (2) the ability to interpret correctly mathematical expressions in which parentheses are used, (3) the ability to employ parentheses correctly in situations where they are necessary or helpful, and (4) the ability to transform expressions involving parentheses into equivalent expressions which do not contain parentheses.

It is questionable whether a topical study of parentheses is either necessary or desirable, although most textbooks in beginning algebra do offer such a treatment. Much of the difficulty which students experience in the use of parentheses in algebra is probably due to the formal way in which the subject is presented to them. If they can be taught to think of parentheses simply as a symbol which indicates that the terms enclosed therein are to be regarded all together as one quantity, much, if not most, of the difficulty will disappear. Such a concept will enable the student to make his own analysis of every operation affecting or affected by the parenthetical quantity without the need of having special rules.

The most troublesome cases probably are those involving the "removal of parentheses" containing expressions of two or more terms. Special rules for the removal are generally given, often without adequate explanation. Hence students tend to look upon the removal of parentheses in such cases as a mechanical, rather than a rational, process. There follows a natural tendency to perform the operations with little or no thought of their meaning.

To correct this situation, it is suggested that the students' attention be focused upon the idea of writing an equivalent expression without parentheses rather than upon the removal of the parentheses and that the latter expression be completely discarded. Such a case as $3x - 4y + 11 - (2x + 3y - 5)$ will then become merely a problem in rewriting. It is apparent that each term must be rewritten with due regard to its sign, and since the entire expression $2x + 3y - 5$ is to be subtracted from the foregoing terms, it is apparent that this means that each of its terms must be subtracted individually. Hence we write $3x - 4y + 11$ and then proceed to subtract, in turn, the terms $2x$, $3y$, and -5. This procedure obviously gives

$$3x - 4y + 11 - (2x) - (3y) - (-5)$$

or $3x - 4y + 11 - 2x - 3y + 5$, which upon collecting terms gives $x - 7y + 16$ as the net result. Thus the expression has been rewritten without parentheses, and it has been accomplished without any special rule for the removal of the parentheses. The whole operation thus becomes one based upon understanding rather than merely upon the authority of an arbitrary rule.

It is probable that a freer and more systematic use of parentheses in such matters as the evaluation of formulas, the solution of literal and fractional equations, the addition of fractions, and various other algebraic operations would do much to prevent mistakes and clarify the meaning and emphasize the usefulness of parentheses. The foregoing illustration is a case in point. Some mention of this has been made in certain sections of this and the preceding chapter, but for emphasis two additional illustrations will be given here.

1. Given the formula for the sides of a right triangle $h^2 = a^2 + b^2$, let it be required to find the value of h in terms of a and b. Many students will thoughtlessly write, "Since $h^2 = a^2 + b^2$, therefore

$$\sqrt{h^2} = \sqrt{a^2} + \sqrt{b^2}, \qquad \text{or} \qquad h = a + b."$$

The square root is taken of the separate terms of the right member of the equation rather than the right member as a whole. The fact that here $a^2 + b^2$ must be treated as a single quantity could easily be emphasized by writing the equation in the form $h^2 = (a^2 + b^2)$.

2. Given the formula for the volume of a right circular cylinder $V = \pi r^2 h$, let it be required to find the volume of a particular cylinder by using the values $\pi = 3.14$, $r = 1.7$, and $h = 5.5$. The following is not an exaggerated illustration of the careless way in which many students put down their written work for the evaluation of such a formula:

$$\begin{array}{l} \quad\ 3.14 \quad 1.7 \quad 5.5 \\ V = \not\pi \quad \not r^2 \quad \not h = \cdots \end{array}$$

Such carelessness in writing is responsible for many arithmetical mistakes. If the students were trained to write out such a form as the following for the evaluation before substituting the numerical values, there would be much less likelihood of mistakes occurring either in the substitution or the subsequent evaluation.

$$\begin{aligned} V &= \pi \cdot r^2 \cdot h \\ &= (\quad)(\quad)^2(\quad) \\ &= (3.14)(1.7)^2(5.5) \\ &= \ldots\ldots\ldots\ldots \end{aligned}$$

Illustrative Tabular Analysis of a Teaching Problem

Radicals and radical equations

I. What background may the students be expected to have with reference to this topic?
  A. Use of radical sign and index to indicate square roots and cube roots of numbers, including proper use in indicating principal roots
  B. Meaning of literal symbols
  C. Meaning and laws of positive integral exponents
  D. Finding square roots and some cube roots, squares and cubes of numbers

II. What are the particular understandings and abilities which the student should acquire or strengthen through his study of this topic?
  A. Things to know:
    1. The precise meaning to be associated with a radical
    2. The precise meaning of rational and irrational numbers
    3. The precise meaning of similar radicals
    4. The fact that in general only similar radicals may be combined by addition or subtraction
    5. The precise conditions under which a radical is said to be in its simplest form
    6. The fact that $\sqrt[n]{a \cdot b} \equiv \sqrt[n]{a} \cdot \sqrt[n]{b}$, and conversely*
    7. The fact that $\sqrt[n]{a/b} \equiv \sqrt[n]{a}/\sqrt[n]{b}$, and conversely*
    8. The fact that in general $\sqrt[n]{a} \pm \sqrt[n]{b} \neq \sqrt[n]{a \pm b}$*
    9. The principles which underlie the solution of radical equations
    10. The meaning of extraneous roots and the necessity as well as the method of guarding against them in the solution of radical equations
  B. Things to be able to do:
    1. To combine similar radicals by addition or subtraction
    2. To change radical expressions of the forms $\sqrt[n]{a \cdot b}$ and $\sqrt[n]{x/y}$ into the equivalent forms $\sqrt[n]{a} \cdot \sqrt[n]{b}$ and $\sqrt[n]{x}/\sqrt[n]{y}$ (and conversely) with assurance and facility
    3. To "simplify" radicals readily
    4. To change radicals with different indices to similar radicals when possible so that they may be combined by addition or subtraction
    5. To solve radical equations
    6. To check the solution of radical equations and detect and discard extraneous roots

III. What activities or procedures will most effectively enable the student to gain these desired understandings and abilities?

Each of the foregoing items should be subjected to a careful individual analysis before teaching. In general, careful explanations by the teacher should be freely illustrated by numerical examples and accompanied by questions and discussion in which both the teacher and the students participate. Understanding should be followed by

*The exceptions to these properties need not be considered here.

supervised practice or drill on the skills listed under II*B*. The drill should be specific but with examples sufficiently varied to foster generalization and give the students a feeling of assurance in identifying meanings and recognizing appropriate procedures. Subsequent diagnostic testing and remedial instruction will probably be needed.

IV. What special difficulties may the students be expected to encounter in acquiring the desired understandings and skills?
   A. Learning to simplify radicals such as $\sqrt{54}$ or $\sqrt{3x^3y}$
   B. Learning to simplify fractional radicals such as $\sqrt{a/b}$
   C. Combining radicals which are not given as similar radicals (e.g., $\sqrt{27} + \sqrt{48}$). Instead of reducing these to similar radicals and then combining, some students are likely to say $\sqrt{27} + \sqrt{48} = \sqrt{75}$
   D. Failing to check solutions of radical equations in the original equations

V. What specific suggestions, devices, and procedures will be most likely to help the student overcome these difficulties and avoid these mistakes?

The particular shortcomings listed under IV give rise to mistakes which may be traced to inadequate understanding of the principles involved and to lack of experience in using these principles. Doubtlessly the principles will have to be re-explained and discussed and the procedures will have to be re-illustrated, perhaps several times. Each new discussion should aim to produce more complete and specific understanding and should be followed by specific and carefully supervised practice.

Considerable difficulty may be avoided if the students are taught to *write out in detail all the steps in the operations*, as follows:

$$\sqrt{54} = \sqrt{9 \cdot 6} = \sqrt{9} \cdot \sqrt{6} = 3\sqrt{6}$$

$$\sqrt{3x^3y} = \sqrt{x^2(3xy)} = \sqrt{x^2} \cdot \sqrt{3xy} = x\sqrt{3xy}$$

$$\sqrt{a/b} = \sqrt{ab/b^2} = \sqrt{ab}/\sqrt{b^2} = \sqrt{ab}/b$$

$$\sqrt{27} + \sqrt{48} = \sqrt{9 \cdot 3} + \sqrt{16 \cdot 3} = \sqrt{9} \cdot \sqrt{3} + \sqrt{16} \cdot \sqrt{3}$$

$$= 3\sqrt{3} + 4\sqrt{3} = 7\sqrt{3}$$

Students often object to this detailed writing out of all the steps because they feel it slows up their work. As a matter of fact, however, it really has the opposite effect by materially decreasing the number of mistakes. More important still, it is the best possible guarantee that the students will fully understand what they are doing and why they are doing it.

The foregoing section is illustrative of a pattern of analysis which can be made by any teacher with reference to any topic of algebra. The making of such an analysis serves several useful purposes. It forces the teacher to a consideration of relative values in planning the various parts of his work. This enables him more effectively to disregard nonessentials and build his teaching with appropriate emphases toward the attainment of the really significant outcomes. Again, it gives the teacher a more complete and organic view of the whole topic and enables him to see the various important elements in their relation to each other and to the whole. This makes for freedom, clarity, interest, and effectiveness in the developmental work. Finally, it calls his attention to the specific danger points which are, after all, the critical points in teaching. It forces the careful analysis of every individual concept and process to be taught from the standpoints of anticipating inherent difficulties, tracing them to their specific causes, and then determining specific means for preventing or overcoming them. It will become increasingly valuable if it is revised from year to year in the light of students' mistakes in oral and written work.

No such analysis will ever be complete or perfect, because there will always be unpredictable factors. But every such analysis will be helpful in motivating the work and making it more efficient and effective through the judicious selection and organization of subject matter, the considered allocation of emphasis, and the selection of procedures and devices specifically designed to produce optimum understanding and mastery and to avoid, minimize, or correct specific misunderstandings or mistakes.

Provision for superior students As in arithmetic, algebra classes must be conducted as classes, and the main body of the subject matter must be studied by all the students. Therefore, that which is to be considered as the required subject matter must be kept within the intellectual reach of practically all the students. Apart from the general developmental discussions, teachers tend to spend more time and effort in helping the poorer students come up to an acceptable level of attainment than in planning ways to help the superior students and the occasional very exceptional student develop their talents to greatest advantage. This is entirely understandable, because the need of the poor students appears the more obvious and more immediately urgent of the two, and it is also the easier to try to satisfy. Appropriate provision for the superior students, and especially for the unusually talented students, cannot ordinarily be made on the spur of the moment, and heavy teaching loads usually leave the teacher little time for the special study and planning that would be required.

This issue is too important to be neglected or ignored, however, and ways need to be found to facilitate the efforts of teachers in this direction. In Norton's view:[9]

[9]Monte S. Norton, Enrichment as a Provision for the Gifted in Mathematics, *School Science and Mathematics*, **57** (1957), 339–345.

> Many of the people involved with the current problem of providing for the gifted pupil in mathematics appear to be in need of specific suggestions for providing for the gifted pupils in their charge: techniques, devices, activities, and other experiences that have been successfully administered and have produced successful results.

In the article from which this quotation was taken the reader will find a considerable number and variety of such specific suggestions under the following headings:

1. Reading and writing activities
2. Individual and group projects in mathematics
3. Additional exercises and supplementary problems
4. Building vocabulary in mathematics
5. Applications of mathematics
6. Mathematical assemblies
7. Mathematical clubs and organizations

The article also contains a list of 15 specific avenues for enrichment of the student's work. These suggestions, however, are not slanted explicitly toward any particular course or grade.

With particular reference to elementary algebra some provision can be made in several ways:

1. Superior students who have completed the regular assignments may be permitted to work ahead of the class on advance assignments. Often this appears to be the easiest way to meet the situation, but eventually it can give rise to serious problems of instruction and management.

2. Superior students who have completed the regular assignments may be given additional and more difficult problems related to the same topic or unit that the class is currently studying. Unless such supplementary work is provided in the basic textbook, the teacher will need to plan the assignments. Review or "refresher" books or more advanced textbooks in algebra can often be used to economize time in this. The plan may make considerable initial demands on the teacher's time, but it has the advantage of keeping the class together in the sense that at any time all are working on the same topic or unit.

3. Superior students who have completed an assignment chapter or unit ahead of schedule may be permitted to study (perhaps in small discussion groups where it is feasible) extensions or variations of the work of that unit. This requires that other texts or reference books be easily accessible. An interesting variant of this is to have these students critically examine the presentation of this unit in several elementary algebra textbooks and report critical comparisons of the several texts with respect to this unit. Most better-than-average students will respond well to such an assignment. It seems to capture their interest, and the comparisons necessarily elicit the best kind of

good, well-motivated study with consequent broadening and reinforcement of their mastery of the unit.

Since about the same major topics or units are presented in nearly all elementary algebra texts, this type of activity could be carried on with respect to practically any unit or chapter. Individual or group written reports could be required and made to the teacher on each unit studied in this way, and these reports should form a basis for student-teacher or group-teacher discussion. These reports may provide the teacher with helpful cues to what the students consider the more effective ways of presenting the details of the unit. Thus they could help the teacher improve his instruction and they might eventually be helpful in the reappraisal or selection of a basic textbook for the class in subsequent years.

4. The extremely talented and interested student will probably be helped most by permitting him to select some topic or area which he would like to investigate extensively and independently, providing him with suitable materials in the way of reference books, and getting him started at his undertaking. He should be permitted to work on his special study only after he has done the work currently assigned to the class, because sometimes brilliant students are so impatient to get to the superstructure that they will slight the routine necessary to lay a proper groundwork. His study might extend over a semester or even a year. He would need to have some guidance and supervision, and to this end he should be required to make progress reports at designated intervals. Eventually he should be held responsible for both a written and an oral report on his work. The written report would be supervised by the teacher, and the oral report would be made to a group of perhaps one or more teachers and some of the outstanding students in his own or more advanced classes in algebra.[10]

[10]For a discussion of this topic see Howard F. Fehr, Mathematics for the Gifted, *Bulletin of the National Association of Secondary-School Principals*, **38** (1954), 103–110.

EXERCISES

1. Make a careful large-scale graphic solution of the system of equations $2a + 5b = 29/4$ and $7a - b = 9/4$. Consider the domain of each of the variables a and b to be the set of real numbers. Explain your work, estimate the solution as nearly as you can from the graph, and tell what the numerical values represent. Check your solution by substituting the values of a and b in both equations.

2. Consider the two relations $x + y \geqq 2$ and $2x + y = 4$ with the domains of both x and y the set of integers such that $-3 \leqq x \leqq +4$ and $-2 \leqq y \leqq +5$.
   a. Draw the graph of each relation.
   b. What is the solution set when the two relations are considered simultaneously?
   c. What is the solution set for the two relations when the "is greater than" (>) is removed from $x + y \geqq 2$?

3. Rework all parts of exercise 2, but this time let the domains of both x and y be the set of all real numbers.

4. Consider the following problem: The length of a rectangle is 2 inches less than twice its width, and its perimeter is 20 inches. What are its dimensions? Solve this problem by using just one equation in one unknown. Then solve it by using two equations in two unknowns. Show that in the first case you really used two equations in two unknowns but solved one of them mentally.

5. It frequently happens that beginning algebra students who can combine numerical fractions have trouble in performing the same operations with fractions involving literal symbols. What, in your opinion, is the explanation of this?

6. Why is it important that students learn how to factor algebraic expressions before undertaking work with algebraic fractions?

7. In your opinion what are the things that a student must understand in order to take reducible algebraic fractions and reduce them to simpler terms? Give examples to illustrate why these understandings are needed in order to perform this operation intelligently.

8. In the process of reducing a fraction or changing it to higher terms the original value of the fraction must be preserved. Explain why the value of a fraction is changed if the same nonzero number is added to or subtracted from both the numerator and the denominator of the fraction.

9. Point out the potential dangers of using the terms "cancel" and "cancellation" in elementary algebra. Give examples to illustrate.

10. In dividing one fraction by another, the rule "Invert the divisor, then multiply" is generally used. Most students know this rule and know how to use it, but very few can justify it. If a student should ask you why the rule is valid, what explanation would you give him?

11. In explaining to beginning algebra students how to perform the operation $(6n/5) \div 3$, would you teach them to divide the numerator by 3, or would you teach them to regard the divisor as a fraction $^3/_1$ and then use the customary rule for dividing by a fraction? What advantage can you see in the method you prefer?

12. Explain as simply as you can the procedure for converting fractions with unlike denominators into equivalent fractions having the same denominator. Give the reasoning that underlies and justifies the procedure.

13. Make a list of the specific difficulties and kinds of mistakes which students in first-year algebra can be expected to make in combining algebraic fractions by addition or subtraction. Prepare explanations designed to help students overcome these difficulties and avoid these mistakes.

14. If one of your students should write $a/x + 5/(x + 3) = (a + 5)/(2x + 3)$, just what would you do to get him to see his error and understand why it is an error? What would you do to help him understand how to correct his mistake and check his result?

15. In adding fractions it is necessary to preserve the original value of each of the fractions involved. Explain why this is not necessary in solving equations containing fractions. Explain what it is that *must* be preserved in such equations.

16. In this chapter there is a discussion of some important considerations related to teaching the solution of equations containing fractions. Give a clear and connected résumé of this discussion, emphasizing its salient points.

17. How do you account for the fact that students generally have more trouble with verbal problems than with other parts of algebra? Be as specific as you can.

18. Students characteristically have difficulty in reading verbal problems with understanding, interpreting them correctly, and in translating them into the symbolic language of the equation. How serious is the handicap imposed by these shortcomings? What, if anything, can be done about it?

19. Verbal problems usually are solved by solving one or more equations arising from the problems. Explain why, in checking the solutions, it is necessary to check them in the actual statements of the problems and why it is not enough merely to check them against the equations.

20. Rules and formulas of algebra can often be illustrated effectively by numerical examples. For instance, the general relation $a^2 - b^2 = (a - b)(a + b)$ can be illustrated by expressing 21 as $25 - 4$, or as $5^2 + 2^2$, and in turn as $(5 - 2)(5 + 2)$, or $(3)(7)$. Select other algebraic rules and illustrate them in a similar manner. Do you think this practice would serve to clarify the meanings of the rules to the students?

21. Explain in detail how you would make it clear and convincing to a class that the following definitions are consistent with the laws of operation with positive integral exponents:

$$x^{1/3} = \sqrt[3]{x} \qquad x^{-3} = 1/x^3 \qquad x^0 = 1$$

22. Does your explanation of the relations set forth in exercise 21 constitute a proof of these relations, or does it merely define fractional, negative, and zero exponents? Explain.

23. What are the reasons for teaching special products and factoring? Why should they be taught together?

24. What special products and what types of factoring are suitable for the beginning course in algebra? Examine some elementary algebra textbooks and see whether you find included any types of factoring which in your opinion are not suitable for the beginning course.

25. Make up a set of expressions or problems designed to promote understanding and appreciation of the use of parentheses. How important is this? Why? Give illustrations to show how failure to use or interpret the use of parentheses properly may lead to numerical mistakes.

BIBLIOGRAPHY

Beberman, Max, and Bruce E. Meserve: An Exploratory Approach to Solving Equations, *Mathematics Teacher*, **49** (1956), 15–18.

Bellman, Richard: On the Concepts of a Problem and Problem-solving, *American Mathematical Monthly*, **67** (1960), 119–134.

Brown, Claude H.: "The Teaching of Secondary Mathematics" (New York: Harper & Row, Publishers, Inc., 1953), pp. 180–222.

Butler, Charles H.: Home-made Problems for Algebra, *Mathematics Teacher*, **45** (1952), 384–386.

———: A Note on Writing Fractions, *Mathematics Teacher*, **47** (1954), 527.

Clements, C. Robert: Work Problems Made Easy, *Mathematics Teacher*, **48** (1955), 582–585.

Commission on Mathematics: "Concepts of Equation and Inequality" (New York: College Entrance Examination Board, 1958). (Sample classroom unit for high school algebra students.)

———: "Appendices" (New York: College Entrance Examination Board, 1959), pp. 2–7.

Davis, David R.: "The Teaching of Mathematics" (Reading, Mass.: Addison-Wesley Publishing Company, Inc., 1951), pp. 200–209.

Denbow, Carl H.: On the Use of Variators in the Teaching of Algebra, *School Science and Mathematics*, **54** (1954), 65–68.

Fehr, Howard F.: Operations in the Systems of Positive and Negative Numbers and Zero, *Mathematics Teacher*, **42** (1949), 171–176.

Fouch, Robert S.: On the Definability of Zero to the Power Zero, *School Science and Mathematics*, **53** (1953), 693–696.

Fulkerson, Elbert: Teaching Signs in Fractions, *Mathematics Teacher*, **40** (1947), 71–74.

Georges, J. S.: Learning to Solve Problems Intelligently, *School Science and Mathematics*, **56** (1956), 701–707.

Grove, Ethel L., and others: Models for Introducing Special Products, *School Science and Mathematics*, **50** (1950), 662–664.

Hartung, Maurice L., and Robert L. Erickson: Graphical Methods in Science and Mathematics Teaching, *School Science and Mathematics*, **50** (1950), 200–208.

Henderson, K. B., and R. E. Pingry: Problem Solving in Mathematics, *Twenty-first*

Yearbook (Washington, D.C.: National Council of Teachers of Mathematics, 1953), pp. 228–270.

Henderson, Ronald: How I Teach Analysis of Verbal Problems, *Mathematics Teacher*, **47** (1954), 275–276.

Holder, Doyne: Polynomials: Factorable or Non-factorable, *School Science and Mathematics*, **62** (1962), 22–25.

Ingraham, W. W.: The Graphic Solution of a Problem Involving Simple Linear Equations, *Mathematics Teacher*, **38** (1945), 175–176.

Jerbert, A. R.: Division by Zero, *School Science and Mathematics*, **49** (1949), 484–488.

Kocher, Frank T., and Ralph T. Heimer: Techniques of Solving Rational Equations, *Mathematics Teacher*, **56** (1963), 486–489.

Lichtenberg, Don. R., and Marilyn Zweng: Linear Programming Problems for First-year Algebra, *Mathematics Teacher*, **53** (1960), 171–176.

Manheim, Jerome: Word Problems or Problems with Words, *Mathematics Teacher*, **54** (1961), 234–238.

Meighan, John N.: Methods of Solving Elementary Systems of Equations in Two Unknowns, *School Science and Mathematics*, **47** (1947), 709–714.

Merriman, Gaylord M.: Sets and Some Elementary Problems, *Mathematics Teacher*, **53** (1960), 266–269.

Meserve, Bruce E., and Max A. Sobel: "Mathematics for Secondary School Teachers" (Englewood Cliffs, N.J.: Prentice-Hall, Inc., 1962), pp. 77–173.

Miller, G. H.: Difficulties in Algebra: A Study, *School Science and Mathematics*, **58** (1958), 714–720.

"Modern Elementary Algebra" (Chicago: Society for Visual Education, Inc., 1963). (Two sets of filmstrips in color.)

"Modern Mathematics" (New York: McGraw-Hill Book Company, 1963). (Filmstrips on set theory.)

Myers, Sheldon S. (Editor): Applications, *Mathematics Teacher*, **45** (1952), 210–214, 522–524.

Niessen, Abraham M.: The Extension of the Exponent Concept, *School Science and Mathematics*, **48** (1948), 605–610.

O'Brien, Katherine: Problem Solving, *Mathematics Teacher*, **49** (1956), 79–86.

Perisho, Clarence R.: A Non-commutative Algebra, *School Science and Mathematics*, **58** (1958), 727–730.

Reeve, William David: "Mathematics for the Secondary School" (New York: Holt, Rinehart and Winston, Inc., 1954), pp. 245–294.

Rich, Barnett: The Place of the Variable in the Teaching of Mathematics, *Mathematics Teacher*, **48** (1955), 538–541.

Schaaf, William L.: "Basic Concepts of Elementary Mathematics" (New York: John Wiley & Sons, Inc., 1960).

School Mathematics Study Group: "Elementary Functions" (New Haven, Conn.: Yale University Press, 1960).

______: "Intermediate Mathematics" (New Haven, Conn.: Yale University Press, 1959).

______: "First Course in Algebra" (New Haven, Conn.: Yale University Press, 1960).

Singleton, Marilyn C.: An Approach to Solving Word Problems, *Mathematics Teacher*, **51** (1958), 212–213.

Torreyson, Homer O.: Equation Balances, *School Science and Mathematics*, **55** (1955), 104–108.

Tucker, A. N.: On the Meaning, Use, and Importance of Zero, *School Science and Mathematics*, **52** (1952), 443–444.

Vavoulis, Alex: Teaching the Linear Equation in Intermediate Algebra, *School Science and Mathematics*, **62** (1962), 261–263.

Webber, G. Cuthbert, and John A. Brown: "Basic Concepts of Mathematics" (Reading, Mass.: Addison-Wesley Publishing Company, Inc., 1963).

Winthrop, Henry: The Structure of Simple Problems and Their Solutions, *School Science and Mathematics*, **63** (1963), 38–42.

FIFTEEN

The teaching of algebra in the senior high school and the junior college

THE SUBJECT MATTER of algebra is very cumulative; hence at the higher levels it makes continual use of the concepts, principles, and operations developed in the first course at the same time that new concepts, new principles, and new operations are introduced and studied. From one standpoint the broader objectives of the instruction at the more advanced level offer certain points of contrast with the objectives of the junior high school. In particular, the elective status of the higher courses implies a somewhat different personnel in such classes. The students are likely to be inherently more interested and capable than typical junior high school students. It is also quite probable that they are studying algebra because of its usefulness in academic or professional fields. In view of these facts, the technical aspects of algebra may legitimately come to occupy a relatively more important place among the instructional aims. This, of course, does not imply any lessening of the emphasis upon understanding, but it does imply a progressively increasing insistence upon the mastery of the algebraic tools.

Qualitatively, the general aims are the same as before, viz., to develop and clarify understandings, to produce familiarity with the terminology, notation, and symbolism of algebra, and to perfect operational facility. The expanding field introduces new difficulties which are offset only in part by added maturity of the students and by the operation of the principle of progressive selectivity. Intelligence and reasonable mastery of prerequisite work are necessary conditions for the successful study of algebra at these higher levels, but they are not in themselves sufficient. The teacher's role is still one of extreme importance, and his effectiveness will depend in great measure upon his ability to anticipate and overcome specific difficulties which the students are likely to have with particular topics.

Review work in beginning intermediate algebra In beginning the course in intermediate algebra, teachers generally find it necessary to make some review of the work of elementary algebra. Indeed, most textbooks in the more advanced algebra courses begin with several chapters which are essentially reviews of various phases of the earlier work. Much time may be wasted in this review work, however, unless it is carefully and purposefully planned. It is well at the outset to take a rather careful inventory of the algebraic equipment of the class. This may be done by administering a comprehensive inventory test. If it is done at the beginning and if the results are immediately tabulated and analyzed, it is possible for the teacher to have very soon a fairly accurate picture of the needs of the class for review work. If these tabulated results are used as a basis for planning and conducting the review, it will be possible to concentrate attention on those places where the need is evident and to dispense with unnecessary work on other topics.

There is an advantage in spreading the review over some two or three weeks and giving it in small doses interspersed with new work instead of concentrating it all in the first few days and leaving it as finished business. If the students get nothing but review work for several days, it becomes tiresome. Some new work offered along with the review provides both variety and incentive. The distribution of time in this way also makes for more effective learning. Among the things which are likely to need special attention in this review work may be mentioned the language of algebra (substitution and evaluation), positive and negative numbers, easy formal work in the fundamental operations, review of the field postulates, the solution of literal equations, and easy work with fractions.

Need for teaching even simple details specifically Teachers often overlook the very important fact that much of the difficulty which students have with algebra is due to their failure to understand and generalize certain critical *details* of the work or to appreciate the bearing of these details upon the work as a whole. It is not at all uncommon for students to find themselves confused and their progress blocked merely because of lack of understanding of some apparently minor point. In many cases when the proper cue is given or the troublesome detail is cleared up, the student is able to proceed with independence and satisfaction. Many such details appear so familiar, simple, and obvious that teachers do not recognize them as troublemakers, but it is not wise to assume too much in this respect, even in the matter of recognizing equivalent expressions and making proper substitution. Following examples will make this clear.

Frequently students experience difficulty because they fail to *recognize* the equivalence or identity of certain algebraic expressions. This is particularly true with reference to indicated products and quotients, roots, and exponents. For example, the expressions $x^3/2$ and $\frac{1}{2}x^3$ are precisely equivalent, but even in such simple cases it is not uncommon to find students who are unable to recognize the fundamental equivalence. Other examples of equivalent expressions in which the identity is not always readily discerned are found in such illustrations as the following:

$$\frac{2}{3}xy,\ \frac{2x}{3}y,\ 2y\frac{x}{3},\ 2\frac{xy}{3},\ \frac{2xy}{3}$$

$$\frac{1}{2}h(b+B),\ \frac{h}{2}(b+B),\ \frac{b+B}{2}h,\ \text{and}\ \frac{(b+B)h}{2}$$

$$\sqrt{7x}\ \text{and}\ \sqrt{7}\cdot\sqrt{x}$$

$$\frac{\sqrt{x}}{\sqrt{y}}\ \text{and}\ \sqrt{\frac{x}{y}}$$

$$\left(\frac{x}{y}\right)^3\ \text{and}\ \frac{x^3}{y^3}$$

$$x^3y^3\ \text{and}\ (xy)^3$$

Students also frequently fail to recognize the fact that, whereas in the multiplication of a polynomial the multiplier must be applied to each term in the polynomial, in the multiplication of an indicated product of two or more factors the multiplier is applied to only one factor (any factor) of the indicated product. Likewise, they do not always recognize that to multiply a fraction means to multiply only its numerator. Hence such erroneous statements as

$$r(x+y)(a+b) = (rx+ry)(ra+rb) \qquad \text{or} \qquad 3\frac{a}{b} = \frac{3a}{3b}$$

are of common occurrence.

Another case in point is found in connection with the substitution of one expression for another in a function or a formula. For example, the teacher immediately sees in the expression $8x^6 - 125y^9$ the difference of two cubes and associates the expression at once with the form $a^3 - b^3$. It seems so natural to identify $2x^2$ with a and $5y^3$ with b that it may not even occur to him that the student will have any difficulty. However, it takes specific teaching, deliberately designed to emphasize this particular association, to give the students a feeling of security and assurance in handling such situations. The acts of recognition, identification, association, and substitution which are involved will be successfully mastered in most cases only if they are taught specifically and if considerable special practice is given in performing them.

Many other illustrations could be given. There is nothing in these situations themselves which is inherently difficult. The correct interpretations can invariably be explained easily and to the entire satisfaction of the students by dealing with them deliberately and specifically. Numerical examples are often sufficient, but the students must be continually impressed with the need for associating the specific illustration with the generalized procedure. The trouble is that teachers do not keep themselves sensitive to the fact that the students need to be taught to generalize these details. They take too much for granted. The reason why most students do not react properly to such situations is that they are not taught to do so. The teacher, if he gives any thought to it at all, generally assumes that the principles or the generalizations are so obvious that they need no discussion. It is a fact, however, that this assumption cannot be made safely. The only reasonable assurance of the effective functioning of these recognitions, identifications, and generalizations is to give special instruction and carefully planned practice designed specifically to this end.

This instruction, however, needs to be more than superficial. It needs to stress the basic principles that apply to the different operations, particularly the commutative, associative, and distributive laws. Students need to be kept sensitive to the fact that these laws are taken as axioms and that as such, they provide the formal justification for asserting that two or more algebraic expressions are equivalent, or are names for the same thing. The students in these classes will already have had one course in algebra, and they should now be given a more mathematically mature approach to material with which they had previously worked in an earlier grade.

More about simultaneous linear equations When more than two equations are involved in a system of linear equations, the most effective techniques for solving are based on the concept of a rectangular array of the coefficients of the system. Such a rectangular array is called a *matrix*. Consider the system of equations

$$x - y + 2z = 5 \qquad (1)$$
$$4x - 2y + 3z = 9 \qquad (2)$$
$$3x + 4y - 5z = -4 \qquad (3)$$

There are basically two matrices associated with such a system of equations, the *coefficient matrix* and the *augmented matrix*. The coefficient matrix is merely the rectangular array consisting of the coefficients of the system. Here it is

$$\begin{pmatrix} 1 & -1 & 2 \\ 4 & -2 & 3 \\ 3 & 4 & -5 \end{pmatrix}$$

The augmented matrix is obtained by annexing to the coefficient matrix the column of constant terms. The augmented matrix of the above system is

$$\begin{pmatrix} 1 & -1 & 2 & 5 \\ 4 & -2 & 3 & 9 \\ 3 & 4 & -5 & -4 \end{pmatrix}$$

The two methods to be discussed here are essentially methods of synthetic elimination in that the process is concerned with the detached coefficients of a system of equations as displayed in the augmented matrix of the system. No proof will be given of the validity of either technique, but a bit of careful examination will reveal the fact that each technique is closely related to the process of elimination by addition or subtraction.

The pivotal-element method. Consider the elements of the augmented matrix of the system of equations with an annexed column in which each element is the sum of the numbers in the row in which it occurs. In row (1), for example, $7 = 1 + (-1) + 2 + 5$. The technique of

	x	y	z	c	S
(1)	1	−1	2	5	7
(2)	4	−2	3	9	14
(3)	3	4	−5	−4	−2
(2′)		2	−5	−11	−14
(3′)		7	−11	−19	−23
(3″)			13	39	52

the pivotal-element method involves the selection of any nonzero element of the coefficient matrix as the pivotal element. If there is a 1 among these coefficients, it should be used in order to simplify the computation as much as possible. Here the coefficient of x in the first equation is 1, and it is chosen as the pivotal element. The row and column to which this chosen element belongs are then blocked out (here row 1 and column 1). The augmented matrix is then transformed in the following manner:

1. Each element of the augmented matrix, not included in either the row or column which is blocked out, is replaced by a determinant of order two. The corresponding elements of the sum column are replaced in the same manner. For example, the elements of the second row in the matrix of the given system of equations, which are to be replaced, are -2, 3, 9, and 14.

If we use P to represent the pivotal element and R to represent the replaced element, then, for this illustration, P is 1 and R is, in turn, $-2, 3, 9$, and 14. For equation (3) R will be 4, -5, -4, and -2, respectively, while P, of course, remains 1. The symbol e_{pr} will be used to represent the element in the same row as the pivotal element and the same column as the replaced element, and e_{rp} will represent the element in the same row as the replaced element and the same column as the pivotal element.

2. Construct the determinant

$$\begin{vmatrix} P & e_{pr} \\ e_{rp} & R \end{vmatrix} = PR - e_{pr}e_{rp}$$

for each element which is to be replaced. For example,

-2 is replaced by $\begin{vmatrix} 1 & -1 \\ 4 & -2 \end{vmatrix} = (1)(-2) - (-1)(4) = 2$

3 by $\begin{vmatrix} 1 & 2 \\ 4 & 3 \end{vmatrix} = (1)(3) - (2)(4) = -5$

9 by $\begin{vmatrix} 1 & 5 \\ 4 & 9 \end{vmatrix} = (1)(9) - (5)(4) = -11$

14 by $\begin{vmatrix} 1 & 7 \\ 4 & 14 \end{vmatrix} = (1)(14) - (7)(4) = -14$

The elements in row 3 are replaced in a similar manner.

3. The new element in the sum column must be equal to the sum of the remaining elements in the same row. For example,

$$-14 = 2 + (-5) + (-11)$$

This is a good rapid check, but it is not an infallible check. If the equality does not hold, there is an error. It should be evident, however, that owing to the possibility of compensating errors, the equality might hold even though errors would be present.

4. Continue the process, each time choosing as the pivotal element a nonzero element from the transformed coefficient matrix. Each transformation has the effect of eliminating the unknown for which the pivotal element was the coefficient. For example, if x were eliminated by subtraction from the above system of equations, the resulting system would be the two equations whose coefficients are displayed in rows $2'$ and $3'$. Since 2, a coefficient of y, is chosen as the pivotal element in the second transformation, the row $3''$ represents the equation $13z = 39$.

5. From the final equation determine the value of one of the unknowns. Use this value in an equation of the immediately previous system to determine a second unknown. Use these two values to determine a third unknown, and continue until values for all unknowns have been determined. For example, $13z = 39$ gives $z = 3$; use either 2′ or 3′ to find $y = 2$; use either 1, 2, or 3 to find $x = 1$. Check in the remaining equations of the original system.

In the above discussion of the pivotal-element technique three equations with simple integral coefficients were chosen. All the computations can be made mentally in all such cases. The process is effective for any number of equations and with complicated coefficients. In such cases computing machines can make the computations effectively and rapidly, the most difficult problem being the control on the proper number of significant digits to retain in the rounding process that becomes necessary.

There are systems of equations which do not produce unique solutions. In such cases some of the unknowns may be expressed in terms of the remaining unknowns. If a system of equations in n unknowns is such that r of the unknowns can be expressed in terms of the remaining $n - r$ unknowns, then the pivotal-element technique will produce proportional rows after $r - 1$ transformations. For example, consider the system of equations

$$2x - 3y + z - u = -1 \qquad (1)$$
$$3x + y - z + 2u = 5 \qquad (2)$$
$$5x - 2y + u = 4 \qquad (3)$$
$$5x + 9y - 5z + 8u = 17 \qquad (4)$$

The augmented matrix with the sum column is

	x	y	z	u	c	S
(1)	2	−3	1	−1	−1	−2
(2)	3	1	−1	2	5	10
(3)	5	−2	0	1	4	8
(4)	5	9	−5	8	17	34
(2′)	5	−2		1	4	8
(3′)	5	−2		1	4	8
(4′)	15	−6		3	12	24

One transformation has produced rows which are proportional, so two of the unknowns may be expressed in terms of the remaining $4 - 2$, or 2, unknowns. For example, from row 2′ $u = 4 - 5x + 2y$. This value used in equation (1) gives $z = 3 - 7x + 5y$. These values will check in equations (3) and (4).

It is important to note that the determinant $\begin{vmatrix} P & e_{pr} \\ e_{rp} & R \end{vmatrix}$ is used to replace the element R, although the pivotal element, P, is not in the first column. The rows and columns in which P and R occur have no effect on the second-order determinant used to replace R.

In the illustrative example the number of equations is the same as the number of the unknowns. This is not necessary.

The sweep-out process. This process is quite similar to the pivotal-element process. Again, consider the augmented matrix of the first system of equations. In each row divide all elements by the element which is the coefficient of x in the corresponding equation. (If this coefficient is zero, use the first nonzero element in the row.) This process produces equations (1′), (2′), and (3′). Subtract the elements of row 1′ from the corresponding elements of rows 2′ and 3′ to produce rows 4 and 5, respectively. This has, in effect, eliminated x from the

	x	y	z	c	S
(1)	1	−1	2	5	7
(2)	4	−2	3	9	14
(3)	3	4	−5	−4	−2
(1′)	1	−1	2	5	7
(2′)	1	$-1/2$	$3/4$	$9/4$	$7/2$
(3′)	1	$4/3$	$-5/3$	$-4/3$	$-2/3$
(4)	[(2′) − (1′)]	$1/2$	$-5/4$	$-11/4$	$-7/2$
(5)	[(3′) − (1′)]	$7/3$	$-11/3$	$-19/3$	$-23/3$
(4′)		1	$-5/2$	$-11/2$	−7
(5′)		1	$-11/7$	$-19/7$	$-23/7$
(6)	[(5′) − (4′)]		$13/14$	$39/14$	$26/7$

three equations and produced two equations in two unknowns, y and z. Divide the elements in rows 4 and 5 by the leading nonzero coefficient to produce rows 4′ and 5′ and then subtract 4′ from 5′. This operation has, in effect, eliminated y from the two equations, leaving the one equation $13/14z = 39/14$, or $z = 3$. This value of z can be substituted in row 4′, 5′, 4, or 5 to determine a value for y. The values of y and z can then be substituted in any one of the three original equations to determine a value for x. The three values thus determined can then be checked in the remaining two equations.

As in the pivotal-element method, each operation can be checked by the fact that the element in the sum column must be the same as the sum of the remaining elements in that particular row.

Solving quadratic equations in one unknown Five methods for solving quadratic equations are commonly taught. They are (1) solving by the graphical method, (2) solving by inspection (in the case of incomplete quadratics), (3) solving by factoring, (4) solving by completing the square, and (5) solving by use of the quadratic formula.

The graphical method is not strictly an algebraic method and can give only approximate solutions, but it is very valuable in clarifying the meaning and nature of the two roots, just as the graph itself is useful in bringing out certain important characteristics of the function. There are four essential things for the students to understand: (1) The graph is the geometric picture of a *function* of the independent variable and, as the independent variable takes on different values, the function also takes on different values; (2) since the general form of the quadratic equation is $ax^2 + bx + c = 0$, we seek to find those values of x which will make the function $y = ax^2 + bx + c$ have the value zero; (3) the only points on the graph for which the function can have value zero are those points which are on the x axis; and (4) consequently, the abscissas of those points give the values of the independent variable which satisfy the equation. These values are sometimes called the *zeros of the function*. The graph also can be used effectively to show why two real and distinct roots may exist, why the roots are sometimes real and equal, and why, in certain cases, there are no real roots.

Just as in the case of the linear relations, it is important that the student have a clear understanding of just what is represented by a quadratic relation. Consider the two relations

$$x^2 + y^2 \leqq 25 \qquad (1)$$

$$y = x^2 - 5 \qquad (2)$$

Example 1: Let the domain and range of $x^2 + y^2 \leqq 25$ be the set of integers, and for $y = x^2 - 5$ let the domain be the set of integers such that $-4 \leqq x \leqq 4$ while the range is the set of integers such that $-5 \leqq y \leqq 11$. The *complete* graph for relation (1) consists of all those points marked by dots in Figure 15-1, and the *complete* graph for relation 2 consists of all those points marked by crosses. When the two relations are considered simultaneously, the solution set consists of all those points common to the two graphs, namely, those marked by a crossed-over dot. It is the set $\{(0,-5), (-1,-4), (1,-4), (-2,-1), (2,-1), (-3,4), (3,4)\}$.

Example 2: Let the domain and range of the two relations be the set of all real numbers. The *complete* graph of the relation $x^2 + y^2 \leqq 25$ will be the circle and the area which

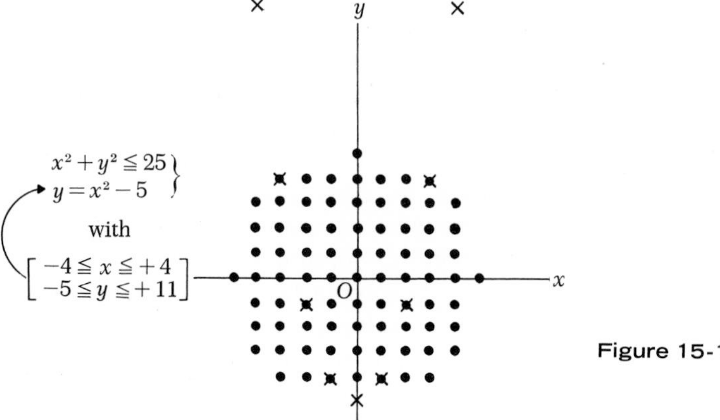

Figure 15-1

it encloses, as is indicated by the shaded portion of Figure 15-2. An *incomplete* graph of the relation $y = x^2 - 5$ will be the portion of the parabola that is shown in the figure. When the two relations are considered simultaneously, the solution set will consist of all the points on the portion of the parabola that lies within the shaded part of the figure. If the condition of "less than" (<) is removed from relation (1), then the graph of this relation becomes the circle. In this case the solution set of relations (1) and (2), considered simultaneously, becomes the set {(0,−5), (−3,4), and (3,4)}.

Similar considerations are present when a quadratic relation and a linear relation are considered simultaneously.

The graph of $y = x^2 - 5$ is a special case of the graph of the quadratic function

$$y = ax^2 + bx + c \qquad a \neq 0$$

The condition $a \neq 0$ guarantees that the function has the characteristics of a quadratic function; it also guarantees the possibility of

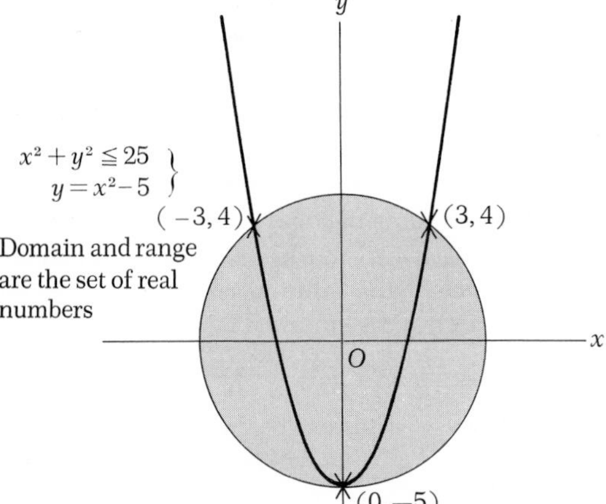

Figure 15-2

certain operational procedures which are desirable in dealing with the function. For a proper understanding of the essential characteristics of this function it is necessary to examine the effect which each coefficient in the formula has on the graph. For the illustrative examples it will be sufficient to specify the set of real numbers as both the domain and range of the function.

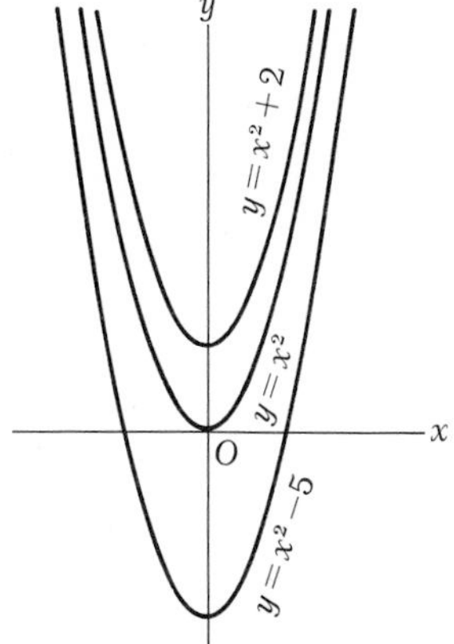

Figure 15-3

Example 3: The effect of c on the graph of $y = ax^2 + bx + c$, Figure 15-3. It should be evident that $(0, c)$ is always a point on the graph; that is, c is the y intercept of the graph. A comparison of the graphs of the functions $y = x^2 + 2$, $y = x^2$, and $y = x^2 - 5$ is sufficient to show that a change in the value of c merely shifts the position of the intercept on the y axis. Note that in each of these three cases the curve is open upward and the y intercept is the lowest point on the curve. It is a *minimum point;* that is, the function has a *minimum value* at this point.

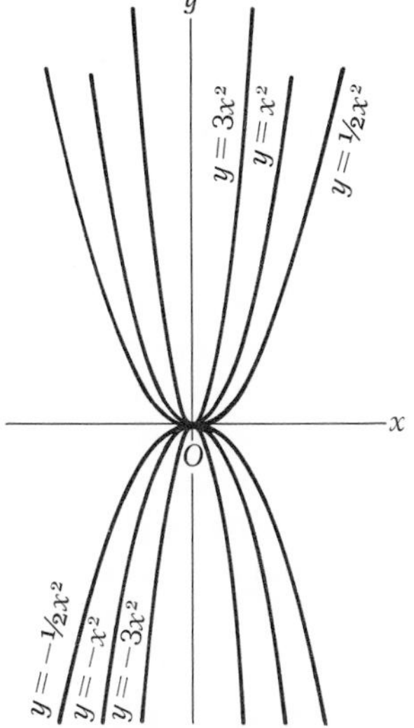

Figure 15-4

Example 4: The effect of a on the graph of the function $y = ax^2 + bx + c$. This effect is of two types. In Figure 15-4 a comparison of the graphs of the functions $y = ax^2$, where the coefficients a are numerically equal but opposite in sign, will reveal the following facts: When $a > 0$, the curves are open upward and have a minimum point; when $a < 0$, the curves are open downward and have a maximum (highest) point.

Furthermore, a comparison of curves for the equations in which the coefficients a have the same sign but differ in numerical value will reveal that, as a gets larger in numerical value, the curve tends to close up toward the y axis and, as a gets smaller in numerical value, the curve tends to stretch out away from the y axis.

In both of the above examples all of the curves are symmetric with respect to the y axis. This means that $x = \pm k$ substituted into a quadratic function of the form $y = ax^2 + c$, where $a \neq 0$, will produce the same value for y, namely, $y = ak^2 + c$.

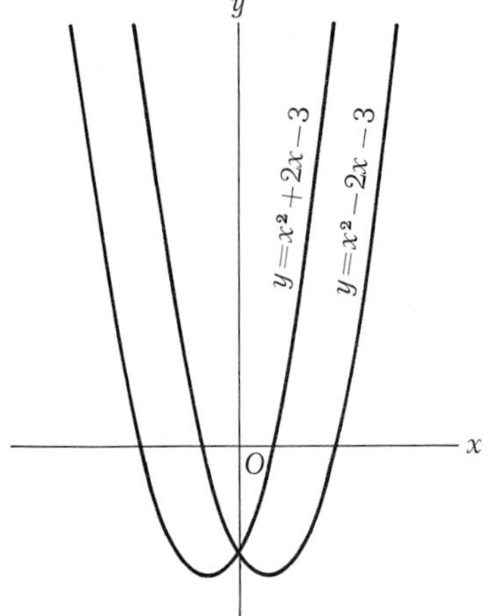

Figure 15-5

Example 5: The effect of b on the graph of the function $y = ax^2 + bx + c$. A simple illustration of the effect which a change in b will have on the graph of the quadratic function can be obtained from a comparison of the graphs of the two functions $y = x^2 - 2x - 3$ and $y = x^2 + 2x - 3$. Here simple values of a and c are used, but they remain the same for the two functions. The only difference is in the value of the coefficient b. The effect on the graph, Figure 15-5, has been to shift along the x axis both the minimum point [from $(+1,-4)$ to $(-1,-4)$] and the axis of symmetry (from $x = 1$ to $x = -1$).

These special examples have portrayed in simplified form the characteristic effects which the respective coefficients of the quadratic function $y = ax^2 + bx + c$ have on the shape and position of the graph of the function. Each case can be argued more rigorously for the general case by directing attention to the equivalent form of the function

$$y = a\left(x + \frac{b}{2a}\right)^2 + \frac{4ac - b^2}{4a}$$

which exhibits $x = -b/2a$ as the axis of symmetry of the graph and the point $[-b/2a, (4ac - b^2)/4a]$ as the minimum point (if $a > 0$) or the maximum point (if $a < 0$).[1]

Because it is slow and tedious, the graphical solution should not be required for many problems. Its purpose will have been served when it has been used in sufficient cases to clarify and amplify the students' understanding of quadratic equations and inequalities and their solution sets. The major part of the work with quadratic equations should be concerned with algebraic rather than graphical solutions.

The second method mentioned above—that of solving by inspection—is so simple and obvious that often it is not even listed as a method of solution. The third offers little difficulty to students except possibly in the factoring, and this will merely require careful attention. There is nothing inherently new about the process, but there is one point that may need re-explanation. When an equation such as $x^2 + 5x - 14 = 0$

[1]For a more detailed discussion of the quadratic function see the Report of the Commission on Mathematics, "Appendices" (New York: College Entrance Examination Board, 1959), pp. 36–57.

is given in factored form as $(x + 7)(x - 2) = 0$, it is not always clear to the students why one has the right to set the factors separately equal to zero and thus get two linear equations. The justification for this should be made clear. That is, it should be explained that, if either of the factors is zero, the function itself will be equal to zero and the equation is thus satisfied, and conversely, the *only* way in which the equation can be satisfied is for at least one of the factors to be equal to zero.

In taking up the method of solving quadratics by completing the square, it will be well to review briefly the characteristics of the perfect trinomial square of the form $x^2 + 2bx + b^2$ in order that the students may get well in mind the relation between the coefficient of x and the term free of x. This is the crux of the whole matter, and it should be carefully explained and freely illustrated. It is desirable that the students themselves should make the generalization and be able to state it in words. After this special case has been thoroughly understood, the technique should be extended to the general quadratic expression $ax^2 + bx + c$. The generality of this method of solution should be emphasized and contrasted with the lack of generality (in terms of real numbers) of the factoring method. It will not be necessary, however, to spend much time in actually solving equations by this method, since its principal function here is to provide a means for developing the general quadratic formula.

The general quadratic formula is of such special importance and usefulness that it should be thoroughly mastered by every student. Its development requires the use of the method of completing the square and provides an excellent review of operations with literal symbols. The development should be carefully explained, and the students should be tested for their understanding of every step. The formula itself is indispensable, and every student should memorize it and use it until he is perfectly familiar with its form and meaning.

In connection with the study of this formula, the teacher should see to it that the students understand the meaning of the discriminant and that they understand why it is possible, in a quadratic equation under proper hypotheses of reality or rationality of the coefficients, to determine the nature of the roots from a study of the discriminant alone, without solving the equation. To this end it is desirable for the teacher and students to examine and discuss together a variety of quadratic equations with numerical coefficients, after which the students may well be given exercises such as the following.

Exercise: In each of the following quadratic equations the coefficients are rational numbers. Indicate in each case the nature of the roots so far as this can be determined from the discriminant alone. Do not solve the equations.

Equation	Discriminant* $b^2 - 4ac$	Nature of roots		
		Real or imaginary	Equal or unequal	Rational or irrational
$x^2 + 7x + 6 = 0$				
$3y^2 + 7y + 2 = 0$				
$2x^2 - 2x + 11 = 0$				
$x^2 - 10x + 25 = 0$				
$5x^2 + x - 7 = 0$				

Exercises of this sort demand and develop insight into the role of the discriminant in determining the nature of the roots and contribute materially to the understanding and appreciation of the generality of the formula. In any discussion of the use of the discriminant, exercises of the form (1) $x^2 - \sqrt{5}x - 5 = 0$ and (2) $2x^2 + 6ix - 9 = 0$ should be used by way of contrast to those listed in the table. The purpose is to place specific emphasis on the importance of the hypotheses of rationality and reality on the coefficients of the quadratic. In example 1 the discriminant is rational but the roots are irrational. (The coefficients are *not* rational.) In example 2 the discriminant is positive but the roots are not real. (The coefficients are *not* real.)

Not infrequently students have difficulty in dealing with equations such as $x^6 + 13x^3 + 36 = 0$. The difficulty almost invariably lies in the failure to recognize that, while this, for example, is a sixth-degree equation in x, it may be regarded as a quadratic equation in x^3 and so may be solved easily for x^3, the values of x itself then being readily found by taking the cube roots of x^3. To help the students become sensitive to the possibility of reducing such equations to quadratic form, a variety of examples should be given, the quadratic form being written out in each case. Thus $x^8 + 5x^4 - 2 = 0$ may be written

*In actuality $b^2 - 4ac$ is not the discriminant of the quadratic equation $ax^2 + bx + c = 0$, but it is its value in terms of the coefficients of the equation. By definition the discriminant of the polynomial equation

$$a_0x^n + a_1x^{n-1} + a_2x^{n-2} + \cdots + a_{n-1}x + a_n = 0$$

is

$$a_0^{2n-2}(x_1 - x_2)^2(x_1 - x_3)^2 \cdots (x_1 - x_r)^2(x_2 - x_3)^2 \cdots (x_{n-1} - x_n)^2$$

where $x_1, x_2, \cdots, x_n$ are roots of the equation and the factor a_0^{2n-2} serves merely to render the discriminant an integral expression in the coefficients of the polynomial. For the quadratic equation the discriminant is

$$a^2(x_1 - x_2)^2 = a^2\left(\frac{-b + \sqrt{b^2 - 4ac}}{2a} - \frac{-b - \sqrt{b^2 - 4ac}}{2a}\right)^2 = b^2 - 4ac$$

$(x^4)^2 + 5(x^4) - 2 = 0$, or, if preferred, a different letter, say z, may be substituted for x^4 so that the equation becomes $z^2 + 5z - 2 = 0$. The illustrations should include examples involving radicals and fractional exponents, such as $x + 3\sqrt{x} - 18 = 0$ and $2x^{2/5} + 8x^{1/5} + 12 = 0$. After a number of illustrative examples have been given, the principle may be generalized to help in subsequent recognition of such cases.

In work of the twelfth grade or of the first year of college algebra there should be extensive applications of the foregoing methods to the solution of quadratic equations in one unknown. This work would necessarily involve the use of radicals and imaginary and complex numbers. The quadratic formula as a general solution should be stressed. Such work may be extended appropriately to include the investigation of certain other general properties of quadratic equations, particularly the relations existing among the roots and the coefficients. It should lead to the subsequent study of quadratic equations and systems of equations in two unknowns.

Many students who are able to apply the quadratic formula explicitly in determining the roots of a given equation find themselves at a loss when confronted with situations in which the formula is implicitly involved. The following illustrative examples are cases in point.

Example 6: In each of the following equations determine the real values of k for which the roots will be equal:

$$4x^2 - 12x + k = 0$$
$$2kx^2 + 5x + 1 = 0$$
$$x^2 - 8kx + 4 = 0$$

There usually will be a few students who will be able to sense for themselves the role of the discriminant in such cases, but for many of them it will need to be pointed out and illustrated specifically. In particular it will be necessary to review the fact that the equality or inequality of the roots of such equations is determined solely according to whether the discriminant $b^2 - 4ac$ is or is not equal to zero, and consequently the condition for their equality is that k must be of such value as will make this discriminant zero. That is, the student must come to sense the fact that, in order to produce the required condition and to discover the required value of k, the discriminant of the particular equation must be set equal to zero and the resulting equation solved for k.

The relations between the roots and the coefficients should be carefully developed. Most textbooks give the bare symbolic development of these formulas but are usually lacking in explanatory comment. To supply adequate explanation of the development and pointed comment with reference to applying these relations must be the task of the teacher. He must use a variety of problems which will provide the student with the opportunity of seeing the formulas applied both explicitly and implicitly. For example:

Example 7: Find the sum and product of the roots without solving.

$$5x^2 - 3x + 8 = 0$$
$$2x + 5 = x^2$$

Example 8: Given the equation and one root, as indicated, find the other root without solving.

$$x^2 - 11x + 24 = 0 \qquad \text{(one root is 8)}$$
$$2x^2 - 17x + 33 = 0 \qquad \text{(one root is 3)}$$

Example 9: Given the roots as indicated, write the equations.

Roots are 5/2 and -6
Roots are k and k/a

Other and varied examples will be found in any text in college algebra. Those which are to be used for illustrative purposes or for practice work should be carefully selected by the teacher. The main criterion should be the extent to which the exercise lends itself to clarifying and emphasizing the particular point in question.

Systems involving quadratic equations in two unknowns The students' previous experience in solving simultaneous equations may be assumed to have been confined to systems of linear equations. In teaching the solution of such systems of equations there is a tendency on the part of many to overlook the method of substitution. The disadvantage of failing to give due emphasis to this method now becomes apparent, because it is generally applicable to the solution of systems involving quadratics, while other methods of solving systems of linear equations are not applicable. Therefore it may be advisable, in taking up the study of this topic, to give a *brief* review of the solution of systems of linear equations by substitution. The students should be made sensitive to the importance of the method as a general algebraic method for solving quadratic systems in two unknowns.

Systems of equations involving quadratics fall into two general classes: (1) systems containing one linear and one quadratic equation and (2) systems in which both equations are quadratics. The latter class may be further divided to advantage into homogeneous and nonhomogeneous systems. The special methods and devices used in the solution of these systems vary according to the forms of the equations involved in the particular systems under consideration. Teachers should make every effort to see that students do not use these various devices blindly but are trained to look for the reasons why the devices work. In doing this they will be acquiring the ability to analyze systems of equations and to determine for themselves what procedures will be most likely to yield the desired solutions. It is highly important that the teachers use discretion and care in the selection of problems to be assigned.

Textbooks generally present these devices with appropriate illustrations but often without emphasizing either the peculiar characteristics of the forms to which the various methods are especially adapted or the

Figure 15-6
Quadratic systems: (a) *two distinct real solutions, two real and equal solutions, two imaginary solutions;* (b) *four real solutions;* (c) *four real solutions (equal in pairs);* (d) *two real and two imaginary solutions;* (e) *four real solutions (two equal);* (f) *four imaginary solutions.*

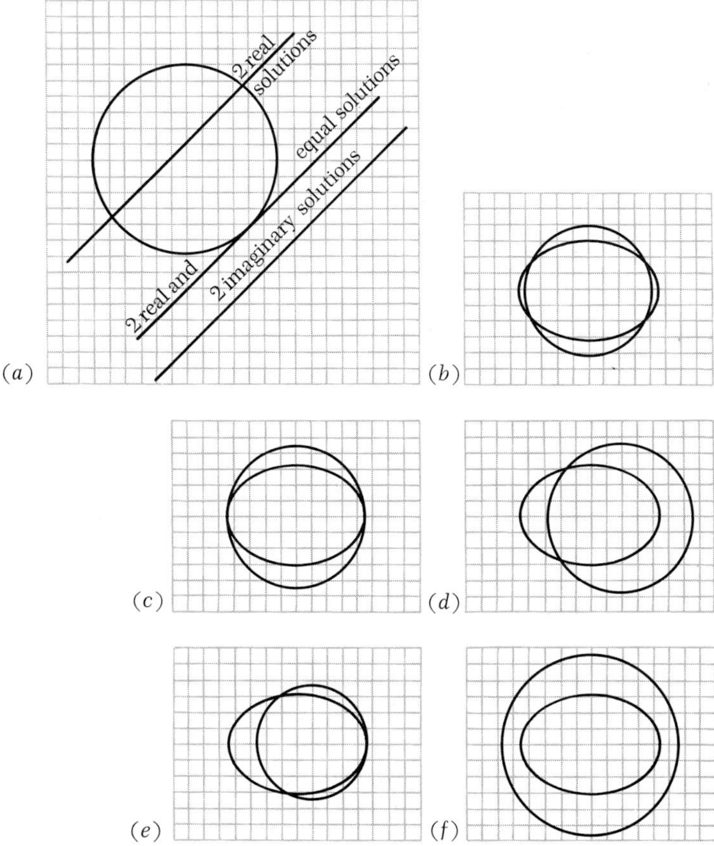

reasons why a particular method is especially suitable for handling a particular form. It must be the teacher's primary task to see that the students are given insight into the reasons underlying the use of the various devices in particular situations as well as a knowledge of the devices themselves. Otherwise, rote work is inevitable.

Useful and economical as these special procedures are, the student should not be allowed to forget that as a rule they are merely means for reducing the tedious labor often involved in the more general method of solving one equation for one variable in terms of the other and then substituting the result in the other equation.

The graphical method of solving quadratic systems is a laborious method and, of course, gives only approximate solutions, but it probably gives the average student more real intuitive insight into the nature of the solutions than any of the strictly algebraic methods of attack. In particular, it is useful in explaining why a system containing two quadratic equations has four solutions (real or imaginary) and why a system containing one quadratic equation and one linear equation has only two solutions.

The set of graphs in Figure 15-6 includes representation of all types possible in quadratic systems. A thorough discussion and comparison of such graphs as these and their associated equations should give the students an intuitive basis, which they too often fail to get, for interpreting the solutions of such systems. Moreover, the use of graphs in this connection will give the student an initial acquaintance with some of the basic concepts of analytic geometry. In this way it serves not only to clarify his present work in algebra but also to stimulate his interest in and provide a basis for a thorough understanding of the analytic geometry that lies ahead.

Ratio, proportion, and variation Most students have a fairly clear understanding of the meaning of ratio and proportion by the time they reach the second algebra course. The concepts of ratio and proportion are used, at least intuitively and by implication, even in the arithmetic of the elementary school and to a greater extent in the subsequent work of the junior high school. Most textbooks in elementary algebra or general mathematics contain some systematic, though elementary, treatment of this subject, and a more extensive treatment is found in the study of similar geometric figures in intuitive and demonstrative geometry and in numerical trigonometry. Consequently, students in the advanced courses may be expected to have some familiarity with the concepts and techniques of ratio and proportion.

The concept of variation also will be familiar to the students, but with intuitive rather than analytical implications. In all probability the form and meaning of the symbolic representation will be new. However, since it is often more convenient and effective to use the variation form of notation than the proportion form, the systematic analytic study of variation should undoubtedly find a place in the advanced work in algebra. It is not a particularly difficult topic to teach, but it needs to be taught thoroughly. Such explanation as may be given in the textbook will necessarily be condensed and will need to be materially supplemented by the teacher.

The teacher should have in mind two specific objectives: (1) to see that the students get a clear understanding of what is meant by direct variation, inverse variation, and joint variation and (2) to see that the students learn how to set up these relations in the form of equations involving a constant of variation or a proportion and understand why the equations necessarily represent the different types of variation. A variety of illustrative formulas, graphs, and problems can be used effectively to bring out the meaning of the equations $y = kx$, $y = k/x$, $x = kyz$, $y = kx^2$, $y = kx^2/z^3$, etc. Innumerable examples involving variation may be drawn from arithmetic, geometry, physics, and other sources. The following illustrative examples are designed to give the students training in translating verbal statements of relationships into equations of these types. In each case the students should be asked to translate the statement into an equation involving a constant k and to indicate the numerical value of k where he can.

1. The perimeter of a square varies directly as the side.
2. The area of a square varies directly as the square of a side.
3. The circumference of a circle varies directly as the radius.
4. The volume of a sphere varies directly as the cube of the radius.
5. The base of a rectangle of constant area varies inversely as the altitude.
6. The strength of an electric current (amperage) varies directly as the voltage and inversely as the resistance.
7. The amount of simple interest varies jointly as the principal, rate, and time.
8. The volume of a confined gas varies directly as the absolute temperature and inversely as the pressure.
9. The intensity of illumination from a given source varies inversely as the square of the distance from that source.

Many applications should be given in the form of problems in order that the students may become thoroughly familiar with these forms and acquire the ability to apply them correctly in appropriate situations and use them with proficiency and assurance. The students will realize, of course, that there are many situations involving variation in which the relationships are so complex that the mathematical laws governing them are not known. They should be impressed, however, with the fact that, whenever we can set up an analytical representation of the mathematical law governing such variation, we are thereby providing ourselves with a powerful instrument for studying and predicting the behavior of the variables.

The study of variation affords an excellent opportunity to clarify and emphasize the nature of functional relationship and functional thinking. In fact, the concept of variation is inseparable from the concept of function, and the two should be stressed together, both concepts being abstracted and clarified through the interweaving of graphic illustrations and numerical evaluation of formulas of polynomial functions. The concept of continuity should be emphasized in connection with the graphs of such functions. This concept should be associated with the concept of the *changing values* of the variables. These, in turn, are to be associated with the shifting coordinates of a point moving at will on the graph, and the graph itself should be associated, through these notions, with the formula or function which it represents. Proper attention to these concepts and associations of ideas will go far toward developing a real idea of the nature of variation at the same time that it gives clear emphasis to the general notion of dependence as an aspect of functionality.

Arithmetic and geometric progressions The first fundamental necessity in teaching progressions is to see that the students become really sensitive to the way in which the progressions are built up, i.e., the precise way in which each term after the first one is obtained from the preceding term. There are two approaches to this problem. Textbooks generally start by giving in each case a definition of the type of progression being discussed, calling attention to its distinguishing characteristic (the common difference between two consecutive terms or the common ratio of the one to the other), giving a few numerical illustrations, presenting the first few terms in symbolic form, and proceeding then to the development of the formula for the nth term. In this procedure the definition and the concept forms the starting point, and the numerical examples merely illustrate, supplement, and enrich the concept.

Some teachers feel, however, that better results are to be secured by more or less reversing this order of things. Under this plan various simple numerical illustrations of progressions are presented at the beginning without any definite laws or conditions governing the relations among the terms being given. The students are merely asked to try to find the way in which each series is built up or to discover for themselves the characteristic relation governing each of the series. This approach obviously stresses discovery rather than definition as a starting point. After the student has discovered the relations governing several progressions, he is asked to formulate a statement expressing this relation for each type of progression and finally to express these laws or relationships symbolically as formulas for the nth term of the series. It is held that many students can do this if the illustrative series are simple and appropriately chosen.

Advocates of this approach contend that students who discover the relationships for themselves are likely to understand the characteristic laws better, remember them more vividly, and apply them more readily than those who start with ready-made definitions and formulas. There are probably some grounds for this contention. There is no conclusive evidence, however, that either of these approaches is markedly superior to the other. In either case numerical illustrations are indispensable, and in either case it will probably be necessary for the teacher to help many of the students in setting up the symbolic formula for the typical nth term in the particular type of progression being considered.

Derivation of the formulas for the sums of the first n terms demands careful attention. Some texts offer "simplified proofs" which avoid explicit application but require tacit assumption of the principle of finite induction. This does not seem to be justifiable practice. Rather, the proofs of these propositions afford simple, yet very effective, means for introducing the students to the important technique of proof by mathematical induction. The procedural pattern in the application of the principle of finite induction to these particular propositions is simple in content but of sufficient general import to offer real opportunity for the development of basic understanding of this important mathematical technique.

The most serious difficulty which most students encounter in the study of progressions is in knowing how to go about the insertion of a given number of arithmetic or geometric means between two given numbers. This difficulty can easily be dispelled, however, if the students can be made sensitive to the fact that all they need to do is to find the common difference or the common ratio and that they can do this in either case by taking the formula for the nth term and solving it for the common difference or the common ratio in terms of the other elements of the formula. For several reasons it is better for them to carry out these solutions as they are needed rather than to memorize the formula for d and r. Besides reducing the amount of memorizing, it enhances the students' understanding of the formulas and provides excellent practice in the solution of literal equations.

Arithmetic and geometric progressions have extremely interesting and important applications which should be pointed out to the students. In any linear function, for consecutive integral values (in terms of any real unit) of the independent variable, the corresponding values of the function form an arithmetic progression, and conversely. This may be illustrated both graphically and numerically. Doubtless the most important general application of the geometric progression is the compound interest law. Here the teacher has the opportunity to emphasize the usefulness of geometric progressions by showing that this law is applied not only to the computation of compound interest but also to important problems in various fields. The following examples are illustrative:

Chemistry: problems associated with the disintegration of radioactive substances

Physics: the adiabatic law for gases; rates of cooling

Biology: problems associated with the growth of colonies of bacteria and abnormal tissue growth

Economics: problems of investment, insurance, debt funding, and installment buying

Sociology: problems associated with population growth

The study of harmonic progressions is a topic which has important but highly specialized application, and it is usually taught (or retaught) in connection with these applications. It is of less general interest than arithmetic and geometric progressions and is often omitted even from courses in college algebra. Because of the specialized application of this topic, no discussion of it will be given in the present chapter.

Mathematical induction As pointed out in the previous section, proofs of the sum formulas in arithmetic and geometric progressions afford simple but effective media for introducing proof by mathematical induction. This pattern of deductive reasoning not only is of tremendous importance in further mathematical study but also affords excellent illustrations of the significance of, and distinction between, necessary and sufficient conditions.

The principle of finite induction, stated on page 64 for natural numbers, will be restated here for positive integers. The two statements, of course, are equivalent, since there exists an isomorphism under addition and multiplication between the set of all natural numbers and the set of all positive integers.

Principle of finite induction. If P is a set of positive integers such that 1 is an element of P, and also such that if k is an element of P, then $k + 1$ is also an element of P, then P is the set of all positive integers.

In this statement there are two conditions that must be satisfied before the conclusion can be drawn that P is the set of all integers. Each condition is a necessary condition, but neither condition by itself is a sufficient condition for drawing the desired conclusion.

Two illustrations may be cited of the truth of this last statement. Suppose we make the statement that the formula $n^2 - n + 11$ gives a prime number for all positive integers. If this is a true statement it certainly must be true for the positive integer 1; and it is, since $(1)^2 - 1 + 11 = 11$ and 11 is a prime number. If $n = 11$, however, we have $(11)^2 - 11 + 11 = (11)^2$, which is not a prime number. Here the second necessary condition fails, for the formula does give a prime for $n = 10$ but not for $n = 10 + 1 = 11$. Similar illustrations are found in the formula $n^2 - n + 41$, which renders a prime for all positive integers from 1 through 40 but not for 41, and in the formula $n^2 - 79n + 1601$, which yields a prime for each positive integer from 1 through 79 but not for $n = 80$.

In the study of arithmetic progressions one of the important principles to be developed is that the sum of the first n consecutive positive integers is given by the formula $S = n(n + 1)/2$. It thus would be incorrect to say that this sum is given by the formula $S = [n(n + 1)/2] + 1 = (n^2 + n + 2)/2$. However, let us assume that there exists some positive integer k such that

$$1 + 2 + 3 + \cdots + k = \frac{k^2 + k + 2}{2}$$

It then follows from the additive property of equality that

$$\begin{aligned}(1 + 2 + 3 + \cdots + k) + (k + 1) &= \frac{k^2 + k + 2}{2} + (k + 1)\\ &= \frac{(k^2 + k + 2) + 2(k + 1)}{2}\\ &= \frac{(k^2 + 2k + 1) + (k + 1) + 2}{2}\\ &= \frac{(k + 1)^2 + (k + 1) + 2}{2}\end{aligned}$$

It thus follows that if the formula is true for any positive integer k it is also true for the positive integer $k + 1$.

If $n = 1$ is used the formula produces 2, and $1 \neq 2$. In fact we know that there is no positive integer for which this formula produces a correct result.

These two illustrations underscore the fact that, while each condition of the principle of finite induction is a necessary condition, neither alone is sufficient for the conclusion. The conclusion can be drawn *only* when both conditions are met simultaneously.

Complex numbers In introducing students to the study of imaginary and complex numbers it is well to review the previous steps in the extension of their number concepts from positive integers to common and decimal fractions and later to irrational numbers and negative numbers. They will be interested in realizing that each of these extensions was made in response to a need; that, when situations were encountered which could not be interpreted or explained adequately by use of positive integers alone, fractions were invented to do the job; and similarly for negative numbers. The point should be stressed that these new kinds of numbers have been sheer *inventions* made to serve a purpose and that they take their meanings from definition. This having been established, the students will tend to be in a receptive frame of mind for further extension of their number ideas.

The meaning of an imaginary number should be made clear at the outset. There should be no mystery about it, and there need be none. An explanation along the following lines will make clear the meaning which is to be attached to such numbers and will dispel much of the intellectual reservation and even antagonism which often exist with reference to this radically new concept.

Let us consider some negative number, say, -9. Can we find its square root? The square root of -9 cannot be $+3$, because $(+3)(+3) = +9$; nor can the square root be -3, because $(-3)(-3) = +9$. In fact the square root of -9 cannot be any positive number and it cannot be any negative number, because the square of either a positive or a negative number is positive. Obviously it cannot be zero. What then can it be? The only kinds of numbers we know about up to now are positive and negative numbers and zero. Since the square root of -9 cannot be any of these, we must *invent* another kind of number which we shall *define* as being the square root of a negative number and which we shall *call* an *imaginary number*. This is, in fact, what mathematicians have done. They have recalled that the square of either square root of any number gives that number [i.e., $\sqrt{7} \cdot \sqrt{7} = 7$, $(-\sqrt{7})(-\sqrt{7}) = 7$, etc.] and they have said that since this is the meaning of a square root, it must follow that $\sqrt{-9}\,\sqrt{-9} = -9$ and $(-\sqrt{-9})(-\sqrt{-9}) = -9$. Since they call both nonnegative and negative numbers *real* numbers, and since neither square root of (-9) can be a real number, they call it a *pure imaginary* number. Such symbols as $\sqrt{-48}$, $-\sqrt{-2}$, $\sqrt{-1}$, $-\sqrt{-364}$, etc., represent other pure imaginary numbers. The special symbol i is used to designate the imaginary number $\sqrt{-1}$, which is used as the *imaginary unit*. Thus, in seeking the square root of (-9) we might use the imaginary unit to write (-9) as $9i^2$. When this is done we have $+3i$ and $-3i$ as the two square roots of (-9). This is verified by the fact that $(+3i)(+3i) = (-3i)(-3i) = 9i^2 = -9$. There are occasional situations in which it may be convenient to identify i with $\sqrt{-1}$, where this symbol is to be interpreted such that $(\sqrt{-1})(\sqrt{-1}) = -1$.

This explanation will, of course, need to be amplified by the teacher, but it indicates the main avenue along which the students' thinking should be directed. It should be made clear that, in thus defining imaginary numbers, we make them subject to all the normal laws of operation which we use with real numbers. It is very important that students understand this clearly, and this understanding is facilitated, and confusion avoided, by the consistent use of the symbol i in place of the radical $\sqrt{-1}$. Thus there is no difference between applying the laws of exponents, the law of signs in multiplication, etc., to numbers expressed in terms of i and applying these laws to numbers expressed in terms of x or y or a or any other literal symbol. The peculiar cyclic nature of the successive integral powers of i often makes it possible to simplify the results of such operations, but this characteristic itself is a direct consequence of the laws of exponents applied in the usual manner to the number i, and of the definition of that number.

The principal points at which difficulty may be anticipated are the establishment of the definition and meaning of imaginary numbers, the definition of the symbol i, the firm fixation of the principle that *operations* with numbers in terms of i are carried on in exactly the same fashion as operations with numbers expressed in terms of any other letter, and the establishment of the successive positive integral powers of i which give a recurring series of numbers $+i$, -1, $-i$, $+1$.

When these properties of imaginary numbers have been well established in the minds of the students, the subsequent definition of and work with complex numbers should present little difficulty. Care should be taken in defining complex numbers to make sure that the full significance of the definition is understood. A complex number is of the form $a + bi$, where a and b are real numbers. This is not clearly understood until one realizes that the real numbers can be put into one-to-one correspondence with the complex numbers of the form $a + 0i$ and the pure imaginary numbers with the complex numbers of the form $0 + bi$. Once this understanding has been attained, the student is ready for the definition of conjugate complex numbers, equal complex numbers, and the four fundamental operations for working with complex numbers. The student should understand clearly that these definitions are such that the associative, commutative, and distributive properties are preserved. Furthermore, they are such that, when applied to numbers of the form $a + 0 \cdot i$, the results are consistent with those obtained with real numbers.

The geometrical representation and treatment of complex numbers is extremely interesting to students and helps to make their concepts of these numbers much more tangible. This work is not extremely difficult and may well be introduced even in the second course in algebra, at least to the extent of making the students familiar with the method of representing complex numbers graphically and with the basic principles of simple vector addition. For those students who have had trigonometry, this work may well be extended to include the representation of complex numbers in trigonometric form, multiplication of two numbers in polar form, De Moivre's theorem, finding the nth roots of a complex number, and the division of complex numbers expressed in polar form.

The teaching of logarithms Most students make their first acquaintance with logarithms when they study trigonometry. This acquaintance too often is limited to the use of logarithms as a means of reducing the laborious computation incident to the solution of triangles. It is certainly true that logarithms have played an important role in this connection, but students should not be left with the impression that logarithms are a part of trigonometry per se or that their usefulness is limited to numerical work in this branch of mathematics. Actually, the theory of logarithms is algebraic, and the application of logarithms in trigonometry is incidental rather than organic. The systematic study of logarithms should therefore form a part of the second year of algebra, and the analytic properties of logarithms should be developed in connection with their inverse counterpart, exponentials.

The approach to a basic understanding of the fundamental relationship between logarithmic functions and exponential functions can best be made through a clear comprehension of the definition of a logarithm as an exponent. First this definition should be developed and its implications followed to the derivation of the laws of operation with logarithms from the appropriate laws of exponents. This should be followed by a review of these fundamental properties, laws, and uses of exponents by means of taking some convenient small positive integer as a base and building a partial table of exponents of numbers with respect to that base. For example:

Base 2		*Base* 8	
$2^0 = 1$	$2^4 = 16$	$8^{0/3} = 1$	$8^{5/3} = 32$
$2^1 = 2$	$2^5 = 32$	$8^{1/3} = 2$	$8^{6/3} = 64$
$2^2 = 4$	$2^6 = 64$	$8^{2/3} = 4$	$8^{7/3} = 128$
$2^3 = 8$	etc.	$8^{3/3} = 8$	$8^{8/3} = 256$
		$8^{4/3} = 16$	etc.

By using the first of these tables (extended if desired), simple operations in finding powers and roots, products, and quotients can be performed. Thus,

$$\sqrt[3]{64} = \sqrt[3]{2^6} = 2^{6/3} = 2^2 = 4$$
$$4 \cdot 4 = 2^2 \cdot 2^2 = 2^{2+2} = 2^4 = 16$$
$$64 \div 4 = 2^6 \div 2^2 = 2^{6-2} = 2^4 = 16$$

It will be obvious to the student, however, that these tables or any other tables similarly constructed would be very limited in their application. For example, the first table above contains no logarithms for 3, 5, 6, 7, 9, 10, or other number which is not an integral power of 2. The logarithms of such numbers, with reference to the base 2, would necessarily be fractional, since the numbers lie between numbers which are integral powers of 2. A similar observation should be made, of course, with reference to a table similarly constructed with any positive number as a base. However, the students should also be told that, although they do not know how to determine these fractional exponents, there are methods by which they can be computed and really serviceable tables compiled. They should also be reminded that, since our number system is a decimal system, the number 10 would seem to be a more convenient base than 2 or 8 or any other number, because the integral powers of 10 give our familiar units of enumeration, namely, 1, 10, 100, 1,000, etc.

By this time the stage is set for introducing the students to the system of common logarithms in which the base is 10. The following step-by-step procedure has been found effective in producing understanding of this system and skill and facility in its use. The order of the steps is important because each new idea or principle developed rests upon those preceding it and, in turn, provides an additional idea or principle as a basis for those yet to come. The key sentence or idea in each step is italicized. The teacher may enlarge upon these italicized statements and give such explanations, illustrations, and practice as may be desired. Some suggestions are given.

1. *Any number in the decimal system can be expressed as an integral power of* 10 *or as the product of two factors, one of which is between* 1 *and* 10, *the other being an integral power of* 10.

$32.78 = 3.278 \times 10^{1}$ $\quad$ $35{,}200 = 3.52 \times 10^{4}$

$0.346 = 3.46 \times 10^{-1}$ $\quad$ $0.00682 = 6.82 \times 10^{-3}$

Give considerable practice in writing numbers in this way. Such consideration would afford further opportunities for calling attention to the nature and importance of scientific notation (see page 302). If the students have difficulty in determining the integral power of 10 to be used, the following rule will be helpful: Place the pencil point after the nonzero digit on the extreme left of the given number and count to the position of the decimal point. The number of digits (or places) thus counted gives the integral power of 10 to be used. Counting to the right in this way indicates a positive power of 10, while counting to the left indicates a negative power of 10. This integral power of 10 is the characteristic of the logarithm of the number, but it is better not to use the terms "logarithm" or "characteristic" until a little later.

2. *If we could express all numbers between* 1 *and* 10 *as powers of* 10, *then it is evident that we could express all numbers in the decimal system as powers of* 10. Point out that this follows from the fact that every number in the decimal system can be expressed as an integral power of 10 or as the product of such a power of 10 by a number between 1 and 10. Refer to the illustrations under step 1 above.

3. *Any number between* 1 *and* 10 *can be expressed either exactly or approximately as a power of* 10. Do not try to prove this, but make it appear plausible. Remind the students that since $1 = 10^0$ and $10 = 10^1$, then surely any number between 1 and 10 must be expressible (at least approximately) in the form 10^x, where $0 < x < 1$. For example, if $x = 1/3$, we have $10^{1/3} = 2.154$ (approximately), or 2.154 is approximately 10 to the one-third power. Similarly, $10^{1/2} = 3.162$ (approximately); $10^{2/3} = 4.642$ (approximately); etc.

4. *Mathematicians have given us a table of numbers between* 1 *and* 10 *expressed as powers of* 10. Make it clear that the numbers in the left margin of the table of logarithms should be read as if there were a decimal point after the first digit at the left in the number. This is, in fact, the number for which the logarithm is given in the table, since only mantissas are given; and these, themselves, are logarithms only of numbers between 1 and 10. This number will be the first of the two factors referred to in step 1. It may also be explained to the students that the omission of the decimal point in the numbers printed in the tables makes for convenience and for the conservation of space. When the students have learned to read and interpret the numbers in the left margin of the table of logarithms in this way, have them refer to their tables of mantissas and read from these the powers of 10 representing various numbers between 1 and 10. For example, $5 = 10^{.69897}$; $3.27 = 10^{.51455}$; $7.84 = 10^{.89432}$; etc. For the present have the students think of these as exponents rather than as logarithms. Point out that the decimal point precedes the first figure in the number taken from the table, whether it is printed there or not. Give practice in reading and writing down these exponents and in interpreting them.

5. *We can make certain computations by use of this table alone so long, and only so long, as the numbers we use are between* 1 *and* 10 *and the answers are also between* 1 *and* 10. Give practice, using examples in multiplication and division and in finding powers and roots, but be sure that at this stage no number used or answer sought is less than 1 or greater than 10, emphasizing again that they are approximate.

6. *We may now use our tables for any positive numbers.* Give practice in multiplication, powers, roots, and appropriate division, but for the present avoid division that would lead to negative exponents. This is a problem in itself. In connection with the use of the tables for the inverse cases, teach the students to express the numbers as the product of two factors. For example, have them express $10^{3.82367}$ as $10^{.82367} \times 10^3$.

7. *We are now ready to begin thinking, speaking, writing, and working in terms of logarithms instead of exponents.* Some practice, but not a great deal, will be needed now in reviewing and associating the logarithmic form with the exponential form.

Example 10:

Exponential form	*Logarithmic form*
$8 = 2^3$	$\log_2 8 = 3$
$100 = 10^2$	$\log_{10} 100 = 2$
$a = b^c$	$\log_b a = c$

In each case the logarithm is the exponent, but explain to the students that in the common system of logarithms the base ten is understood and is generally not written.

Now give considerable practice in the use of the logarithmic form and notation in finding products, roots, powers, and quotients. Negative characteristics should still be avoided.

Example 11: Find the product of 782 and 3.96.

log 782 =
log 3.96 =

log product =
Product =

At this stage of development it is probably advisable to emphasize that previously the practice work was for understanding, but now it is mainly for efficiency.

8. *Special difficulties with logarithms with negative characteristics.* Go back to the exponential form for a little while.

Example 12: Find log .0342.

$$.0342 = 3.42 \times 10^{-2} = 10^{.53403} \times 10^{-2} = 10^{-2+.53403}$$

This, however, cannot be written as $10^{-2.53403}$ because the .53403 is positive. It is sometimes written as $10^{\bar{2}.53403}$. A more convenient way of writing the same thing is $10^{8.53403-10}$. In logarithmic form this would be given as log .0342 = 8.53403 − 10.

Considerable special practice will be needed on this, and it should be very carefully supervised until the students have acquired a substantial understanding of the nature of negative logarithms and reasonable proficiency in handling the special notation which it is necessary to use.

Having learned how to use the table of natural functions and the table of common logarithms, the student should have no difficulty in understanding the meaning or mastering the use of the tables of logarithms of the trigonometric functions. These tables are not, in fact, indispensable but are provided merely to speed up the work. The question of whether or not to use cologarithms is debatable. Some teachers and writers feel that cologarithms are nonessential and superfluous, while others prefer to have them used. This matter is probably of little moment and may safely be left to the judgment of the individual teacher.

An explanation of the slide rule, showing how its construction and use are based upon the principles of logarithms, will add interest and value to the study of logarithms.

Logarithmic and exponential functions If two variables are so related that the first can be expressed as some function of the second and the second can be expressed as some function of the first, then the two functions are said to be *inverse* to each other. For example, if $y = f(x)$ and $x = g(y)$, then $g(y)$ is the inverse of $f(x)$ and $f(x)$ is the inverse of $g(y)$. Thus, if $y = 7x + 2$, then the inverse function is $x = (y - 2)/7$. This is an example of two inverse algebraic functions.

Logarithmic and exponential functions have this inverse relationship, since either can be expressed in terms of the other. Thus if $y = a^x$, then by taking logarithms of both members we get $\log y = x \log a$, or $x = (\log y)/(\log a)$. Similarly, if $y = \log_a x$, then $x = a^y$; hence it is possible to take a function given in either form and convert it into an equivalent inverse expression in the other form.

Attention should be called to the fact that this concept of inverse function is consistent with the concept of inverse element included among the properties of a number field. For each element a of a field there exists an additive inverse $-a$ such that $a + (-a) = (-a) + a = 0$, and for each nonzero element b there exists a multiplicative inverse b^{-1} such that $b \cdot b^{-1} = b^{-1} \cdot b = 1$. In each case, the result of combining an element with its respective inverse is to produce the identity element. The analogous situation in the case of functions is that the composite function of a function and its inverse, in either order, is the identity function. That is, it is a function which may be represented by an ordered pair in which the first and second elements are the same, for example, (x,x).

Example 13: For the linear function $y = 7x + 2$ and its inverse function $x = (y - 2)/7$, we have

$$y = 7x + 2 = 7\,[(y - 2)/7] + 2 = (y - 2) + 2 = y$$

and

$$x = (y - 2)/7 = [(7x + 2) - 2]/7 = 7x/7 = x$$

Similarly, for the function $y = \log_a x$ and its inverse function $x = a^y$, we have

$$y = \log_a x = \log_a (a^y) = y$$

and

$$x = a^y = a^{\log_a x} = x$$

As a part of mathematical literacy beyond the most elementary level, it is important for students to become aware of this inverse relationship between logarithmic and exponential functions. As an instrument in the study of analytic geometry, calculus, statistics, and subsequent courses it is necessary for students to understand this relationship and be able to make interconversions with assurance and facility. This objective has often been sadly neglected, to the detriment of the students, who too often have been taught only how to use logarithms numerically.

Other topics in algebra In a volume such as this it is impossible to consider in detail the teaching procedures connected with all the topics of intermediate and college algebra. It is hoped that the preceding pages will in some measure have set a pattern for the study of such problems. It is hoped further that the discussion will encourage teachers to apply themselves assiduously to the task of specifying the major relationships and concepts to be developed in connection with each topic and discovering the main characteristic difficulties which the study of each topic presents to the students.

Among the topics which are of first-rate importance at their appropriate levels but which it has not been possible to discuss in this chapter may be mentioned the binomial theorem, special properties of functions and equations of degree higher than second, permutations and combinations, probability, determinants, general theorems on algebraic functions and equations, and the mathematics of investment and insurance. In concluding this chapter, a few general suggestions may be made with a view to helping teachers plan their instruction in these and other topics effectively.

Perhaps the most important objective of mathematical instruction at the higher levels is the development of the ability to understand *generalized* principles and concepts and to apply these generalizations properly to particular situations or problems. At the same time, this seems to present to students greater difficulty than almost anything else. It is therefore a matter to which special attention needs to be given very consistently. The following examples may be cited by way of illustration.

1. The recognition of type forms in factorable expressions which in themselves may be rather complicated, such as

   $12y^3 - 4y^6 + x^{2a} - 9$ (difference of two squares)
   $a^3 + 8b^3 + c^3 + 6a^2b + 12ab^2$ (sum of two cubes)

2. The recognition of possibilities for reducing equations or expressions to standard forms which can be more readily handled, such as

   $x^{16} + 5x^8 + 6 = 0$ (quadratic equation in x^8)
   $x^4 + x^2 + 1 = 0$ (factorable by difference of two squares)

3. Interpretation of the implications of consistency and inconsistency of a system of m linear equations in n unknowns

4. Understanding the generality of the relations given by the remainder theorem, the factor theorem, the fundamental theorem of algebra, the theorems giving relations between roots and coefficients, etc.
5. Understanding the significance of the procedures used in solving and checking literal equations and formulas
6. Applying the formula for the rth term in a binomial expansion for a given value of r, and similarly applying other generalized formulas to the determination of values in particularized cases

It is important that instruction be carried on at suitable levels of difficulty and expectation. At times there is an unwarranted, though not unnatural, tendency among teachers to assume that all the material in a textbook is suitable for the students in the grade in which the textbook is used. In connection with any given topic the teacher should try to decide how far he can carry his particular class profitably in relation to that topic and what should be the nature and difficulty of the exercises which he should use and the assignments he should make. It is to be expected that a spiral treatment of topics in algebra will generally produce better results than too intensive treatment, carried beyond appropriate levels, in any one year. Thus, instead of trying to teach all of factoring in the first course, a few simple and easily understandable cases are given at that level. Later, at the more advanced level of instruction, these are reviewed and more difficult ones considered, and this process is repeated in subsequent years. The work should always challenge the best efforts of the students, but if it is carried beyond their capacities, it will lose its meaning and value.

Finally, the elements of time, practice, review, application, and maintenance are of extreme importance. They are all involved in a program of instruction that looks to a fundamental mastery of algebra. The great generalities do not emerge in an instant or a year. They are the result of a long process of assimilation and familiarization. They require not hours but years of concentrated attention and sheer hard intellectual work, beginning with simple concepts and proceeding to ever more difficult and abstract relationships. Rome was not built in a day, nor is there any quick, easy short cut to a real mastery of algebra. Persistent review and practice, both in the skills of algebra and in their application, are required. Otherwise, the skills and understandings will deteriorate through disuse.

Under a program of subject matter selected to present a reasonable challenge to ability, to provide a gradual expansion of the horizon of mathematical understanding, and to demand an incessant program of maintenance, the student may expect to arrive at a *real mastery* of algebra. Such a mastery of appropriate subject matter of algebra not only will provide that student with a sound basis for exploring mathematics at its higher levels but also will give him a richness of insight into the related fields of science.

Provision for superior students Students who take algebra beyond the first course usually do so voluntarily, through some special interest in the subject. The problem of motivation is thus less acute, and some degree of selection with respect to mathematical aptitude will have been operative. At the same time the subject is sufficiently demanding that the regular work of the course will call forth serious effort on the part of most of the students. There will be a few, however, for whom the regular work is easy, and there may be an occasional student for whom the regular course is not much of a challenge. These are the students who possess that rare combination of mathematical insight and originality which marks them as potential leaders in mathematics, and the shortage of such leaders is regarded in high places as a matter of grave and increasing concern.

We cannot afford to let mathematical talent go to waste. Yet this will happen unless students of exceptional talent are given work which will call forth their interest and their best efforts. For those students who are simply above average, varied assignments with perhaps less routine work and more emphasis on relatively difficult problems may suffice. It is usually easy to find some such problems in the regular textbook or in collateral textbooks. They may be oriented to the unit or to topics currently being studied by the class, but this need not be the case. Students with marked ability and a taste for originality will often take keen delight in working on challenging problems which may be quite unrelated to the current work of the class. Such journals as the *Mathematics Student Journal*, the *Pentagon*, *School Science and Mathematics*, and the *Mathematics Teacher* are good sources of problems suitable for this purpose, as are some of the numerous books on mathematical recreations.

Once in a while one may find a student not merely superior but of truly exceptional insight and endowed with insatiable curiosity and the capacity for sustained effort. Such a student may work with more keen interest in carrying on independently an intensive investigation of some collateral topic than in working on short-term special assignments. Serious work of this kind should be encouraged, though with suitable safeguards. For high school students such topics as the following could serve as foci for such investigations: theorems about polynomials of higher degree; properties of determinants; exponential and logarithmic functions; mathematical induction and the binomial formula; permutations, combinations, and probability; notation for and operations with sets; elements of symbolic logic.

Only the student who is capable of a high order of independent and sustained work should be given this sort of collateral assignment. The teacher's role will be to recommend appropriate reference works, to receive and comment on the progress reports that the student will make from time to time, and to appraise the final oral and written reports that should be presented. This will make extra work for the teacher, but if the assignment is well carried out, it can yield high dividends.

One caution is in order. Special projects of this kind should be regarded as complementing but not replacing the regular course in algebra, and such assignments should be made only with the most careful discrimination. Sometimes the enthusiasm of highly capable students makes them impatient with the need to master routine but necessary skills and details. But such neglect of fundamental groundwork imposes severe limitations on eventual progress, and it should not be permitted. Talented students may not require so much time as their less capable classmates to acquire the necessary details and skills, but they should be held responsible for their mastery, just as the other students are.

EXERCISES

1. The usual way of beginning the second year's work in algebra is to give a concentrated and extensive review of the fundamental operations. What are the reasons for this? What disadvantages does it entail? Can you suggest a better plan? What is it?

2. Use both the pivotal-element and sweep-out processes to solve these systems of equations:

a.
$$\begin{aligned} x + y + z + u &= 5 \\ 2x - y + z - 2u &= -1 \\ x - 2y + z - 2u &= -1 \\ 3x + 2y - 2z + u &= 0 \end{aligned}$$

b.
$$\begin{aligned} x + y + z + u &= 3 \\ 2x + 2y + 3z - u &= 8 \\ z - 3u &= 2 \\ 3x + 3y + 5z - 3u &= 13 \end{aligned}$$

3. Consider the two relations $y \geqq x^2$ and $y^2 = 8x$ (1) with the domain for both x and y the set of integers such that $-3 \leqq x \leqq +8$ and $-5 < y < +10$ and (2) with the domain for both x and y the set of real numbers. (*a*) Draw the graph of each relation. (*b*) What is the solution set when the two relations are considered simultaneously? (*c*) What is the solution set for the two relations when the "is greater than" (>) is removed from $y \geqq x^2$?

4. List the specific things you would want your students to know or be able to do as a result of their study of quadratic equations in their second year of algebra?

5. What difficulties would you expect your students to encounter in their work with quadratic equations? How could you help them avoid or overcome these difficulties? Consider each separately and be as specific as you can.

6. Give reasons for the appropriateness of teaching logarithms in the algebra course rather than in connection with the trigonometry course.

7. Make a list of the main outcomes you would strive for in teaching logarithms and exponentials in a second course in algebra. Why is it desirable to teach these two topics together?

8. What specific outcomes should be sought in work with radicals? What specific difficulties can students be expected to have in connection with this work?

9. Show that the equation $\sqrt{3x - 5} + \sqrt{2x + 3} + 1 = 0$ has no solution, although the derived quadratic equation does have two real solutions. (Such problems illustrate and emphasize the importance of thoughtful checking of algebraic work.)

10. Given: $f(x) = x^2 - 5x + 28$ and $g(x) = 12 - 5x + x^2$. Many students, if instructed to write the correct expressions for $f(12)$ or

$g(h + 17)$, would report that they could not do it. Do you think this is because of mathematical disability or do you think it is due mainly to not knowing how to interpret the notation used? How important is this question? Discuss.

11. With reference to exercise 10, what are some steps you would take to remedy the situation?

12. The resistance of a wire to the passage of an electric current is directly proportional to the length of the wire and inversely proportional to the square of the diameter. Write this as a variation equation, using R, L, and D to represent resistance, in ohms; length, in feet; and diameter, in mils, respectively, and K to represent the constant of variation.

13. A 24-gauge copper wire of diameter 20.1 mils and length 150 feet has a resistance of 3.85 ohms. Compute the constant of variation K and determine the length of 30-gauge copper wire (diameter 10.0 mils) required to make a coil whose resistance is 75 ohms. Explain the part which the constant K plays in the solution.

14. Show how the compound interest law, and consequently the study of annuities and the mathematics of life insurance, is based upon a geometric progression. Give illustrations to show applications of the compound interest law to fields other than finance.

15. The study of inequalities often receives no attention in high school algebra and little attention in college algebra. What do you think is the reason for this? Criticize or justify this practice, giving arguments to support your position.

16. Graph each of the following and discuss each graph: $y = 3$, $y \geqq 3$, $y < 3$, $y < -1$, $y \leqq x$, $y \geqq x - 1$, $3y < 2x$, $y = x^2$, $y \geqq x^2$, and $y < x^2$. Take the domains of x and y to be the set of real numbers.

17. Prove the remainder theorem and show that the factor theorem is actually just a special case of the remainder theorem. Do you think students generally get the full significance of the remainder theorem? If not, why don't they?

18. Explain to the class the principle of mathematical induction. As an illustration of this principle, prove that, if n represents any positive integer, then

$$\sum_{i=1}^{n} i(i + 1)(i + 2) = \tfrac{1}{4}n(n + 1)(n + 2)(n + 3)$$

19. Make a list of specific difficulties which students may be expected to encounter in the study of one of the following topics and suggest ways of helping them avoid or overcome the difficulties: progressions, logarithms, irrational roots, determinants, complex numbers, inequalities, quadratic equations, equations of third or higher degree, mathematical induction, binomial theorem, permutations and combinations, and probability.

20. What advantages, if any, accrue to students from the practice of checking their own solutions of, say, quadratic equations or equations involving radicals?

21. What advantages, if any, accrue to students from having printed answer lists available for some of the problems they are to solve? What disadvantages may attend this practice?

The next four problems were taken from the Problem Section of School Science and Mathematics. *Present your solutions.*

22. Solve for x: $\sqrt[3]{e^{2+x}}\,\sqrt[4]{e^{4-x}}\,\sqrt[5]{e^{5x-1}} = 1$.

23. If $\log (x + z) + \log (x - 2y + z) = 2 \log (x - z)$, show that x, y, and z are in harmonic progression.

24. Find two numbers such that their sum multiplied by the sum of their squares is 5,500 and their difference multiplied by the difference of their squares is 352.

25. Eliminate x and y from the following system of equations: $x^2y = a$, $x(x + y) = b$, $2x + y = c$.

26. Assume that you have discovered in your class a student of extraordinary ability who does the regular work of the class with little effort and who wishes also to carry on an independent study of transfinite numbers. Compile a list of suitable references which you would recommend for him.

BIBLIOGRAPHY

Barnes, George: An Easily Constructed Chart for Finding the Roots of Quadratic Equations, *Mathematics Teacher,* **50** (1957), 40–42.

Beckenbach, Edwin, and Richard Bellman: "An Introduction to Inequalities" (New York: Random House, Inc., 1961).

Bellman, Richard: On the Concepts of a Problem and Problem-solving, *American Mathematical Monthly,* **67** (1960), 119–134.

Bennett, Howard C.: A Graphical Method Useful in Solving Certain Algebraic and Trigonometric Inequalities, *Mathematics Teacher,* **46** (1953), 82–85.

Brown, Elizabeth F.: Roots and Logarithms, *Mathematics Teacher,* **49** (1956), 544–547.

Brown, James P.: Further Deciphering of the General Trinomial, *Mathematics Teacher,* **48** (1955), 586–587.

Byrkit, Donald R.: Linear Indeterminate Equations: An Aid to Enrichment, *School Science and Mathematics,* **60** (1960), 627–631.

Clair, H. S.: The Laws of Algebra and Modern Algebra, *School Science and Mathe*matics, **53** (1953), 29–33.

Commission on Mathematics, Report of: "Appendices" (New York: College Entrance Examination Board, 1959), pp. 29–63, 74–93.

Dalton, Leroy C.: Complex Numbers and Loci, *Mathematics Teacher,* **54** (1961), 229–233.

Diamond, Louis E.: Introduction to Complex Numbers, *Mathematics Magazine,* **30** (1957), 233–249.

Fehr, Howard F.: "Secondary Mathematics: A Functional Approach for Teachers" (Boston: D. C. Heath and Company, 1951), pp. 36–73, 123–167.

Gruenberger, Fred: Imaginaries, *Mathematics Teacher,* **47** (1954), 11–12.

Hohfeld, Joseph F.: An Analysis of the Quadratic, *Mathematics Teacher,* **54** (1961), 138–141.

Jones, Phillip S.: Complex Numbers: An Example of Recurring Themes in the Development of Mathematics, *Mathematics Teacher,* **47** (1954), 106–114, 257–263, 340–345.

Kane, Robert B.: Linear Programming: An Aid to Decision Making, *Mathematics Teacher,* **53** (1960), 177–179.

Lange, Lester H.: Another Encounter with Geometric Series, *School Science and Mathematics,* **55** (1955), 472–476.

Law, Carol: Arithmetical Congruences with Practical Applications, *Mathematics Magazine,* **32** (1958), 221–227.

Lewis, Jesse C.: An Interesting Problem Involving Indeterminate Equations, *Mathematics Teacher,* **53** (1960), 540–542.

Maskewitsch, D.: On the Equation $ax + by = c$, *School Science and Mathematics,* **60** (1960), 288–290.

______: Geometric Solution of a Quadratic Equation, *School Science and Mathematics,* **61** (1961), 457–461.

McGaughey, A. W.: The Imaginary Number Problem, *American Mathematical Monthly,* **64** (1957), 193–194.

Meserve, Bruce E.: Using Geometry in Teaching Algebra, *Mathematics Teacher,* **45** (1952), 567–571.

______: Foundations of Algebra, *Mathematics Teacher,* **50** (1957), 356–360.

Mirsky, Robert: Streamlining the Proof of the Binomial Theorem, *Mathematics Teacher,* **48** (1955), 96.

National Council of Teachers of Mathematics: *Twenty-third Yearbook* (Washington, D.C.: National Council of Teachers of Mathematics, 1957).

______: *Twenty-fourth Yearbook* (Washington, D.C.: National Council of Teachers of Mathematics, 1959).

______: *Twenty-eighth Yearbook* (Washington, D.C.: National Council of Teachers of Mathematics, 1963).

Niven, Ivan: "Numbers: Rational and Irrational" (New York: Random House, Inc., 1961).

Nowlan, F. S.: The Solution of a Radical Equation, *Mathematics Teacher,* **46** (1953), 490

Payne, Joseph H.: Self-instructive Enrichment Topics for Bright Pupils in High School Algebra, *Mathematics Teacher,* **51** (1958), 113–117.

Peters, Max: An Introductory Lesson in Logarithms, *New Jersey Mathematics Teacher,* **13** (1957), 3–6.

Ransom, W. R.: Elementary Calculation of

Logarithms, *Mathematics Teacher,* **47** (1954), 115–116.

_____: Second Order Interpolation, *School Science and Mathematics,* **55** (1955), 460–461.

Read, Cecil B.: Does Unity Divided by Zero Equal Infinity? *School Science and Mathematics,* **52** (1952), 736.

Ringenberg, L. A.: Numbers and Number Systems, *Mathematics Magazine,* **32** (1958), 265–276.

Rio, Sheldon T., and Walter J. Sanders: Interval Graphing, *Mathematics Teacher,* **54** (1961), 194–200.

Schaaf, William L.: Meaning, Rigor and Discipline in Secondary Mathematics, *Mathematics Teacher,* **44** (1951), 259–261.

Schack, Arthur: Two Forms of Mathematical Induction, *Mathematics Magazine,* **32** (1958), 83–85.

School Mathematics Study Group: "Elementary Functions" (New Haven, Conn.: Yale University Press, 1960).

_____: "Intermediate Mathematics" (New Haven, Conn.: Yale University Press, 1959).

_____: "Introduction to Matrix Algebra" (New Haven, Conn.: Yale University Press, 1960).

Scott, C. H.: Dimensional Analysis, *School Science and Mathematics,* **57** (1957), 32–36.

Shuster, Carl N.: The Calculation of Logarithms in the High School, *Mathematics Teacher,* **48** (1955), 322–323.

_____: Graphic Solution of a Quadratic Equation, *Mathematics Teacher,* **54** (1961), 142–144.

Spiegel, M. R.: Reciprocal Quadratic Equations, *American Mathematical Monthly,* **59** (1952), 175–177.

Stewart, Lurline: The Binomial Theorem, *Mathematics Teacher,* **53** (1960), 344–348.

Strickland, Warren: Algebra of Complex Numbers, *School Science and Mathematics,* **58** (1958), 690–692.

Utz, W. R.: Maxima and Minima without the Calculus, *School Science and Mathematics,* **57** (1957), 263–266.

Weiner, L. M.: A Direct Proof of the Binomial Theorem, *Mathematics Teacher,* **48** (1955), 412.

Wendt, Arnold: A Simple Example of a Noncommutative Algebra, *Mathematics Teacher,* **52** (1959), 534–540.

_____: Solving Simultaneous Linear Equations, *Mathematics Teacher,* **53** (1960), 12–17.

Whitford, D. E., and M. S. Klamkin: On an Elementary Derivation of Cramer's Rule, *American Mathematical Monthly,* **60** (1953), 186–187.

Yates, Robert C.: Solving Symmetric Equations, *School Science and Mathematics,* **54** (1954), 234–235.

SIXTEEN

The teaching of geometry in the junior high school

IN THE HANDS of an enthusiastic and competent teacher the geometry of the junior high school becomes for the students not only an important subject of study but a fascinating one as well. Children live and grow in a world that abounds in geometric form. They see circles in coins and wheels, angles in the hands of clocks and in gables of houses, and cylinders in tree trunks and tiles and tin cans. Cones are filled with ice cream and are found on the ends of newly sharpened pencils. Doors and sheets of paper are rectangles. Kites are polygons. Marbles and oranges are spheres. Some figures are thin and flat, while others are not. Some are symmetrical, while others have very irregular outlines or surfaces. All children have countless times observed common geometrical forms such as those mentioned above, and often even very young children know the names of some of them.

But perhaps because of their very familiarity these geometric configurations are often seen without being sensed, and even when attention is focused upon them their properties may not be understood. Yet children of junior high school age have great curiosity, and well-conducted study of the properties of geometric figures seldom fails to capture their interest. The main objective of geometrical instruction in the junior high school is to help the students learn to clarify, organize, and extend their understanding of geometrical concepts and relationships and to increase their interest in doing so. The approach is informal in the sense that it stresses understanding rather than formal proof and draws upon intuition and experimentation as well as upon clear thinking. The purpose of this chapter is to consider some matters which seem important in connection with geometrical instruction at this preformal level.

The objectives of junior high school geometry According to the Commission on Mathematics there are three main objectives for the study of geometry in high school.[1] They are:

1. The acquisition of information about geometric figures in the plane and in space
2. The development of an understanding of the deductive method as a way of thinking, and a reasonable skill in applying this method to mathematical situations
3. The provision of opportunities for original and creative thinking

The third objective is, of course, a major objective of instruction in geometry whether in the junior high school, senior high school, or junior college. The second objective is a principal responsibility of the senior high school. The first objective is primarily the concern of the junior high school.

The geometrical experience of the student entering the junior high school has been somewhat limited and quite casual. It has extended from the more or less incidental perceptions of size, shape, and position that take place during preschool days to the more systematic treatment of measurement, drawing to scale, and calculation of perimeters, areas, and volumes in the arithmetic of the sixth grade. The geometrical information of the preschool and elementary school period has been acquired largely through manipulation and computation. It is the function of the junior high school (1) to systematize this information and extend it to some of the broader and more general aspects of the geometry of everyday life; (2) to aid the student in becoming familiar with the basic geometrical concepts and in understanding the fundamental techniques, such as the use of the straightedge, protractor, compass, and the techniques of measurement and construction; (3) to acquaint the student with the characteristics of good geometrical notation; and (4) to bridge the gap from the largely manipulative type of geometric experiences to the more formal logical processes of demonstrative

[1] "Report of the Commission on Mathematics" (New York: College Entrance Examination Board, 1959), pp. 22–23.

geometry. Such a geometry has been called "intuitive," but it is rather a geometry *sui generis* which is characterized by intuition, experiment, and an informal approach to the more formal processes of demonstrative geometry. To omit any one of these three aspects would be to give an imperfect description of the province and function of the geometry of the junior high school.

Committee recommendations. While the major concern over the secondary school program in geometry has been directed at the senior high school, it has been recognized that the foundation for effective work at that level must be laid in the elementary school and the junior high school. For many years some aspects of informal geometry have been included in the work of the seventh and eighth grades. Since the middle of the century the awakening concern about the mathematical program of the secondary school has brought increased attention to the importance of work in preformal geometry. Experimental materials have been and are being prepared and tried out both in experimental projects and by regular teachers in many schools throughout the country. The importance of the matter is such that both the Secondary School Curriculum Committee and the Commission on Mathematics felt it urgent to include in their reports recommendations relative to basic aspects of the work in geometry at both the junior and senior high school levels.

With respect to the program in geometry in the junior high school the report of the Secondary School Curriculum Committee contains the following statement:[2]

1. The learning experiences in geometry that precede the one-year [senior high school] course should be *valuable in themselves* and not solely as prerequisites for the deductive geometry that is to follow. We must remember that we are concerned with the education of all youth, not merely those who are college-capable. This consideration is particularly important in grades seven and eight. In these grades there must be provided a program of instruction which is appropriate for pupils whose future study of geometry must be confined largely to its applications, as well as one which is appropriate for those who will later study geometry as a deductive system.
2. Those learning experiences that are designed as preparation for deductive geometry should not require any great amount of verbalization of theorems that are to be proved later in the formal course. The time can be employed to better advantage in developing certain concepts that provide a foundation for the subsequent study of deductive proof. In cases where it is necessary to deal with statements pertaining to congruence, similarity, relations between the sides of a right triangle, etc., there should be constant emphasis on the difference between proof and experimental verification.

[2]Report of the Secondary School Curriculum Committee, *Mathematics Teacher*, **52** (1959), 406.

The report then proceeds to outline the program for grades 7 to 9 in this fashion:

Grades seven and eight (the introduction or observation stage):
Drawing, both freehand and with straightedge and compass
Drawings that represent three-dimensional objects
Perspective drawing
Conjectures based on inductive and intuitive reasoning
Use of measuring instruments, ruler and protractor
Recognition of the fact that all measures are approximate
Relative error; distinction between precision and accuracy
Experiments designed to test conjectures about the areas and volumes of certain solids
Construction of templates for some solids

Concepts: Application of set language to geometry; the set of points on a line, the set of lines on a point, the set of lines on a plane, the set of planes on a line, intersection of two sets; one-to-one correspondence; simple locus problems in two and three dimensions; congruence, ratio, similarity, concurrence of lines, collinearity of points; "inside" and "outside" of a closed curve; the if-then form of a statement; exercises which are "open-ended" in the sense that the pupil is given a certain set of data or a certain drawing and asked to draw as many conclusions as he can.

The above material might well constitute 20 or 30 per cent of that presented in grades seven and eight.

Grade 9:

Liberal use should be made of geometric drawing in illustrating problems wherever possible. The one-to-one correspondence idea should be applied to the number scale and to the development and use of the Cartesian coordinate system.

The Commission on Mathematics did not list any specific geometric content for the ninth grade, but it did describe a program for grades 7 and 8 in these words:[3]

Geometry

Measurement: The ability to operate with and transform the several systems of measure, including the metric system of length, area, volume, and weight. Geometric measurements, including length of a line segment, perimeter of a polygon, and circumference of a circle, areas of regions enclosed by polygons and circles, surface areas of solids, volumes of solids, measure of angles (by degrees). The student should know the difference between the process of measuring and the measure of the quantity. Ability to apply measurement to practical situations. Use of measurement in drawing to scale and finding lengths indirectly.

Relationships among geometric elements: These include the concepts of parallel, perpendicular, intersecting, and oblique lines (in a plane and in a

[3]"Report of the Commission on Mathematics," *op. cit.*, p. 19.

space); acute, right, obtuse, complementary, supplementary, and vertical angles; scalene, isosceles, and equilateral triangles; right triangles and the Pythagorean relation; sum of the interior angles of a triangle. The use of instruments in constructing figures; ideas of symmetry about a point and a line.

Analysis of the content of junior high school geometry The kinds of geometric configurations studied in the junior high school are relatively simple and relatively few. Line segments, angles, triangles and other polygons, and circles are about the only planar figures to be considered, while the list of solids included only prisms, pyramids, cylinders, cones, and spheres. Thus it might seem at first thought that the instructional problems would be equally few and simple.

However, one must consider that while the word "circle" represents only a single type of figure, there are many concepts to be taught and learned about circles. Line segments and angles are not to be disposed of merely by defining or illustrating them. The mere naming and identification of these configurations is only a first step in studying them. Their properties must be investigated. Comparisons must be made. Ways of measuring them must be discovered and means devised for making indirect measurements when direct measurement is not possible. The very meaning of "direct measurement" needs to be clarified, as also does the meaning of a "unit" and the need for and the definitions of certain standard units. Estimating and the approximate nature of measurement need to be stressed. A technical nomenclature and terminology needs to be mastered and associated with various geometric concepts. Measuring instruments need to be studied, and students need to acquire some skill and facility in their use. Properties of geometric figures and relations among such figures and their properties need to be formulated, both in words and in terms of equations or inequalities in which the variables are expressed in terms of literal symbols. Formulas need to be evaluated. Symmetry, which characterizes many common geometric forms, should be given special study. The list could be extended, but there is no need. Enough has been said to make it clear that any analysis of the content of the informal geometry of the junior high school is a complex task.

The subject matter for study can be classified and organized in various ways. With each kind of figure are associated certain properties, concepts, and technical terms, and these need to be learned and associated with that type of figure. For example, with the study of angles it would be important to associate the classification of angles as acute, right, obtuse, straight, and reflex, and such concepts and terms as (among others) the vertex and sides of an angle, adjacent angles, complementary and supplementary angles, alternate-interior angles and corresponding angles of a pair of lines cut by a transversal, interior and exterior angles of a triangle or polygon, how angles are measured, degree, protractor, equal angles, vertical angles, and an acceptable notation.

On the other hand, some properties, or characteristics, per se are associated with different kinds of figures. For example, all closed plane figures have characteristics which we call *perimeter* and *area.* The study of the perimeters and areas of such figures as rectangles, triangles, parallelograms, trapezoids, and circles forms an important part of the geometry of the junior high school. Similarly, volume and surface area are attributes of all solids, and the study of these attributes of certain simple three-dimensional figures is important at this level of instruction.

Thus the analysis of the content of junior high school geometry solely according to types of figures would be incomplete, as would an analysis solely in terms of properties of figures. Certainly each type of figure needs to be studied individually for determination of its properties, but this is not enough. Different types of figures sometimes are found to have similar properties, and this can be brought out only through comparisons. Yet the discovery of these similarities is no less important than discovery of the properties of the individual kinds of figures. Some of the significant generalizations of geometry emerge only through the cross association of the different properties of individual kinds of figures with the different types of figures which exhibit various particular properties.

Analysis of a unit of instruction: circles The present section represents an analysis, such as a teacher might make, of a unit built around a particular type of geometric figure, in this case, circles. It cannot be considered complete, but it at least suggests some of the important objectives and activities.

Vocabulary and understandings to be mastered. Circle, arc, major arc, minor arc, semicircle, quadrant, radius, radii, diameter, chord, center, circumference, area, central angle, inscribed angle, compass, tangent, secant, segment, sector, locus, pi (π), ratio, equal circles, concentric circles, intersecting circles, circle graph, inscribed circle, inscribed polygon, inside and outside of a circle, degree, protractor.

Important facts, relations, and principles to be established. Value of the ratio $\frac{\text{circumference}}{\text{diameter}}$ and how to find either of the terms when the other is known; how to find the area of a circle; circumferences of circles are proportional to their respective diameters or radii; measures of arcs on a circle are proportional to the measures of their central angles and vice versa; measures of arcs or measures of central angles in a circle are not in general proportional to the lengths of their respective chords; doubling the radius length doubles the circumference but does not double the area; doubling the area does not double the circumference or the diameter; any angle inscribed in a semicircle is a right angle.

Constructions. Drawing circles with given radii or diameters; drawing central angles of given sizes, using protractor; constructing chords of given lengths; constructing perpendicular bisectors of line segments; constructing tangents at given points on circles; constructing angles equal to given angles; constructing angle bisectors; measuring central angles with the protractor; making circle graphs; making designs involving circles or arcs.

Types of activities and problems. Measuring diameters, radii, and chords; measuring circumferences experimentally by rolling or string wrapping; determining experimentally the approximate value of pi (π); laying out circles experimentally on the ground by use of an angle mirror, and testing with tape; solving many numerical problems for determination of such values as circumferences, radii, central angles; areas of circles, sectors, or rings; arc lengths; ratios of areas, central angles, or arc lengths. At least some of the numerical problems should be based on data obtained by measurement.

Appreciations. The many places where circular forms are found in things we see in everyday life (coins, wheels, clock faces, dishes, etc.); the use of circular forms in designs; the use and the usefulness of circular forms in manufactured products; the role of the wheel (as a circle) in our civilization; the symmetries of the circle.

Problems and methods of instruction The particular instructional problems that will arise in connection with any unit of subject matter will depend on the specific objectives of that unit. Many of these problems can be foreseen by a careful, detailed listing of the particular understandings and abilities sought through the study of the unit. Every unit, whether it is built around a particular kind of geometric configuration (e.g., angles or circles) or around a particular geometric property of certain figures (e.g., perimeters or areas) will aim at the understanding and mastery of several kinds of things. These will usually include the mastery of an associated mathematical vocabulary; clarification of certain geometrical concepts; understanding of relationships within and among particular geometric figures under given conditions; the ability to make acceptable and helpful drawings and to use a suitable notation; the ability to make, interpret, and evaluate formulas; and the ability to understand certain geometric "facts" which in the future will come to be known as "theorems." These are the kinds of learning problems which the student will face in his study of informal geometry at this stage in his education.

The teacher, of course, will face them too, but from a different viewpoint. His concern must be to see that none of these problems is neglected, to provide suitable learning situations and activities through which the students will have optimal opportunity for attaining the desired understandings and abilities, and to help the students in appropriate ways to mastery of the objectives toward which the instruction is aimed.

The means at the teacher's disposal are numerous and varied. Since the principal aim at this stage is knowledge and understanding rather than formal proof, and methods or devices that will further such knowledge and understanding are appropriate. Direct measurement with measuring instruments, including the scaled ruler and protractor, may be used both to build clear understanding of the meaning and the approximate nature of measurement and to provide numerical data for experimental study of geometric figures and their properties. Chalkboard drawings accompanied by suitable explanatory comment serve to clarify many ideas. Meter sticks and balances borrowed from the science laboratory can be helpful in comparing systems of measurement, in obtaining numerical information, and in making clear the principles of proportion and the solution of equations.

Experiments in paper folding can lead to discovery of principles about angles and lines. Cross-section paper facilitates understanding of relationships through the construction and interpretation of graphs. Hollow cylinders and cones filled with sand lead to conclusions about relative volumes. The principle that volumes of similar solids are proportional to the cubes of corresponding dimensions can be verified by weighing, say, wooden spheres of different sizes. Field work with simple instruments, such as alidades, angle mirrors, and tapes, and even simple surveying equipment, provides interesting work in mapping small areas, and this, in turn, involves the use of many of the concepts, relations, and facts of geometry. In addition to this, it can contribute much to giving a sense of reality and importance to the classroom work in geometry. Indeed, there is no stage at which the mathematics laboratory plays a more important part than in connection with the informal work in geometry in the junior high school grades.

Thus the variety of means or methods of instruction appropriate to the subject and available to the teacher is large, and the ingenious teacher will find many ways of helping his students develop clear geometric concepts and understandings. Drawing, measuring, comparing, experimenting, discussing, explaining, questioning, conjecturing, verifying and testing—all these provide appropriate and helpful avenues for attaining the objectives of geometry at this stage of the students' education, so all are grist for the teacher's mill. Among them all, however, nothing is more important than his ability to "chalk-talk" well—to make good, clear chalkboard sketches and to accompany these with clear explanations of the ideas which he is trying to emphasize.

Junior high school geometry from a modern viewpoint Since the early 1960s the mathematics of the junior high school has begun to reflect the modern spirit which is in line with the recommendations of such groups as the Secondary School Curriculum Committee and the Commission on Mathematics and which characterizes the work of such important experimental projects as SMSG and UICSM, the University of Maryland Mathematics Project, the Ball State Project, the Greater Cleveland Program, the Madison Project, and others. This is true of geometry no less than of arithmetic and algebra. The work on geometry which will appear in junior high school textbooks of 1965 and later will exhibit marked differences from that which was found in books published in 1955. The geometrical configurations to be studied will be the same, but the discussions will involve new concepts, terminology, notation, and emphases that were not found in the earlier textbooks. These should serve the double purpose of giving greater preciseness, clarity, and interest to the study of geometry and of pointing up those permeating and unifying concepts which link parts of geometry to other parts and which link geometry to arithmetic and algebra.

The geometry in a modern course in junior high school mathematics will give increased attention to sharpness of definition, to new and more precise ways of thinking about geometric figures and their properties, and to the use of some modern terminology and symbolism. The concept and notation of sets will be prominent. Simple work with inequalities will receive appropriate attention, as will graphs and the association of ordered pairs of numbers with points in the coordinate plane. Geometric figures will often be described in terms of sets of points and their descriptions given by the use of formal set notation, terminology, and symbolism.

The following list of words or expressions, all of which were found in recent seventh- and eighth-grade textbooks, is illustrative of the increasing demands of the work at this level with respect to concepts and vocabulary:

Cartesian plane
Cartesian product
closed interval
collinear points
complement of a subset
congruence
congruent angles
congruent line segments
convex polygon
coordinates
coordinate axes
coplanar
endpoints
half line
inequality
intersection (of subsets)
locus
open interval
ordered pairs
ordered triples
quadrant
ray
set
simple closed curve
subset
union (of subsets)
variable
Venn diagram

Most of these terms would not have been found in seventh- and eighth-grade textbooks even as recently as 1960. A few which would probably have been found in earlier textbooks (e.g., congruent, locus) are now being used in a more sharply definitive sense than before.

Further evidence of this tendency to sharpen concepts and discussion of the subject matter can be found in the increasing use of the definitive symbolism and notation of contemporary mathematics, such as the following:

$\{\ \}$ for a set
$\cup$ for the union of two sets
$\cap$ for the intersection of two sets
ϵ for "is a member of"
$\wedge$ for "and also"
$\sim$ for "complement of" or for "not"
$\approx$ for "is approximately equal to"
$\cong$ for "is congruent to"
$AB < AC$ for "segment $\overline{AB}$ is less than segment $\overline{AC}$"
$\{x|x = \qquad\}$ "set builder" notation
$n \cap m$ for "the point of intersection of lines n and m"
(a,b) for "the ordered pair consisting of a and b in that order"
Graph S if $S = \{x,y|3x - y = 1, 0 \leq x \leq 5\}$ for "Make a graph of the set of all points (x,y) for which $3x - y = 1$, such that x shall not be negative and x shall not be greater than 5"

The hope is that the use of notation such as that illustrated above will serve both to make the statements compact and to clarify the concepts and relations under discussion.

The introduction of a technical terminology and symbolism which was not found in the older textbooks will, of course, mean that hereafter junior high school students will have to learn to avoid vagueness in their study of geometry, to read statements very carefully, to interpret statements and symbols exactly, and to make their written work precise and unambiguous, using appropriate symbolism where it can be helpful. This, of course, increases the demands made on the students with respect to these matters, and one might be inclined a priori to expect that students would react to these increased demands in a negative fashion. Actually, however, this seems not to be the case. Testimony of experienced teachers who have used "modern" materials in the seventh and eighth grades indicates that for the most part students appear to take the new vocabulary and symbolism in stride and to enjoy using it. Indeed, it may be that this material presents no more difficulty to many students in these grades than it does to some teachers who have not had previous experience with it.

Student problems

On the whole, students in the junior high school grades who are well-motivated should not be expected to have much difficulty with the informal geometry that they study. Normally they can already identify by name some of the common figures: circles, triangles, rectangles, squares, cones, cylinders, and spheres. They will need to learn the meanings of some new words, such as chord, arc, central angle, degree, vertex, corresponding parts, perpendicular and parallel lines, intersection, altitude, base, diagonal, prism, pyramid, formula, perimeter, area, volume, and the like, as well as to associate these words with the concepts which they represent. These, however, soon become familiar through illustration and repeated use in drawing, direct measurement, experimentation, and discussion. Many kinds of laboratory exercises can be used to advantage in clarifying such concepts and in building skill and facility in direct linear and angular measurement. It is important that mastery of the fundamental concepts and associated vocabulary not be slighted, but it is easily motivated and little difficulty need be anticipated. Estimating lengths and angles presents more of a problem. Considerable experience in drawing and measuring will usually be necessary to give students a basis for forming reliably good estimates, but through practice they can markedly improve their ability in this direction.

Probably the greatest difficulty which students encounter in their work in informal geometry is in connection with the mensuration formulas. For some students the use of literal notation to represent numbers will be new, and they will have to learn that a formula is simply a rule that tells what to do with certain numbers in order to get a desired number. This idea can be facilitated by showing how a rule stated in words can be translated into a more concise and convenient form by using letters or other symbols to represent the various component measures that were originally stated in words. It is helpful to show them schematically just how the verbally stated rule can lead to a more condensed form in which phrases are replaced by words and how these words, in turn, can be replaced by literal symbols.

(The area of a triangle)	(is found by taking)	(one half)	(the product of the base and the altitude)
Area	=	$\frac{1}{2}$	(base × altitude)
A	=	$\frac{1}{2}$	($b \times h$)

Conversely, students should be given many opportunities to translate formulas back into rules stated in verbal form.

Formulas for the perimeters and areas of some of the simple plane figures and for the volumes of some of the common geometric solids need to be learned: in particular, the formulas for the areas of the square, circle, rectangle, triangle, parallelogram, and trapezoid, for the surface of a sphere, and for the volumes of prisms or cylinders (altitude times area of base), cones or pyramids (one-third altitude times area of base), and the volume of a sphere. With these in hand students should be able to see how to find lateral surfaces of right regular prisms and pyramids and of right circular cylinders and cones when the necessary component data are known. A good deal of practice will be needed, however, both for making the students reasonably adept in selecting or making correct formulas to fit given cases and for giving training in making numerical substitutions and performing correctly the computations involved.

EXERCISES

1. The geometry of the junior high school has been called by various names: intuitive geometry, experimental geometry, observational geometry, practical geometry, and informal geometry. Comment on the implications of each of these designations and show in what ways it is appropriate.

2. In this chapter there is an analysis of a unit of instruction organized about the study of circles. Make a similar analysis of a unit of instruction organized about one of the following types of figure: triangles, polygons, cylinders, prisms, cones, pyramids, or spheres.

3. Make an analysis of a unit of instruction organized for the study of perimeters of familiar plane figures.

4. Make an analysis of a unit of instruction organized for the study of the areas of simple plane geometric figures.

5. Make an analysis of a unit of instruction organized for the study of volumes of the simple geometric solids.

6. Make an analysis of a unit of instruction organized for the study of surface areas of right regular prisms and pyramids, right circular cylinders and cones, and spheres.

7. Construct a spelling list of fifty words encountered in the study of informal geometry. If you give it as a test to your classes, it is likely that you will get some misspellings.

8. In the junior high school how much emphasis should be placed on the approximate nature of measurement and on the results of computing with approximate data?

9. Explain how to find the relative error in a measured value, and give some illustrations.

10. Compile a conversion table for translating measurements of length and area and volume made in our common English system of units into units of the metric system, and vice versa.

11. Make a large 360° protractor by trimming a piece of polar coordinate paper around its largest circle and cutting a small hole in the center through which the vertex of an angle can be seen. This can be used satisfactorily as a chalkboard protractor.

12. In connection with symmetrical figures, explain and give examples to illustrate what is meant by "symmetry" with respect to a line, with respect to a plane, and with respect to a point.

13. Explain to your class what is meant by drawing to scale. What properties of similar figures are involved in a scale drawing? Is a map in effect a scale drawing? Discuss this.

14. Find at least one method of mapping small outdoor areas by use of simple field instruments, such as the plane table, alidade, and tape, and demonstrate or describe this to your class.

15. Figure A, on page 448, is a rectangular figure in which the curved lines are composed of quadrantal arcs of circles whose radii can be determined from the dimensions shown. Make a formula for the area of the shaded part of the figure in terms of a. Evaluate this area if $a = 5$.

16. Explain as you would to a seventh-

grade class how to find the total surface and the volume of the tank shown in Figure B in terms of the dimensions r, s, and t shown on the diagram. Make formulas for finding the total surface and the volume. What difficulties would you expect seventh-graders to have with this problem, and why?

17. Let the diameter of a circle be divided into a number of segments, not necessarily equal, and on each of these segments as a diameter let a small circle be made. If the circumferences of all the little circles were added together, would the sum be less than, equal to, or greater than the circumference

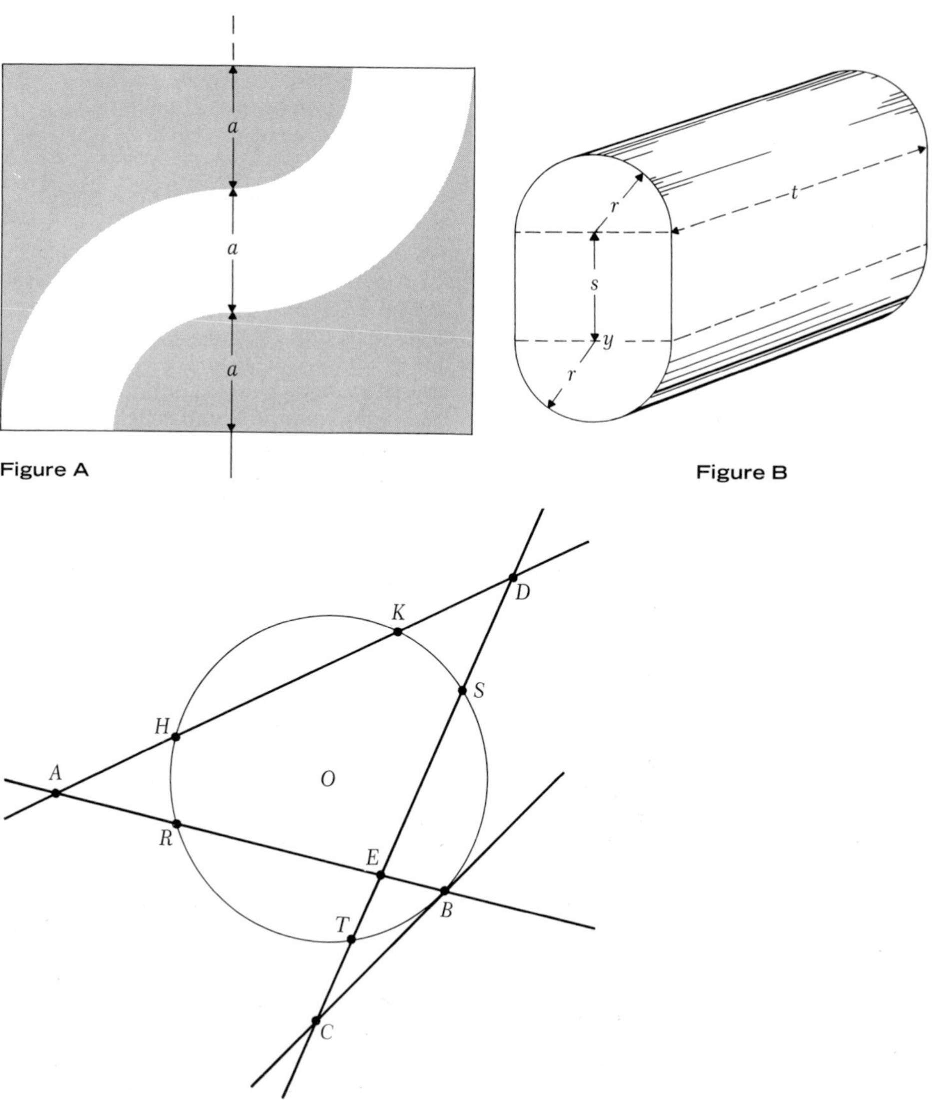

Figure A

Figure B

Figure C

of the original circle? How do you know? Is the answer intuitively evident?

18. If $ABCD$ is a trapezoid with bases $\overline{AB}$ and DC, and with diagonals $\overline{AC}$ and $\overline{BD}$ intersecting at E, compare the areas of triangles AED and CEB, and write down the numerical ratio of these areas. Explain as you would to a junior high school class.

19. Using compass and straightedge only, construct some designs which you think would be interesting examples for a junior high school class. What values can be gained by having the students construct some such designs?

20. How would you get a seventh-grade class to understand what is meant by the statement that areas of similar plane figures are proportional to the squares of the lengths of corresponding line segments in the figures? Give some examples to illustrate this principle.

21. Find the lateral area, total area, and volume of a right circular cone whose base has a radius of 4.00 inches, if the slant height of the cone is 7.00 inches. Explain.

22. Explain and illustrate the following terms as you would to a junior high school class: ray, coplanar, variable, ordered pair, locus, closed interval (on a number line), open interval, set, subset, union and intersection (of subsets), coordinate axes, coordinates of a point, and convex polygon.

23. In Figure C, identify and describe each of the following:

a. $\overline{AE} \cup \overline{ED}$ *b.* $\overline{ED} \cup \overline{DA}$
c. $(\overline{AE} \cup \overline{ED}) \cup \overline{DA}$ *d.* $\overline{AE} \cup (\overline{ED} \cup \overline{DA})$
e. $\overline{AB} \cap \overline{CD}$ *f.* $\overline{RB} \cap \overline{TD}$
g. $\{H\} \cap \{K\}$ *h.* $\overline{EB} \cap \overline{HK}$

24. Make graphs of the subsets R, S, and T of the set of numbers on the real number line if $S = \{n|\ 3 \leqq n \leqq 5\}$, $T = \{n|\ 0 \leqq n \leqq 3\}$, and $R = \{n|\ 4 \leqq n \leqq 6\}$. Describe and graph $(R \cup S) \cup T$.

25. Is $(7,2) \in S$, where $S = \{x,y|\ 3x - y = 1\}$? Translate this question into words, and explain and justify your answer as you would to a junior high school class. What difficulties might the students be expected to have?

26. Let $S = \{x,y|\ x^2 + y^2 = 25\}$. Make a good graph of S, and explain it as you would to a junior high school class.

27. Compare the sections on geometry in three different textbooks on junior high school mathematics published since 1962 with those found in textbooks published before 1960. In what ways are they alike, and in what ways do they differ? Report your findings to the class.

BIBLIOGRAPHY

Amir-Moez, Ali R.: "Ruler, Compasses, and Fun" (Lafayette, Ind.: Lafayette Printing Company, 1961).

Archer, Allene: Aids for Junior High Mathematics, *Twenty-second Yearbook* (Washington D.C.: National Council of Teachers of Mathematics, 1954), pp. 134–142.

Beeman, W. E.: Originality in Geometry, *Mathematics Teacher*, **50** (1957), 589–593.

Brandes, Louis Grant: "Geometry Can Be Fun" (Portland, Me.: J. Weston Walch, Publisher, 1958).

Brune, Irvin H.: Some Geometric Ideas for the Junior High School, *Mathematics Teacher*, **53** (1960), 620–626.

———: Geometry in the Grades, *Arithmetic Teacher*, **8** (1961), 210–219.

Dunn-Rankin, Peter, and Raymond Sweet: Enrichment: A Geometry Laboratory, *Mathematics Teacher*, **56** (1963), 134–140.

Hertzig, M.: Notes on the Teaching of Geometry in Junior High Schools, *High Points*, **40** (1958), 68–70.

Hinkel, Wilfred H.: The Trapezoid—and Area, *Mathematics Teacher*, **53** (1960), 106–108.

Johnson, Donovan A.: "Paper Folding for the Mathematics Class" (Washington, D.C.: National Council of Teachers of Mathematics, 1962).

———: Topology, *Twenty-seventh Yearbook* (Washington, D.C.: National Council of Teachers of Mathematics, 1963), pp. 148–164.

_____ and William H. Glenn: "Topology: The Rubber Sheet Geometry" (New York: McGraw-Hill Book Company, 1960).

_____ and William H. Glenn: "The World of Measurement" (New York: McGraw-Hill Book Company, 1961).

Johnson, Pauline: "Creating with Paper" (Seattle: University of Washington Press, 1958).

Jones, Burton W.: Reflections and Rotations, *Mathematics Teacher*, **54** (1961), 406–410.

Kluttz, Marguerite: The Mathematics Laboratory: A Meaningful Approach to Mathematics Instruction, *Mathematics Teacher*, **56** (1963), 141–145.

"Measurement: A Resource Unit for a Course in Basic Mathematics" (Albany, N.Y.: Bureau of Secondary Curriculum Development, The New York State Education Department, 1958).

Meserve, Bruce, and Max A. Sobel: "Mathematics for Secondary Schools" (Englewood Cliffs, N.J.: Prentice-Hall, Inc., 1962), pp. 177–191.

Payne, Joseph N., and Robert C. Seber: Measurement and Approximation, *Twenty-fourth Yearbook* (Washington, D.C.: National Council of Teachers of Mathematics, 1959), pp. 182–228.

Ravielli, A.: "An Adventure in Geometry" (New York: The Viking Press, Inc., 1957).

Reeve, W. D.: Informal Geometry in the Junior High School, *School Science and Mathematics*, **56** (1956), 371–380.

Rosskopf, Myron F.: Geometric Proof in the Eighth Grade, *Mathematics Teacher*, **54** (1961), 402–405.

Ruchlis, Hy, and Jack Engelhardt: "The Story of Mathematics: Geometry for the Young Scientist" (Irvington-on-Hudson, N.Y.: Harvey House, 1958).

Rutland, Leon, and Max Hosier: Some Basic Geometric Ideas for the Elementary Teacher, *Arithmetic Teacher*, **8** (1961), 357–362.

Scannel, A., and M. Fridrich: Finding Art in the Geometry Classroom, *School Arts*, **55** (1956), 33–34.

Schaaf, William L.: "Basic Concepts of Elementary Mathematics" (New York: John Wiley & Sons, Inc., 1960), pp. 59–64.

School Mathematics Study Group: "Mathematics for Junior High School," vols. 1 and 2 (New Haven, Conn: Yale University Press, 1960).

Sensiba, Daniel E.: Geometry and Transformations, *Twenty-seventh Yearbook* (Washington, D.C.: National Council of Teachers of Mathematics, 1963), pp. 302–311.

Sister Mary Fides: Geometry Decorates Our Lunch Room, *Catholic School Journal*, **54** (1954), 20–21.

Smith, D. E., and W. D. Reeve: "The Teaching of Junior High School Mathematics" (Boston: Ginn and Company, 1927).

Spooner, George: "Sets, Geometry, Numeration: Mathematics Enrichment Programs A, B, and C" (New York: Harcourt, Brace & World, Inc., 1962).

Steinhaus, Hugo: "Mathematical Snapshots" (Fair Lawn, N.J.: Oxford University Press, 1956).

University of Maryland Mathematics Project: "Mathematics for the Junior High School," books 1 and 2 (College Park, Md.: University of Maryland, 1959).

Webber, G. Cuthbert, and John A. Brown: "Basic Concepts of Mathematics" (Reading, Mass: Addison-Wesley Publishing Company, Inc., 1963).

Woodby, Lauren G.: How Far Can You See? *Twenty-seventh Yearbook* (Washington, D.C.: National Council of Teachers of Mathematics, 1963), pp. 269–272.

"You Will Like Geometry" (Chicago: Museum of Science and Industry).

SEVENTEEN

The teaching of geometry in the senior high school

THE INFORMAL GEOMETRY of the junior high school will constitute the complete geometry program of many students. For those who continue their study of geometry in the senior high school, intuition and experiment will still be an effective aid, but the major purposes of instruction will be to instill in the students an appreciation of the significance of logical demonstration; to acquaint them with effective methods of clear, impartial thinking, critical evaluation, and intelligent generalization; to train them in the techniques of discovery of truth; and to introduce them to the meaning of mathematical rigor and precision.

The demonstrative geometry of the senior high school should aim to develop the habits of independent and careful thinking rather than strive to present the subject matter of geometry as a *finished* model of deductive thinking. It is extremely important that each pupil do his own thinking, observing, and comparing and that new ideas, statements, truths, and theorems be discovered by the pupil himself. Teachers should therefore give thoughtful and conscientious consideration to the most effective means of attaining these goals of instruction. Each teacher should have a clear comprehension of the nature of deductive reasoning and of the significance of demonstration. He needs to know the distinguishing characteristics of various techniques and patterns of careful reasoning, and he needs to be aware of the difficulties that students have in their efforts to attain these understandings.

Nature of the program As pointed out in the preceding chapter, there is general agreement that many of the important properties of, and relations among, geometric figures can be learned and understood by students in the junior high school grades. Some seem intuitively evident. Others can be made to seem plausible and convincing through informal inductive methods such as drawing, measurement, observation, simple experiments, and simple inferences based upon these activities. Thus students should normally be expected to begin the study of demonstrative geometry with a fairly extensive background of geometrical concepts and "facts." It is a responsibility of the junior high school to see that they do.

The responsibility of senior high school geometry, by contrast, is defined mainly within the province of postulational reasoning. This implies, of course, the mastery of a body of significant theorems, but more importantly it implies intelligent comprehension of the methods involved in arriving at and establishing the truths embodied within such theorems. There is a definite propaedeutic value in the mastery of a number of geometric theorems which is to be neither overlooked nor minimized. In the main, however, such academic value is overshadowed by the importance to the individual of the technique of discovery, evaluation, and establishment of truth. The clear statement of definitions, the critical analysis of assumptions, the careful weighing of evidence, and the impartial deduction of implied conclusions are invaluable contributions which the intelligent study of demonstrative geometry may make to the general education of senior high school pupils.

Furthermore, students should be led to an appreciation of the postulational structure of geometry. They should recognize that different geometries with distinct basic postulates can be structured, some infinite and some finite.[1] They should have the opportunity to know of the existence of non-Euclidean geometries as well as Euclidean, projective as well as metric, and of the basic distinctions between such classifications of geometrical subject matter. Also they should have their consideration of geometric configurations oriented in three dimensions as well as in one and two dimensions, and the techniques they use should be extended to include those basic to analytic coordinate geometry as well as those basic to synthetic pure geometry.

One of the major problems that confront the teacher of demonstrative geometry is to teach the pupil to reason without reference to unestablished circumstantial evidence. For example, in proving a theorem related to triangles, a pupil is inclined to think in terms of a right triangle if one of the angles looks like a right angle, or in terms

[1]Burton W. Jones, Miniature Geometries, *Mathematics Teacher*, **52** (1959), 66–71.

of an equilateral triangle if the diagram looks as if the three sides are equal. The pupil's attention should be called to the dangerous pitfalls of inaccurate reasoning that lie behind such diagrammatic camouflages. An inexperienced pupil is likely to use such special diagrams and is just as likely to draw general conclusions from specific situations. Emphasis should be given to the necessity for drawing accurate diagrams with ruler and compass in situations that demand them, such as construction problems, prescribed written work, or any situation which places a great deal of emphasis on accuracy of figure. Freehand drawings that are approximately accurate may be used occasionally, particularly for the drawing of figures that are purely demonstration figures, such as in proofs of theorems or solutions of original exercises where the emphasis is on the method of attack. In every case the argument for the establishment of a truth should place the figure in the background; i.e., only known and established facts related to the figure should be used.

The above remarks do not intend to imply that there will be no place for intuition in senior high school geometry. A great many of the intuitive truths from junior high school geometry should be accepted as a background for senior high school geometry. Furthermore, there should be opportunities for experimentation and intuitive thinking in senior high school geometry. Intuition may often lead to understanding through conjectures, even though these may need to be validated subsequently by demonstration. But the teacher must make sure that a clearly defined distinction is drawn between the techniques and functions of experimentation, intuition, and demonstration. The subject matter of geometry offers a body of materials concerning which individuals can think impartially and critically and about which they can form conclusions entirely uninfluenced by their emotions. It is for this reason that the study of geometry can be used so effectively as a means for demonstrating and analyzing the techniques of careful argumentation and clear thinking.

Committee recommendations No area of the secondary school mathematics curriculum has received more critical study than has the geometry program. This has been due to the recognized inadequacies of the traditional pattern of Euclidean geometry that has dominated the high school program.[2] The Secondary School Curriculum Committee devoted 4 pages of its report to the discussion of this problem.[3] Likewise, the Commission on Mathematics devoted better than 5½ pages of

[2]Albert E. Meder, Jr., What's Wrong with Euclid? *Mathematics Teacher*, **51** (1958), 578–584.

[3]Secondary School Curriculum Committee, Report of, *ibid.*, **52** (1959), 404–408.

its report to the same problem,[4] and an additional 2 pages to presenting a proposed outline for a geometry program for grade 10.[5] Though there is some divergence in these two reports, particularly concerning the relative emphasis to be devoted to synthetic geometry and analytic (algebraic) geometry, there is a great deal of agreement on fundamental questions relating to an improved program in geometry. In particular, the two reports agree on the desirability of (1) the use of techniques and concepts from coordinate geometry, (2) an integrated treatment of plane and solid geometry, (3) more careful attention to the postulational structure of geometry, (4) providing opportunity for students to learn of the existence of geometries other than the Euclidean type, and (5) capitalizing on a basic geometric foundation which should be recognized as the responsibility of the junior high school.

The Secondary School Curriculum Committee, in placing a stronger emphasis on the synthetic study of geometry, underscores the need for "a sharper delineation of the meaning of deductive proof." It states that this implies a need for a better understanding of the nature of an indirect proof and for becoming familiar with the distinctions and relations between a theorem and its converses, inverses, and contrapositives. Also, it makes the very important point that "the kind of thinking that pupils are called upon to do in solving geometric originals is somewhat like that required of the mature classical mathematician.[6]

The recommendations of the two committees mentioned above are consonant with the things undertaken in important experimental programs such as the SMSG program, the UICSM program, and others. It is significant that these recommendations are being reflected in most of the recent commercially published textbooks on high school geometry, especially those published since 1962. This is indicated by the following summary statement of trends in geometry.[7]

1. The use of geometric and logical patterns to stimulate pupil discovery and thinking,
2. Careful definitions and the use of precise terminology,
3. Proofs of statements using either coordinate geometry or synthetic methods,
4. An emphasis upon the sets of elements under consideration and the relations among these elements,
5. The integration of some solid geometry with plane geometry.

[4]"Report of the Commission on Mathematics" (New York: College Entrance Examination Board, 1959), pp. 22–28.

[5]*Ibid.*, pp. 38–39. Also see the second volume of the report, entitled "Appendices," pp. 109–174, for discussions and illustrative examples of possible revisions in the treatment of the geometry program of the secondary school.

[6]Secondary School Curriculum Committee. *op. cit.*, p. 407.

[7]Bruce E. Meserve, New Trends in Algebra and Geometry, *Mathematics Teacher,* **55** (1962), p. 457.

Difficulties students have in geometry Mortality in high school geometry has traditionally been high, and this has been ascribed to various causes. Some have felt that it has been due to the difficulty of the subject. Others have blamed it on ineptitude or laziness on the part of the students. Still others have held that students lose interest in geometry because of its abstract nature, which they regard as having no practical value. There is probably something to each of these arguments. Admittedly demonstrative geometry is not the easiest of subjects to learn. It demands careful and sustained attention, perseverance, and a measure of ingenuity; in order to attain a real mastery of it most students do have to do some hard work. There probably are some students who, no matter how hard they might work, could never really master the subject, and undoubtedly there are persons whose preoccupation with matters of immediate practical usefulness leads them to deprecate any activity which to their minds is not obviously in this category. There may be some who are just too lazy to work at it, though in many cases this diagnosis is likely to be wrong.

There is, however, good reason to believe that in most cases the real reason for much of the failure in geometry and apathy toward the subject lies mainly in poor motivation and failure to provide clear insights into the meaning and method of the subject. Normally children simply are not lazy. When they appear to be, they are probably just bored. They will work hard at things which interest them, and they delight in games and puzzles. Probably much of the unsatisfactory work in geometry, and the dissatisfaction with which students view the subject, can be traced to the fact that it has not been taught to them in such a way as to excite their curiosity and present them with an intellectual challenge, but just as a rather dull job to be done. Geometry has the characteristics of both a game and a puzzle: an intellectual game to be played under accepted rules and a puzzle to challenge the ingenuity of the students. Indeed, these two characteristics in effect constitute the spirit of demonstrative geometry, and when students can be brought to approach the subject in this spirit the problem of boredom ceases to be a problem at all.

At the same time even good students who are interested in the subject do face some real problems in learning geometry. The more clearly teachers can identify these problems, the more effectively they can diagnose and understand the difficulties and so be in a better position to help the students to clearer insights and better habits of work. The listing which follows indicates some of the troubles which students do have from time to time in their study of geometry. Some teachers would doubtless suggest items which have not been included or would state the items differently. The list is certainly not exhaustive, but it may serve to alert teachers to the benefits which might come from rather careful study of the difficulties of individual students.

Some troubles which students have in studying geometry.

1. Inability to read well and to understand clearly the meanings of theorems or problems
2. Inability to restate theorems or problems in other words—especially in an "if-then" form
3. Failing to have the background of geometrical information well organized so as to facilitate the search for theorems or postulates which might be helpful in given situations
4. Not knowing how to get started
5. Failing to sketch out a skeleton plan of proof at the outset
6. Failing to justify each step in a proof, leaving weak links
7. Falling into the trap of circular reasoning
8. Trying to memorize proofs, sometimes without understanding them
9. Short attention span
10. Impatience to "get through"
11. Hurried, careless, unsystematic written work
12. Poor drawing and sketching of geometric figures
13. Drawing conclusions merely from the appearance of figures and diagrams

Some important things to teach students in geometry The practice of medicine has two fundamental aspects or objectives: curative and preventive. The one is pointed toward the treatment and amelioration of physical ailments after they have developed. The other is aimed at preventing the development of such ailments. Similarly, the teacher of mathematics should be concerned not only with diagnosing difficulties which his students have in their study of the subject and helping them overcome these but also with anticipating potential difficulties and trying to head these off and prevent them from becoming serious impediments to the students in their work.

The difficulties which students have in their work in geometry stem from the things, physical or mental, which they need to do or to know. Some of these are fairly definite and concrete. Others are less simple and more abstract. It is impossible to enumerate all the detailed things, overt and otherwise, which students will need to know or to do, or to try to do, in studying geometry. However, the following list does suggest in as definite a way as seems possible a considerable number of things which it seems important to try to teach to students; if mastered, they would do a good deal to help students avoid difficulties which often do arise.

Some important things to teach students in demonstrative geometry.

1. To understand the arbitrary nature of axioms (postulates, assumptions) and definitions

2. To understand the role which axioms, definitions, and undefined terms play in deductive reasoning and the contingent nature of the conclusion in a deductive proof
3. To be clear as to what axioms are accepted in the course being studied
4. To understand what a theorem is and why, in a deductive system, each theorem must be proved
5. To understand precisely what a deductive proof entails
6. To understand precisely what a construction problem entails
7. To translate verbal statements of theorems into the "if-then" form
8. To draw and sketch good representative diagrams and figures
9. To restate hypotheses and conclusions in "if-then" form, using the notation on the representative figure being used
10. To acquire the habit of sketching a plan of proof in attacking a theorem and of going through it rapidly to get it well in mind before starting to write out the detailed proof in finished form
11. To write out finished proofs correctly, completely, and in good form
12. To understand, for a given theorem, the meanings of inverse, converse, and contrapositive theorems and to be able to state these in "if-then" form, using the notation and the diagram used for the original theorem
13. To make some inverses and converses of their own and to try to prove these or to disprove them
14. To understand what the method of indirect proof is and why it is valid
15. To understand the pattern for using the method of indirect proof
16. To draw diagrams carefully and to label them appropriately
17. Where overlapping parts (e.g., triangles) of a figure are involved, to redraw and label these separately
18. To avoid drawing conclusions, except as conjectures, merely from the appearance of figures
19. To avoid drawing general conclusions, except as conjectures, from special cases
20. To use the analytic-synthetic approach in trying to formulate a plan of proof in cases where the method of attack is not readily apparent
21. To form the habit of stating and illustrating three-dimensional counterparts of figures and theorems of plane geometry
22. To look for generalizations (e.g., citing a single theorem which subsumes one or more other theorems as special cases)
23. To give careful attention to inequalities in geometry, as well as to equalities
24. To make up theorems of their own and try to prove or disprove these
25. To try to find counterexamples in the effort to disprove statements which they suspect of being false
26. To learn how to use the methods of coordinate geometry in describing geometric configurations and in proving some suitable theorems
27. To know and be able to use the terminology and notation associated with sets in connection with appropriate situations (e.g., locus problems) in geometry
28. To avoid vagueness and ambiguity and to be articulate and precise in discussion and written work

Remarks on teaching deductive reasoning The principal characteristic which distinguishes the geometry program of the junior high school from that of the senior high school is, of course, the different points of view with which the subject is approached in the two cases. As pointed out, the junior high school program is aimed primarily at establishing the feeling of a good acquaintance with common geometric forms and relationships by whatever means seem calculated to contribute effectively to this end. Conclusions are accepted on the basis of informal procedures of observation, measurement, comparison by appearance, and simple inductive inferences. By contrast, the prime objective in the geometry of the senior high school is to build a feeling for a deductive system in which the validity of conclusions is accepted only when these have been established by formal reasoning from bases already accepted or established. While much of the subject matter (that is, the figures and relationships studied) is the same in the two cases, the point of view is not at all the same.

The transition from the one point of view to the other is difficult for many students. The work of the junior high school will have stressed the presumption of "truth" of geometric facts and principles in terms of their consistency with intuition and with observed physical (geometric) phenomena and inductive reasoning, rather than investigating their validity solely in terms of their logical consistency with a set of facts previously established or assumed. It is no simple matter for a child thirteen or fourteen years old to see the sense of wanting to "prove" something which appears obvious to him and which he feels that he knows already.

An analogy which may help to give the point of view which we want the students to have is to compare a deductive proof with a game which must be played under a given set of rules, just as any other game must be. Children like games, and they understand the role which the rules of the game play in prescribing what is permissible and in determining the validity and the acceptability of the outcome. If they can be brought to look upon the attempt to make a deductive proof of a theorem as a sort of game in which the outcome (conclusion) will be regarded as valid and acceptable only if it is reached without violating any of an accepted set of rules, then they will have attained the view of demonstrative geometry which we want them to have. The rules are few and simple, but inflexible:

1. Certain undefined terms, definitions, and assumptions are accepted arbitrarily in the beginning. These may be used, when applicable, to justify steps in proofs.
2. To be acceptable the proof must consist of an unbroken chain or sequence of steps starting with the hypothesis which is specified for the theorem and leading to the conclusion.

3. Each step (statement) in the sequence, without exception, must be justified either by an accepted definition or assumption or by some theorem which has already been proved.

When students can be brought to look upon demonstrative geometry not merely as a job to be done but rather as a sort of intellectual game to be played according to these rules, they will have attained a feeling for the subject which not only is correct but which can lend interest to their work. Fortunately, since about 1960 a good many students in the junior high school will have had some introduction to this type of reasoning and to this view of mathematics in connection with their work in arithmetic and beginning algebra. Those who have had such experience will find less difficulty in accepting the postulational approach than those who have not.

One point upon which considerable stress ought to be laid is the arbitrary nature of the definitions and especially the assumptions (axioms, postulates, and specially stated hypotheses) upon which the proofs are based. The usual postulates of Euclidean geometry are such that people intuitively feel that they are "true" in the sense of correctly representing properties of space as it is commonly sensed. With respect to teaching geometry, this is both an advantage and a disadvantage. The big advantages are that they are easy for students to accept and that they do give rise to a system of geometric theorems which seems to agree with what are thought of as "real" properties of ordinary space. This is important in that it gives learners a feeling that the geometry they are studying makes sense.

The disadvantage lies in the fact that too often students tend to look upon these reasonable-sounding axioms and postulates as facts or absolute truths rather than as assumptions. This tends to obscure the contingent nature of the postulational approach and to give students the feeling that the geometric structure built upon the set of postulates which they are using is the one and only "true" geometry. If we are to get students to develop the feeling we want them to have for the nature of an axiomatic structure it will have to be emphasized again and again that conclusions based on sound reasoning are "true" only if the assumptions upon which they are based are true. The striking illustration in geometry is the development of non-Euclidean geometries different from the usual school (Euclidean) geometry but just as consistent, the differences resulting solely from using a different parallel postulate.

All theorems are statements of "if-then" form or can be put in this form. The special hypotheses or "given" parts of the statement of a theorem are in effect the "if" parts. The arbitrary nature of these can be illustrated nicely by considering a theorem and, along with it, one of its inverses. The specially stated hypotheses are clearly different, but still acceptable, in the two cases. Although the axioms or postulates which have been accepted once and for all are not explicitly restated as hypotheses in each theorem, they are implicitly included among the hypotheses for every theorem and must be regarded in the same light as the specially stated hypotheses.

Consider, for example, the statement that the area of a 3- by 2-inch rectangle is 6 square inches. Put in "if-then" form, it might read about as follows: *If* a quadrilateral is a 3- by 2-inch rectangle (hypothesis), *then* its area is 6 square inches (conclusion). Here the conclusion necessarily follows from the hypothesis, and the proposition is considered to be true.

By contrast, a related but different proposition might read as follows: *If* a quadrilateral is not a 3- by 2-inch rectangle (hypothesis), *then* its area is not 6 square inches (conclusion). This proposition is not necessarily true, as can easily be shown by producing a counterexample. Yet it is clearly an "if-then" statement. There is no difficulty in accepting the hypothesis, and consequently its implications are subject to investigation.

The role of speculation and conjecture While the emphasis in high school geometry is properly on deductive reasoning and the nature and practice of proof, it would be a mistake to overlook the importance of having students speculate about the things being studied and try to form their own tentative conclusions. Indeed, this is the way theorems (statements to be proved) normally arise. Conjecture and proof in a sense are teammates and complement each other. Deductive proof is used to establish the truth or validity (or lack of it) of propositions, but the propositions themselves almost invariably have their origins in speculation. Conjecture can be regarded as the inventive or creative implement which leads to discovery or arouses speculation.

Conjectures can arise through intuition or through inductive reasoning based on observation of limited numbers of cases. For example, students may be asked what relation, if any, they think exists between the lengths of unequal chords of a circle and the distances of these chords from the center. The intuitive reaction is almost certain to give immediately the correct conjecture that the longer the chord, the nearer it is to the center; and this can then be formally stated in "if-then" form and subjected to formal proof to determine whether or not this conjecture is correct. Or they may be asked whether they think there is any relation between the number of sides of a convex polygon and the sum of the exterior angles of the polygon, and if so, what that relation is. Intuitive or experimental examination of this question will probably bring forth the conjecture that regardless of the number of sides, the sum of the exterior angles is always the same—namely, 360°—and the conjecture can then be subjected to formal proof. Not all relations in geometry lend themselves so easily as those in the foregoing examples to conjecture, but many do. Others may give rise to controversy and perhaps to a need for re-examining definitions or hypotheses. Such an instance would arise in the second of the foregoing examples if the word "convex" were omitted. In this case the theorem would hold only if the exterior angles were carefully defined to be directed angles with their positive and negative directions indicated. Speculation and discussion can be very fruitful in focusing the attention of the students on critical points at issue.

There are two principal advantages of having students try to formulate their own conjectures about their problems as a preliminary to undertaking to establish their conjectures by formal proof. One is that it ensures a clear insight into what is being investigated. The second is that it can give the students a feeling of creativity or discovery, and in this way it can add a good deal of interest to their work. Teachers who capitalize on this approach will find that it yields good dividends. Those who neglect to make use of its possibilities are overlooking a potent source of motivation.

Indirect proof[8] In Chapter 3 the nature of the indirect form of argumentation is discussed. Since there are many situations in geometry which can be investigated most effectively by applying the techniques of indirect proof, it is desirable to examine the procedure more in detail in such a context. One feature of the indirect proof which frequently proves to be troublesome is the clumsy wordiness that is inseparable from the verbal statement of the denial of the hypothesis. This use of negative statements can become very confusing.

A plan that has been used very satisfactorily in overcoming this difficulty is that of writing out separately the complete and careful statements of the two contradictory propositions in step 1 *and then substituting for each of these statements a single identifying symbol.* The Greek letters θ and ϕ were chosen merely because it was felt that they were not likely to be confused with the customary symbols used in identifying points, lines, etc. The choice turned out to be a happy one for another reason, viz., the newness of these symbols aroused the curiosity and interest of the students and, as a by-product of this focusing of attention, the mechanical outline of indirect proof tended to crystallize in the students' minds more quickly and more definitely than had been expected.

The use of these symbols made it possible to eliminate a great deal of

[8]See the Report of the Commission on Mathematics, "Appendices," *op. cit.*, pp. 116–119.

the verbal confusion mentioned above and to shorten both written and oral exposition, with a corresponding increase in understanding of the mechanics and the nature of indirect proof.

To illustrate, let us consider the proposition concerning two straight lines perpendicular to the same line. The demonstration following the outline described, but not employing the symbolic representation of the contradictory statements, would be set up in some such manner as the following:

Theorem: Two straight lines, lying in the same plane and both perpendicular to the same straight line, are parallel to each other.

Given: $a \perp l$ and $b \perp l$.

To prove: $a \parallel b$.

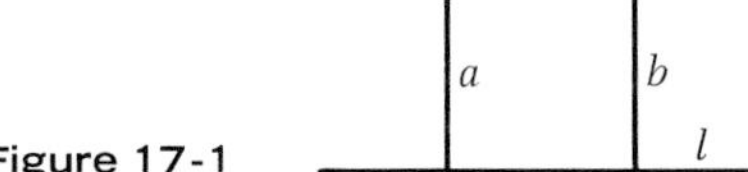

Figure 17-1

Proof:

1. Either $a \parallel b$ or a is not $\parallel b$. — 1. *Contradictory statements.*
2. Suppose a is not $\parallel b$. — 2. *Tentative assumption.*
3. If a is not $\parallel b$, then a intersects b. — 3. *Definition of $\parallel$ lines.*
4. In this case we should have two lines both $\perp$ a line from the same point, which is impossible. — 4. *One and only one line can be drawn from a point perpendicular to a line.*
5. $\therefore$ It is not true that a is not $\parallel b$. — 5. *Because this assumption leads to a contradiction of a previously proved theorem.*
6. $\therefore a \parallel b$. — 6. *If one of two contradictory propositions is false, the other one must be true.*

This is a perfectly correct and valid proof, but its statement is rather confusing in step 5, where it is necessary to use the double negative or else avoid the use of the word "parallel."

If this proposition were set up in the symbolic form which has been described, the argument could be developed as follows (the same diagram and statement of hypothesis and conclusion may be used):

1. $\theta \ldots a \parallel b$, $\phi \ldots a$ is not $\parallel b$. — 1. *Two contradictory statements.*
2. Suppose ϕ is true. — 2. *Tentative assumption.*
3. If a is not $\parallel b$, then a intersects b. — 3. *Definition of $\parallel$ lines.*
4. In this case we should have two lines $\perp$ a line from the same point, which is impossible. — 4. *One and only one line can be drawn from a point perpendicular to a line.*

5. $\therefore\ \phi$ is not true.	5. *Because the assumption led to a contradiction of a previously proved theorem.*
6. $\therefore\ \theta$ is true.	6. *If one of two contradictory statements is false, the other one must be true.*

Observe that the statement "ϕ is not true" is much more concise and less confusing than the verbal statement "It is not true that a is not parallel to b." Moreover, experience has shown beyond doubt that the use of this symbolic representation of the two possibilities in setting up the theorem distinctly increases the students' perception of the essentially contradictory nature of the two statements and clarifies for them the mechanics of the proof.

There are, of course, cases in which the setup of the problem contains more than two possibilities. Take, for example, the following:

Theorem: If the measures of two angles of a triangle are equal then the lengths of the sides opposite these two angles are also equal.

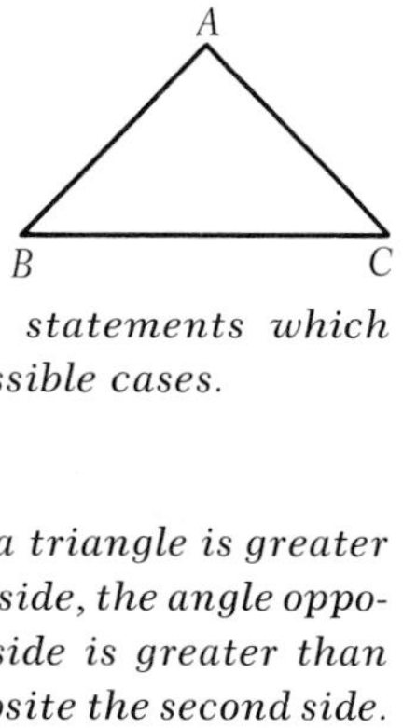

Given: $m < B = m < C$.

To prove: $AB = AC$.

Figure 17-2

Proof:

1. θ . . . $AB = AC$, ϕ . . . $AB \neq AC$, or $\begin{cases}\phi_1 \ldots AB > AC,\\ \phi_2 \ldots AB < AC.\end{cases}$	1. *Contradictory statements which involve all possible cases.*
2. Suppose ϕ_1 true, then $\angle C > \angle B$, contradictory to hypothesis.	2. *If one side of a triangle is greater than a second side, the angle opposite the first side is greater than the angle opposite the second side.*
3. Suppose ϕ_2 true, then $\angle B > \angle C$, contradictory to hypothesis.	3. *Same reason as step 2.*
4. $\therefore\ \theta$ is true, and $AB = AC$.	4. *All other possible relationships between AB and AC have led to contradictions of the hypothesis.*

In the above two illustrations the argument proceeded directly from the negation of the conclusion to the implication of the negation of the hypothesis. This is, as pointed out on page 73, the proof of the contrapositive of the given theorem, and it is equivalent to proving the original theorem. Not all indirect arguments are of this type. Another technique is to establish that the contradiction of the conclusion leads to the implication of a known inconsistency. This procedure is illustrated in the following proof of the converse of the first of the above two theorems.

Theorem: If a line is perpendicular to one of two parallel lines and lies in the plane of these lines, then it is perpendicular to the other.

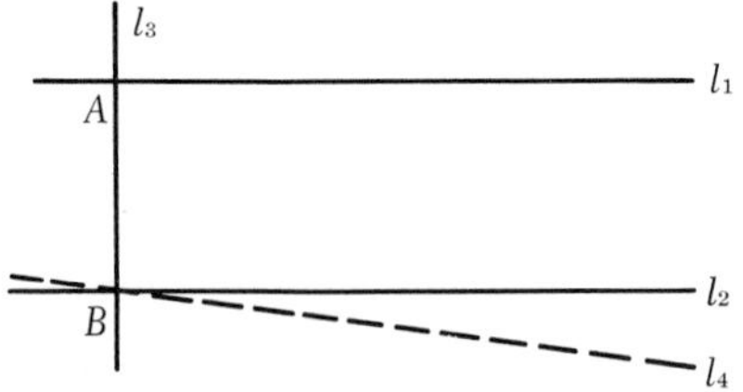

Figure 17-3

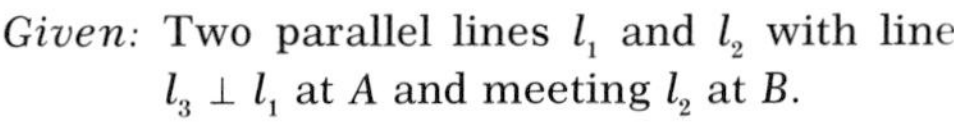

Given: Two parallel lines l_1 and l_2 with line $l_3 \perp l_1$ at A and meeting l_2 at B.

To prove: $l_3 \perp l_2$.

Proof:

1. Either $l_3 \perp l_2$ or l_3 is not $\perp l_2$. — 1. *Contradictory statements which involve all possible cases.*
2. Assume l_3 is not $\perp l_2$. — 2. *Tentative assumption.*
3. Through B, and in the plane of l_1 and l_3, draw $l_4 \perp l_3$.
4. $l_4 \parallel l_1$. — 4. *Two straight lines lying in the same plane and perpendicular to the same straight line are parallel.*
5. $l_2 \parallel l_1$. — 5. *By hypothesis.*
6. There are two lines through B, both $\parallel l_1$, which is impossible. — 6. *A contradiction of the parallel postulate.*
7. $\therefore l_3 \perp l_2$ — 7. *If one of two contradictory statements is false, the other one must be true.*

It may be remarked in passing that indirect proof is not limited to school geometry but is used extensively and increasingly in higher mathematics. The following example provides one illustration of the use of indirect proof in algebra to establish a conjecture. Suppose that a student says that he believes that the sum of any positive number and its reciprocal cannot be less than 2 but cannot prove it. He shows that he has tested it out with several positive numbers and found his belief verified in every case, but he has not been able to find a proof that his guess is valid for all positive numbers and wants to see such a proof. The following indirect proof is short, easy, and conclusive.

Given: A positive number x and its reciprocal $1/x$.

To prove: $x + 1/x \geqq 2$.

Set up the following contradictory propositions:

1. $\theta : x + 1/x \geqslant 2$.
   $\phi : x + 1/x < 2$. — 1. *Contradictory statements which include all possibilities.*
2. Suppose ϕ is true. — 2. *Working hypothesis.*
3. Then $x + 1/x < 2$. — 3. *Given.*
4. Then $x^2 + 1 < 2x$. — 4. *Multiplication by x (positive).*
5. Then $x^2 - 2x + 1 < 0$. — 5. *Subtraction of 2x from both sides of inequality.*
6. Then $(x - 1)^2 < 0$. — 6. *Same as step 5 in another form.*

But this is contrary to the fact that the square of a real number is never negative, so we must reject ϕ.

7. Therefore θ must be true, and $x + 1/x \geqq 2$ QED.	7. *If one of two contradictory statements is false, the other one must be true.*

Although the indirect proof is a very powerful instrument in the investigation of truth, it is at times dangerous. One using the indirect type of argument can very easily become guilty of reasoning in a circle, i.e., using the theorem in question either explicitly or implicitly as a reason in its proof. This, however, is but one type of faulty argument which can be the source of error in any form of deductive proof whether direct or indirect, synthetic or analytic. The teacher should be aware of these sources of error and shape his instructional program to ensure against them. Probably the most prominent and persistent are the following:

1. Omission of statements
2. Inclusion of irrelevant statements
3. A disregard for a correct order of statements
4. The use of reasons not yet established
5. Reasoning in a circle, i.e., the use of the proposition in question as a reason in its proof
6. The confusion of definitions with theorems
7. The confusion of the hypothesis with conclusion
8. The confusion of a statement with its converse and inverse

Planning proofs: the analytic-synthetic approach A good many of the propositions and problems of elementary geometry are quite simple and involve proofs which are short and rather obvious. Others, however, are less simple, and the proofs of some are rather long and involved. In many cases, when no approaches seem intuitively evident, students are likely to have difficulty in getting started and in discovering and mapping out connected plans for their proofs. Yet a plan of proof is always important, and the less simple and obvious it is, the more important it is for the student to have his plan completely sketched out in his mind, and perhaps on paper, before starting to write out the formal proof of the proposition.

In cases where students have trouble in getting started or are unable to formulate a connected plan leading to the required conclusion, it may often be helpful to consider the proposition, as it were, in reverse. If a set of hypotheses implies a certain conclusion, then the conclusion *is implied by* the given set of hypotheses. By supposing the conclusion to be true and then asking, "Under what circumstances would this be true?" or "By what is this implied?" one may be able to back-track or blaze a trail of "is implied by" statements leading without break backward from conclusion to hypotheses. If this can be done, then, since the conclusion is connected by a chain of "is implied by" statements to the hypotheses, it follows conversely that the hypotheses are connected by an unbroken chain of "implies" statements to the conclusion. The plan of proof is then complete, and by reversing the order of the steps the synthetic proof is established and can be written down formally.

As suggested in chapter 3, the procedure can be represented schematically as follows:

Analysis Conclusion $\leftarrow a \leftarrow b \leftarrow \cdots \leftarrow m \leftarrow n \leftarrow$ Hypotheses
Synthesis Hypotheses $\rightarrow n \rightarrow m \rightarrow \cdots \rightarrow b \rightarrow a \rightarrow$ Conclusion

However, since schematic representations can often be clarified by concrete illustrations, the following example is given to illustrate such an analytic-synthetic attack upon a problem.

Suppose we wish to prove this theorem.

Theorem: If a straight line joins the midpoints of two sides of a triangle, then it is parallel to the third side.

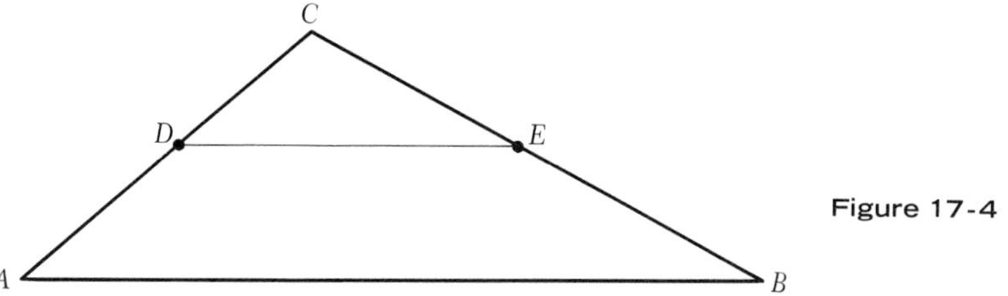

Figure 17-4

Given: ABC with $\overline{AD} \cong \overline{DC}$ and $\overline{BE} \cong \overline{EC}$.

Prove: $\overline{DE} \parallel \overline{AB}$.

Since nothing is known initially about the angles in the figure, we cannot prove $\overline{DE} \parallel \overline{AB}$ directly by using any of the theorems about transversals and associated angles. An alternative method is to show that $\overline{DE}$ and $\overline{AB}$ are, or lie in, opposite sides of a parallelogram. Clearly $ABED$ is not a parallelogram, and the figure does not appear to contain one. However, there might be a parallelogram having $\overline{AB}$ as one side and such that we could show that $\overline{DE}$ is part of the opposite side. If we could show that this is the case, our proposition would be proved.

Now if we should construct a parallelogram $ABFD$ on $\overline{AD}$ and $\overline{AB}$ as adjacent sides, then DF would be parallel to AB and would cut $\overline{BC}$ in some point H, so we would have $\overline{DH} \parallel \overline{AB}$. Then if we could show that points E and H coincide, this would make $\overline{DE}$ coincide with DH, which is constructed parallel to $\overline{AB}$, whence $\overline{DE}$ would be parallel to $\overline{AB}$, as required. Moreover, the coincidence of points E and H would be established if we could prove $\triangle DHC \cong \triangle FHB$ because this would give $\overline{CH}$

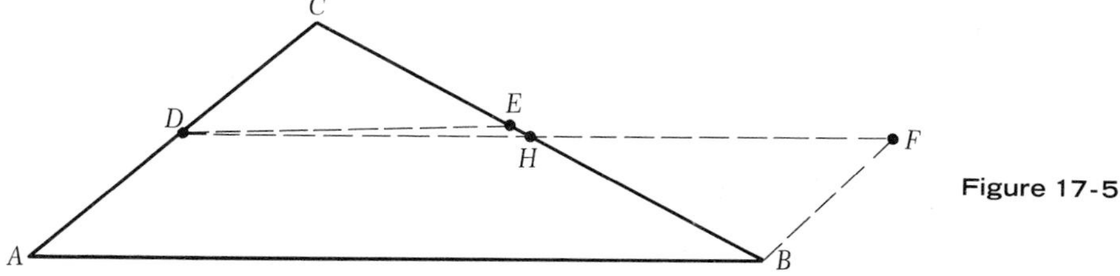

Figure 17-5

$\cong \overline{HB}$, making H the midpoint of $\overline{BC}$, whereas we know that E is the midpoint of $\overline{BC}$, and a line segment has only one midpoint. Finally, we see that we can actually accomplish all this because we can prove $\triangle DHC \cong \triangle FHB$ by use of the angle-side-angle theorem. That is, $\angle CDH \cong \angle BFH$, being alternate-interior angles of parallel lines; $\angle DCH \cong \angle FBH$ for the same reason; and $\overline{CD} \cong \overline{FB}$, since each is known to be equal to $\overline{AD}$.

This analysis of the problem has done two valuable things. It has given us a place to get started (proving $\triangle DHC \cong \triangle FHB$), and it has charted a sequence of steps through which we can pass from this starting point to the desired conclusion. If we start by proving $\triangle DHC \cong \triangle FHB$ we can show that H is the mid-point of $\overline{BC}$ and consequently is the same point as E. Thus $\overline{DE}$ coincides with $\overline{DH}$, which is constructed parallel to $\overline{AB}$, whence $\overline{DE} \parallel \overline{AB}$ as required. Once this plan is in mind, the students should have no difficulty in writing out the details of the formal proof. It may be remarked that this is not the only way of proving this proposition, but it is an interesting one.

Converse, inverse (opposite), and contrapositive The analysis of geometric theorems and their proofs is often facilitated by clear understanding of certain related theorems known, respectively, as *converses*, *inverses*, and *contrapositives* of the given theorems. These types of theorems can be obtained from the original theorems to which they are related by the denial and/or the interchange of hypotheses and conclusions of the original theorems. Because their statements often appear to be superficially similar to statements of the original theorems, casual reading may sometimes lead the reader to confuse them with the originals, whereas they are fundamentally different. The truth of an original theorem does not imply that a converse or an inverse is necessarily true, so care is necessary in drawing conclusions. An introduction to a clear understanding of these descriptive terms may be secured by examining a simple theorem containing only one hypothesis and one conclusion.

Theorem. If a triangle is equilateral, then it is isosceles. (Obviously true.)
Converse theorem. If a triangle is isosceles, then it is equilateral. (Not necessarily true.)

Inverse theorem. If a triangle is not equilateral, then it is not isosceles. (Not necessarily true.)
Contrapositive theorem. If a triangle is not isosceles, then it is not equilateral. (Obviously true.)

In this simple case the method of derivation of the different types of theorems is rather evident. For a theorem with one hypothesis and one conclusion:

1. The converse theorem is obtained by interchanging the hypothesis and conclusion.
2. The inverse (or opposite) theorem is obtained by taking the contradiction of the hypothesis as the new hypothesis and the contradiction of the conclusion as the new conclusion.
3. The contrapositive theorem is obtained by taking the contradiction of the conclusion as the new hypothesis and the contradiction of the hypothesis as the new conclusion.

If H represents the hypothesis of a given theorem and C the conclusion, the above definitions may be stated diagrammatically as follows:

Theorem. If H is true, then C is true.
Converse theorem. If C is true, then H is true.
Inverse theorem. If H is not true, then C is not true.
Contrapositive theorem. If C is not true, then H is not true.

It must be remembered that, as demonstrated in the truth tables of page 74, the fact that a theorem is true makes no implication about the truth or falsity of the statement in its converse or its inverse. The truth of each must be investigated upon its own merits. The law of contraposition, however, states that a theorem and its contrapositive are equivalent; i.e., if one is true, the other is true, and if one is false, the other is false.[9]

The above definitions must be modified for theorems that involve more than one hypothesis or more than one conclusion. The following definitions have been suggested as satisfactory generalizations:[10]

1. A converse of a theorem may be obtained by interchanging *any* number of conclusions with an *equal number* of hypotheses.
2. An inverse of a proposition having one conclusion may be formed by contradicting one of the hypotheses and the conclusion.
3. A contrapositive of a theorem containing more than one hypothesis and only one conclusion may be obtained by the interchange of the contradictory of one of the hypotheses with the contradictory of the conclusion.

[9]N. Lazar, The Importance of Certain Concepts and Laws of Logic for the Study and Teaching of Geometry, *Mathematics Teacher*, **31** (1938), 107 *ff.*

[10]*Ibid.*

It will be noticed that the definitions given here for inverses and contrapositives of theorems are somewhat more restrictive than the one given for converses. Less restrictive definitions could be given, but logical difficulties which would then be encountered suggest that the definitions given here are more desirable for elementary geometry.

As an illustration of the nature of converse propositions, consider the following:

Theorem: If two right triangles have the hypotenuse and a leg of one equal respectively to the hypotenuse and a leg of the other, the triangles are congruent.

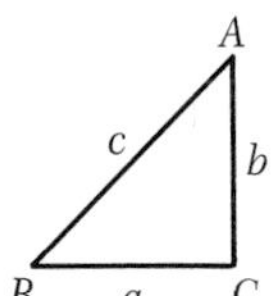

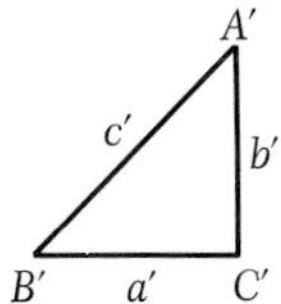

Figure 17-6

Hypotheses	*Conclusions*
⊿s ABC and $A'B'C'$ (Figure 17-6).	⊿s are $\cong$.
$H_1 : \angle C$ and $\angle C'$ are rt. $\angle$s.	$C_1 : a = a'$.
$H_2 : c = c'$.	$C_2 : \angle B = \angle B'$.
$H_3 : b = b'$.	$C_3 : \angle A = \angle A'$.

There is a temptation on the part of the immature pupil to consider the statement that the triangles are congruent as the one conclusion of the theorem. Upon analysis, however, it is seen that there are in fact many conclusions, since equality of any pair of corresponding parts of the two triangles follows as a consequence of the three stated hypotheses. Only the three basic conclusions are listed above for purposes of the desired illustration. Symbolically the above theorem may be written

$$(H_1)(H_2)(H_3) \rightarrow (C_1)(C_2)(C_3)$$

It is then evident that the following converses can be obtained by the interchange of one hypothesis and one conclusion.

1. $(H_1)(H_2)(C_1) \rightarrow (H_3)(C_2)(C_3)$
2. $(H_1)(C_1)(H_3) \rightarrow (H_2)(C_2)(C_3)$
3. $(C_1)(H_2)(H_3) \rightarrow (H_1)(C_2)(C_3)$
4. $(H_1)(H_2)(C_2) \rightarrow (C_1)(H_3)(C_3)$
5. $(H_1)(C_2)(H_3) \rightarrow (C_1)(H_2)(C_3)$
6. $(C_2)(H_2)(H_3) \rightarrow (C_1)(H_1)(C_3)$
7. $(H_1)(H_2)(C_3) \rightarrow (C_1)(C_2)(H_3)$
8. $(H_1)(C_3)(H_3) \rightarrow (C_1)(C_2)(H_2)$
9. $(C_3)(H_2)(H_3) \rightarrow (C_1)(C_2)(H_1)$

Careful examination of these nine theorems reveals the fact that in each case but one there is a combination of hypotheses sufficient to give congruent triangles. The exception is theorem 6, in which case the hypothesis would imply the ambiguous case for a triangle. In each theorem, however, which involves H_1 as one of the conclusions there is not necessarily a true statement. Thus, of the nine converse theorems, only six (1, 2, 4, 5, 7, 8) are necessarily true theorems.

Since converse theorems may be obtained by the interchange of two hypotheses with two conclusions and of the three hypotheses with the three conclusions, we have the following additional converses of the original theorem:

10. $(H_1)(C_1)(C_2) \to (H_2)(H_3)(C_3)$ 11. $(H_1)(C_1)(C_3) \to (H_2)(C_2)(H_3)$
12. $(H_1)(C_2)(C_3) \to (C_1)(H_2)(H_3)$ 13. $(C_1)(H_2)(C_2) \to (H_1)(H_3)(C_3)$
14. $(C_1)(H_2)(C_3) \to (H_1)(C_2)(H_3)$ 15. $(C_2)(H_2)(C_3) \to (C_1)(H_1)(H_3)$
16. $(C_1)(C_2)(H_3) \to (H_1)(H_2)(C_3)$ 17. $(C_1)(C_3)(H_3) \to (H_1)(C_2)(H_2)$
18. $(C_2)(C_3)(H_3) \to (C_1)(H_1)(H_2)$ 19. $(C_1)(C_2)(C_3) \to (H_1)(H_2)(H_3)$

As above, it is evident that no theorem which has the clause H_1 as a part of its conclusion is necessarily a true theorem. Furthermore, the hypothesis of theorem 12, $(H_1)(C_2)(C_3)$, is not sufficient to establish congruence. Hence, of the above converse theorems, only theorems 10 and 11 are necessarily true theorems. Thus out of the total of 19 possible converse theorems to the original true theorem there are only eight (1, 2, 4, 5, 7, 8, 10, 11) which are necessarily true theorems.

For an illustration of inverses and contrapositives of a theorem consider the following:

Theorem: If two triangles have two sides of the one equal, respectively, to two sides of the other, but the included angle of the first greater than the included angle of the second, then the third side of the first is greater than the third side of the second.

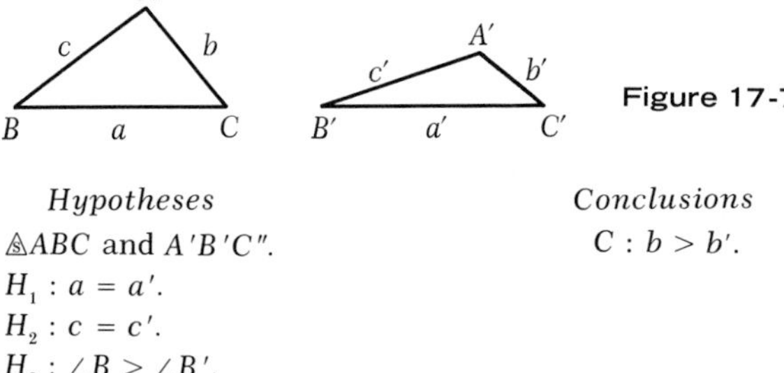

Figure 17-7

Hypotheses
$\triangle ABC$ and $A'B'C''$.
$H_1 : a = a'$.
$H_2 : c = c'$.
$H_3 : \angle B > \angle B'$.

Conclusions
$C : b > b'$.

This theorem is well adapted to the consideration of inverses and contrapositives because it has only one conclusion. In the discussion which follows, we shall use $\overline{H}_1$ to represent the contradiction of H_1, $\overline{H}_2$ of H_2, $\overline{H}_3$ of H_3, and $\overline{C}$ of C. Thus $\overline{H}_1$ becomes $a \neq a'$ (or $a \gtrless a'$); $\overline{H}_2$ becomes $c \neq c'$ (or $c \gtrless c'$); $\overline{H}_3$ becomes $\angle B \ngtr \angle B'$ (or $\angle B \leqq \angle B'$); and $\overline{C}$ becomes $b \ngtr b'$ (or $b \leqq b'$). From the definition of the inverse of a theorem it is evident that there are three inverses to the given theorem. They are:

1. Hypotheses: $\overline{H}_1, H_2, H_3$; Conclusion: $\overline{C}$.
2. Hypotheses: $H_1, \overline{H}_2, H_3$; Conclusion: $\overline{C}$.
3. Hypotheses: $H_1, H_2, \overline{H}_3$; Conclusion: $\overline{C}$.

Analysis of these three theorems establishes that theorem 3 is the only true theorem.

Similarly, there are three contrapositives of the given theorem. They are:

1. Hypotheses: $\overline{C}, H_2, H_3$; Conclusion: $\overline{H}_1$.
2. Hypotheses: $H_1, \overline{C}, H_3$; Conclusion: $\overline{H}_2$.
3. Hypotheses: $H_1, H_2, \overline{C}$; Conclusion: $\overline{H}_3$.

By the contrapositive law all three of these theorems should be true theorems. Careful analysis reveals that this is the case.

Original exercises For many years it has been recognized that original exercises provide probably the most effective means for the development of originality, ingenuity, and the power to do independent work in geometry. Here the student is on his own. Given a proposition to be proved or a construction problem to be solved, he needs first to interpret it so as to get his working conditions or hypotheses clearly in mind and to determine just what it is that he is to try to do. He then has to try to formulate a plan that will bring him to his objective. Finally he must synthesize and formalize his work, justifying each step in his synthesis. He is thus faced with a variety of problems which may tax any or all of his mathematical resources. These will include not only his accumulated store of geometric facts (theorems) but also his quickness of insight, his power of analysis, his inventiveness, his ability to discriminate between relevant and irrelevant details and to synthesize those which are relevant into sound sequential argument, his tenacity and persistence, and his ability to write clear, lucid exposition. These are the characteristics which we like to see our students develop.

From careful study of the expositions of theorems that are proved in the textbook, students can learn much about correct synthetic form and, of course, can continually increase their store of important geometric facts and insights. But when they tackle original exercises they have to invent their own analyses and formulate their own proofs. This calls upon a higher order of insight and ingenuity than that which is required merely for following a demonstration that somebody else has worked out. When a student works out an original exercise he is, in fact, engaging in creative mathematical activity. The proposition which he proves or the construction which he devises and validates will doubtless have been worked out by many people before, but to him it is new, and his accomplishment can bring the satisfaction that always accompanies the successful completion of a piece of original work. Hence original exercises furnish not only the most effective medium for developing the ability to do original work and independent thinking in geometry but they also constitute a powerful built-in means of motivating students to put their best efforts into their work.

Moreover, teachers can probably learn more about the abilities and work habits and the strengths and weaknesses of their students (especially students with potential talent) by studying their work on original exercises than in any other way. In routine matters the student who is quick, curious, inventive, and self-reliant may often become bored and do only good ordinary but unimpressive work. On the other hand, his work on original exercises will almost certainly manifest these characteristics in a way and to a degree not usually reflected in the work of the conscientious but unimaginative plodder. Even the plodders, however, have an important stake in this creative aspect of geometry because imagination and ingenuity can be cultivated, at least to a degree, and the cultivation as well as the recognition of these characteristics is a very important objective.

For most students it is important that the original exercises be rather carefully graduated, and this is recognized by most textbook writers. A common practice is to divide sets of exercises into subsets on the basis of probable difficulty. Usually authors do pretty well in such classification, but sometimes exercises will be found which seem to be placed in wrong categories. It is a good thing for teachers to check every exercise which is to be assigned to students to be sure that its level of difficulty is appropriate for the students who are expected to work on it and for the purpose of the assignment.

It would be easy to make an extensive list of particular difficulties which students have and particular errors which they make in working on original problems in geometry, and such listings have been made. However, most of these detailed troubles will be found to stem from a few sources. Successful work invariably requires a well-organized fund of knowledge of the theorems that have been proved and of the postulates and definitions that have been accepted. For each exercise it requires that the student get very clearly in mind precisely what he has given to work from and precisely what he aims to accomplish. Lacking any of these, the student is in for trouble. Given all of them, success will depend largely upon his ingenuity in devising tentative plans of proof or tentative constructions and upon his ability to draw readily and extensively upon his funded information about geometry for hints and for supporting argument. Well-drawn diagrams may often suggest promising lines of attack. Careful notation and neat, orderly writing may appear to be peripheral considerations, but they are real assets. Many people feel that it is helpful to keep classified summary lists of ways of establishing particular properties or relations of geometric figures, such as the following:

1. Ways of proving triangles congruent
2. Ways of proving angles equal
3. Ways of proving lines parallel
4. Ways of proving lines perpendicular
5. Ways of proving line segments equal in length
6. Ways of proving triangles similar
7. Ways of proving that an angle is a right angle
8. Ways of proving that a quadrilateral is a parallelogram
9. Ways of proving one angle greater than another
10. Ways of proving one line segment longer than another
11. Ways of proving chords of circles equal or unequal

Such classifications and lists can be made as detailed and as extensive as desired. They would probably prove useful to many students. It has long been a fairly common practice among authors of geometry textbooks to include some such classified lists or summaries in their books.

Generalization and special cases The fact that converses, inverses, and contrapositives are related in specified ways to given original theorems suggests another way in which theorems are frequently related. Sometimes groups of theorems can be found such that they all can be shown to be special cases under a single inclusive proposition. In such cases it is a good thing to call attention to the fact, because recognition of this relationship can be beneficial to students in several ways. It forces them to examine and compare the geometric properties of the figures involved and to test critically each of the special cases to determine whether or not it actually is a special case under the general theorem. Pedagogically it is helpful because the close attention which it demands of students and the element of discovery which it involves are almost sure to enlist and hold their interest and thus to obviate boredom. Above all, it helps to connect and give organization to sets of separate but related theorems and to clarify the concept of generalization. It has received little emphasis in textbooks on geometry, but it can be used to advantage by any good teacher.[11]

Two examples which follow will serve to illustrate how certain groups of theorems can be generalized so that each proposition in the group can be shown to be a particular case under a single general theorem.

[11]For an old but excellent article on this, see F. P. Hennessey, The Principle of Continuity, *Mathematics Teacher,* **24** (1931), 32–40.

1. Consider the familiar formulas, usually defined or developed separately, for the areas of the square, the rectangle, the parallelogram, the triangle, and the trapezoid. The formula for the area of a trapezoid is usually stated as half the product of the altitude and the sum of the two bases. However, it can equally well be stated as the product of half the sum of the lengths of a pair of parallel sides and the distance between them. If this latter statement is used, then the area formulas for all five figures listed above can be subsumed under this single formula or rule. In each of the five cases it yields the special formula, or rule, for determining the area of the figure being considered, though in the case of the triangle the length of one of the "parallel" sides must be regarded as zero.

2. A second and perhaps more interesting case involves a group of theorems giving the measures of angles formed by lines associated with a circle. These measure formulas are always developed separately, commonly in the following order:

a. The measure of a central angle
b. The measure of an angle formed by two chords intersecting inside the circle
c. The measure of an inscribed angle
d. The measure of an angle formed by a tangent and a chord
e. The measure of an angle formed by two secants intersecting outside the circle
f. The measure of an angle formed by a secant and a tangent which intersect outside the circle
g. The measure of an angle formed by two tangents to the circle

As they are usually given in textbooks, the formulas for the measures of angles formed under the several conditions described above all imply that only the absolute values of all arcs involved are to be considered. Under this restriction there is no single theorem which would include all the cases. But by introducing the notion of *directed* arcs (counterclockwise, positive; clockwise, negative), each of these separate measure formulas can be subsumed under the general theorem "The angle formed by two lines each of which cuts or is tangent to a circle is measured by half the *algebraic* sum of the intercepted arcs." It is very possible that students will not find this generalized theorem stated in their textbooks, but this may make it all the more interesting to them. They will find that testing the separate theorems against this generalization is an interesting and valuable experience.

Not all theorems fit into such patterns of generalization, and the cases cited above admittedly represent unusually large groupings. There are a good many cases, however, both in plane and solid geometry, in which two or three theorems can be subsumed under a single covering theorem. For example, to cite a very simple case, the theorem "The measure of each interior angle of a regular polygon is $(n-2)180°/n$" includes, among others, as special cases the propositions (1) "The measure of each interior angle of a square is 90°" and (2) "The measure of each interior angle of an equilateral triangle is 60°."

It is important in all mathematical instruction to try to help students develop a feeling for the unity and coherence of the subject and for ways in which different parts of the subject may be related to each other. The device suggested here can contribute significantly to the attainment of this objective in geometry. The generalization of theorems and the search for groups of theorems that can be classed as special cases under a single generalization provides one avenue through which mathematical interest, insight, and growth may be nurtured.

EXERCISES

1. Explain the difference between the point of view and the main objectives for instruction in geometry in the junior high school and in the senior high school.

2. In the junior high school students learn to understand a good many facts or principles of geometry which they later encounter as theorems in high school geometry. Sometimes they ask, in effect, and in good faith, "Why do we need to prove this now, when we have already learned it?" How would you answer this question if you were the teacher?

3. Suppose that student A received a good, thorough grounding in the informal geometry of the junior high school and that student B did not. If they both subsequently take demonstrative geometry in high school, what particular advantages will student A have over student B? Be as specific as you can, and give illustrative examples to reinforce your points.

4. Study the report of the Secondary School Curriculum Committee of the National Council of Teachers of Mathematics and the report of the Commission on Mathematics of the College Entrance Examination Board, and give a comparative review of their recommendations relative to high school geometry.

5. In 1940 a textbook on geometry[12] was published which differed considerably from other standard textbooks of that time. Compare it with some other standard textbook on plane geometry published before 1960. What points of difference do you find?

6. Compare the SMSG course in geometry with that represented in some standard geometry text published before 1960. Make a list of the important differences which you find.

7. Compare the UICSM course in geometry with that represented in some standard geometry text published before 1960. Make a list of the important differences which you find.

8. Enumerate five problems which in your opinion cause serious difficulties to students in their work in geometry. Discuss each of these, explaining what you think a teacher might do to help students avoid or overcome these difficulties.

9. Explain clearly the difference between the inductive method and the deductive method of arriving at conclusions. Give examples of each.

10. Explain the nature of each of the following and the role of each in the process of deductive thinking: (*a*) undefined terms,

[12]G. D. Birkhoff and Ralph Beatley, 3d ed., "Basic Geometry" (New York: Chelsea Publishing Company, 1959.)

(*b*) definitions, (*c*) assumptions (axioms or postulates), and (*d*) theorems.

11. Discuss the values of encouraging students to speculate and form conjectures about problems, even though they may not be able to prove that their conjectures are correct.

12. Consider that $1 = 1$; $1 + 3 = 4$; $1 + 3 + 5 = 9$; $1 + 3 + 5 + 7 = 16$. See whether you can make up a formula which gives the sum of the first n positive odd integers in terms of n for these four cases. If you can, try it out on several cases where n is greater than 4. Does it work in each case you try?

13. Do you believe your formula in the foregoing problem would work for all values of n? On what reasoning do you base your answer? Have you proved it? Explain.

14. Prove the following theorems:

a. The areas of two similar triangles are proportional to the squares of any pair of corresponding sides of the two triangles.

b. The areas of two similar polygons are proportional to the squares of any pair of corresponding lines in the two polygons.

c. The areas of two circles are proportional to the squares of the diameters or of the radii of the two circles.

15. The foregoing theorems all deal with measures of the areas of pairs of similar figures. See if you can formulate a statement of a more general theorem which you think might include all these as special cases. If you can, then write it down and test each of the given theorems against it to see whether it really is a special case under your general theorem.

16. Describe the essential steps in the method of indirect proof. Try to find an example from a plane geometry textbook which you can use to illustrate the method.

17. In a direct synthetic proof of a proposition, an unbroken sequence of statements leads directly from the hypotheses to the conclusion. But sometimes students do not know how to get started or do not see why certain steps are taken. Explain how an analytic-synthetic attack on a proposition may help them to discover for themselves a correct synthetic proof. Illustrate by at least one example.

18. Exhibit an analytic-synthetic proof of this theorem: If ABC is an equilateral triangle inscribed in a circle and if P is any point on the arc $\overline{BC}$, then $\overline{PA} = \overline{PB} + \overline{PC}$.

19. Show that the three common theorems relating to the congruence of triangles can be obtained by taking converses (as defined in this chapter) of any one of them. What other theorems can also be obtained? Which, if any, are not true theorems?

20. Given the theorem: In equal circles, equal chords are equidistant from the centers. (*a*) Restate this theorem in "if-then" form, indicating the hypotheses and the conclusions. (*b*) State a converse and tell whether it is a true theorem or not. (*c*) Do the same for an inverse. (*d*) State a contrapositive.

21. For what particular reasons is it desirable to have students do a great deal of work with original exercises?

22. Consider the theorem which states that two right triangles are congruent if the legs of one are congruent respectively to the legs of the other. Is this a special case under another more general theorem? If so, state it and justify your answer.

23. Consider this proposition: If three or more lines are parallel, the segments which they cut off on any transversal are proportional to those cut off on any other transversal. Find and state as many theorems of plane geometry as you can which can be shown to be special cases under this single general theorem.

24. Select ten theorems of plane geometry for which you can give counterparts in solid geometry, and make clear statements of these counterparts.

25. Consider a triangle of base b and altitude h. If a rectangle of height x is inscribed in the triangle with the base of the rectangle in the base of the triangle, express the area of this rectangle in terms of b, h, and x.

26. What difficulties do you think high school students would be likely to have with the problem in exercise 25?

BIBLIOGRAPHY

Abbott, Edwin A.: "Flatland" (New York: Dover Publications, Inc., 1953).

Annotated Bibliography of Articles from Periodicals: *Twenty-eighth Yearbook* (Washington, D.C.: National Council of Teachers of Mathematics, 1963), pp. 225–235.

Birkhoff, George David, and Ralph Beatley: "Basic Geometry," 3d ed. (New York: Chelsea Publishing Company, 1959).

Blumenthal, L. M.: "A Modern View of Geometry". (San Francisco: W. H. Freeman and Company, 1961).

Charosh, Mannis (Educational Adviser): "Modern Geometry" (New York: McGraw-Hill Book Company, 1963). (Set of six color filmstrips on geometry.)

Chipman, Hope: When I Teach Geometry, *Mathematics Teacher,* **53** (1960), 140–142.

Christian, Robert R.: A New Role for High School Geometry, *Mathematics Teacher,* **53** (1960), 433–436.

Commission on Mathematics: "Appendices" (New York: College Entrance Examination Board, 1959), pp. 109–174.

Eves, Howard: "A Survey of Geometry," vol. 1 (Englewood Cliffs, N.J.: Allyn and Bacon, Inc., 1963).

Fehr, Howard F.: Reform of Instruction in Geometry, *American Mathematical Monthly,* **70** (1963), 323–327.

Hallerberg, Arthur E.: The Geometry of the Fixed Compass, *Mathematics Teacher,* **52** (1959), 230–244.

Halley, Robert R.: Prove As Much As You Can, *Mathematics Teacher,* **49** (1956), 491–492.

Hausner, Melvin: "The Geometry of Color" (Washington, D.C.: National Council of Teachers of Mathematics, 1963), pp. 301–310.

Hendrix, Gertrude: The Psychological Appeal of Deductive Proof, *Mathematics Teacher,* **54** (1961), 515–520.

______: "Non-verbal Awareness in the Learning of Mathematics," *Research Problems in Mathematical Education,* Cooperative Research Monograph No. 3 (U.S. Government Printing Office, 1960).

Hirsch, Martin: Pythagorean Converse, *Mathematics Teacher,* **54** (1961), 632–634.

Hlavaty, Julius: The Nature and Content of Geometry in the High Schools, *Mathematics Teacher,* **52** (1959), 115–118.

Katsoff, Louis O.: The Saccheri Quadrilateral, *Mathematics Teacher,* **55** (1962), 630–636.

Meserve, Bruce E.: New Trends in Algebra and Geometry, *Mathematics Teacher,* **55** (1962), 452–461.

______ and Max A. Sobel: "Mathematics for Secondary School Teachers" (Englewood Cliffs, N.J.: Prentice-Hall, Inc., 1961), pp. 192–337.

Mirra, Julio A.: "Geometry through Practical Applications" (New York: Barnes & Noble, Inc., 1961).

Ness, Harald M.: A Method of Proof for High School Geometry, *Mathematics Teacher,* **55** (1962), 567–569.

Pólya, George: "Mathematical Discovery," vol. I (New York: John Wiley & Sons, Inc., 1962).

Schaaf, William L.: "Basic Concepts of Elementary Mathematics" (New York: John Wiley & Sons, Inc., 1960), pp. 59–88.

Scheid, Francis: Square Circles, *Mathematics Teacher,* **54** (1961), 307–312.

School Mathematics Study Group: "Mathematics for High School: Geometry," parts 1 and 2 (New Haven, Conn: Yale University Press, 1960).

Schor, Harry: An Introduction to the Angle Measurement Theorems in Plane Geometry, *Mathematics Teacher,* **56** (1963), 107–108.

University of Illinois Committee on School Mathematics: "High School Mathematics: Unit 6, Geometry" (Urbana, Ill.: The University of Illinois Press, 1960).

Unkrich, Harmon: Using the Overhead Projector in Teaching Geometry, *Mathematics Teacher,* **55** (1962), 502–505.

Webber, G. Cuthbert, and John A. Brown: "Basic Concepts of Mathematics" (Reading, Mass.: Addison-Wesley Publishing Company, Inc., 1963), pp. 236–271, 290–302.

Wiseman, John D.: Some Related Theorems on Triangles and Circles, *Mathematics Teacher,* **54** (1961), 14–16.

EIGHTEEN

More on the teaching of geometry

The concept of locus The concept of locus is one of the most pervasive ideas in geometry. Explicitly or tacitly, loci are involved in all geometric constructions, and the very descriptions of many figures are in effect the descriptions of loci which satisfy certain given conditions. Children in the seventh grade learn how to make simple constructions in which they continually make use of intuitive ideas about loci, even though they may not have had any formal definition of the word.

Conversely, a very effective approach to a clear understanding of locus can be made with the aid of some of these elementary constructions. Through the use of such constructions the student can frequently be made aware of the truths of certain locus theorems before he actually comes into formal contact with them. The proper use of experimental geometry in the junior high school provides for just such an approach to the understanding of the locus concept. A few constructions which provide experimental material suitable for this purpose are as follows:

1. Bisect the angles of a given triangle.
2. Draw the perpendicular bisectors of the sides of a given triangle.
3. Draw the altitudes of a given triangle.
4. Draw the medians of a given triangle.

Through the use of these simple constructions, the general experiences of the child, and the use of simple geometric models the introduction of the concept of locus can be made very meaningful to the pupil.

The language of sets frequently affords a convenient method for describing a locus. For example, a circle might be described as the set of points in the plane at a fixed distance from a fixed point. Also, the perpendicular bisector of a line segment might be described as the set of all points which are equidistant from the endpoints of the line segment. This could be a point, a line, or a plane, depending upon the dimensionality of the universe of points from which the specified set is selected.

Both the dynamic and the static, or "set of points," concepts of locus should be introduced and developed. The concept of motion provides for the dynamic interpretation of a locus as the path of a point moving in such a way that its position satisfies at all times certain prescribed conditions. This is especially useful in construction problems. In using the concept of a moving point and of a locus as the path which it traces out under certain restrictions, attention should be directed to the fact that this path consists of those points, and only those points, which satisfy the given conditions. Sometimes this concept of a locus as the path of a moving point is easier for immature students to grasp than is the static interpretation of the locus as a set of points which, and only which, satisfy the prescribed conditions. Clearly, where both apply the two interpretations are in no sense contradictory or inconsistent, though there are some loci to which the term "path" is hardly applicable. For example, the locus of points 1 inch from a given straight line or the locus of points less than 1 inch from a given straight line would be illustrative of this situation. On the other hand, the "set of points" interpretation applies to all loci and should be strongly emphasized.

It is generally recommended that locus problems be considered in conjunction with the four fundamental theorems on concurrent lines:

1. The altitudes of a triangle meet in a point.
2. The medians of a triangle meet in a point.
3. The bisectors of the angles of a triangle meet in a point.
4. The perpendicular bisectors of the sides of a triangle meet in a point.

These theorems will have been intuitively established through experimentation with the simple constructions mentioned on page 478. They form the basis for two other fundamental locus constructions, that is:

1. Inscribe a circle within a given triangle.
2. Circumscribe a circle about a given triangle.

As an aid to general construction problems there are seven locus theorems which should be considered as fundamental and which should be thoroughly understood by everyone. These are as follows:

1. The locus of points lying in a plane and at a fixed distance from a fixed point in the plane is precisely the set of those points each of which satisfies the given conditions. This locus is called a *circle*.

2. The locus of points lying in a plane and at a fixed distance from a fixed straight line in the plane is precisely the set of those points each of which satisfies the given conditions. This locus is a pair of straight lines parallel to the given fixed line and lying at the given distance from it.
3. The locus of points lying in a plane and equidistant from two fixed points in the plane is precisely the set of those points each of which satisfies the given conditions. This locus is the perpendicular bisector of the line segment joining the two fixed points.
4. The locus of points lying in a plane and equidistant from two fixed intersecting lines in the plane is precisely the set of points each of which satisfies the given conditions. This locus is a pair of lines each bisecting a pair of vertical angles formed by the two given fixed lines.
5. The locus of points lying in a plane equidistant from two fixed parallel lines is precisely the set of points in the plane of the parallel lines each of which satisfies the given conditions. This locus is a single straight line parallel to the two given parallel lines and midway between them.
6. Consider the set of right triangles ABC for each of which a given line segment $\overline{AB}$ is the hypotenuse and point C is at the vertex of the right angle. The plane locus of the vertexes of the right angles of these right triangles is precisely the set of points C each of which satisfies the given conditions. This locus is a circle having the segment $\overline{AB}$ as a diameter.
7. Consider the set of triangles ABC for each of which a given line segment $\overline{AB}$ is the base, the vertex of the angle opposite the base is at C, and for which the measure of angle ACB is a fixed value. The plane locus of the vertex of the angle opposite the base is precisely the set of points C each of which satisfies the given conditions. This locus is a pair of congruent arcs, one on either side of AB, such that each is an arc of a circle of which $\overline{AB}$ is a chord, and each is an arc in which angle ACB can be inscribed.

The traditional method of proving a locus problem has been to prove a theorem and either one of its converses or one of its inverses. Since the contrapositive of a theorem is true if the theorem is true, this two-way proof can also be accomplished by proving one of the contrapositives of the theorem and one of the contrapositives of a converse. The two-way method of proof of any locus problem may then be established by proving two theorems, one each from groups I and II.

Group I: Theorem and all its contrapositives
Group II: A converse of the theorem and all the contrapositives of this converse

Since an inverse of a given theorem is also a contrapositive of a converse, such a pairing of theorems exhausts all possibilities for a two-way proof of any locus and provides many choices of method. For example, if a given statement of a locus involves two hypotheses H_1 and H_2 and one conclusion C, we have as one pattern of the two groups.

Group I:

1. Theorem: $(H_1)(H_2) \rightarrow (C)$.

2. Contrapositive: $(H_1)(\overline{C}) \rightarrow (\overline{H_2})$.
3. Contrapositive: $(\overline{C})(H_2) \rightarrow (\overline{H_1})$.

Group II:

1. Converse: $(H_1)(C) \rightarrow (H_2)$.
2. Contrapositive: $(H_1)(\overline{H_2}) \rightarrow (\overline{C})$.
3. Contrapositive: $(\overline{H_2})(C) \rightarrow (\overline{H_1})$.

As an illustration, consider the following:

Theorem: The locus of a point equidistant from the sides of a given angle is the bisector of the angle.

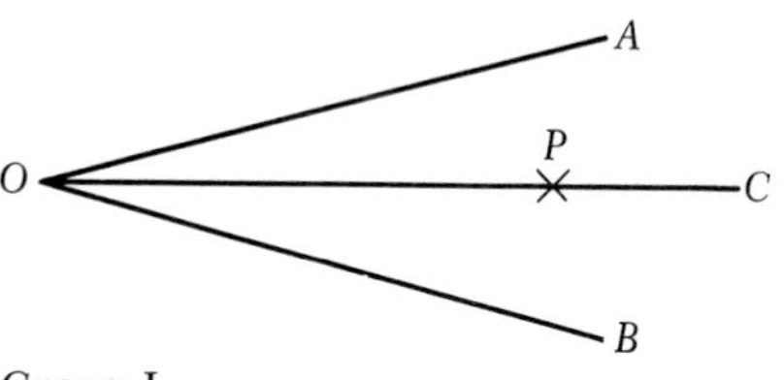

Figure 18-1

Group I

Theorem: If $\overrightarrow{OC}$ is the bisector of $\angle AOB$ and P lies on $\overrightarrow{OC}$, then P is equidistant from $\overrightarrow{OA}$ and $\overrightarrow{OB}$.

Contrapositive. If $\overrightarrow{OC}$ is the bisector of $\angle AOB$ and P is not equidistant from $\overrightarrow{OA}$ and $\overrightarrow{OB}$, then P does not lie on $\overrightarrow{OC}$.

Contrapositive. If P is not equidistant from $\overrightarrow{OA}$ and $\overrightarrow{OB}$ and P lies on $\overrightarrow{OC}$, then $\overrightarrow{OC}$ is not the bisector of $\angle AOB$.

Group II

Converse. If $\overrightarrow{OC}$ is the bisector of $\angle AOB$ and P is equidistant from OA and OB, then P lies on $\overrightarrow{OC}$.

Contrapositive. If $\overrightarrow{OC}$ is the bisector of $\angle AOB$ and P does not lie on $\overrightarrow{OC}$, then P is not equidistant from $\overrightarrow{OA}$ and $\overrightarrow{OB}$.

Contrapositive. If P does not lie on $\overrightarrow{OC}$ and P is equidistant from $\overrightarrow{OA}$ and $\overrightarrow{OB}$, then $\overrightarrow{OC}$ is not the bisector of $\angle AOB$.

The proof of any theorem of Group I and any theorem of Group II will constitute a two-way proof of the above locus problem. Thus from these two groups there are nine ways of establishing the given locus by a two-way proof. There exists still a second converse of the stated theorem, namely: If the point P lies on the ray $\overrightarrow{OC}$ which passes through the vertex of angle AOB, and if P is equidistant from rays $\overrightarrow{OA}$ and $\overrightarrow{OB}$, then $\overrightarrow{OC}$ is the bisector of angle AOB. Nine additional patterns for two-way proofs can be obtained by pairing each theorem of Group I with any one of the group of theorems composed of this converse and its two contrapositive theorems.

If the seven fundamental locus theorems on pages 479 and 480 are established by the two-way method, or merely postulated, then a one-way proof can be used effectively in practically all other locus situations. In order to avoid the two-way proof, some recommend that the seven fundamental loci be postulated. As an illustration of the one-way proof, two locus problems will be considered.

Problem: Find the locus of the mid-point of a rod whose ends always touch two fixed rods which are perpendicular to each other.

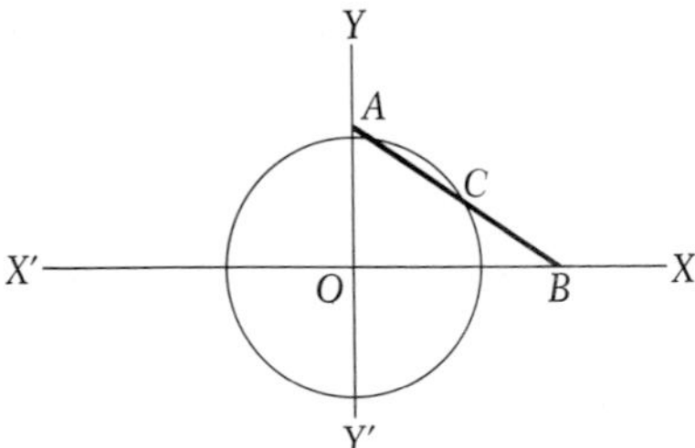

Figure 18-2

Given: Rods $\overline{XX'}$ and $\overline{YY'}$ $\perp$ each other at O. $\overline{AB}$ a rod moving so that end A is always on $\overline{YY'}$ and end B is always on the rod $\overline{XX'}$.

To find: The locus of C, the mid-point of $\overline{AB}$.

Solution:

1. $\overline{AB}$ in any position forms a rt. $\triangle$ with $\overline{AB}$ as hypotenuse.	1. *$\overline{XX'}$ and $\overline{YY'}$ given $\perp$ each other.*
2. $\overline{OC} \cong \overline{AC} \cong \overline{CB}$.	2. *The mid-point of the hypotenuse of a rt. $\triangle$ is equidistant from the three vertexes.*
3. $\therefore$The locus of C is a circle with O as center and $\overline{OC}$ as radius.	3. *The locus of points lying in a plane and at a fixed distance from a fixed point in the plane is a circle.*

Problem: Find the locus of the points of contact of tangents drawn from a given point to concentric circles.

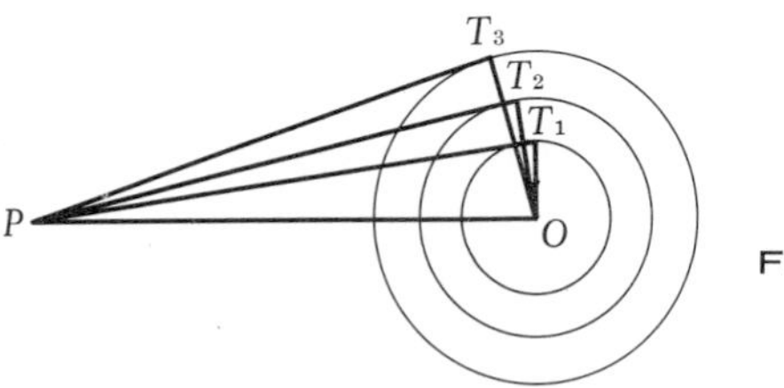

Figure 18-3

Given: Concentric circles with center at O and tangents drawn from fixed point P.

To find: The locus of the points of contact of these tangents.

Solution:

1. In any position $\overline{OT}$ will pass through O.	1. *In each case $\overline{OT}$ is a radius of a circle.*
2. In any position $\overline{PT}$ will pass through P.	2. *Given condition.*
3. In any position the $\angle PTO$ is a rt. $\angle$.	3. *The radius of a circle is always $\perp$ a tangent at the point of contact.*

4. ∴The locus of the point T is a circle on $\overline{PO}$ as diameter.

4. *The locus of the vertex of the rt. ∠ of a rt. △ with a given fixed hypotenuse is the circumference of the circle with the hypotenuse as diameter. (Theorem 6, page 480.)*

Each of the above problems can be established by a two-way proof, but the directness and simplicity of the one-way method make it very desirable.

Another important aspect of the concept of locus is that it offers many rich opportunities for exhibiting relations and counterparts of plane and solid geometry and thus provides a correlating link between them. Thus, for example, the locus of points in space which are equidistant from two fixed points might well be examined in connection with the locus of points in a plane which are equidistant from two fixed points in the plane. The result of studying these loci together could hardly fail to enrich the students' conception of both. Many other similar cases are readily found.

Conversely, the consideration of some of the more familiar space concepts might lead to a more natural and a better motivated approach to the somewhat abstract concept of locus. The consideration of the parallel walls of a room, the parallelism of floor and ceiling, or parallel rows of trees in an orchard might lead to a more intelligent comprehension of the true nature of parallelism than the mere drawing of lines on paper or on the board.

The close relationship existing between some of the two- and three-dimensional loci is indicated in the following discussion. The plane locus is stated, and then the concept of motion is introduced to develop the space locus.

I. The locus of a point moving in a plane so that it is always at a given distance from a fixed point is a circle with the fixed point as center and the given distance as the radius.

If in Figure 18-4 the circle is allowed to turn on $\overline{AB}$ as an axis, we obtain the sphere of Figure 18-5 whose diameter $\overline{A'B'}$ is congruent to $\overline{AB}$. Every point on the surface of the sphere is equidistant from O', the mid-point of $\overline{A'B'}$. Hence

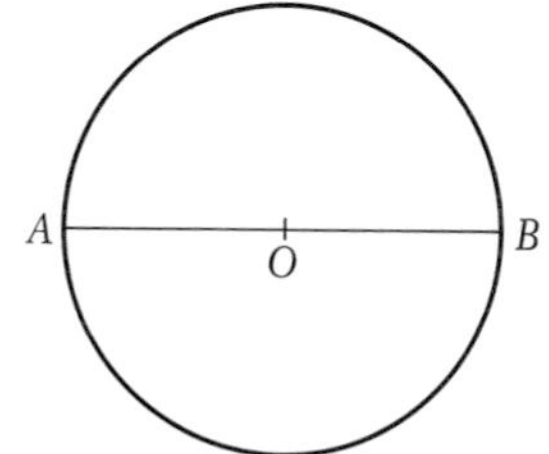

Figure 18-4

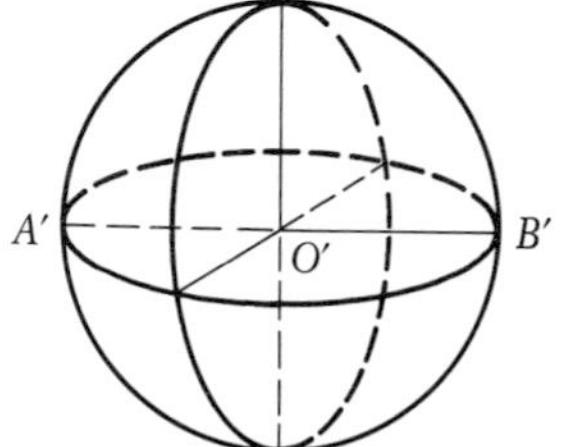

Figure 18-5

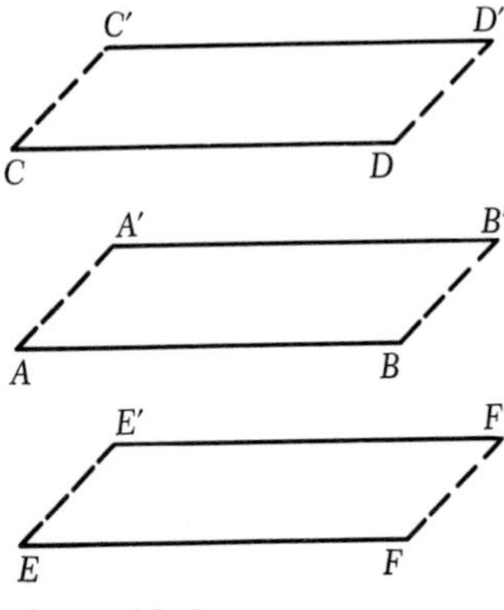

Figure 18-6

I. The locus of a point moving in space so that it is always at a given distance from a fixed point is a sphere with the fixed point as center and the given distance as the radius.

II. The locus of a point moving in a plane so that it is always at a given distance from a fixed line is a pair of lines parallel to the fixed line and at the given distance from it.

In Figure 18-6 consider first the lines $\overleftrightarrow{AB}$, $\overleftrightarrow{CD}$, and $\overleftrightarrow{EF}$. If the distance between $\overleftrightarrow{CD}$ and $\overleftrightarrow{AB} = d$ $=$ distance between $\overleftrightarrow{EF}$ and $\overleftrightarrow{AB}$, then $\overleftrightarrow{CD}$ and $\overleftrightarrow{EF}$ are the lines of the plane locus II. Now, if $\overleftrightarrow{AB}$ moves to the position $\overleftrightarrow{A'B'}$ and at the same time $\overleftrightarrow{CD}$ moves to $\overleftrightarrow{C'D'}$ and $\overleftrightarrow{EF}$ to $\overleftrightarrow{E'F'}$ and they each remain at all times the distance d from $\overleftrightarrow{AB}$, then the planes $CDD'C'$ and $EFF'E'$ are each d distance from the plane $ABB'A'$. Hence

2. The locus of a point moving in space so that it is always at a given distance from a fixed plane is a pair of planes parallel to the fixed plane and at the given distance from it.

III. The locus of a point moving in a plane so that it remains equidistant from two fixed points is the perpendicular bisector of the line segment joining the two fixed points.

If in Figure 18-7 the line $\overline{AB}$ is allowed to revolve around $\overleftrightarrow{CD}$ as an axis, then we obtain Figure 18-8, in which every point on $\overleftrightarrow{CD}$ is equidistant from the points on the circle XYZ whose center is O and whose radius is $\overline{OA} \cong \overline{OB}$. Furthermore, if C is a fixed point, then $\overline{CA} \cong \overline{CB}$. Hence

3. The locus of a point moving in space equidistant from the points of a circle is a line perpendicular to the plane of the circle at the center of the circle.

4. The locus of a point moving in space so that it remains equidistant from the three vertexes of a triangle is a line perpendicular to the plane of the triangle at the point which is the center of the circumscribed circle of the triangle.

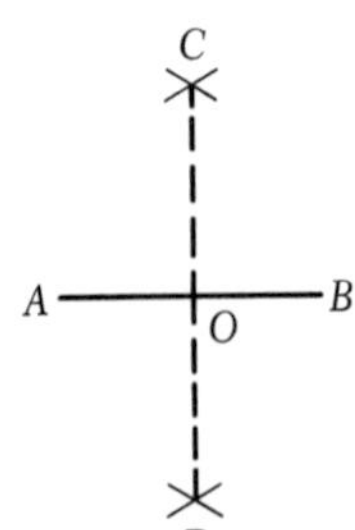

Figure 18-7

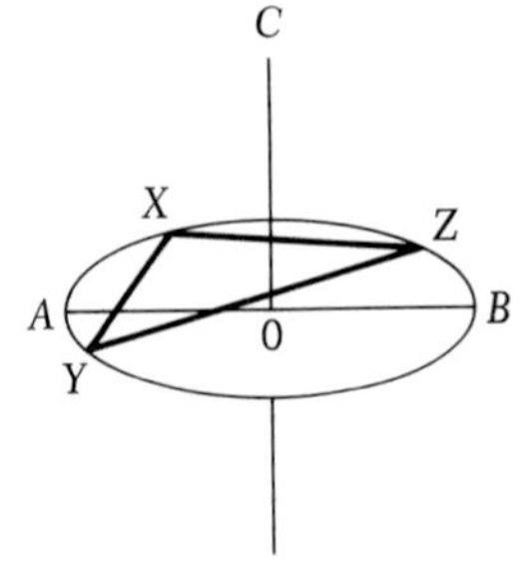

Figure 18-8

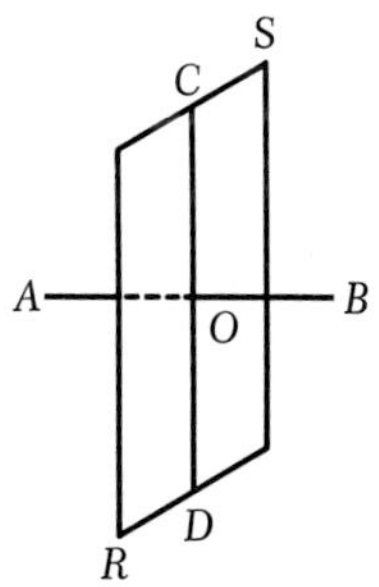

Figure 18-9

5. The locus of a point moving in a plane so that it is at a given distance from a fixed point not in the plane is a circle whose center is the projection of the point on the plane and whose radius is the projection of the given distance upon the plane.

If in Figure 18-7 the line $\overleftrightarrow{CD}$ is allowed to revolve around $\overleftrightarrow{AB}$ as an axis and if it is remembered that $\overleftrightarrow{CD}$ is unlimited in extent, then we obtain a figure represented by Figure 18-9, in which every point in the plane *RS* is equidistant from the points *A* and *B*. Hence

6. The locus of a point moving in space so that it remains equidistant from two fixed points is a plane perpendicular to the line segment joining the two points and at its mid-point.

IV. The locus of a point moving in a plane so that it remains equidistant from a pair of fixed intersecting lines is a pair of lines bisecting the angles formed by the two fixed lines.

In Figure 18-10 first consider the angles formed by the lines $\overleftrightarrow{AB}$ and $\overleftrightarrow{CD}$ with their bisectors $\overleftrightarrow{EF}$ and $\overleftrightarrow{GH}$. Then, if the lines are allowed to move so that the respective planes are generated, it follows that

7. The locus of a point moving in space so that it remains equidistant from the faces of two intersecting planes is a pair of planes bisecting the dihedral angles formed by the planes.

V. The locus of a point moving in a plane so that it remains equidistant from two parallel lines is a line parallel to the two lines and midway between them.

In Figure 18-11 first consider the parallel lines $\overleftrightarrow{CD}$ and $\overleftrightarrow{EF}$ with $\overleftrightarrow{AB}$ midway between and parallel to them. Let the point *C* move along the line $\overleftrightarrow{CX}$ while the given lines move in such a way that the initial relationship remains true. Then we have

Figure 18-10

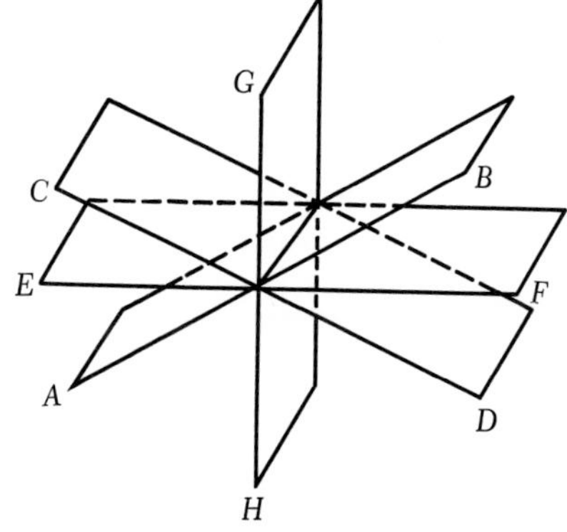

Figure 18-11

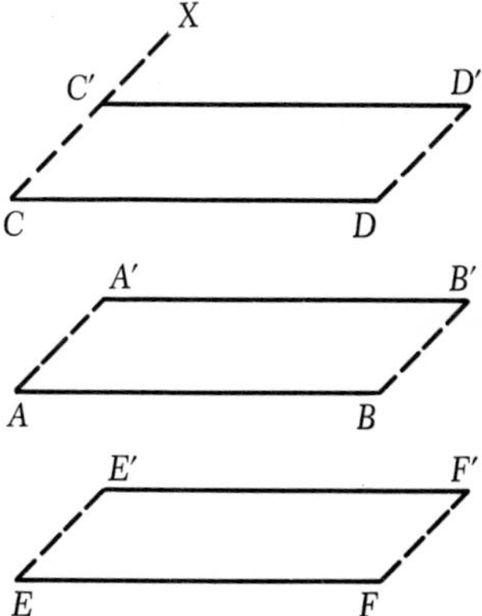

8. The locus of a point moving in space so that it remains equidistant from the faces of two parallel planes is a plane parallel to the two planes and midway between them.

Thus by using motion in space as the generalizing technique, the two- and three-dimensional concepts of locus can be shown to be closely associated with each other, and each may be effectively used to supplement the discussion of the other.

The concept of dependence The dynamic concept of locus emphasizes the importance of functional dependence in the analysis of geometric configurations. This concept of the interdependence of geometrical magnitudes is by no means new. Most of the emphasis in the study of functionality on the secondary level, however, has been confined to the analysis of interdependent variation by means of algebraic techniques. In plane geometry this has resulted in a tendency to overlook the fact that there are many aspects of dependence which are not expressible in the conciseness of an algebraic formula but which are deeply significant to a fundamental understanding and appreciation of the real nature of geometrical subject matter.

In 1872 Felix Klein, in outlining his famous Erlanger program, gave the following definition of geometry: "Geometry is the study of the invariants of a configuration under a group of transformations." Thus the structure of geometry may be outlined as follows:[1]

1. Select the space, i.e., determine whether the geometry to be studied is in one, two, three, or higher dimensions.
2. Select the element, i.e., specify the undefined elements. In ordinary two- or three-dimensional geometry the undefined element is generally taken to be either the point or the straight line. This, however, is not necessary.
3. Build configurations such as triangles, quadrilaterals, circles, and polygons.
4. Select transformations. In elementary geometry, the two most frequently used groups of transformations are those of rigid motion and projection.
5. Study invariants. An invariant of a geometric configuration is a property that does not change in the process of being transformed. For example, of a line segment does not change when the line is moved about in space, but it does change if the segment is projected from one plane to another; hence, length is an invariant under rigid motion but not under projection.

From the above outline of the structure of geometry it is evident that the very nature of the geometry to be studied is dependent upon making

[1]*Cf.* E. P. Lane, Definition and Classification of Geometries, *School Science and Mathematics*, **30** (1930), 50–56.

certain basic choices. In the geometry of the secondary school the space in which we are interested is either two-dimensional (plane) or three-dimensional (solid). The undefined element is the point, and the transformations are those of rigid motion, viz., rotation and translation. Under these transformations, such geometric properties as length, distance, size of an angle, united position of point and line, and area are invariant properties. We proceed, then, to analyze the geometric configurations in terms of these invariants; for example:

1. Two triangles are congruent when their sides are of the same respective lengths.
2. Two triangles are congruent when two pairs of sides of the same respective lengths include angles of the same size.
3. A circle is the locus of a point moving at a given distance from a fixed point.
4. Two circles are congruent if their radii are of the same length.

Although the point may be taken as the undefined element of the geometry of the secondary school and all other elements defined in terms of it, from a pedagogical point of view, this is very undesirable. It is not good psychology to crowd the young mind with so many formal definitions. No significant mathematical rigor is lost in taking for undefined elements in secondary geometry such terms as point, line, surface, plane, solid, and space. An intelligent comprehension of such concepts can be established intuitively, and it is pedagogically unsound to attempt to build up definitions of these concepts that could be accepted as technically correct.

In any geometric configuration there exist intrinsic interrelations among the constituent elements. An analysis of this interdependence of elements is one of the most effective techniques for discovering the characteristic properties of the configuration and portraying its complete geometric significance. For example:

1. The area of a triangle depends upon the lengths of the altitude and base. What happens to the area when either the altitude or the base is doubled? What happens when both are doubled?
2. How do the circumference and area of the circle depend upon the radius? Which is affected more by a change in the length of the radius?
3. In a cylinder, $V = \pi r^2 h$. Which would increase the volume more, to double h or to double r?
4. In a triangle how is a side affected by increasing the opposite angle if the lengths of the two including sides remain constant?

Questions such as these help to bring to light the exact nature of any geometric configuration under investigation. Critical analysis and intelligent interpretation of such configurational dependence will contribute to enriched geometrical comprehension.

The study of geometrical dependence is further enhanced by the principle of continuity, which asserts that a proposition that has been established in relation to a given figure will remain true when that figure changes continuously subject to the conditions controlling its initial construction. The interrelated concepts of dependence and continuity unite to replace a static, mechanical treatment of geometrical subject matter by a dynamic, functional program of instruction. It behooves every teacher of geometry to utilize the full benefits of such an approach to the study of geometrical subject matter. As an illustration of the full significance of the introduction of these dynamic concepts into the teaching of plane geometry, consider the implications for relational thinking embodied in the two following theorems:

1. The angle formed by two intersecting lines of unlimited length which meet a circle is measured by one-half the algebraic sum of the intercepted arcs.
2. In a triangle the square of the side opposite a given angle is equal to the sum of the squares of the other two sides diminished by twice the algebraic product of one of these sides by its directed projection upon the other.

It is true that the concept of directed line and arc lengths must be introduced in the consideration of the above theorems for their full significance. Why should we not use such concepts of directed line lengths in the teaching of plane geometry as a significant aspect of the concept of directed numbers introduced in the algebra of the junior high school? The consideration of similar groupings of significant theorems will enhance the value of these dynamic concepts of dependence and continuity as instructional mediums in plane geometry.

Since it takes only two points to determine a line, we say that three points are dependent if they are on the same line. This concept of dependence has some very interesting and important applications to the construction of geometric figures. A triangle is uniquely determined by three points not on the same line. In more general terminology this statement would read: A triangle is uniquely determined by three independent points; or still more generally, a triangle is uniquely determined by three independent elements (or conditions). The truth of this last statement is illustrated by the congruence theorems which require three independent elements.

Since the sum of angles of a triangle is always two right angles, the three angles are dependent elements. Why are two triangles whose three angles are respectively congruent not necessarily congruent? Why do three lines through the same point not determine a triangle? Two other less evident illustrations of dependent elements are to be seen in Figures 18-12 and 18-13.

In Figure 18-12 it is to be noted that any angle inscribed in the arc BAC will be congruent to angle A. Hence it is evident that the elements a, A, R (radius of circumscribed circle) are dependent elements; i.e., given any two of them, the third is determined.

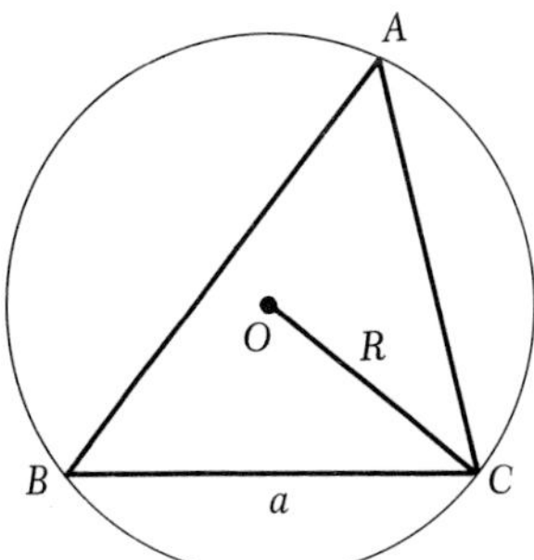

Figure 18-12

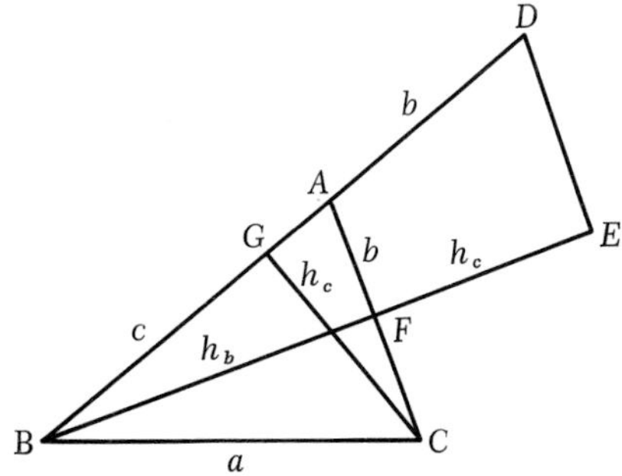

Figure 18-13

In the triangle ABC (Figure 18-13) let h_b and h_c represent the altitudes upon the sides b and c, respectively. In the rt. ⊿s BFC and BGC, respectively, it is evident that a, h_b, $\angle C$ and a, h_c, $\angle B$ are sets of dependent elements, since, in each case, any two of the elements determine the right triangle and the third element is then uniquely determined. Now let $\overline{BA}$ be extended to D so that $\overline{AD} \cong \overline{AC}$; then $BD = b + c$. Draw $\overline{DE} \perp \overline{BF}$ extended. $\overline{DE} \parallel \overline{AC}$; hence $\angle D \cong \angle CAB$. Also $\overline{BE} = h_b + h_c$. It then follows immediately from the right triangle BDE that the elements $b + c$, $h_c + h_b$, $\angle A$ are dependent elements.

By using both direct and indirect elements related to the unique determination of triangles, five sets of three dependent elements each have been exhibited. They are

I. A, B, C
II. a, A, R
III. $b + c, h_c + h_b, A$
IV. a, h_b, C
V. a, h_c, B

Such sets of dependent elements are important aids in an effective approach to exercises in the construction of triangles. It is the purpose of this discussion to call attention to an aspect of this concept of dependence that seems to be generally overlooked in the teaching of plane geometry. To simplify the discussion, two specific examples will be developed in the hope that inferences will lead to the individual development of many others.

A simple construction problem that frequently comes early in the geometry course is to construct a triangle having given two angles and the included side. Let us specify that the given elements are B, C, a. After this construction has been completed, additional construction problems may be derived from it by using the dependent elements of sets I, II, IV, and V. These problems may be used as instructional aids, supplementary drill material, or as material for enriching the study of construction. It would indeed be fine instructional technique to have the students derive and construct such supplementary problems. From set I it is evident that, once angles B and C are known, angle A is also known. Hence the given elements imply the following elements as given:

1. A, B, a
2. A, C, a

From set II it is evident that, since angle A and side a are known, R, the radius of the circumscribed circle, is also known, so that we have

3. A, B, R
4. A, C, R
5. B, C, R
6. R, B, a
7. R, C, a

Now, if we apply sets IV and V, in turn, to the original problem and derived problems 1, 2, 6, and 7, we obtain

8. B, C, h_b
9. h_c, C, a
10. h_b, C, h_c
11. B, C, h_c
12. B, h_b, a
13. h_b, h_c, a
14. B, h_c, h_b
15. A, h_b, a
16. A, B, h_b
17. A, h_c, a
18. A, C, h_c
19. R, B, h_c
20. R, h_b, a
21. R, C, h_b
22. R, h_c, a

Another interpretation of set I is that if we have given one angle of a triangle, we also know the sum of the other two. By applying this to problems 6, 7, 9, 10, 12, 14, 15, 17, 19, and 21 above, we obtain

23. $R, A + C, a$
24. $R, A + B, a$
25. $h_c, A + B, a$
26. $h_b, A + B, h_c$
27. $A + C, h_b, a$
28. $A + C, h_c, h_b$
29. $B + C, h_b, a$
30. $B + C, h_c, a$
31. $R, A + C, h_c$
32. $R, A + B, h_b$

Hence from the original set of elements there have been derived 32 additional sets of given elements with which triangles may be constructed. Each of these problems may have an individual construction which is independent of the original problem B, C, a. It is quite evident, however, that all of the problems may be reduced to the original problem. Still others may be derived.

Another illustration of interest may be found in the application of these techniques to derive additional construction problems from the one whose construction is carried out on pages 492 to 493.

From the use of set I we have the following:

1. $a, B + C, b + c$

An application of set II to the original problem and to the derived problem gives

2. $R, A, b + c$
3. $a, R, b + c$
4. $R, B + C, b + c$

An application of set III then gives

5. $a, h_c + h_b, b + c$
6. $a, A, h_c + h_b$
7. $R, h_c + h_b, b + c$
8. $R, A, h_c + h_b$

Applications of sets I and II to problems 6 and 8 give

9. $a, B + C, h_c + h_b$
10. $a, R, h_c + h_b$
11. $R, B + C, h_c + h_b$

If it is furthermore recalled that the perimeter $2p$ is the sum of the sides, i.e.,

$$2p = a + b + c$$

the following 12 sets may be derived:

12. $2p, A, a$
13. $2p, R, a$
14. $2p, A, R$
15. $2p, b + c, R$
16. $2p, B + C, a$
17. $2p, B + C, b + c$
18. $2p, b + c, A$
19. $2p, R, B + C$
20. $2p, h_c + h_b, a$
21. $2p, h_c + h_b, A$
22. $2p, h_c + h_b, B + C$
23. $2p, h_c + h_b, b + c$

Thus 23 additional construction problems have been derived from the original one through successive applications of the concept of geometric dependence.

Similar possibilities exist in all construction situations in geometry. Such instructional technique not only provides the teacher with an enriched program for teaching geometry but also affords the student the opportunity for a more significant understanding of the real nature of geometric construction.

Construction problems There is no more fascinating or provocative activity in school mathematics than the solution of construction problems in geometry. This aspect of the subject brings into play all the geometrical assets which students possess: their knowledge of the accepted postulates, stated definitions, and proved theorems; their ability to analyze problems; their ingenuity in making plausible conjectures and in seeking for methods of verification; their skill in planning formal proofs; their ability to recognize in carrying out the synthesis whether the proposed proof is valid or not; their care in considering all the possible cases that might arise under the given hypotheses; and their ability to determine whether or not the construction is unique or, indeed, whether or not it is possible. Thus construction problems form an extremely valuable part of the experience of students in geometry.

Most students in plane geometry will have had some experience in making simple constructions empirically and without proofs in their work in the junior high school. This is a helpful start and serves to give the students an intuitive feeling for certain loci and combinations of figures. It is sufficient for making interesting designs, but it is not sufficient to meet the objectives we have in mind in proposing construction problems for students in demonstrative geometry.

Most of the construction problems which occur as principal "Problems" along with the sequence of principal "Theorems" in the textbooks are quite simple of analysis and easy of proof. For example, it is relatively easy to devise a method for constructing a tangent to a circle at a given point on the circle and to prove that this method is valid. However, there are many interesting problems whose solutions are far from obvious and which do tax the ingenuity and ability of the students. Such problems provide valuable experience, especially for the better students, and can do much to stimulate interest in the course.

There are four aspects of any construction problem in geometry: (1) Determine how to use the given elements to construct the required figure; (2) construct the figure; (3) prove that the construction is correct; i.e., prove that the constructed figure has the given elements in it, either directly or indirectly; and (4) discuss the possibilities of construction, i.e., the conditions under which the construction is possible and whether the construction, when possible, is unique. These four aspects might be more briefly labeled: (1) analysis, (2) construction, (3) proof, and (4) discussion. To illustrate, let us consider the following:

Problem: To construct a triangle, given the base, the angle opposite the base, and the sum of the other two sides.

Given: $a, b + c, \angle A$.

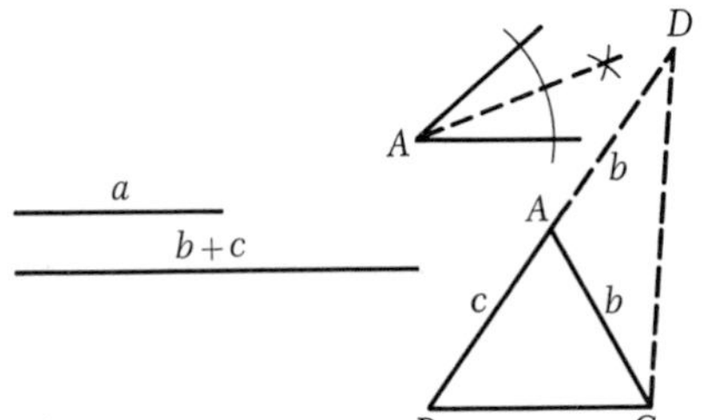

Figure 18-14

To construct: $\triangle ABC$.

Analysis: Suppose $\triangle ABC$ is the required triangle. How can $b + c$ be used to get the triangle? Is there an auxiliary triangle, using $b + c$ and the other given elements, which can be constructed and from which the $\triangle ABC$ can be obtained? It is to be observed that, if $\overline{BA}$ is extended to D so that $\overline{AD} \cong \overline{AC}$, then $\overline{BD} = b + c$. Furthermore, since $\triangle ADC$ is isosceles, $\angle D = \frac{1}{2}\angle A$. Therefore, $\triangle BDC$ can be constructed, since two of its sides and the angle opposite one of them are known. The $\perp$ bisector of $\overline{DC}$ will then intersect $\overline{BD}$ in the point A, thus determining the required $\triangle ABC$.

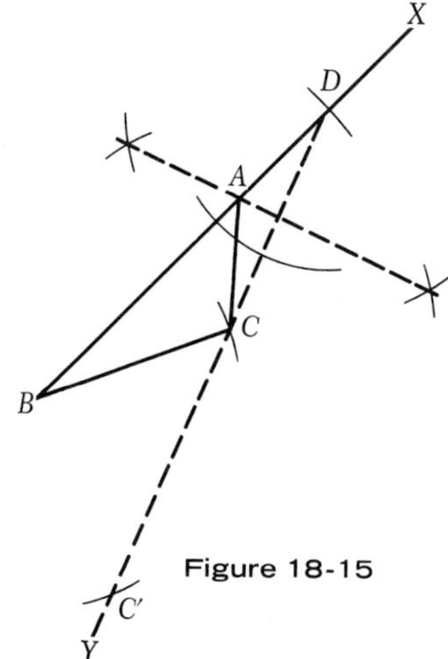

Figure 18-15

Construction: On a working line $\overleftrightarrow{BX}$ lay off $\overline{BD} = b + c$. At D construct $\angle D = \frac{1}{2}\angle A$. With B as a center and a radius $= a$, describe a circle intersecting $\overleftrightarrow{DY}$ in C and C'.
Draw $\overline{BC}$.
Erect the $\perp$ bisector of $\overline{DC}$.
It will intersect $\overline{BD}$ in A.
Draw $\overline{AC}$.
$\triangle ABC$ is the required triangle.

Proof:

1. $\overline{BC} \cong a$.	1. *By construction.*
2. $\triangle ADC$ is isosceles.	2. *A lies on* $\perp$ *bisector of* $\overline{DC}$ *by construction.*
3. $\overline{AD} \cong \overline{AC}$.	3. *Legs of isosceles* $\triangle$.
4. $\therefore \overline{BA} + \overline{AC} \cong \overline{BA} + \overline{AD} \cong \overline{BD} \cong b + c$.	4. $BD = b + c$ *by construction.*
5. $\angle ADC \cong \angle ACD$.	5. *Base* $\angle$s *of isosceles* $\triangle$.
6. $m\angle BAC = m\angle ADC + m\angle ACD = 2m\angle ADC$.	6. *Ext.* $\angle$ *of* $\triangle$ = *sum of two opposite int.* $\angle$s.
7. $\therefore \angle BAC \cong \angle A$.	7. $\angle ADC \cong \frac{1}{2}\angle A$ *by construction.*

Discussion: For the construction to be possible, $b + c$ must be greater than a, since the sum of two sides of a triangle must be greater than the third side. In the construction of the auxiliary $\triangle BCD$, the circle with B as a center and a as a radius might intersect the line $\overleftrightarrow{DY}$ in two points C and C' (as in Figure 18-15), in which case there would be two solutions for the $\triangle BCD$. If a were equal in length to the $\perp$ distance from B to $\overleftrightarrow{DY}$, this circle would be tangent to $\overleftrightarrow{DY}$ and there would be only one $\triangle BCD$. If a were less than the $\perp$ distance from B to $\overleftrightarrow{DY}$, the circle would not intersect the line $\overleftrightarrow{DY}$ and there would be no $\triangle BCD$ possible. From each auxiliary $\triangle BCD$ there can be obtained one and only one required $\triangle ABC$, since the $\perp$ bisector of $\overline{DC}$ will intersect $\overline{BD}$ in one and only one point. Therefore, there may be two solutions, one solution, or no solution for the given problem.

No construction problem should be considered a finished product until it has been subjected to the complete treatment outlined above.

Much of the most important information concerning a construction is frequently hidden until the discussion brings it to light. It should be emphasized that such procedure as this gives system to the attack on construction problems and eliminates a great deal of the futile effort expended and feeling of helplessness developed in the hit-or-miss, trial-and-error technique so frequently used.

Solid and spherical geometry During the first half of this century it was quite customary for high schools to offer a one-semester course in deductive solid geometry. This is no longer the case. Expansion of the high school curriculum and considerations of relative values have brought about widespread abandonment of solid geometry as a separate course. At the same time, however, it continues to be recognized that understanding of many of the space concepts and relations with which solid geometry deals is important, and there is a marked tendency now toward associating some study of these concepts and relations with related parts of plane geometry.

Perhaps the three principal values to be hoped for from any study of solid geometry are the acquisition of a sense of space perception and the ability to visualize figures in three-dimensional space, understanding of important space relationships and of the terminology used to describe them, and knowledge of the metric properties and relationships in and among the common simple solids. To a large extent these values can be attained through informal methods. These would include such things as the examination, comparison, and perhaps the construction of physical models, measurement, careful and realistic-looking drawings, well-planned discussion of matters to be emphasized, and plausible reasoning.

Concepts to be stressed include parallel and skew lines, parallel planes, lines and planes which are parallel, lines perpendicular to planes, projections of lines on planes and the concept of the angle between a line and a plane, the line of intersection of two planes, dihedral angles, the plane angle and measure of a dihedral angle, perpendicular planes, and the common simple solids studied in the junior high school. Even an informal study of these concepts and figures will bring to light a considerable number of important properties and relationships which may be discussed verbally and taken as theorems without proof. Clear understanding of these relationships through discussion based upon models and drawings both depends upon and at the same time serves to clarify the students' sense of space perception and imagination.

In the part of the work dealing with mensuration, the formulas for the surface areas and volumes of certain of the familiar simple solids are needed. Most students should have encountered these in their work in the junior high school. These formulas need to be known so well now that they can be called to mind instantly and applied without hesitation to mensuration problems. Solids involved in this part of the work will be prisms, cylinders, pyramids, cones, spheres, and composite figures that can be decomposed into some of these forms. The analysis, or decomposition, of such composite figures is usually not difficult, though the numerical evaluations may be tedious. Problems of this kind are very common in the physical sciences, industrial technology, and engineering.

The ability to make good drawings of space figures is an important asset. It is important to the student because it requires some feeling of space perception in depth, and at the same time it helps to clarify and crystallize this feeling. It is important for the teacher because it helps him to make his explanations realistic. It is hard to build correct intuitive feelings about objects unless the representations of these objects correspond pretty closely to the appearance which the objects themselves (or models of them) would have. Unfortunately, few students, and by no means all teachers, are gifted with the native ability to make good three-dimensional drawings. Lines have to be foreshortened, angles distorted, and shapes changed, but without destroying the illusions which they are intended to convey. Only an artist's intuition can provide the full measure of competence in this, yet by following a few simple principles of drawing, and with patience, care, and practice, most people can learn to do this reasonably well. Some good hints and numerous examples of drawings of three-dimensional figures can be found in the "Appendices" volume of the Report of the Commission on Mathematics.[2] Teachers of geometry should feel a special responsibility for making themselves competent in this respect.

The trend toward modernization The traditional course in high school geometry has been criticized in recent years by many members of the mathematical community, both among college and university faculties and among high school teachers themselves. The criticisms have been leveled not so much against the objectives and content of the subject as against certain alleged defects in its logical foundations and upon instructional approaches which seem not to have yielded full educational dividends in terms of understandings and attitudes.

Mathematicians have long recognized that Euclid's presentation of geometry, splendid as it is, contains certain logical inadequacies which come more sharply into focus and become more acute in the light of contemporary thinking.[3] There are cases in which proofs are made to

[2]Report of the Commission on Mathematics, "Appendices" (New York: College Entrance Examination Board, 1959), pp. 140–158.

[3]See, for example, the Report of the Commission on Mathematics (New York: College Entrance Examination Board, 1959), pp. 23–24.

depend upon tacit assumptions which seem intuitively evident but which are not explicitly postulated. We may note the absence of any explicit postulates about order relations (as, for example, the order of points on a line) and of definitive statements of what is meant by a point lying between two points or between two lines. Such logical defects becloud the rigor which is commonly supposed to undergird the structure of school geometry and thus seem to call for some modification of the traditional course.

Apart from these logical defects in the exposition of the subject itself, there has been serious criticism of the teaching of geometry. Some shortcomings of traditional instruction in geometry have been summarized by the Commission on Mathematics as follows:[4]

1. An overemphasis on logical formalism as opposed to mathematical insight, or even to the understanding of deductive reasoning.
2. A failure to utilize the altogether adequate algebra of the present day.
3. A failure to fuse instruction in plane and solid geometry.
4. A failure to emphasize adequately intuition and "plausible reasoning," particularly in the development of spatial imagination.

As a result of such criticisms, massive efforts have been made in recent years to improve the traditional treatment of school geometry in line with contemporary mathematical thought. Under the UICSM project, the SMSG project, the Ball State Mathematics Project, and other experimental programs, courses and textbooks have been produced which differ rather radically from the traditional course and textbooks. The observable differences reflect a trend toward modernization of the treatment of the subject, and this trend can be observed in practically all textbooks in school geometry published since about 1960.

The concept of sets, with appropriate terminology, notation, and operations, is being given prominence, and the language of sets is being used to give precision and clarity to definitions. Geometric figures are regarded as sets of points or as subsets of sets of points. For example, a segment is regarded as a subset of the set of points on a line, while a quadrilateral is taken to be the union of four sets of points each of which is a subset of a line. An angle is defined to be the union of two rays and its vertex as the intersection of these two rays. A circle is defined as the set of all points in a plane that are at a given distance from a given point in the plane. Many other illustrations could easily be given.

Order relations and the concept of betweenness, missing from the traditional courses, are now receiving explicit and careful attention. Precise definitions and adequate postulates are serving to clarify and

[4]*Ibid.*, "Appendices," p. 111.

make precise some notions which in the past could be apprehended only intuitively. Examples of this are the meanings to be attached to the statement that a point lies between two other points or that a point lies in the interior of an angle.

In contrast to earlier practice, distinction is being made between geometric configurations themselves, considered as sets of points, and the measures of their magnitudes, the latter being represented as real numbers. Traditionally the distinction has been implied by the context, but it is becoming common practice to indicate the distinction by different notations. For example, instead of $\angle ABC + \angle CBD$, one now commonly finds such notation as $m\angle ABC + m\angle CBD$ to represent the measure of the sum of the measures of two angles. This distinction is not trivial. It promotes precise and incisive statements based on precise and incisive thinking in which ambiguity and fuzziness have no place. Moreover, by regarding measures as real numbers a link is provided by which the geometry of sets of points is associated with the real number system. Thus an adequate algebra and arithmetic are made available not only for precise quantitative descriptions of geometrical figures but also as helpful instruments that can be used in the analysis and solution of many geometric problems.

The notation and the algebraic properties of inequalities will be treated more adequately than in the courses of a decade ago. The arbitrary nature of definitions and postulates will be emphasized by the fact that definitions may differ from textbook to textbook and that statements which are found as theorems in some textbooks will be postulated in others. Parts of solid geometry will be studied in connection with similar ideas in plane geometry. Specific rather than tacit reference will be made to transformations of rigid motion (translation, rotation, and reflection), and attention will be given to the properties and uses of symmetry. The methods of coordinate geometry will at times be used to supplement the usual synthetic geometry for purposes of both definition and proof.

These are illustrations of things which are likely to be found in textbooks on school geometry of the 1960s but which were not generally found in the textbooks of the 1950s. They indicate a clear trend toward modernizing school geometry and toward erasing the hitherto sharp demarcation between geometry and algebra. Some textbooks will go further in this direction than others, but there will be few if any in which the trend is not clearly discernible.

Methods of coordinate geometry The reports of both the Commission on Mathematics and the Secondary School Curriculum Committee point out the desirability of introducing some of the most fundamental ideas and methods of coordinate geometry in the high school course.

Neither report recommends a complete course in analytic geometry in the high school, but both recognize that there are advantages to be gained by making some use of coordinate methods. Perhaps the greatest advantage is the expanded outlook and the deeper insight which students would gain through becoming aware of ways in which these methods serve to bring the powerful methods of algebra to bear upon geometrical problems.

Concepts to be developed would include:

1. The notion of a system of coordinates (one-to-one correspondence between the set of points in the coordinate plane and the set of ordered pairs of real numbers)
2. The concept of a locus as a set of points and of its intercepts on the coordinate axes
3. The concept of a straight line as a special type of locus with special properties
4. The concept of the slope of a straight line and the conditions (in terms of slopes) for parallelism and perpendicularity of lines
5. The distance formula, for which, of course, the Pythagorean theorem is needed
6. The mid-point formula
7. What is meant by the equation of a locus and the locus of an equation
8. Forms for the equation of a straight line and the relations of the coefficients in the equation to the geometrical properties of the line, such as slope and intercepts
9. The concept of a circle as another special type of locus having a characteristic type of equation, and the relations of the coefficients in the equation to the geometrical properties (location of the center and length of radius) of the circle
10. The geometric and algebraic significance of the intersection of two loci
11. Geometrical interpretation of inequalities such as, for example, $y \leqq \frac{1}{2}x$, or $x > -3$, or $(x - 3)^2 + (y - 2)^2 \leqq 5$

Since loci are sets of points, the formal notation of sets will sometimes be used to describe them. For example, the circle C whose center is at $(-2,5)$ and whose radius is 3 units long may be described by the notation $C = \{(x,y) \mid x \text{ and } y \text{ real numbers}, (x + 2)^2 + (y - 5)^2 = 3\}$. The line l whose y intercept is -1 and whose slope is $3/4$ may be described by the notation $l = \{(x,y) \mid x \text{ and } y \text{ real numbers}, y = \frac{3}{4}x - 1\}$. If p and q are two given lines having different slopes, their point of intersection may be designated in set notation as $p \cap q$. If the equations of the two lines are given, algebraic solution of the system will yield an ordered pair of real numbers which will be the solution set $p \cap q$.

These are all simple concepts which, if well presented, can be understood without serious difficulty by high school sophomores. Some excellent sets of exercises for developing and clarifying such ideas as these are found in textbooks published since about 1960. In addition to such developmental exercises there is a considerable number of theorems and exercises for which synthetic proofs have traditionally been given but which are susceptible of proof by coordinate methods. For example, it can easily be shown analytically that the diagonals of a parallelogram bisect each other or that the line segment joining the mid-points of two sides of a triangle is parallel to the third side and half as long as the third side. Many such examples can be found in recent textbooks, and the "Appendices" volume of the Report of the Commission on Mathematics lists a set of thirty such theorems, together with suggestions for their proofs or solutions by coordinate methods.

The study of coordinate methods can do much to supplement, enrich, and motivate work in high school geometry and at the same time to lay a valuable foundation for subsequent work in mathematics.

Topics for bright students There are some students who are able to master the usual course in high school geometry with so little effort that their full mathematical potential is hardly more than tapped. These are the students who, with proper motivation, could go furthest in mathematics but who are often neglected in the sense that they are not given work which will "stretch their minds" but are allowed to coast along with the rest of the class and are not forced to extend themselves very much. These students need, and usually like, work which will challenge their best intellectual efforts. The discussion which follows suggests two examples of topics which could serve this purpose. Others could be given. With suitable reference books available, and with some guidance and perhaps some help from the teacher, either of these could be investigated with interest and profit by high school students of exceptional insight and ability.

Mirror geometry. This is a geometry in which the basic transformation is the reflection of points in a straight line or the construction of the images of points and figures which are symmetric to given points and figures with respect to a straight line. The idea of symmetry with respect to a line is central, and the construction of the images is achieved through use of the definition of this concept. To construct the image P' of a point P in a line l, one needs only to construct a line from P perpendicular to l and prolong this line to a point P' such that P' and P are equidistant from l. The image of a figure F is the aggregate of the images P' of all points P on F. Thus little is required from the usual Euclidean geometry except the construction of a perpendicular from a point to a line, the theorem that this perpendicular is unique, and the definition of congruent figures and a few congruence theorems.

By constructing carefully a number of plane figures and their images (reflections), certain general observations soon become intuitively evident. Repeated reflections (reflections of images in the same line or in other lines) yield other and more interesting observations which the student may set down as conjectures and for which he may then seek proofs. Observant and ingenious students may be able to discover and prove several theorems in such a "mirror geometry." More importantly, their understandings of transformations will be somewhat generalized and clarified, and they will almost certainly get a sense of achievement and a high degree of motivation through investigation of this special topic.

Finite geometries. In Euclidean plane geometry it is assumed that there are infinitely many lines in the plane and infinitely many points on each line. In a finite geometry, by contrast, it is stipulated at the outset that only a finite number of points and lines are to be considered and that for purposes of this geometry there are no other points or lines. Such terms as "parallel" or "perpendicular lines," "bisector," "triangle," "congruent," and other concepts to be involved are not to have the usual meanings intuitively attached to them but must be defined explicitly in terms of admissible points. Likewise all assumptions must be stated categorically and without ambiguity. These conditions are very important because except for its axiomatic structure such a geometry will have little in common with ordinary plane geometry. Unfamiliar meanings will be attached to familiar terms. The definitions and graphic or physical models will seem strangely different from those of Euclidean plane geometry, and intuition can play no part in arriving at conclusions. Even theorems which may sound verbally familiar cannot have the familiar interpretations.

On the other hand, the very necessity of working without the aid of intuition can do much to clarify the feeling for what the axiomatic method is and how it operates. Because they depend considerably on intuition, working with such a geometry would likely have little appeal to most students except, perhaps, as a puzzle. But to those who have a natural liking and flair for abstractions, the search for proofs of theorems in a finite geometry can be a fascinating and truly productive experience.

The foregoing are but two examples taken from a considerable list of topics that would be suitable for investigation by exceptionally able high school students. Proofs in plane geometry by vector methods, topologically equivalent curves and surfaces, and traversable networks are among the numerous other topics that have been suggested by various writers.

EXERCISES

1. Give verbally both a dynamic and a static statement describing the geometric conditions for each of the following two-dimensional locus concepts: circle, angle bisector, perpendicular bisector of a line segment.

2. Give three-dimensional analogues for the loci described in the foregoing exercise.

3. Explain why it is necessary, in order to prove a locus, to prove two theorems. Discuss this in terms of necessary and sufficient conditions, using an example to illustrate your discussion.

4. Consider this proposition: If a point is equidistant from the ends of a line segment, it lies on the perpendicular bisector of the segment. The proof of this proposition, together with the proof of its converse, would establish a locus theorem. State it.

5. If the original theorem of exercise 4 and its inverse were both proved, would this establish a locus theorem? If so, try to prove the locus in this way.

6. Of the following sets of three elements of a triangle, which are sets of dependent elements? (*a*) a, b, c; (*b*) a, A, R; (*c*) A, B, C; (*d*) A, b, C; (*e*) A, h_c, b; (*f*) a, h_b, h_c; (*g*) a, h_b, C; (*h*) A, a, h_a; (*i*) b, R, h_c; (*j*) A, R, b.

7. Explain the construction of a common internal tangent to two circles. Discuss the problem fully, examining all cases.

8. Let it be required to construct a triangle, given the length of side a, the radius R of the circumscribed circle, and the altitude h_b on the side b. Give the analysis, construction, proof, and discussion of this problem.

9. Construct triangle ABC if the only elements given are side a, angle B, and the median to side c. Give the analysis, construction, proof, and discussion of this problem.

10. Construct triangle ABC if the only elements given are the lengths of the medians to the three sides. Give the analysis, construction, proof, and discussion of this problem.

11. Select five locus theorems from plane geometry, and for each of these state a proposition which would be a counterpart in three-dimensional space.

12. Find the total surface area and the volume of a spherical wedge of the sphere circumscribed about a cube whose edges are each 2 inches long, if the dihedral angle of the wedge has a measure of 45°. Express your answer in terms of π.

13. Let P and Q be two right regular pyramids each having a square base 2 inches on each side. If the altitude t of Q is twice the altitude n of P, show that the volume of Q is twice the volume of P.

14. If two pyramids P and Q have congruent bases, show that their volumes are proportional to their altitudes.

15. Using the information of exercise 13, make a formula showing in terms of n the ratio of the lateral surface of P to the lateral surface of Q.

16. Suppose that in exercise 13 it had been stipulated that $t = kn$, where k is some constant other than zero. Explain why the formula for the ratio of the volume of P to the volume of Q is independent of both n and t.

17. Make good realistic drawings to represent

a. Three lines perpendicular to a plane
b. The diagonal of a rectangular box
c. A right circular cone and its altitude
d. A line segment inclined to a plane and its projection on the plane
e. A right prism whose base is a pentagon
f. A sphere
g. A right circular cone cut by a plane parallel to its base

18. Take two geometry textbooks of recent date, and, as you examine them, make a list of pages on which you find discussion, illustrations, or applications of sets and associated terminology and notation. Present some of these to the class as illustrative examples of what you find.

19. Let c represent a circle and let s represent a secant of c, t a tangent to c,

and m a line outside of c. How many points are in the set $c \cap s$? How many are in $c \cap t$? How many are in $c \cap m$?

20. See if you can find in a recent geometry textbook any examples of the application of formal logic in the form of truth tables. Present and explain such examples if you find any.

21. The term "congruence" has been applied traditionally to closed or bounded geometric figures, such as triangles, polygons, etc. See how the term is defined in several recent textbooks. Under these definitions, would it be proper to speak of two line segments as being congruent? Of two angles as being congruent?

22. Explain what is meant by the "absolute value" of a number. Illustrate by use of a number line the set of numbers x such that $|x| \leq 3$. Do the same for the set of numbers x such that $|x| \geq 3$.

23. Is the measure of an angle a space concept, or is it a number? Explain and illustrate how the geometric concept of a set of angles is associated with the set of real numbers.

24. Explain and illustrate how a one-to-one correspondence can be set up between the set of points on a line and the set of real numbers. Between the set of angles having a common vertex and the set of real numbers.

25. Consider the following statements: (*a*) angle $ABC \cong$ angle PQR; (*b*) the measure of angle ABC = the measure of angle PQR. Do these statements mean the same thing? If not, what does each statement mean and how do the meanings differ?

26. Precisely what is meant by the statement that if points A, B, and C are on a line, point B lies between points A and C?

27. Explain precisely what is meant by the statement that a point X lies on the inside of an angle and that another point Y lies outside the angle.

28. Explain precisely what is meant by saying that one ray r lies between two other rays s and t. Illustrate.

29. In its 1959 report, the Commission on Mathematics gave arguments for including some work in coordinate geometry in the high school course in geometry. Review and defend or criticize these arguments.

30. Give both a synthetic proof and a proof by coordinate methods of the theorem that the line joining the mid-points of two sides of a triangle is parallel to the third side and is equal to half of the third side. Present these proofs to the class and discuss them fully.

31. Select some supplementary topic which you think is a good one for investigation by exceptional students in geometry, develop the topic, and give a good discussion of it before the class.

BIBLIOGRAPHY

Albert, A. A.: Finite Planes for the High School, *Mathematics Teacher*, **55** (1962), 165–169.

Ash, Carol: Locus Proofs, *Mathematics Teacher*, **55** (1962), 175–176.

Bell, Max: High School Geometry via Ruler-and-protractor Axioms: Report on a Classroom Trial, *Mathematics Teacher*, **54** (1961), 353–360.

Botts, Truman: Finite Planes and Latin Squares, *Mathematics Teacher*, **54** (1961), 300–306.

Brumfiel, Charles F.: Geometry: Right or Left, *Twenty-eighth Yearbook* (Washington, D.C.: National Council of Teachers of Mathematics, 1963), pp. 100–108.

Buseman, Herbert: The Role of Geometry for the Mathematics Student, *American Mathematical Monthly*, **67** (1960), 281–285.

Charosh, Mannis (Educational Adviser): "Modern Geometry" (New York: McGraw-Hill Book Company, 1963). (Set of six filmstrips on plane geometry.)

Commission on Mathematics: "Appendices" (New York: College Entrance Examination Board, 1959), pp. 109–174.

Daus, Paul: Why and How We Should

Correct the Mistakes of Euclid, *Mathematics Teacher*, **53** (1960), 576–581.

Eves, Howard: "A Survey of Geometry," vol. 1 (Englewood Cliffs, N.J.: Allyn and Bacon, Inc., 1963).

Fehr, Howard F.: New Thinking in Mathematical Education *Mathematics Teacher*, **53** (1960), 424–429.

Hewitt, Frances: A New Look at Some Old Geometry Problems, *Twenty-eighth Yearbook* (Washington, D.C.: National Council of Teachers of Mathematics, 1963), pp. 65–75.

Hlavaty, Julius H.: Mascheroni Constructions, *Mathematics Teacher*, **50** (1957), 482–487.

Jones, Burton W.: Reflections and Rotations, *Mathematics Teacher*, **54** (1961), 406–410.

______: Miniature Geometries, *Mathematics Teacher*, **52** (1959), 66–71.

Kazarinoff, Nicholas D.: "Geometric Inequalities" (New York: Random House, Inc., 1961).

Kelley, Paul J.: Plane Convex Figures, *Twenty-eighth Yearbook* (Washington, D.C.: National Council of Teachers of Mathematics, 1963), pp. 251–264.

Kline, Morris: The Straight Line, *Scientific American*, **192** (1956), 104–114.

MacLane, Saunders: Metric Postulates for Plane Geometry, *American Mathematical Monthly*, **66** (1959), 543–545.

Mathematics Staff of the College, University of Chicago: Coloring Maps, *Mathematics Teacher*, **50** (1957), 546–550.

Meserve, Bruce E.: New Trends in Algebra and Geometry, *Mathematics Teacher*, **55** (1962), 452–461.

______ and Max A. Sobel: "Mathematics for Secondary School Teachers" (Englewood Cliffs, N.J.: Prentice-Hall, Inc., 1962), pp. 192–337.

Miller, William G.: Tangent Circles and Conic Sections, *Mathematics Teacher*, **46** (1953), 78–81.

Moise, Edwin: The SMSG Geometry Program, *Mathematics Teacher*, **53** (1960), 437–442.

______: Some reflections on the Teaching of Area and Volume, *American Mathematical Monthly*, **70** (1963), 459–466.

______: "Elementary Geometry from an Advanced Standpoint" (Reading, Mass.: Addison-Wesley Publishing Company, Inc., 1963).

Munro, Thomas: "Coordinate Geometry" (New York: Oxford Book Company, Inc., 1960). (A booklet designed as a supplement to plane geometry.)

Prenowitz, Walter: Geometric Vector Analysis and the Concept of a Vector Space, *Twenty-third Yearbook* (Washington, D.C.: National Council of Teachers of Mathematics, 1957), pp. 145–199.

Rosskopf, M.F., and R. M. Exner: Some Concepts of Logic and Their Applications in Elementary Mathematics, *Mathematics Teacher*, **48** (1955), 290–298.

Schaaf, William L.: "Basic Concepts of Elementary Mathematics" (New York: John Wiley & Sons, Inc., 1960), pp. 59–88.

Scholomiti, N. C., and R. G. Hill: A Triangle Construction, *Mathematics Teacher*, **56** (1963), 323–324.

School Mathematics Study Group: "Mathematics for High School: Geometry," parts 1 and 2 (New Haven, Conn: Yale University Press, 1960).

Schor, Harry: Altitudes, Medians, Angle Bisectors, and Perpendicular Bisectors of the Sides of Triangles, *Mathematics Teacher*, **56** (1963), 105–107.

Serwais, W.: Equations and Geometric Loci: A Logical Synthesis, *Mathematics Teacher*, **50** (1957), 114–122.

Small, Dwain E.: Selection of Topics from Solid Geometry for a One-year Course in Geometry, *Mathematics Teacher*, **52** (1959), 546–548.

Smiley, Charles H., and David K. Peterson: No Space Geometry in the Space Age? *Mathematics Teacher*, **53** (1960), 18–21.

Smith, Dan: Vectors: An Aid to Mathematical Understanding, *Mathematics Teacher*, **52** (1959), 608–613.

Smith, Haus: Perimeter Relations of Enveloping and Inscribed Polygons and Circles, *School Science and Mathematics*, **62** (1962), 629–637.

Trigg, Charles W.: Geometry of Paper Folding I: Properties of a Drinking Cup, *School Science and Mathematics*, **54** (1954), 453–455.

Troyer, Robert J.: An Approach to Vector Geometry, *Mathematics Teacher*, **56** (1963), 290–297.

University of Illinois Committee on School Mathematics: "High School Mathematics: Unit 6, Geometry" (Urbana, Ill.: The University of Illinois Press, 1960).

University of the State of New York: "Tenth Year Mathematics: Coordinate Geometry" (Albany, N.Y.: The State Education Department, 1957). (A bulletin.)

Webber, G. Cuthbert, and John A. Brown: "Basic Concepts of Mathematics" (Reading, Mass.: Addison-Wesley Publishing Company, Inc., 1963), pp. 236–271, 290–302.

Wiseman, John D.: Chains of Reasoning in Geometry, *Mathematics Teacher*, **52** (1959), 457–458.

———: Some Related Theorems on Triangles and Circles, *Mathematics Teacher*, **54** (1961), 14–16.

———: Introducing Proof with a Finite System, *Mathematics Teacher*, **54** (1961), 351–352.

Wright, Adril Lindsay: Applications of Combinations and Mathematical Induction to a Geometry Lesson, *Mathematics Teacher*, **56** (1963), 325–328.

NINETEEN

The teaching of trigonometry

THERE WAS a time when few people other than mathematicians or engineers studied trigonometry or knew anything about the subject. This is no longer the case. It is common practice now to introduce some of the simple ideas and applications of right-triangle trigonometry even in the seventh grade. The more comprehensive and systematic study of the subject, although it is still offered in most colleges (sometimes without credit), has come to be regarded as essentially a high school subject and is generally offered in the eleventh or twelfth grade. More and more students are taking trigonometry in high school.

Also, there can be noted a new emphasis in the courses in trigonometry being taught in the senior high school. The numerical aspect, as represented in the solution of triangles by laborious logarithmic methods, is fading from prominence, and increased attention is being given to the analytical properties of the trigonometric functions and the relations among them. This trend is of large and increasing importance.

Trigonometry draws heavily upon ideas and procedures of arithmetic, elementary algebra, and geometry, and by synthesizing these with a few new ideas, concepts and relations are opened up beyond the scope of the earlier courses. It is not inherently a very difficult course, but there are some important and fairly definite problems of learning which will inevitably be encountered and of which teachers should be aware. The purpose of this chapter is to consider some of these instructional problems.

Trigonometry in the junior high school The justification of some work in numerical trigonometry in the junior high school lies partly in its propaedeutic value but more in its contribution to the general enrichment of the mathematics course at this level. It includes extension and application of the concept of ratio and of the use of symbolism; appreciation of the power of indirect measurement; understanding of methods of accomplishing such measurement through the use of the right triangle and the tangent, sine, and cosine ratios; correlation of ideas and procedures drawn from arithmetic, algebra, and geometry; and the solution of simple problems. It offers opportunities for experimental activities and inductive reasoning, and it aims at stimulation of interest in mathematics as a whole.

The subject matter of the numerical trigonometry of the junior high school is simple; it consists primarily of instances dealing with the indirect measurement of distances. Much impetus can be given to this work by allowing the students to undertake actual field projects, but before this is done, a considerable amount of preliminary groundwork should be laid. Presumably the students will already be familiar, through their work in informal geometry, with the principles of drawing to scale and with the use of the protractor and tape for measuring angles and distances directly. This is about all that can be assumed safely. It is necessary, however, that they have clear concepts of the meaning of similar figures (especially similar triangles), of a ratio as a comparison of two quantities in the sense that one is a certain fraction of the other or that one is a certain number of times the other, and also of a ratio as a single number (fractional or integral) which may be used as a multiplier. They also need to understand the particular meanings of the tangent ratio, the sine ratio, and the cosine ratio; and they must know how to use the table of natural functions either to find the value of a particular function of a given angle or to find the value of an angle if the numerical value of one of its functions is known. They need to know the meaning of such terms as "angle of elevation" and "angle of depression." They need practice in analyzing problem situations, in making working drawings, in selecting the appropriate functions to use, in setting up and solving equations involving these functions, and in substitution and evaluation. These things need to be carefully and clearly explained by the teacher. In order to develop comprehensive understanding of the techniques used in field projects, the students should work a large number of illustrative problems. Furthermore, the teacher should carefully discuss the full implications of such problems with the students.

Developing the meaning of a trigonometric function In beginning the study of numerical trigonometry the first thing to be done is to make clear the meaning of the trigonometric functions as ratios and as numbers. Probably the best way to accomplish this is to have the students actually make careful measurements of the angles and sides of right triangles and compute the numerical values of the ratios representing the tangent, sine, and cosine. It is well to have several students com-

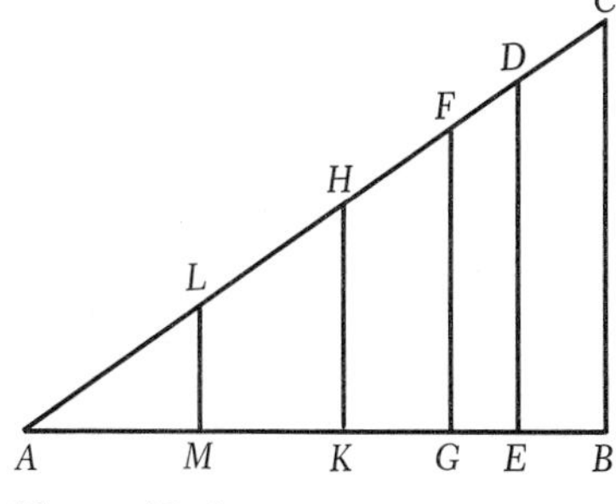

Figure 19-1

pute the values of these functions for angles of a given size so that they may compare their results. Generally, their results will show a fairly close correspondence, and the fact that they may not agree exactly offers a good opportunity to emphasize the approximate nature of measurement. Thus, any discrepancies may be attributed either to mistakes in computation or to errors in taking the measurements. This approach, through measurement and computation, to the meaning of a trigonometric function emphasizes the concept of the function both as a comparison of the lengths of two sides of a right triangle and as a single numerical quantity or quotient. Common agreement on the value to be accepted may be reached by averaging the values found by several students.

A variation of the foregoing procedure may be made by having each student make several sets of measurements and computations leading to the determination of the values of the functions of a particular angle, such as angle A in Figure 19-1. Thus the value of the tangent of angle A might be determined by using several different ratios, such as CB/AB, DE/AE, FG/AG, HK/AK, or LM/AM. This would give emphasis to the principle that the value of a given function of any angle is independent of the actual lengths of the sides of the triangle and depends only on the *ratio* of the lengths of the two sides involved.

The functions that are introduced in the study of trigonometry in the junior high school are generally limited to the tangent, sine, and cosine. The others would add nothing toward making the meaning of a function clear, and they are not needed for the solution of the simple applied problems that make up the work of this period. For obvious reasons this work is limited to situations that involve functions of acute angles. With this in mind, the functions of an acute angle may be defined in terms of the sides of a right triangle containing that angle. Let angle BAC be the given angle, Figure 19-2.

Figure 19-2

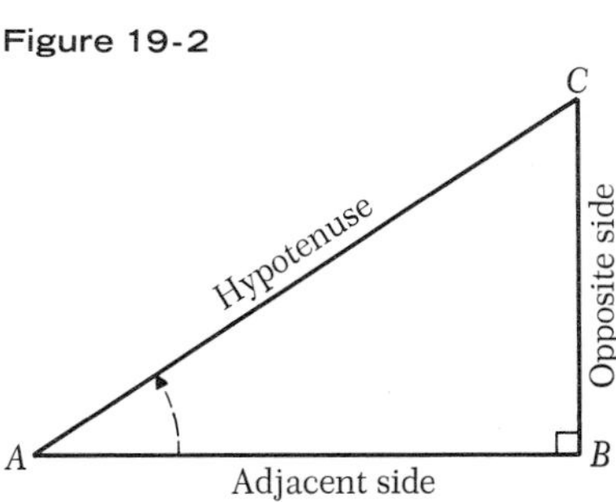

$$\text{Tangent } \angle BAC = \frac{\text{opposite side}}{\text{adjacent side}}$$

$$\text{Sine } \angle BAC = \frac{\text{opposite side}}{\text{hypotenuse}}$$

$$\text{Cosine } \angle BAC = \frac{\text{adjacent side}}{\text{hypotenuse}}$$

An interesting and valuable exercise can now be introduced by having the class as a whole make measurements and computations necessary for the compilation of a table of sines, cosines, and tangents for the acute angles, say, which are integral multiples of 5°. This exercise would provide well-motivated practice in accurate drawing and measurement of lines and angles and in careful computation. Diagrams for the measurements should be rather large and should be very carefully drawn. For each of the angles considered, at least two or three students should make determinations of the functions for purposes of comparison, checking, and averaging of the results. The values of the functions as shown by the computed results should be expressed to three significant figures.

Teaching students how to use the trigonometric functions The meanings of the trigonometric functions and the ways in which they are to be used will be more quickly and adequately comprehended if the meanings and uses are illustrated in problem situations. There need be no delay about this. As soon as the meaning of the tangent ratio has been explained to the point of understanding, the teacher should show how it is used in finding distances or angles without direct measurement. Hypothetical or "made-up" problems will serve for this purpose quite as well as "real" problems, and perhaps better, because the assumed elements (an angle and a distance or two given distances) can be selected at will and with a view to convenience, and there will be no extraneous details of actual measurement, the manipulation of instruments, or unnecessarily difficult computations to draw the students' attention from the basic principles and procedures involved. Substantial mastery of the basic theory and procedure should be assured before the students are thrown into situations in which they will have to provide their own data. Initial interest is usually high, and the artificial motivation afforded by field projects is unnecessary at the outset. Thus, such problems as the following serve well to introduce students to the applications of the functions. The fact that convenient data are arbitrarily chosen in no way lessens the value of the problems. The steps in the solution are about in the form in which they should be explained to the students.

Example: From a point $5\underline{0}$ feet from the base of a tree, the angle of elevation A of the top of the tree is found to be 29°. Find the height of the tree.

1. First we shall make a picture or diagram to represent the problem. On this diagram we shall indicate all data that are given, such as the distance from point A to the base of the tree and the size of the angle of elevation at A. (The diagram is made and data are indicated as shown, see Figure 19-3.)
2. Since the height of the tree represents the unknown distance, we should designate it by some letter; for example, let us use h.
3. We know that the ratio $h/50$ represents the tangent of angle A, so we may now write the equation $h/50$ = tangent of 29°.

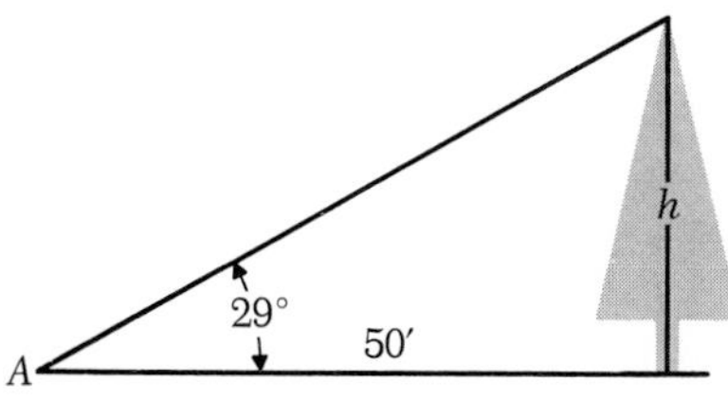

Figure 19-3

4. We know that the tangent of an angle can be expressed as a number. From our table of tangents we find that the numerical value of the tangent of 29° is 0.5543. Therefore we may substitute this numerical value for the expression "tangent of 29°" and write the equation $h/50 = 0.5543$.
5. Now, if we solve this equation for h, we shall get the equation $50(h)/50 = (0.554)(50)$, or $h = 27.72$ feet, i.e., about 28 feet. Thus we know that the tree is about 28 feet high.

In presenting this explanation, the students' attention should be deliberately focused both upon the particular activities and the basic concepts presented in each of the various steps and upon the order in which the steps are taken. The order reveals to the students a pattern for their work. This pattern not only helps them to systematize their written work and their computations but also helps them in analyzing such problems and in organizing their thinking about them. Each step stresses one important element in the analysis and solution of the problem. Drawing and lettering the figure and indicating the given data (step 1) give the problem a concrete setting and facilitate the job of translating it into an equation. The selection and indication of a literal symbol to represent the unknown part of the figure (step 2) direct attention to the fact that the object of the work is to determine the magnitude of this particular part. Writing the equation (step 3) requires analysis of the problem to determine which of the trignometric functions is the appropriate one to use.

In this connection the following points should be stressed: (1) If one side and an angle of the triangle are given and it is required to find another side, that function should be selected which is represented by the ratio that involves both the unknown side and the known side. (2) If two sides are given and an angle is required, then that function should be selected which is represented by the ratio of one of these known sides to the other. A scheme that is slightly mechanical yet rather helpful in selecting the proper function is to emphasize that the sine and cosine should be used if one of the given sides is the hypotenuse. It should further be emphasized that the hypotenuse occurs in the denominator of each of these functions.

The transition from the ratio concept to the numerical concept of a trigonometric function and the substitution of the numerical value for the ratio (step 4) are of vital importance in understanding the use of the functions in indirect measurement. The actual solution of the equation for the unknown part and the reinterpretation of this in terms of the diagram or of the original problem situation (step 5) bring a realization of how the laws of algebra operate to give the required information by giving explicit form to a relationship which was merely implicit before. In the calculations involved, care should be taken to observe the rules for computation with approximate data. The order in which these steps have been indicated is the order in which they logically occur in the analysis and solution of the problem. Fortunately there is no conflict between this logical order and the natural or "psychological organization" of the analysis from the standpoint of the immature student.

The problem upon which the foregoing discussion is based involves the use of the tangent. Similar illustrative problems involving the sine and the cosine should also be used. Such problems should be selected or devised with care, but they are available in countless numbers and with many variations. The following are examples involving, respectively, the sine and cosine:

Example: A ladder 22 feet long is placed against a vertical wall so that it makes an angle of 62° with the ground. At what height above the ground does the ladder touch the wall, Figure 19-4?

Example: To find the distance across a lake, some surveyors sighted an east-west line *AB* across the lake and then a north-south line *BC*. Then they measured the distance *AC* and the angle *BAC*. They found that *AC* = 4,100 feet and that angle *BAC* = 43°. Find how far it was from *A* to *B*, Figure 19-5.

In setting up the earlier problems care should be taken to arrange the data so that, when the equations are set up, the symbols for the unknown parts will occur in the *numerators* of the fractions representing the trigonometric ratios or functions to be used. Later on it will be de-

Figure 19-4

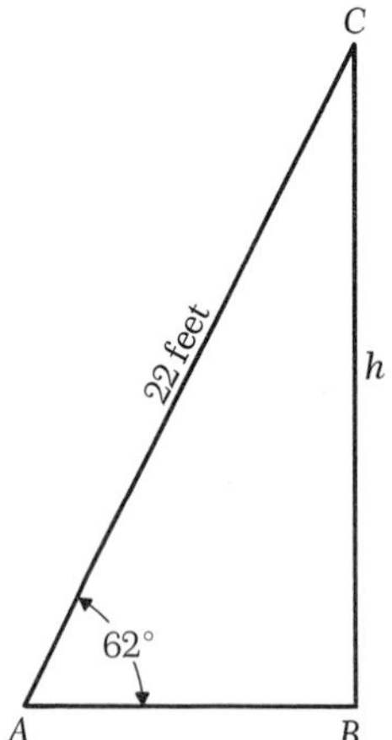

Figure 19-5

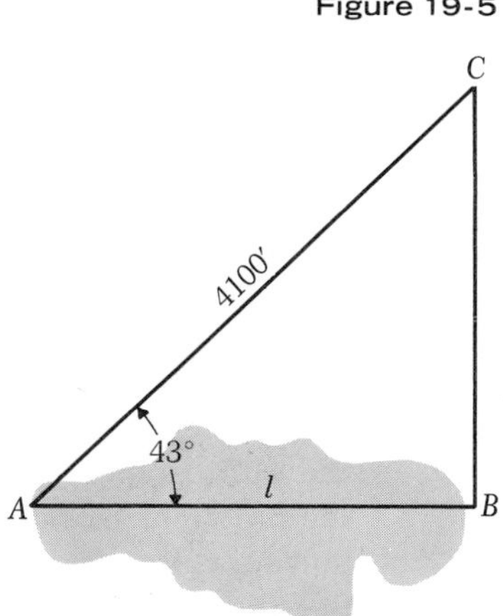

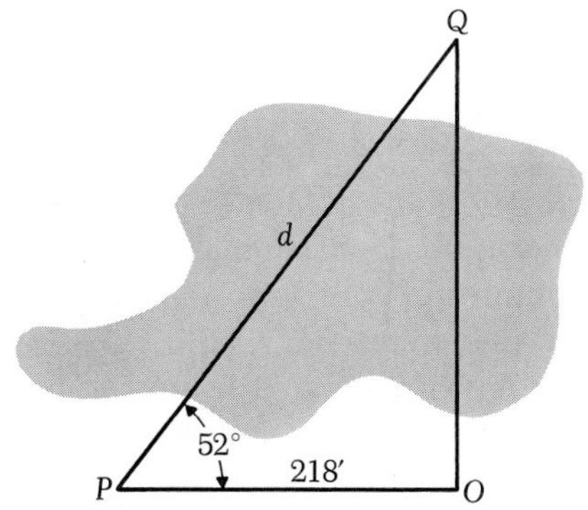

Figure 19-6

sirable to introduce some problems in which the unknown will occur in the *denominator* of the fraction. The following example will illustrate this:

Example: In order to find the distance between two points P and Q on opposite sides of a small lake, two boy scouts decided to set up a right triangle with PQ as the hypotenuse (Figure 19-6). They used an angle mirror to locate a point O such that the lines of sight $\overrightarrow{OP}$ and $\overrightarrow{OQ}$ formed a right angle. The distance from O to Q could not be measured directly, but the distance from O to P was measured and found to be 218 feet. By sighting from P to O and then from P to Q, the size of angle P was established as 52°. From these data the boys found the distance from P to Q. How far was it? (Call this distance d.)

This problem leads to the equation

$$\frac{218}{d} = \cos 52° = 0.6157$$

To simplify the solution, it may be suggested to the students that the equation can be written $218/d = 0.616/1$, that by inverting both of these fractions the equation $d/218 = 1/0.616$ will result, and that, if both members are now multiplied by 218, the equation is solved for d, the required distance, by performing the indicated division.

The work in trigonometry in the junior high school will scarcely go beyond these simple applications of the functions to the general problem of finding certain unknown parts of right triangles. If desired, the cotangent may be introduced, but it is unnecessary and little is to be gained by its use. The secant and cosecant should not be discussed.

Trigonometry in the senior high school and the junior college

The systematic course in trigonometry in the senior high school and the junior college will be in marked contrast to the work offered in the junior high school, both in complexity and in emphasis. It will also differ from the old-time traditional course, which gave excessive emphasis to the solution of triangles. Relative emphasis on this aspect of the course, and upon the massive numerical work that formerly was considered so important, is diminishing, while increasing importance is being attached to the analytic aspects of the subject.

There will still be triangles to be solved, of course, but in view of the changing demands of the physical sciences, engineering, and higher mathematics, there is need today for increased study of such analytic considerations as the variation, graphs, and composition of the trigonometric functions, the inverse functions, proofs of identities, solution of trigonometric equations, polar coordinates and complex numbers in trigonometric form, and a trigonometry of numbers and circular functions. Of the students who take trigonometry today, relatively few will have much occasion later in life to solve oblique triangles, but many will take mathematics and science in college and will need a good understanding of the analytic aspects of trigonometry. In the interests of these students it is important that the course should provide increased emphasis on the analytic side of trigonometry so that a proper balance between the numerical and the analytic aspects of the subject will be maintained.

Such a course will demand of students more intellectual alertness, ingenuity, and insight than the traditional triangle-solving course did, and students will have to accept more responsibility for the analysis and understanding of an expanded theory of the subject. The teacher has the obligation both of keeping them aware of this responsibility and of assisting them in their efforts to discharge it. There are parts of trigonometry which most students would find pretty difficult to "dig out for themselves" but which can easily be made clear and meaningful by a skillful teacher. The teacher of trigonometry has the same obligation to help his class to a clear understanding of the basic principles and techniques of the subject as has the teacher of arithmetic, algebra, or geometry in the earlier years of the secondary school. With this in mind, the remainder of this chapter will be devoted to a discussion of teaching problems that arise in connection with the development of certain concepts and procedures in trigonometry. The topics which will be discussed have been selected on the basis of three criteria: (1) they are fundamental; (2) they are often troublesome; (3) they are based upon relatively simple fundamental principles which, if not properly emphasized, are easily obscured by the mass of detail attending their development but which, if set forth and perceived at the outset, will furnish a clear and helpful guide to the development. In the discussion of these topics the aim will be to present suggestions for developing them in a manner calculated to make clear the underlying principles and thus provide a basic framework around which the details of the development may be organized effectively.

The general angle: degree and radian measure The essential groundwork for the concept of the general angle and its measure will normally have been laid in the junior high school. There the protractor furnishes a means for associating with a given angle a positive real

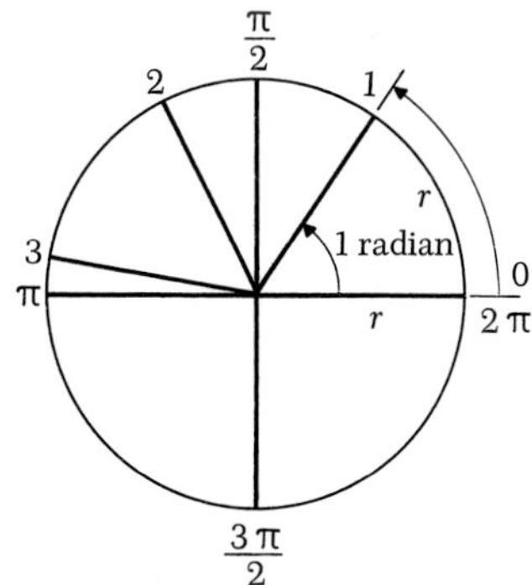

Figure 19-7

number between 0 and 180, called the measure of the angle. Now it becomes desirable to extend the concept of angle to the more general one based on rotation about a point. For such a general angle the domain of permissible measures is the set of all real numbers. Careful explanations illustrated by use of a circular protractor and accompanied by illustrative examples and exercises will serve quickly to enable students to sketch positive or negative angles of any given measure and to measure any given angle.

The concept of radian measure should be developed along with that of the general angle. In order to understand radian measure clearly, the students must first of all have a thorough understanding of the definition and meaning of a radian. The geometrical explanation and illustration should be given repeatedly until the students can readily form a mental picture similar to the one shown in Figure 19-7. This will provide them with a concrete basis for thinking in terms of radians and for understanding the definition. It will provide a means for recalling instantly why the angle π is the same as 180°, why $\pi/2$ is the same as 90°, why $\pi/3$ is the same as 60°, why 2π is the same as 360°, etc. With this sort of picture in mind for reference the student will have no need to memorize the relations between degrees and radian measure because he can easily figure out these relationships for himself. He is thus equipped not only with a knowledge of the facts and relationships which he will need but also with an understanding of how they are determined.

After the students have gained an understanding of the meaning of radian measure, it is well for them to have some special practice in determining the degree equivalents of angles expressed in radians and the radian equivalents of angles expressed in degrees. In this connection it may be desirable to have the degree value of one radian memorized. For the special angles $0, \pi/2, \pi/3, \pi, 2\pi$, 45°, 120°, etc., the students should soon become able to give the corresponding equivalents at sight. The teacher should explain that, in expressing angles in terms of radian measure, it is customary to omit the word "radians." The student needs to be told this so that, when he encounters in his reading such expressions as $\sin \pi$, $\tan 2$, and $\cos 3\pi/4$, he will understand that the angles are given in radians rather than in degrees. It may be pointed out that in higher mathematics radian measure is used almost exclusively.

Trigonometric functions of any angle An angle is said to be in standard position with respect to a rectangular coordinate system if its vertex is at the origin and its initial side lies along the positive half of the X axis. Then if $P(x,y)$ is any point in the XY plane, the distances

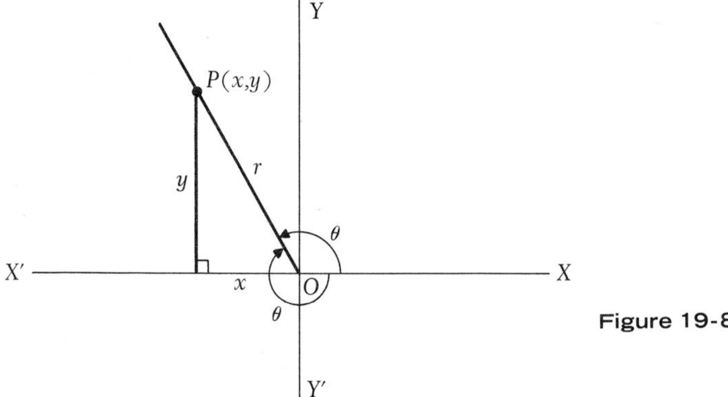

Figure 19-8

x, y, and r ($= OP$) and the angle XOP ($= \theta$) are determined. Except for multiples of 360° the measure of angle θ is determined solely by the position of the terminal side OP, and θ may be either positive or negative.

In this context the trigonometric functions of the general angle θ are defined as follows:

$\sin\theta = y/r \leftarrow$ reciprocals $\rightarrow \csc\theta = r/y$
$\cos\theta = x/r \leftarrow$ reciprocals $\rightarrow \sec\theta = r/x$
$\tan\theta = y/x \leftarrow$ reciprocals $\rightarrow \cot\theta = x/y$

These definitions are general in that they apply both to positive and negative angles of any size for which they are defined. They have clear meanings except when the divisor is zero, in which case the functions are simply undefined. They are entirely consistent with the definitions of the functions of acute angles in terms of the sides of a right triangle, learned earlier in the junior high school. Since they define the fundamental concepts on which all trigonometric work is based, they must be learned to the point of perfection through repeated drills and exercises, both formal and numerical, and much practice based upon sketches such as that shown in Figure 19-8.

Some authors and teachers prefer to define the sine and cosine functions in terms of the coordinates of a point on a unit circle, as shown in Figure 19-9. In this frame of reference the sine and cosine functions are identified respectively with the x and y coordinates themselves, rather than with ratios. This may have some advantage in studying the variation of these functions, but it may also complicate and confuse the interpretation for students. For example, the terminal side of an angle θ may pass through $P(5,7)$, but in this case P does not lie on the unit circle. On the other hand, the ratio definitions offer no problem of interpretation and, if desired, can easily be reduced to the "unit circle" definitions simply by dividing both coordinates of P by $\sqrt{x^2 + y^2}$. Thus in the case above, the coordinates of the point where OP intersects the unit circle are seen to be respectively $5/\sqrt{74}$ and $7/\sqrt{74}$.

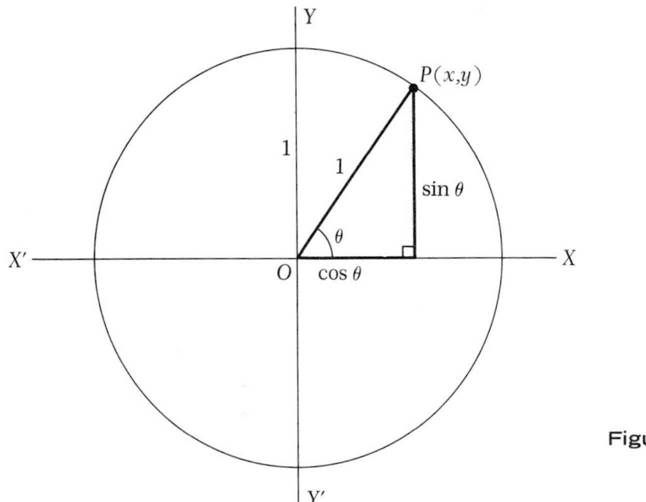

Figure 19-9

Since tables of trigonometric functions generally include only values of functions of angles from 0° to 90°, it is necessary to have some means of expressing functions of any angle whatever in terms of functions of some angle not less than 0° and not greater than 90°. The method of making such transformations may be effectively explained to students somewhat as follows.

Let A be the given angle in standard position as shown in Figure 19-10. If we take a point $P(x,y)$ on the terminal side of angle A and drop a perpendicular to the X axis, there will be formed a right triangle which is called the "triangle of reference." The absolute values of the functions of A are determined by the lengths of the sides of this triangle, since its sides are x, y, and r, that is, the abscissa, ordinate, and distance of P, respectively.

Now, if A is known, we may also find at once the angle θ, without regard to sign. It is the smallest angle which OP makes with the X axis. This will always be the angle XOP or $X'OP$ in the triangle of reference, and its value will never exceed 90°. Thus θ becomes an angle which has the limits $0° \leqq \theta \leqq 90°$, and *the values of the functions of A will be the same as the values of the functions of θ except for sign.* The functions of θ can be found in the tables, and the signs of the corresponding functions of A (whether positive or negative and regardless of size) can be determined by noting the signs of x and y (r is always positive) in the triangle of reference.

Example 1: Find the value of cot 112°5′.

Let A = 112°5′. Then θ = 67°55′ (Figure 19-11). From the tables cot 67°55′ = .40572. But in the triangle of reference, cot θ is negative. Therefore, cot 112°5′ is negative also, and its real value is −.40572.

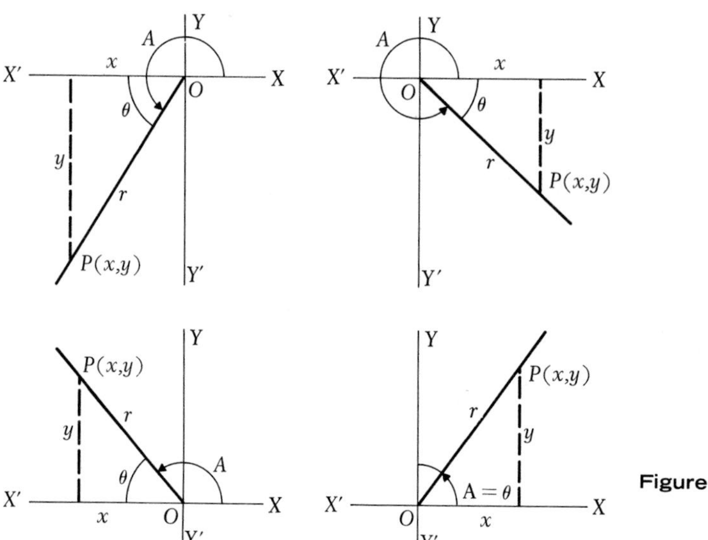

Figure 19-10

Example 2: Find the value of cos 312°.

Let A = 312°. Thus θ = 48°, Figure 19-12. From the tables, cos 48° = .66913. Therefore, the value, except for sign, of cos 312° = .66913. But in the triangle of reference cos θ is positive. Therefore, cos 312° is positive also, and its real value is +.66913.

If the matter is explained and illustrated in this way, the students should have little difficulty in understanding how to find the functions of any given angle from the tables. It is well for them to work out numerous examples of the type given above and to build for themselves tables showing the signs of each of the functions when the angle is in standard position and the terminal side lies in the following eight positions:

In the first quadrant	Along the positive X axis
In the second quadrant	Along the positive Y axis
In the third quadrant	Along the negative X axis
In the fourth quadrant	Along the negative Y axis

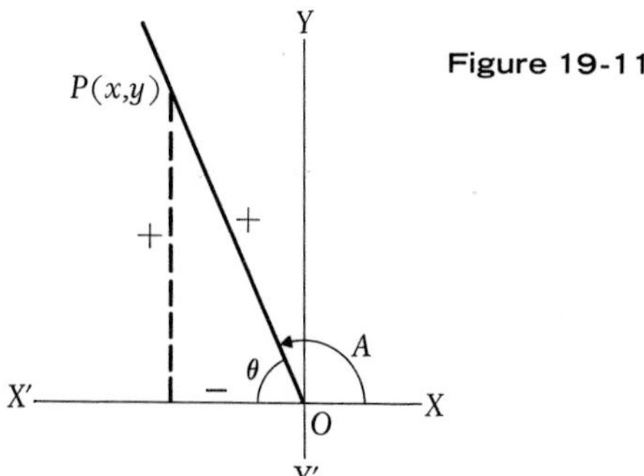

Figure 19-11

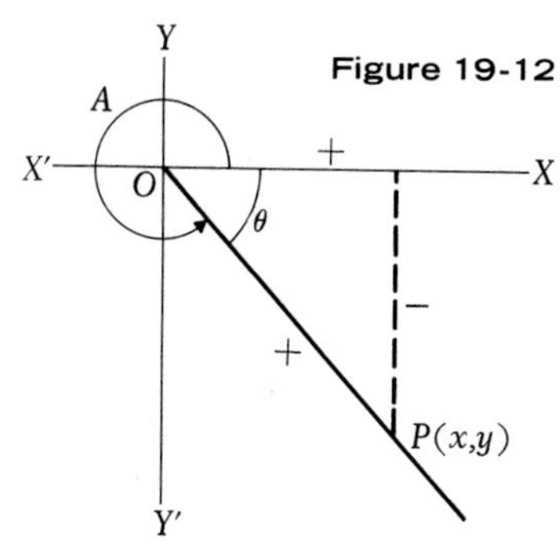

Figure 19-12

When the students have acquired the ability to do this for themselves, they will have attained a real understanding of how the tables can be used to find the functions of any angle whatever. They should experience no further difficulty in this respect, and there will be no need for them to memorize the signs of the functions for the various positions of the terminal side of the angle as indicated in the list given above.

A trigonometry of real numbers The increasing emphasis on the analytic properties of the trigonometric functions makes it desirable to have a way of interpreting these functions and their properties as functions and properties of real numbers, quite apart from any direct reference to angles at all. The need for such interpretation occurs often, both in mathematical and physical contexts, particularly in connection with periodic phenomena.

Such an interpretation is readily available and is easily accomplished through the concept of a "wrapping function," or wrapping process, whereby the real number line is wrapped around the unit circle. Such a process establishes the ordered pair (cos x, sin x), where x is a real number, as the coordinates of points on the unit circle. (See Figure 19-13.) The complete "trigonometry" of these functions can be developed without having to make any reference to angles at any point in the development. However, if at any time it should become desirable to compare the circular functions of real numbers with the trigonometric functions of angles, the comparison can be effected through the medium of radian measure. The one-to-one correspondence which can thus be set up affords a simple method for the evaluation of the circular functions of real numbers. The point should be made, however, that this is a method of evaluation used through convenience and not through necessity. The circular functions can be evaluated without any reference to angles whatsoever.[1]

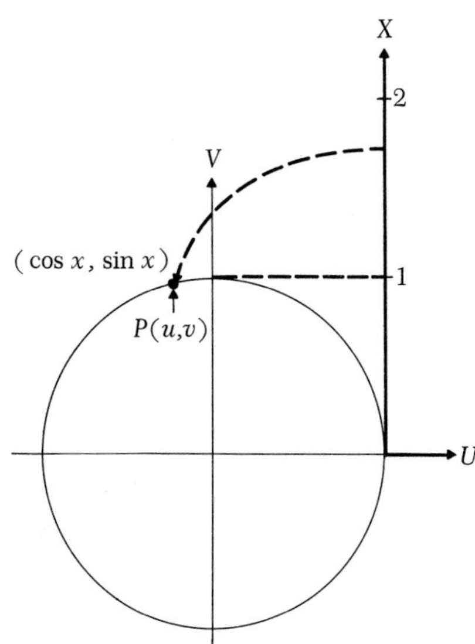

Figure 19-13

Under this one-to-one correspondence the wrapping process guarantees the same domain, range, and periodicity for the circular functions of real numbers as for the corresponding trigonometric functions of angles, and the same relationships and identities among the functions can be established in the two cases. Functions of

[1]For a more detailed discussion of circular functions of real numbers see the Report of the Commission on Mathematics, "Appendices" (New York: College Entrance Examination Board, 1959), pp. 206–213.

real numbers and their inverse functions are evaluated from tables precisely as functions of angles (in radians) and their inverses are evaluated. Indeed the trigonometry of real numbers is in all respects the exact counterpart of the trigonometry of angles.

It is not very difficult to explain all this to students. A good discussion of it can be found in the "Appendices" volume of the Report of the Commission on Mathematics.[2] Some, however, will almost certainly want to know why we should bother with a trigonometry of numbers, when we already have a perfectly good trigonometry of angles. To answer this it may be pointed out that there are at least two good reasons. One is that a trigonometry of numbers can be interpreted more flexibly than a trigonometry based only on angles. In many problems in physics and higher mathematics it is necessary to work with circular functions of numbers apart from any explicit reference to angles. A second reason is that the structure of mathematical systems is a primary concern of mathematicians. It is therefore a matter of great mathematical interest to note that our trigonometry of numbers and circular functions has exactly the same structure as the trigonometry of angles.

Variation and graphs of the trigonometric functions Just as the concept of variation enriches the study of geometry and algebra, so it enriches the study of trigonometry. It is very important for the students to sense the fact that any *change* in the size of an angle is accompanied by a corresponding characteristic change in each of the functions of the angle. This fact should be repeatedly emphasized by the teacher and should be illustrated by all available means and devices. One such means is a thoughtful examination of the tables of functions. It will be immediately noted that increases in the size of the angle are accompanied by characteristic increases or decreases in each of the functions. It should be specifically pointed out that the values given in the tables merely represent particular stages in a continuous variation and that, between any two successive values given in the tables, there exists an infinitude of intermediate values. This concept of variation of the functions can be strengthened by certain mechanical devices which are available commercially or which can be made by the teacher or students. Perhaps the most commonly used and most effective device is the construction and study of graphs of these functions, Figure 19-14.

A real understanding of these graphs makes clear several important things about the variation of the functions. In particular, the following considerations are worthy of note and comment:

1. There is a general similarity in the shape of the graph of any func-

[2] *Ibid.*, pp. 208–210.

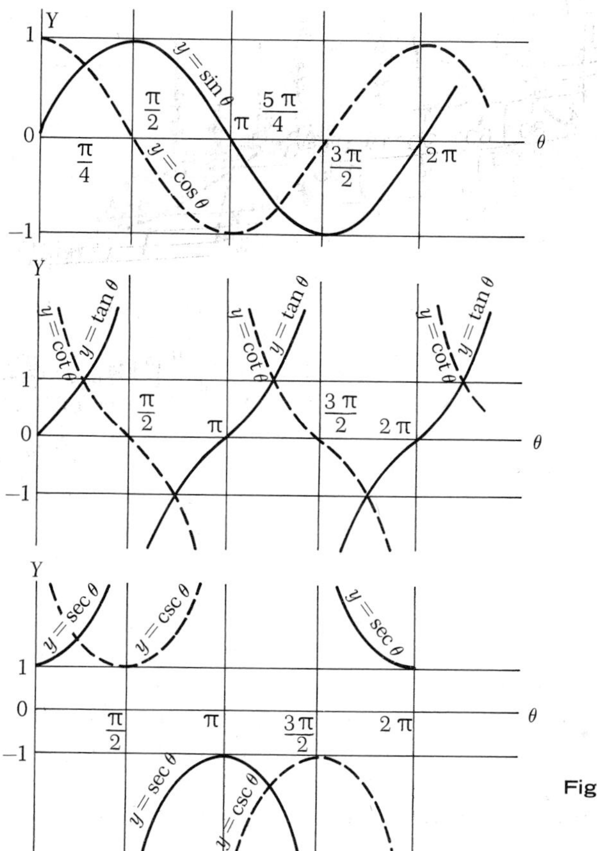

Figure 19-14

tion and its corresponding cofunction.[3] This may be explained by the fact that, for example, the cosine of a given angle is the sine of some other angle (in general, the complement of the given angle), and similarly for the other functions and their corresponding cofunctions.

2. The functions sin θ and cos θ are always finite and continuous over the entire domain of values of θ, while for certain values of θ the other functions become infinite and have points of discontinuity. This may be explained by the fact that each of the other functions is the reciprocal of some function which may take on the value zero and, when this happens, the reciprocal function is undefined. It should also be noted that, at each value of the angle for which a given function becomes discontinuous, the function also changes sign.

3. The sine or cosine of an angle can never be greater than 1 nor less than -1, and the secant and cosecant can never have values between

[3]Here we speak of sin θ and cos θ, for example, as *cofunctions of each other*. Like reference is made to tan θ and cot θ and to sec θ and csc θ.

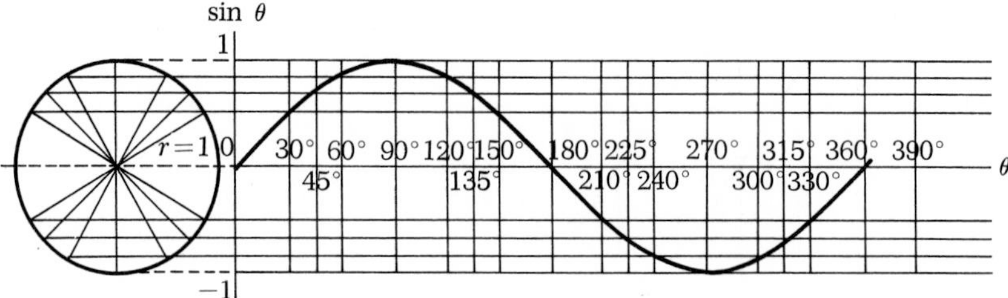

Figure 19-15

these bounds. This is explained by the fact that the secant and cosecant of an angle are respectively reciprocals of the cosine and sine of the angle, and the reciprocal of any number which is not greater than 1 or less than -1 will have a value which must be greater than 1 or less than -1. Numerical illustrations of these facts should be given.

4. From the graphs it will be seen that, when the angle is given by $k\pi + \pi/4$ for all integral values of k, any function of the angle is equal to its corresponding cofunction. The students may be asked to explain this.

Practically all textbooks contain graphs of the functions for reference, and in many cases the students are required to construct their own graphs. Too often, however, the attention given to the graphs of the functions is perfunctory and not very meaningful. If the graphs are to contribute much to developing the concept and the nature of the variation of the functions, considerable time will need to be spent in the interpretation of the graphs and in the discussion of their implications.

Inverse trigonometric functions It must be made clear that the inverse of any trigonometric function is a relation but not a function. The function-to-angle correspondence is not one-to-one but one-to-many. For example, there are infinitely many angles x for which $\sin x = 1/2$. On the other hand, it is desirable to have a way of defining the inverse of a function as a function itself so that for a given value of a function there will correspond exactly one angle instead of many. This is accomplished by restricting the domain of the angle and by designating this restricted domain or interval as the set of *principal values* of x. This restriction is made separately for each function. Reference to either the trigonometric function or its inverse within this restricted domain is generally indicated by capitalizing the initial letter, e.g., $\text{Sin}^{-1}\ 0.8$ or Arctan 3. The intervals defining the principal values of the inverse functions are arbitrary but are usually taken as follows:

Arcsine and Arctangent: from $-90°$ to $90°$, inclusive
Arccosine and Arccotangent: from $0°$ to $180°$, inclusive

In an analogous manner, Sin x is defined to mean sin x, where $-90° \leq x \leq 90°$.

Two notations are commonly used for the inverse trigonometric functions. For example, the angle whose sine is 0.8 is written either as Arcsin 0.8 or as Sin^{-1} 0.8. This is sometimes a little confusing to students at first, but since they will certainly encounter both notations, it is advisable that they become accustomed to both. The matters discussed above need more than casual attention in the classes. The concepts and notation should be made clear through careful definition, pointed questions, and many examples using graphical interpretation. Any difficulties which students may have in working with inverse trigonometric functions are almost sure to have their origins either in wrong interpretations of the meaning of an inverse function and its relation to the parent function or else in failure to attach clear meanings to the terminology and notation employed.

If we consider the graph of any function, say $y = \sin x$, we note that it is a device which will map any number (or angle) x in its domain into the corresponding number y in its range. If we should take y as the independent variable, with $-1 \leq y \leq 1$, then the same graph would map any number y into the corresponding number (or angle) x, where $-\pi/2 \leq x \leq \pi/2$, and we could write $x = \text{Arcsin } y$. In this sense the same set of points could be used both as the graph of the trigonometric function $y = \text{Sin } x$ and as the graph of the inverse function $x = \text{Arcsin } y$, depending on whether x or y is regarded as the independent variable. However, since the letter Y is so often used to represent the axis of the range, and so seldom to represent the axis of the domain, this inverse

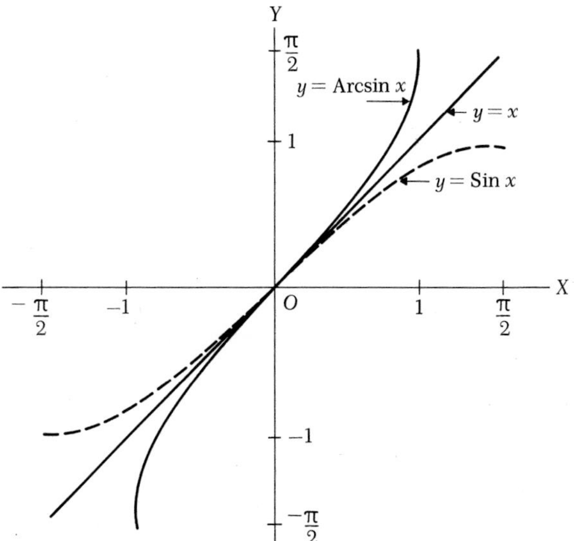

Figure 19-16

function is generally written $y = \text{Arcsin } x$, in which case its domain is the set of numbers x, where $-1 \leq x \leq 1$, and its range is the set of numbers (or angles) y, where $-\pi/2 \leq y \leq \pi/2$.

If the graphs of the trigonometric function $y = \text{Sin } x$ and of the inverse trigonometric function $y = \text{Arcsin } x$ are drawn on the same set of axes scaled to the same unit, it will be noted that they are symmetrical to each other with respect to the straight line $y = x$. The use of the unit circle in drawing the graphs is helpful in bringing out the contrast between the properties of the trigonometric functions and those of their related inverse functions. (See Figures 19-15 and 19-16.)

Values of functions of special angles The special angles 0°, 30°, 45°, 60°, and 90° are of great importance and occur so frequently that students should be able to write down the functions of these angles without having recourse to tables. Some teachers prefer to have their students memorize the values of these functions. It is possible to do this, but it is not necessary because they may all be immediately and easily derived from three elementary geometric considerations.

Consider the right triangle ABC with an acute angle A of 45° and a right angle at B, Figure 19-17. From the illustration we see at once that such a triangle is formed when a diagonal of a square is drawn. If the length of one side of the square is taken as one unit, then each leg of the triangle will be 1 unit in length, and the diagonal of the square, which is the hypotenuse of the triangle, will be found by the Pythagorean theorem to have a length of $\sqrt{2}$ units. With these numbers known, all the functions of 45° can be written down immediately. The only numbers needed are the numbers 1, 1, and $\sqrt{2}$, and even these need not be memorized, since they are immediately apparent from the fact that the

Figure 19-17

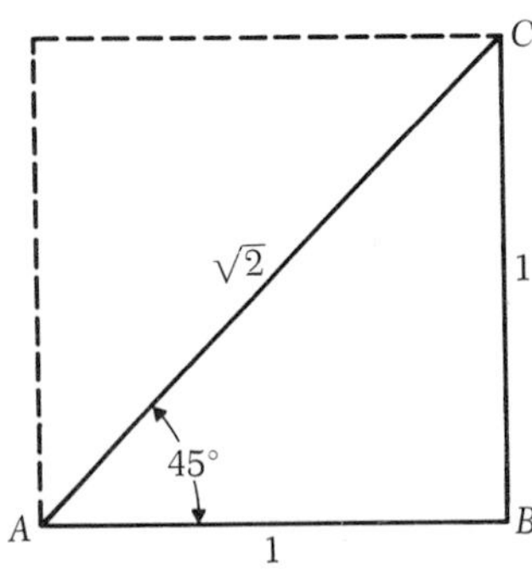

Figure 19-18

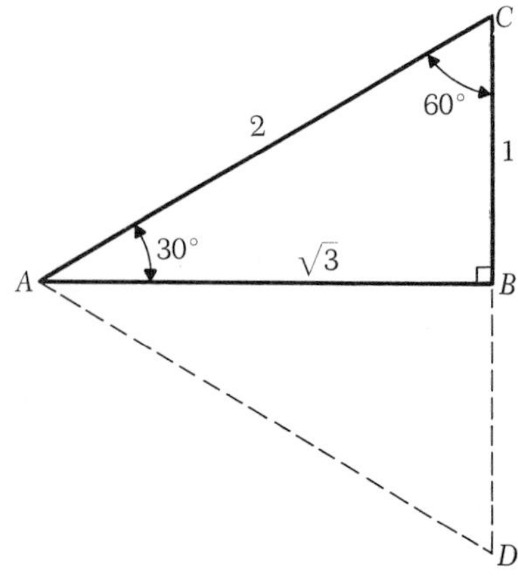

triangle is formed by a diagonal and two adjacent sides of a square. The results are as follows:

$$\sin 45° = \cos 45° = \frac{1}{\sqrt{2}} \qquad \tan 45° = \cot 45° = 1$$

$$\csc 45° = \sec 45° = \sqrt{2}$$

Consider now an equilateral triangle ADC, Figure 19-18, with angle A bisected as shown. The bisector $\overline{AB}$ forms with $\overline{AC}$ an angle of 30° and with $\overline{BC}$ a right angle. Thus we have a 30–60° right triangle ABC whose hypotenuse $\overline{AC}$ is twice as long as the leg $\overline{BC}$ (since $\overline{BC} = \frac{1}{2}\,\overline{DC}$ and $\overline{AC} = \overline{DC}$). If we now consider the length $\overline{BC}$ as one unit, then $\overline{AC}$ has a length of 2 units. Again, using the Pythagorean theorem, we get $\overline{AB} = \sqrt{3}$ units. From Figure 19-18 we have

$$\sin 30° = \tfrac{1}{2} = \cos 60° \qquad \cot 30° = \sqrt{3}/1 = \tan 60°$$
$$\cos 30° = \sqrt{3}/2 = \sin 60° \qquad \sec 30° = 2/\sqrt{3} = \csc 60°$$
$$\tan 30° = 1/\sqrt{3} = \cot 60° \qquad \csc 30° = \tfrac{2}{1} = \sec 60°$$

If the special angles 30°, 45°, and 60° are placed in standard position, they all lie in the first quadrant, but values of the functions of their counterparts in the other quadrants can be found immediately by proper adjustment of signs. These values can be found and the proper adjustment of signs can be made with ease and certainty from sketches showing the angles in standard position.

Values of the functions of the quadrantal angles are immediately obvious if the angle is put in standard position with its vertex at the center of a unit circle, as in Figure 19-9. For any point $P(x,y)$ on this unit circle we have $x = \cos\theta$ and $y = \sin\theta$. These considerations, together with the definitions of the other functions, give us the following values.

TABLE 19-1
Functions of quadrantal angles

	0°	90°	180°	270°
sin	0	1	0	−1
cos	1	0	−1	0
tan	0	undef	0	undef
cot	undef	0	undef	0
sec	1	undef	−1	undef
csc	undef	1	undef	−1

These considerations can be explained easily and are not hard to understand. Students, however, need considerable practice in giving the values of functions of these special angles. Ability to do this is probably best attained by having them make sketches of many of the special angles in standard position and build tables of values based on their sketches. Teachers tend to underestimate, rather than to overestimate, the amount of practice needed for gaining familiarity, facility, and assurance in this.

Some special functions and their graphs Functions such as 3 sin x, sin $3x$, $\frac{1}{2}$ cos x, and cos $\frac{1}{2}x$ occur at times. The function 3 sin x of course is not at all the same as the function sin $3x$, yet sometimes students confuse them unless the difference has been pointed out. Therefore it is important to give some special attention to the interpretation of functions expressed in forms such as those indicated above.

The thing that tends to confuse students in considering, say, 2 sin x and sin $2x$ is the effect of the constant in the two expressions. Failure to interpret such expressions correctly is usually due to lack of careful reading, and it can be corrected, but teachers as a rule will need to give students some help in learning to determine the effect of the constant in each case. An effective way of making students aware of the distinction is to have them construct graphs of both functions on the same set of axes. Direct comparison of the graphs points up the fact that in the one case the constant is a multiplier of the angle (independent variable) and so affects the period of the function but not the amplitude, while in the other case the constant is a multiplier of the function itself and so affects its amplitude but not its period. By constructing the separate graphs on the same axes students should be able to note these

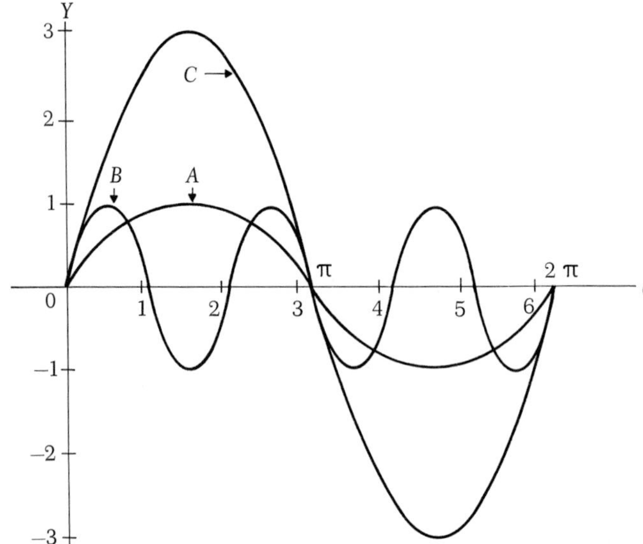

Figure 19-19

Graphs of some sine functions A: $y = \sin \theta$ B: $y = \sin 3\theta$ C: $y = 3 \sin \theta$

effects clearly. They should also become aware of which effect is associated with which position of the constant in the expression. This is the key to proper interpretation. Subsequently, additional experience in this can be given by having students consider and perhaps graph some functions, such as 3 sin $2x$, in which constants are present that affect both the amplitude and the period. Illustrations can be found in most textbooks.

Along with this topic it may be well to mention the construction of graphs of composite functions by addition of ordinates. Students as a rule have little difficulty in making such graphs and usually seem to enjoy it, but they should be given some instruction in interpreting their graphs. They will sometimes be a little surprised when they come to realize that if the graphs of any two functions, no matter what kind, can be made on the same axes, the graph of their sum or difference can be immediately and easily made by this simple method. It will not require much work to develop understanding of the idea, but on the other hand such understanding should not be taken for granted. Teachers should explain and illustrate the procedure, and students should be expected to make at least a few such graphs. As a matter of interest it can be pointed out that approximate solutions for such equations as $\cos\theta = \theta$ can be found by this method, although solutions cannot be obtained by either algebraic or trigonometric methods, and exact solutions are not available in any case.

Figure 19-20
Graph showing method of obtaining approximate solution of the equation $\cos\theta = \theta$

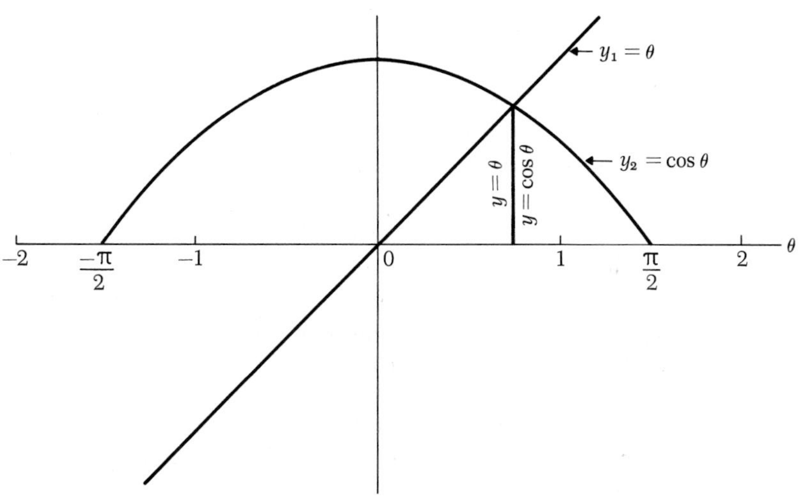

Teaching the functions of the sum or difference of two angles Since there are times when the students will need to use the functions of the sum or difference of two angles, a double angle, a half angle, and perhaps certain other formulas involving two angles, it is necessary that these formulas be developed in terms of the original angles and listed for reference. This is done in practically all textbooks. It is not necessary that students memorize all these formulas. It is desirable, however, that they see and understand the ways in which the formulas are developed and that they memorize a few which are fundamental and which will be needed frequently. Among these may be listed the following:

$\sin(A + B)$	$\cos(A + B)$	$\tan(A + B)$
$\sin 2A$	$\cos 2A$	$\tan 2A$

The development of these formulas is an excellent exercise in the application of algebraic techniques to trigonometric functions and identities. It is an interesting and rather remarkable fact that after one of them is established, the others can all be derived therefrom. It is customary to establish either the identity $\cos(A - B) = \cos A \cos B + \sin A \sin B$ or the identity $\sin(A + B) = \sin A \cos B + \cos A \sin B$ from geometric considerations and then to derive all the rest by using algebraic methods and the fundamental identities. For example, once the identity $\sin(A + B) = \sin A \cos B + \cos A \sin B$ is established, we have at once the following:

$$\begin{aligned}
\sin(A - B) &= \sin[A + (-B)] \\
&= \sin A \cos(-B) + \cos A \sin(-B) \\
&= \sin A \cos B - \cos A \sin B \\
\cos(A + B) &= \sin[90^\circ - (A + B)] \\
&= \sin[(90^\circ - A) - B] \\
&= \sin(90^\circ - A)\cos B - \cos(90^\circ - A)\sin B \\
&= \cos A \cos B - \sin A \sin B
\end{aligned}$$

The table on page 527 indicates lines of association through which many other identities can be derived from this beginning.

If teachers would lay more stress on the interrelations suggested by the table they might bring additional motivation to this work and at the same time give students a sense of the organic relationship and interplay among different parts of trigonometry and, indeed, among different parts of mathematics.

Apart from the derivation of these special formulas or identities, the main difficulty which students have is in memorizing and organizing them to the point of ready recognition and recall and of useful association. The teacher can probably give some help in this by suggesting a method or order for classifying the formulas. There are different

TABLE 19-2
Reduction formulas

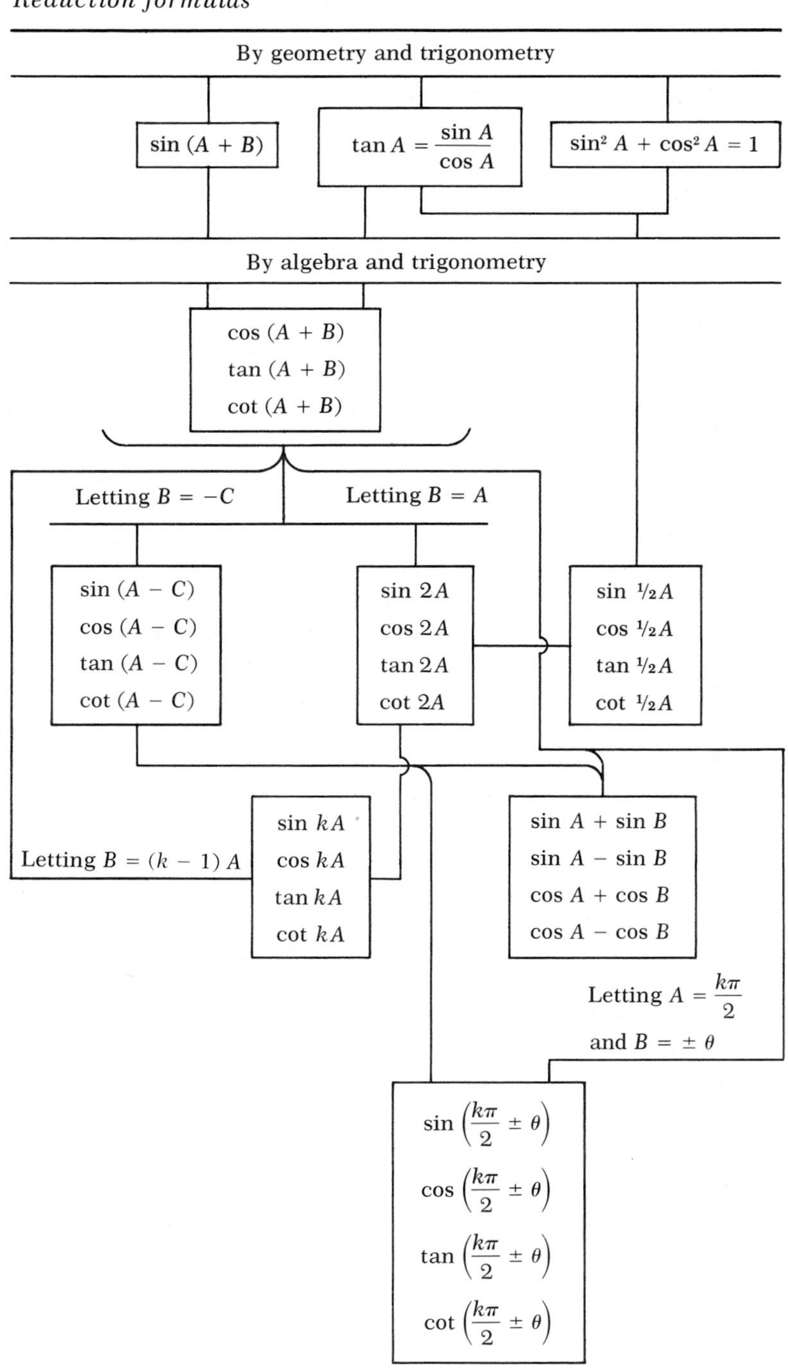

schemes of classification, and each teacher will probably have some scheme which he has found helpful and which he may wish to recommend to his students.

Proving trigonometric identities In this section we shall be concerned with trigonometric identities involving a single independent variable (angle or number). To prove a trigonometric identity means to prove that a given expression involving one or more trigonometric functions can be transformed by legitimate means into the precise form of another given expression. If this can be done the two expressions are said to be identically equal for all admissible values of the variable.

In most textbooks the trigonometric identities proposed for proof are stated in the form of equations. In a way this is unfortunate because with this form of statement students sometimes misinterpret the problem and by treating it as an equation may arrive at a statement that two expressions are equal. From this they sometimes conclude that they have proved the identity of the original expressions, failing to realize that they had essentially assumed this very thing at the outset. The fallacy involved in this sort of reasoning can be shown by taking a case which is evidently absurd on the face of it but which illustrates the point in question. Let it be required to test to see whether or not $\sin x = -\sin x$ is an identity. By treating this as an equation and squaring both members we do get an identity: $\sin^2 x \equiv \sin^2 x$. Clearly, however, this does not justify the conclusion that the original expressions ($\sin x$ and $-\sin x$) are identically equal for all values of x.

A few examples of this sort may serve to clarify the matter for students and to alert them to this type of pitfall. They need to sense clearly that in proving two trigonometric expressions identically equal we may work with only one of them at a time. Either may be changed in form by trigonometric substitutions from known identities or by permissible algebraic operations, and if it can be put in the same form as the other, the identity of the two original expressions will have been established. It is convenient at times to change the forms of both expressions *separately* into other expressions known to be identically equal. Such a procedure establishes a valid proof of the identity of the original expressions if, but only if, all of the steps are reversible.

Once the students have the essential problem and method clearly in mind, their only other need is for a close familiarity with the basic relations among the functions. The eight fundamental identities most commonly needed are:

$$\sin^2 x + \cos^2 x \equiv 1 \qquad (1) \qquad\qquad \sec^2 x - \tan^2 x \equiv 1 \qquad (2)$$

$$\csc^2 x - \cot^2 x \equiv 1 \qquad (3) \qquad\qquad \tan x \equiv \frac{\sin x}{\cos x} \qquad (4)$$

$$\cot x \equiv \frac{\cos x}{\sin x} \qquad (5) \qquad\qquad \cot x \equiv \frac{1}{\tan x} \qquad (6)$$

$$\sec x \equiv \frac{1}{\cos x} \qquad (7) \qquad\qquad \csc x \equiv \frac{1}{\sin x} \qquad (8)$$

These should be thoroughly memorized. The student should already be familiar with formulas (6) to (8), since they are merely the reciprocal relations pointed out in connection with the definition of the functions, and his attention should be called to the fact that formulas (2) and (3) follow immediately from formula (1). In addition to these, the student should also be familiar with the functions of the double angles.

There are other relationships which are sometimes needed but which are so numerous and so much alike that it is difficult to memorize them all. The mnemonic device of Figure 19-21, which we shall call "the function hexagon," provides an easy means for recalling all these fundamental identities except the first three listed above and the functions of double and half angles. The arrangement should be made exactly as shown. This is easy to remember because the sine, tangent, and secant appear in this order from left to right, and each is directly above its corresponding cofunction.

1. The two functions at the ends of any diagonal are reciprocals of each other.

2. Any function is the product of the two functions between which it lies. Thus $\sin x = \tan x \cos x$; $\cot x = \cos x \csc x$; etc.

3. Any function may be expressed as a fraction in which the numerator is either of the adjacent functions and the denominator is the one on beyond that. Thus

$$\tan x = \frac{\sec x}{\csc x} \qquad \cos x = \frac{\cot x}{\csc x}$$

and so on.

4. The product of any three alternate functions is 1. Thus

$$\sin x \cot x \sec x = 1 \qquad \text{and} \qquad \cos x \tan x \csc x = 1$$

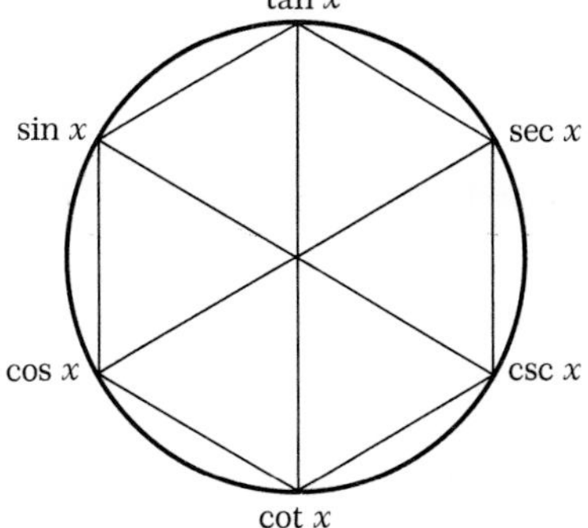

Figure 19-21
The function hexagon

This mechanical device is so simple, economical, and powerful—giving, as it does, 26 separate identities for reference—that students will find it extremely helpful in making trigonometric transformations in their work with trigonometric identities and equations. It does not, of course, *prove* any of these identities, but the proofs are all simple and should be made by the students.

Much interest and motivation can be added to the work on identities by the alternate device of asking students to make up some identities of their own. Have them take some expression involving one or more trigonometric functions of an angle and see how many different expressions they can write that are identically equal to the one they started with. These may then be given to other students to prove. Exercises in making up identities seem to provide a psychological stimulus even for students who may have shown little enthusiasm for proving the ready-made identities in the textbook, and at the same time they provide a valuable learning experience for the students as they become more familiar with the basic identities themselves.

Solving trigonometric equations In contrast to trigonometric identities, which are valid for all admissible values of the independent variable (angle or number), the term "trigonometric equation" is applied in general to an equation involving one or more trigonometric functions of a variable such that the equation is satisfied, if at all, by some, but not all, values of the variable. Thus a trigonometric equation is a conditional equation, and the task which one faces in finding its solution is that of determining the value or values of the variable which satisfy the equation. It is wise to explain and illustrate this to students at the outset in order that their thinking and their efforts may not be misdirected. Trigonometric identities may at times be invoked to advantage in solving trigonometric equations, but their involvement is intermediate and incidental to the solution.

Trigonometric equations really are equations, and they are therefore subject to treatment under the algebraic laws of the equation besides being subject to the algebraic transformation of either member separately or to the trigonometric transformation of the trigonometric elements involved.

Example: Let it be required to solve $\sin 2x = \tan x$. The problem is to find an angle x for which this relation exists. A solution is as follows:

$\sin 2x = 2 \sin x \cos x$ (trigonometric transformation)

$\tan x = \dfrac{\sin x}{\cos x}$ (trigonometric transformation)

$\therefore 2 \sin x \cos x = \dfrac{\sin x}{\cos x}$ (substitution)

$2 \sin x \cos^2 x = \sin x$	(both members multiplied by $\cos x$)
$2 \sin x \cos^2 x - \sin x = 0$	(transposition)
$\sin x(2 \cos^2 x - 1) = 0$	(left member factored)

This can be true only (1) if $\sin x = 0$ or (2) if $2 \cos^2 x - 1 = 0$, which implies $\cos x = \pm \frac{1}{2}\sqrt{2}$.

$\therefore$ if the equation is true, the values of x, such that $0° \leqq x < 360°$, must be

(1) $x = 0°$ or $180°$
(2) $x = 45°, 135°, 225°$, or $315°$

Substitution in the original equation verifies this set of values as the required solution set.

Note that the algebraic transformations which were employed to solve this example are all entirely legitimate because we started with an admitted equation and sought merely the solution of the equation.

Students are sometimes confused or uncertain as to the variable for which they are to solve. This arises from the fact that the problem really involves two main parts. The students need first to solve for an intermediate variable which is typically a trigonometric function of an ultimate independent variable (angle or number). Then, having obtained a solution for this intermediate variable (e.g., $\cos x = \frac{1}{2}$), there still remains the task of determining the value or values of x for which this is true. This is illustrated in the foregoing example. It is an easy thing to understand once it is pointed out, but it should be made clear to the students that the problem is not completed until they have found the set of values for the angle or number which satisfies the original equation.

It should also be pointed out that trigonometric equations which have no solutions may be encountered. Thus there is no number x which satisfies the equation $\sin^2 x + 2 \cos^2 x = 3$. Permissible trigonometric substitutions and algebraic procedures applied to this equation yield the statement that $\cos x = \pm\sqrt{2}$, and $\sqrt{2}$ of course is not within the range of the cosine function. It is probably advisable for teachers to give full and detailed chalkboard explanations of the solutions of several typical trigonometric equations and to make clear, as each step is taken, why it is taken.

Authors of textbooks are not always very careful to graduate the difficulty of the problems given for solution. Students, however, often learn to see patterns and get their insights a step at a time. A set of problems arranged in a sequence or order such that complications are introduced gradually can be a most helpful learning device. Teachers will do well to examine sets of trigonometric equations given in textbooks and if necessary rearrange them in reasonable order of difficulty when they assign the problems to their students for solution.

Polar coordinates and complex numbers in trigonometric form It is likely that a good many students in trigonometry classes will not have had any previous experience in working with polar coordinates, though some may have done so. Therefore it is advisable, in taking up the study of complex numbers in trigonometric form, to begin with a careful explanation of the polar-coordinate system, using diagrams and the basic conversion formulas to clarify the basic equivalence relations between polar and rectangular coordinates.

The definition of the polar coordinates of a point is based upon superimposing a polar system, with pole, polar axis, vectorial angle, and standard position properly defined, directly upon a conventional rectangular coordinate system. This is motivated by the fact that, with respect to an initial point and direction, any point in the plane can be defined as well by a distance and a direction (its polar coordinates) as by two distances (its rectangular coordinates). The relations between these two coordinate systems is easily made clear by reference to a diagram such as Figure 19-22. Evidently $x = r \cos \theta$ and $y = r \sin \theta$. Also, $r = \sqrt{x^2 + y^2}$ and $\tan \theta = y/x$, whence $\theta = \arctan y/x$. These conversion formulas are so simple and so easily reconstructed that there is no need for students to memorize them.

Once these basic relations are established, numerous exercises should be given for the purpose of strengthening understanding and developing facility in applying them. These exercises should include conversions both from rectangular to polar coordinates and from polar to rectangular coordinates. The following are samples: (1) Give the polar coordinates of the point (7,10). (2) Give the rectangular coordinates of the point $(12,\pi/3)$.

Extension of the idea of polar coordinates to polar representation of complex numbers requires setting up a one-to-one correspondence between the complex numbers and the points in a plane. This is accomplished by representing all complex numbers as vectors, or, rather, as vector sums. Since each complex number is of the form $x + yi$, where x and y are real numbers (not excluding zero), it is necessary to designate one of the axes (usually the X axis) as the *axis of reals* and the other (the Y axis) as the *axis of imaginaries*. Then any complex number such as $8 + 5i$ can be represented by a vector drawn from the origin (or pole) to the point (8,5) as referred to the axes. The length, or absolute value, of this vector is known as the *magnitude* or *modulus* of the complex number. In

Figure 19-22

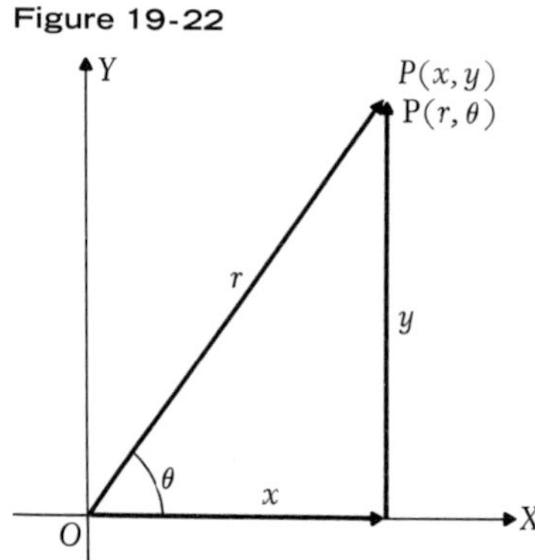

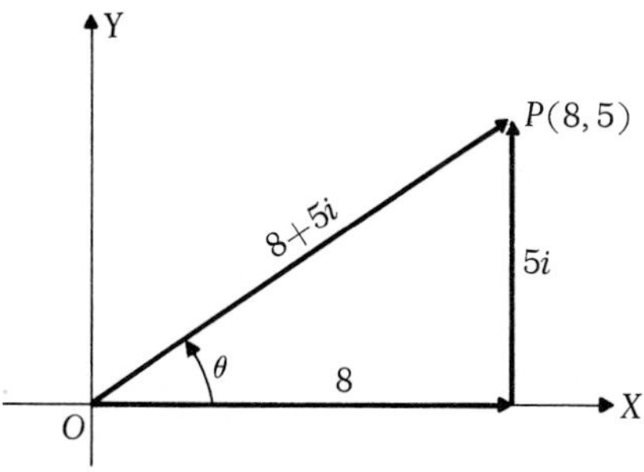

Figure 19-23

this case the modulus is $\sqrt{8^2 + 5^2} = \sqrt{89}$. The positive angle θ which this vector makes with the polar axis is called the *vectorial angle*, or the *amplitude*, of the complex number. In this case $\tan \theta = 5/8$, so the amplitude, or vectorial angle, is *arctan* $5/8$. Hence the polar representation of the complex number $8 + 5i$ in the complex plane is $(\sqrt{89}, \arctan 5/8)$.

None of these ideas should cause any serious difficulty to students if they are carefully explained and adequately illustrated by the teacher. The only new elements are the terms "modulus" and "amptitude" and the designation of the y axis as the *axis of imaginaries*, against which the coefficients of the imaginary parts of complex numbers are plotted. It will probably be necessary to recall to students the methods of forming the sum and product of two complex numbers and the fact that two complex numbers $a + bi$ and $c + di$ are equal if and only if $a = c$ and $b = d$. Then they need only be reminded that (1) the sum of $a + bi$ and $c + di$ can be represented by the vector drawn from the origin to the point corresponding to the complex number $[(a + c), (b + d)]$, which is in fact their sum, and (2) the product of $a + bi$ and $c + di$ can be represented by the vector drawn from the origin to the point corresponding to the complex number $[(ac - bd), (bc + ad)]$, which is in fact their product.

Transition to trigonometric representation is now easily accomplished by recalling that in the rectangular form $x + yi$ the real numbers x and y have the polar representation $x = r \cos \theta$ and $y = r \sin \theta$, with $r > 0$. Therefore, by direct substitution $x + yi$ becomes

$$r \cos \theta + (r \sin \theta)i = r(\cos \theta + i \sin \theta)$$

From this, the passage to the formula for the product is made by direct multiplication. Thus, let $A = r(\cos \theta + i \sin \theta)$ and

$$B = s(\cos \phi + i \sin \phi)$$

Then it needs to be shown that $AB = rs[\cos(\theta + \phi) + i \sin(\theta + \phi)]$. Similarly, the quotient formula $A/B = \dfrac{r}{s}[\cos(\theta - \phi) + i \sin(\theta - \phi)]$ needs to be worked out directly and in detail.

The detailed work involved in developing these formulas is straightforward, but it is somewhat long and tedious. It also requires that certain trigonometric expressions be recognized and replaced by their equivalents as sines and cosines of the sum and difference of two variables. This latter step is not likely to be obvious to students until it is pointed out to them. Therefore it is probably desirable for the teacher to go through all the details of the derivations with the class. Students should eventually memorize the formulas for facility in using them, but not until the derivations have been thoroughly explained and understood.

The product and quotient formulas provide the foundation upon which De Moivre's theorem is established and so lead to a way of finding integral powers and roots of complex numbers in trigonometric form easily and quickly. Students may be helped to a clearer understanding of the procedures implied by the formulas if they are asked to state the formulas verbally and to answer such questions as these: If two complex numbers are given in trigonometric form, what is the amplitude of the product? What is the modulus of the product? Similar questions about the modulus and the amplitude of the quotient of two complex numbers and about the modulus and the amplitude of a power and a root of a complex number should be raised.

Graphical methods should be used freely in all work with complex numbers in trigonometric form, and students should be expected to make graphical representations of sums and differences, products, quotients, powers, and roots of such numbers.

The solution of triangles The trigonometric solution of the right triangle is discussed in the first part of this chapter. The methods are so simple, obvious, and direct that they offer no difficulty and need not be discussed further here. The solution of the oblique or general triangle, however, is not so simple. It requires the development of certain special formulas and a discriminating analysis of the given data in each particular problem to determine the method and the formulas to be used.

There are four different combinations of independent parts any one of which, with one exception which will be mentioned later, may uniquely determine a triangle. These are often referred to as the "four cases of the general[4] triangle." The four combinations of parts are as follows:

Case 1. Given two angles and any side
Case 2. Given two sides and an angle opposite one of them
Case 3. Given two sides and the included angle
Case 4. Given the three sides

To handle the solution of these cases of the general triangle, various special formulas are developed; the most fundamental of them are the

[4]The term "general triangle" is used here instead of "oblique triangle" because the general formulas developed for these cases apply to right triangles as well as to oblique triangles.

law of sines, the law of cosines, and the law of tangents. In addition to these there are numerous more specialized formulas connected with the triangle, including the half-angle formulas in terms of the sides and Heron's formula for the area of the triangle.

The mastery of these formulas and their use in solving the various cases of the general triangle cause a good deal of difficulty to students. The most common difficulties may be enumerated under five main types as follows:

1. Difficulty in following and understanding the derivation of the formulas
2. Difficulty in remembering the various formulas and keeping them in mind without confusing them
3. Difficulty in knowing what formulas to use in particular cases
4. Difficulty due to lack of systematic preplanning and layout of written work
5. Difficulty in checking the solution

Many teachers fail to appreciate either the seriousness of these difficulties or the extent to which failure to master them may impair the effectiveness of the students' work. Yet the teacher has a serious obligation to see that the students are adequately equipped with respect to these points.

The development of the fundamental trigonometric laws is not inherently difficult or complicated. It can be understood without great difficulty by most students if properly presented. The teacher, however, should point the way by laying out the main steps in the development in quick, bold outline just as one lays out the plan of proof for a proposition in geometry before proceeding to write down the complete synthetic proof in finished form. Some geometry teachers and textbook writers have recognized the importance of setting forth the main plan of a proof before proceeding to details. For the most part, trigonometry textbooks have not stressed this very much, so the responsibility must be accepted by the teacher. For example, most students find it difficult to take the bare facts set forth in the proof of the law of cosines and to extract from them much understanding of a plan whereby the proof could be reconstructed without being literally memorized. On the other hand, a rapid "chalk-talk" explanation of the *plan* of development by the teacher will leave the student with a basis of understanding which he can fill in with the necessary details and reconstruct at will. The same may be said for the development of the law of tangents and for the other formulas involved in the solution of the general triangle. In some cases it is necessary to draw upon previously developed formulas. For example, in developing the law of tangents, it is convenient to use the relations

$$\sin A + \sin B = 2 \sin \tfrac{1}{2}(A + B) \cos \tfrac{1}{2}(A - B)$$
$$\sin A - \sin B = 2 \cos \tfrac{1}{2}(A + B) \sin \tfrac{1}{2}(A - B)$$

In such cases the teacher should specifically call attention to these substitutions in discussing the plan of development.

There are a few fundamental formulas which are used so much in the solution of oblique triangles that the student will find it advisable to memorize them. In particular, the law of sines and the law of cosines are indispensable and sufficient. The student should become as familiar with them as with the Pythagorean theorem or the fact that

$$a^2 - b^2 = (a - b)(a + b)$$

For logarithmic solutions the law of tangents is more efficient than the cosine law. Some teachers prefer to have their students memorize other formulas, such as the half-angle formulas (in terms of the sides) and the area formulas. Since courses differ in emphasis, no rigid criterion can be laid down. In general it may be said that students should be required to memorize only such formulas as are fundamental and which, in the judgment of the teacher, will be used sufficiently to warrant memorization; however, those formulas which *are* to be memorized should be memorized to the point of perfection.

The teacher should give the students criteria for determining which formulas to use in particular cases. One criterion is as follows: The formula to be used must be one which expresses an unknown part of the triangle completely in terms of the given parts or from which an unknown part may be found in terms of given parts (as in the case of the law of tangents). By adopting a standard system of notation, listing the fundamental formulas, and setting down the given parts of the triangle in a particular problem, the student may readily determine by inspection which of the formulas should be used. If he is required to do this consistently, he will soon learn that the law of sines is the appropriate formula to use if he is given either two angles and any side or two sides and an angle opposite one of them[5] and that the law of cosines will enable him to solve triangles in which the given parts are either two sides and the included angle or the three sides. The teacher should point out that, in place of the law of cosines, the alternative formulas for the law of tangents and for the tangents of the half angles in terms of the sides may be used when the given parts are respectively two sides and the included angle or the three sides and that these formulas are more amenable to logarithmic treatment than is the law of cosines. The association of the appropriate formulas with the different cases would be strengthened if each formula were developed and immediately applied when the case requiring it is first taken up. In many textbooks, however, the formulas are developed as in an intact body of theory, and the applications are left until later.

[5]The ambiguous case (given two sides and an angle opposite one of them) should be discussed at length and its geometric and trigonometric possibilities pointed out.

In teaching the solution of the general triangle, the teacher should show the students how to make a layout for the work and should give specific training in doing so. Students generally are inclined to start computing as soon as they get hold of two numbers with which they can work. However, since most problems in solving oblique triangles are somewhat long and complicated, this is uneconomical and unwise for several reasons. There is great advantage in thinking the problem through completely and planning the entire solution in detail, but as a whole, before doing anything else. This will ensure an understanding analysis of the problem as a whole. It will prevent the student from becoming confused in a heterogeneous mixture of analysis and computation. It will provide a specific step-by-step guide for all necessary computation and use of the tables. It is economical of time and labor. Finally, it is conducive to orderliness, which in turn is always conducive to effective work.

EXERCISES

1. The two basic problems in solving right triangles (given sufficient data) are (*a*) to solve for an angle and (*b*) to solve for a side. Explain in detail, as you would in introducing the subject to a junior high school class, how to use the trigonometric functions and their numerical values in solving each of these two basic problems. Use examples to illustrate your discussion.

2. Find or make up a good field project, involving the use of right-triangle trigonometry that is suitable for junior high school students. Describe it in detail, and show how it will exemplify the direct practical application of trigonometry.

3. Explain how the circular functions of real numbers are defined, and show that these definitions are consistent with, and equivalent to, the definitions of the corresponding trigonometric functions of angles.

4. Explain the "wrapping function," and show how it enables us to set up a one-to-one correspondence between the set of all angles and the set of all real numbers.

5. Explain what is meant by the "period" of a trigonometric function, and give the period for each of the six trigonometric functions. Explain why the period of the function $y = 2 \sin x$ is not the same as the period of the function $y = \sin 2x$.

6. Summarize the discussion of the teaching of the functions of the special angles as it is given in this chapter.

7. Show that the Pythagorean theorem is a special case of the law of cosines.

8. Why do so many students fail to get an appreciation of the real significance of the following: (*a*) the periodic nature of the trigonometric functions, (*b*) the multiple-valued nature of the inverse trigonometric relations as contrasted with the single-valued nature of the functions themselves, (*c*) the representation of values of functions by line values, and (*d*) the fact that for certain angles the values of certain functions are undefined?

9. List what you feel are the important things to be learned through the study of the variation of the trigonometric functions. Why are these important?

10. By use of graphs of the sine, cosine, and tangent of an angle, construct graphs of the cotangent, secant, and cosecant.

11. Construct a graph of $y = \sin x$. Then, using only this graph and geometric methods, construct on the same axes graphs of the functions: $y = 2 \sin x$, $y = \sin 2x$,

$y = \sin \frac{1}{2}x$, $y = \frac{1}{2} \sin x$, $y = \sin (2 + x)$, $y = 2 + \sin x$, $y = 1 + \frac{1}{2} \sin x$. Explain each of these constructions as you would to a class.

12. What is a radian? Discuss radian measure and the *pi* notation and explain as you would to your students how to convert from degree to radian measure and from radian to degree measure.

13. List the radian equivalents of all numbers x such that x is an integral multiple of $\pi/6$ or $\pi/4$ and $0 \leqq x \leqq 2\pi$. Then make a table giving the values of the six trigonometric functions of each of these, noting any cases in which the functions are not defined.

14. Most tables of trigonometric functions extend only from 0° to 90°, yet it is often necessary to find values of functions of angles not within this domain. Show exactly how you would teach students to determine values from the tables for functions such as cos 153°, tan 289°, and sin (−112°). Explain the use of the triangle of reference, and show how it can be helpful in this connection.

15. Explain why trigonometric identities must sometimes be used in solving trigonometric equations. Give examples to illustrate your explanations.

16. Explain the fundamental distinction between proving identities and solving trigonometric equations. Why is it not legitimate in proving identities to use the algebraic laws of the equation and to operate as if the identity to be proved were an equation? Illustrate.

17. Develop the formula for $\sin (A + B)$ or the formula for $\cos (A - B)$ from geometric considerations.

18. Starting with the formula for $\cos (A - B)$, explain, without using any diagram, how the following formulas are derived: $\cos (A + B)$, $\sin (A + B)$, and $\sin (A - B)$.

19. Explain and illustrate the function hexagon described in this chapter, and show why it is a helpful mnemonic device.

20. List and establish all of the twenty-six identities which the function hexagon can "remember" for you.

21. Take ten simple trigonometric expressions and by means of commonly known identities transform each of them into some other equivalent form. (You will then have established ten "original" trigonometric identities, proofs of which could then be assigned as exercises for your class.)

22. What advantages could students derive from establishing "original" identities themselves?

23. For what values of x in the domain $0° \leqq x \leqq 720°$ is the statement $\cos x < \frac{1}{2}$ valid? For what values of x in this same domain is the statement $\cos x = \frac{1}{2}$ valid?

24. For what value or values of x in the domain $90° < x \leqq 450°$ are the following statements valid? (*a*) $2 \cos 5x = 1$; (*b*) $2 \cos 5x > 1$.

25. Explain as you would to a class the solutions of the following equation and inequality, where $0° \leqq x \leqq 360°$: (*a*) $\sin x = \tan x$; (*b*) $\sin x < \tan x$. [Analysis of part (*b*) makes clear the great care that is needed in examining inequalities. It suggests also the importance of doing some work with inequalities and points up the interest which such work can generate.]

26. Explain, as you would to a class, all the steps in the complete solution of the equation $\cot^2 x = 5 \cot x - 6$.

27. Explain how the graph of the function $y = f(x) = \sin x$ could be used also as the graph of the inverse relation $x = \arcsin y$.

28. Explain how the complex number $u = 4 + 7i$ can be expressed in trigonometric form.

29. Let u and v be complex numbers where $u = r(\cos x + i \sin x)$ and $v = s(\cos y + i \sin y)$. Show why
$u \cdot v = rs \cos (x + y) + i \sin (x + y)$

30. Show why $u^3 = r^3(\cos 3x + i \sin 3x)$.

31. Explain how to find the five fifth roots of the complex number $1 + i$.

32. Construct a graph of the function $f(x) = x + \cos x$ by the addition of ordinates, and explain your method as you would to a class.

BIBLIOGRAPHY

Amir-Moez, Ali R.: Teaching Trigonometry through Vectors, *Mathematics Magazine*, **32** (1958), 19–23.

Andree, Richard V.: Modern Trigonometry, *Mathematics Teacher*, **48** (1955), 82–83.

Baker, G. A.: Multiplication Tables for Trigonometric Functions, *American Mathematical Monthly*, **64** (1957), 502–503.

Bettinger, A. K.: A Derivation for the Formulas for sin $(a + b)$ and cos $(a + b)$, *American Mathematical Monthly*, **60** (1953), 108–110.

Bold, Benjamin: A Geometric Proof for a Number of Trigonometric Theorems, *Mathematics Teacher*, **45** (1952), 43–44.

Bristol, James D.: Construction and Evaluation of Trigonometric Functions of Some Special Angles, *Mathematics Teacher*, **55** (1962), 4–7.

Bruce, Matthew H.: Using the Cathode-ray Oscilloscope in the High School Trigonometry Class, *School Science and Mathematics*, **60** (1960), 593–602.

Bureau of Secondary Curriculum Development: "Mathematics 10-11-12" (Albany, N.Y.: The State Education Department, 1959).

Cohen, Carl: Addition Theorems for the Sine and Cosine, *American Mathematical Monthly*, **63** (1956), 248–249.

Commission on Mathematics: "Appendices" (New York: College Entrance Examination Board, 1959), pp. 175–223.

Dickinson, Frank G.: Some Transformations from a Unit Circle with Line Values of the Sine Function, *Mathematics Teacher*, **45** (1952), 19–24.

Dubisch, Roy: "Trigonometry" (New York: The Ronald Press Company, 1955).

———, with the assistance of Vernon E. Howes: "The Teaching of Mathematics" (New York: John Wiley & Sons, Inc., 1963), pp. 56–70.

Fehr, Howard F.: New Thinking in Mathematics Education, *Mathematics Teacher*, **53** (1960), 424–429.

Greenberg, Benjamin: Transforming the Law of Cosines for Computational Purposes, *Mathematics Teacher*, **48** (1955), 308–309.

———: A Geometric Proof of Half-angle Formulas for Triangle *ABC* by Means of an Escribed Circle, *School Science and Mathematics*, **59** (1959), 682–685.

Grove, Ethel, and others: Model for Introducing Trigonometry on Ninth Grade Level, *School Science and Mathematics*, **51** (1951), 296–297.

Jones, Phillip S.: Angular Measure: Enough of its History to Improve its Teaching, *Mathematics Teacher*, **46** (1953), 419–426.

Jurgensen, Ray: An Interesting Equation: $\tan 2x = \cot x$, *School Science and Mathematics*, **54** (1954), 489–490.

Karpinski, L. C.: The Place of Trigonometry in the Development of Mathematical Ideas, *Scripta Mathematica*, **11** (1945), 268–272.

Mazkewitsch, D.: Geometric Derivations of Some Trigonometric Formulae, *School Science and Mathematics*, **58** (1958), 213–216.

Pedley, Arthur H.: Complex Numbers and Vectors in High School Mathematics, *Mathematics Teacher*, **53** (1960), 198–201.

Ransom, William R.: Some Mirror Trigonometry, *School Science and Mathematics*, **55** (1955), 599–600.

Read, C. B., and Ferna Wrestler: Principal Values of Certain Inverse Trigonometric Functions, *American Mathematical Monthly*, **63** (1956), 184–185.

Rine, T. E.: Integration in the Teaching of Trigonometry in the Secondary School, *School Science and Mathematics*, **53** (1953), 644–649.

Rosenberg, Herman: The Changing Concept of Trigonometry as a School Subject, *Mathematics Teacher*, **51** (1958), 246–252.

Sawyer, W. W.: Trigonometry Abstractly Treated, *American Mathematical Monthly*, **64** (1957), 734–737.

Schumaker, John A.: The Algebra of Sets in the Teaching of Trigonometry, *Mathematics Teacher*, **52** (1959), 20–23.

Steinen, Ramon: Trigonometry in Grade Eight, *Mathematics Teacher*, **50** (1957), 380–383.

Thomas, Robert W.: A New Introduction to the Ideas and Methods of Trigonometry,

Mathematics Teacher, **54** (1961), 427–435.

Tierney, John A.: Trigonometric Functions of Real Numbers, *Mathematics Teacher*, **50** (1957), 38–39.

Trigg, C. W.: A Proof of the Law of Cosines, *School Science and Mathematics*, **54** (1954), 370.

Wegner, Kenneth W.: Trigonometric Values That Are Algebraic Numbers, *Mathematics Teacher*, **50** (1957), 557–561.

Wolfe, J. M.: Proximity of Prerequisite Learning and Success in Trigonometry in College, *Mathematics Teacher*, **49** (1956), 605–606.

Yates, R. C.: The Trigonometric Functions, *Mathematics Teacher*, **51** (1958), 191–193.

Young, Frederick H.: The Addition Formulas, *Mathematics Teacher*, **50** (1957), 45–48.

TWENTY

The teaching of analytic geometry

ANALYTIC GEOMETRY is a borderline subject between the high school courses and the more rigorous work in the calculus and subsequent college courses in mathematics. It contributes to the mathematical development and background of students in at least three important ways. It embraces a body of subject matter which is interesting and beautiful in its own right. Also, by bringing powerful algebraic concepts and techniques to bear upon geometrical problems, it links algebra and geometry together into a unified mathematical structure. Finally, it develops mathematical formulas and techniques, many of which are needed for subsequent work in mathematics, and thus provides an important tool for the mathematician. Analytic geometry may be viewed, therefore, as a mathematical structure, as a method, or as a tool, and it is something of each of these.

Some students find analytic geometry easier than other branches of mathematics which they have studied, but a good many find it harder. Since little has been written on the teaching of analytic geometry, the present chapter undertakes to provide a published source to which teachers can turn for some discussion of certain instructional problems related to the subject. Hence consideration is given in this chapter to some of the key concepts of analytic geometry and to some of the characteristic difficulties which students often have with the subject.

Analytic geometry and the high school program In the past, analytic geometry has been the typical offering for the second half of the freshman year of college mathematics. Until quite recently, few attempts have been made to introduce even its simplest concepts and terminology into the usual courses in high school algebra and geometry, although these subjects afford numerous opportunities for the introduction. To be sure, some work with graphs is included in all algebra courses, but the usual treatment can hardly be said to be analytic; all too often the work has stressed only the point-by-point plotting of graphs, with little emphasis on their interpretation. Except for occasional discussion of the slope of a straight line and of the slope-intercept equation of a line, the standard textbooks in high school algebra and geometry have been practically devoid of any reference to the concepts, notation, or method of analytic geometry.

The years since the middle of the century, however, have seen a marked disposition to introduce new ideas and subject matter into the high school courses. The 1957 revised program in mathematics for the high schools in New York State gave some attention to analytic geometry in the regular work in grades 10 and 11 and in a special course tried out experimentally in grade 12. In the tenth grade it formed one of the seven main divisions of the course. The range of topics was somewhat extended in the eleventh grade. The experimental twelfth-grade course reviewed the topics developed earlier and included study of the conic sections in standard position, study of the properties and type equations of the sections, and some work on polar coordinates and parametric equations.[1]

Subsequently (1959) the Commission on Mathematics of the College Entrance Examination Board included a substantial unit on coordinate geometry as one of the six units comprising its recommended program in mathematics for the tenth grade. The topics proposed for this unit include rectangular coordinates and one-to-one correspondence between points of a plane and ordered number pairs, and rather systematic analytic study of some of the important properties of the straight line and the circle. Emphasis was placed upon the concept of sets, e.g., a locus as a set of points satisfying given conditions and solution sets for equations or inequalities as sets of values satisfying these equations or inequalities. The use of methods of coordinate geometry in proving theorems and solving numerical problems of plane geometry was encouraged.[2]

Since 1960 the experimental textbooks on high school geometry published by the SMSG and the UICSM projects have included substantial amounts of coordinate geometry, and commercial publishers have

[1]For further details on this, see the following documents: "Instruction in Mathematics and Science in New York State Schools" (Albany, N.Y.: The State Education Department, 1957), p. 3; "Tenth Grade Mathematics: Coordinate Geometry," *ibid.*, p. 1; "An Experimental Course in Mathematics for the Twelfth Year," *ibid.*, pp. 25–27.

[2]Report of the Commission on Mathematics, "Program for College Preparatory Mathematics" (New York: College Entrance Examination Board, 1959), p. 39, and "Appendices," *ibid.*, pp. 120–139.

been quick to fall into line. Most of the new commercially published textbooks on high school geometry now include one or two chapters on coordinate geometry.

It seems rather doubtful, however, that analytic geometry as a full systematic course will come to be typically a high school subject as trigonometry has done, though it will doubtless be taught in some schools. It seems more likely that it will remain typically a course for college freshmen. Indications are that it will often be correlated with calculus and that many students will begin their work in college mathematics with such a course.

In the remainder of this chapter some of the key topics of analytic geometry will be considered, along with certain instructional problems.

Some elementary concepts In beginning the study of analytic geometry the students will not encounter immediately any geometric ideas that are essentially new. On the contrary, the introductory work usually consists in a re-examination of the Cartesian coordinate system with which they should already be familiar through their earlier work with graphs. In many cases, however, this earlier work will have been rather casual and not very systematic. Therefore, it is generally advisable at the start to review and refurbish the concepts, terms, and notation associated with rectangular coordinates. This can be done quickly through a little supervised work on plotting points. A few illustrations done at the chalkboard, together with a modicum of practice in plotting points and indicating coordinates in conventional form, will suffice to clear up any questions the students may have.

The concept of ordered pairs of numbers should be stressed in this connection. It should be emphasized that the location of a point in a coordinate system depends not alone on the numerical values of its coordinates but also upon their order, and that the point whose coordinates are (a,b) is not, in general, the same point as the one whose coordinates are (b,a). There is no difficulty involved here, and it would be unnecessary to mention this except that students sometimes get careless about this convention. It is well, however, to stress the importance of giving conscious and explicit attention both to the concept of order in naming the coordinates of a point and to the conventional notation used. Any carelessness or any departure from the accepted notation will induce mistakes in representation and communication. Moreover, it may be pointed out at this time that the modern definition of *function* places emphasis on ordered pairs of elements and that the ordering and its proper representation will be of prime importance throughout all subsequent work in mathematics.

Other matters which probably should be reviewed and clarified in the introductory part of the course include the concept of projections on a line and the notion of directed line segments. Neither of these should require much time or entail any difficulty. The importance of reviewing them at this time lies in the fact that they are basic concepts which must be used continually. Fuzzy conceptions about these terms or the associated notation is likely to lead to fuzzy thinking and uncertainty in their application.

Associated with line segments and projections is the idea of *length* of a line segment, or *distance* from one point to another. The measure of this distance is made through direct application of the Pythagorean theorem to a right triangle, a concept with which the students are already familiar. In connection with any given line segment no difficulty is involved in showing that an associated right triangle may be formed by taking lines respectively parallel to the axes, one through each end of the given segment, and that the projections of the segment on these lines are the legs of the triangle, the segment itself being the hypotenuse. The very simplicity of this concept may tend to throw teachers off guard. It must be remembered that, while it is very elementary, it is also completely fundamental. It needs to be adequately illustrated. Moreover, even after the underlying idea is clearly understood by the students, the general relation needs to be explicitly formulated in terms of the coordinates of the ends of the segment:

$$d = \sqrt{(x_1 - x_2)^2 + (y_1 - y_2)^2} = \sqrt{(x_2 - x_1)^2 + (y_2 - y_1)^2}$$

This is easy to explain and illustrate by a diagram, but it is also the point at which students sometimes begin to become uncertain and confused. Their formulas of synthetic geometry will not usually have involved the use of coordinates, yet from here on they must both make and interpret their formulations in the notation of coordinates. If they can be made to understand both the rationale and the notation of this formula, a long step will have been made in the direction of understanding.

The point-of-division formulas are examples of formulas of analytic geometry which students often attempt to memorize without having a clear understanding of why they are as they are. Like the distance formula, they depend directly on theorems of high school geometry, and the concept is easily explained on this basis. Students bog down on it not because the concept is difficult but because they are unaccustomed to the notation. At this early stage in the course they will not yet have learned either to use or to interpret this notation very readily, and the formulas look forbidding to them. Hence, instead of attempting to interpret the formulas in terms of a figure and then reconstruct them in the new notation, the students often resort to memorizing the formulas. Usually it is not the geometric ideas that trouble them. It is the notation. This is new. It is fundamental and it must become the student's tool and servant throughout this and subsequent courses. It is important, therefore, to give a good deal of attention to this matter of notation in the early part of this work. It may even spell the difference between success and failure in the course.

The mid-point formulas, of course, are merely special cases of the point-of-division formulas, but (again in terms of notation) they are usually stated differently, so the relation is not immediately apparent. Teachers, on the other hand, may tend to assume that the connection is so obvious as not to require any comment. It is desirable to point out this relation explicitly from a geometric viewpoint and also to show how the mid-point formulas can be derived analytically from the point-of-division formulas. This not only serves to clarify this particular case but provides a simple and good illustration of the application of algebraic techniques to geometric problems.

Loci and their equations The associated concepts of loci and their equations are central throughout analytic geometry. In high school mathematics courses little has been done to point up this association, though there are opportunities to do this even in the first course in algebra. The equation is thought of as being a part of algebra, and even the study of graphs of equations is often rather casual and perfunctory. The concept of a locus, on the other hand, is seldom encountered and clarified until the course in plane geometry, and even there the study of loci is confined mainly to its geometrical aspects. Little effort is made to bring the two together in any systematic manner until the course in analytic geometry, when that becomes the central theme. The conditions or restrictions imposed on the points forming a given locus are now expressed analytically or algebraically by equations which specify particular relations among the coordinates of each point in the locus and for no other points. Frequently the loci studied in analytic geometry are described verbally in terms of geometric conditions, but before they can be studied analytically these conditions have to be translated into equations.

The first serious difficulty which students are likely to encounter stems from this fact. Up to this point they have not been accustomed to identify geometric conditions with algebraic forms. Now they must not only learn to make this identification but go even further. In order to be proficient, they must actually learn to think in terms of these forms. For the common and rather simple loci studied, the form of the equation must come to suggest the associated locus, and conversely, the geometric conception of the locus must come to suggest the form of the associated equation. From the outset it should be made clear and kept continually before the students that there is a duality of form and a dual purpose in analytic geometry. The students should be reminded continually that every locus studied is represented by an equation and that every basic equation studied represents a locus. The two fundamental problems of analytic geometry are (1) to learn to associate with each locus studied the characteristic form of its equation and (2) to learn to infer from the type form of the equation the nature and properties of the locus which it represents. These fundamental considerations are not always made clear to students, yet they form the very foundation of understanding. To learn that the equation $(x - h)^2/a^2 + (y - k)^2/b^2 = 1$ represents an ellipse is certainly necessary, but it is not sufficient. Unless the student understands what a and b and h and k represent geometrically, he will have little conception of the form or the properties of the ellipse whose equation is given him as $(x - 5)^2/37 + y^2/10 = 1$. On the other hand, unless he does know this type of equation, he will not be able to write down readily the equation of the ellipse whose center is at (5,0) and whose major and minor axes have lengths of $2\sqrt{37}$ and $2\sqrt{10}$, respectively. Each kind of locus studied in elementary analytic geometry has a characteristic form of equation. The association between the properties of the locus and the form of its type equation needs to be emphasized continually. Indeed, broadly speaking, one may say that this association constitutes one of the fundamental objectives of the course.

The moment a student attains real appreciation of how a statement of geometric restrictions can be translated into an equation and of the fact that the one is the counterpart of the other, he has made a major breakthrough. If he really understands what has taken place, it should then be apparent to him that a powerful new instrument has been added to his working equipment. Once the geometric problem has been translated into algebraic terms, he has at his command all the formal rules and procedures of algebra to assist him. He may manipulate the equation formally and at will without, for the moment, giving any thought to the geometric implications. Then if in the end he can reinterpret the results of his algebraic work back into terms of geometric relations, he will have accomplished his geometric investigation by analytic methods, and these often are more powerful than the direct methods of synthetic geometry.

To some students this concept comes quickly; to others it does not. Yet it is so much the essence of analytic geometry that every effort should be made to ensure that all the students come to appreciate it. Repeated explanations and illustrations will doubtless be necessary, and penetrating questions can often do much to clarify this dual representation and give point to the analytic treatment of geometric problems. Success in this will give the students genuine insight into the method of analytic geometry. Without such insight they often resort to mere profitless memorization and miss the whole point of the course.

Determining the locus of an equation In the beginning, the locus of an equation is usually determined by plotting a considerable number of points whose coordinates satisfy the equation and then drawing a smooth curve through the points. Students have no trouble with this because they have had some experience with graphing and they understand what they are doing. However, despite the fact that constructing the graph of a given equation is one of the fundamental problems of analytic geometry, this method of point-by-point plotting has severe and fundamental limitations. One of them is that it is tedious and slow, and in general one can never plot all the points on the locus. Another is that it is inexact, and exactness is often of great importance, as, for example, in determining the coordinates of points of intersection of loci. Thus, by meticulous point-by-point plotting, a student might obtain carefully made graphs of the loci represented by the equations $x^2 + y^2 + 4x - 5 = 0$ and $y = 1 + 2x$. If the graphs are very carefully made to a large scale, he might well conclude that the one represents a circle and the other a straight line. Indeed, he might decide from observation that the circle has its center at $(-2,0)$, that its radius is 3 units in length, and that one of its points of intersection with the straight line is $(-2,-3)$. He might even make a good estimate of the coordinates of the other point of intersection.

Nobody would question the value of this intuitive observational type of analysis on the part of the students. It should by all means be encouraged because it offers a splendid means for clarifying concepts and interpretations and for stimulating interest in the work. But on the other hand, the students must not be left with the impression that this is sufficient. They must be made to realize that even if all these conjectures were exactly correct (and they might well be so in this case), the graph itself could offer no confirmation of such exactness and that the only way the exact values can be known, or the estimates can be tested for exactness, is through solving simultaneously the equations of the two loci. It should be pointed out also that this observational method cannot bring to light the essential relations between the form of the equation and the general and special properties of the curve.

This is but a single example of the fundamental limitations inherent in this point-by-point plotting of the graphs of equations. Its weakness is that it does not utilize algebraic considerations to determine the characteristics of the locus or to relate them to the form of the equation. It should be explained that the objective of the course is to learn how to apply analytic methods which are at the same time less tedious, more powerful, and more revealing than those of point-by-point plotting and mere observational analysis of graphs. Such analytic methods can bring to light not only the exact coordinates of intersection points but also such characteristics as the coordinates of intercepts, limitations on the extent of the locus if such limitations exist, symmetry or lack of symmetry with respect to either or both of the coordinate axes or to the origin, and discontinuities in the case of horizontal or vertical asymptotes.

Most of the loci usually studied in analytic geometry belong to a few simple types: the straight line, the circle and the conic sections, and a few of the higher plane curves. Each of these types of locus can be defined in terms of certain characteristic geometric properties, and the type equation of each can be identified by certain algebraic characteristics. To infer the type of curve that is represented by one of these equations it is necessary to be familiar with the algebraic characteristics of the equations of the various types of curves. One needs to know, for example, that in a rectangular coordinate system a first-degree equation in two variables is the algebraic representation of a straight line and that a quadratic equation in two variables is to be identified with some type of conic section, the type and specific properties being determined by the form of the equation and by the coefficients of the various terms. In like manner the type equations in polar coordinates of some of the simpler curves must be known if the type of locus is to be inferred from the equation without point-by-point plotting.

Teachers need to focus the attention of their students on these considerations, giving numerous illustrations and considerable practice in identifying simple types of curves and determining their properties merely by examination of their equations. It is a matter which deserves more than the scant attention that is too often accorded to it.

Determining the equation of a locus The general problem of setting up the equation of a locus which is described geometrically usually implies an ordered sequence of steps. The details are sometimes a bit complicated but the pattern is not, at least in the case of the simpler loci studied in elementary analytic geometry.

The first step consists in making a suitable sketch or working drawing. This is done by drawing a pair of axes to represent the coordinate plane, sketching in all given fixed points or lines with their coordinates or equations shown, drawing in a representative point of the locus with variable coordinates (x,y) indicated, and drawing suitable line segments connecting the point (x,y) with the fixed points or lines described in the given conditions. Lengths of these segments may now be denoted (often through their projections on the axes) in terms of the coordinates of the fixed points and the general point of the locus or in terms of the distances of the general point (x,y) from given fixed lines.

Once these details are depicted in a reasonably good sketch, it is not difficult to translate the required conditions from their verbal form into an equation. This equation will always involve the coordinates of the representative point of the locus and the coordinates of some given fixed point or points described in the initial conditions. The actual setting up of the equation in this manner constitutes the second and final step. For the simpler loci it is usually an easy matter. Ordinarily it will involve distances which will be denoted on the sketch and which are either to be equated to each other or set into an equation with given constants. Once the student has identified these distances on the sketch and has noted their forms in terms of coordinates, it is a simple matter to translate them directly into the required equation.

The essential simplicity of this procedure, however, may not be immediately apparent to the students. Through their very familiarity with the subject, teachers are prone to assume too much on this score. These ideas are still new and unfamiliar to most students, and it cannot be assumed that the students will assimilate and use them successfully without help. A few who have unusual perception and insight will have no difficulty, but for most students the topic will probably require careful and repeated explanation, pointed questions, numerous illustrations, and a considerable amount of supervised practice with well-chosen problems.

Example: Determine the equation of the locus of points the sum of whose distances from two fixed points is 10 units.

$$\text{Distance from } P_1 + \text{distance from } P_2 = 10$$
$$d_1 + d_2 = 10$$
$$\sqrt{(x - x_1)^2 + (y - y_1)^2} + \sqrt{(x - x_2)^2 + (y - y_2)^2} = 10$$

Thus the equation is set up without difficulty. To be sure, it is not yet in its simplest form, but the rest is a matter of routine algebraic detail which can be carried on as such, without any further immediate concern about geometric considerations.

One other matter which may well be clarified at this time is the question, which some student will probably ask: "Why shouldn't we write $d_2 = \sqrt{(x_2 - x)^2 + (y - y_2)^2}$ instead of $\sqrt{(x - x_2)^2 + (y - y_2)^2}$?" This often bothers students, and the question is a good one which deserves careful attention. There are two ways of answering it. One is that d_1 and d_2 are thought of here as undirected distances, so we are concerned only with the absolute values of their components, and $|x - x_1| = |x_1 - x|$. In this case, then, the order of the subscripts makes no difference. If we were concerned with d_1 and d_2 as directed distances with correspondingly directed components, the forms $x_2 - x$ and $y_2 - y$ would be the proper ones to use so long as the point P was in a position such as that shown on the following page. In this case, for example, $x - x_1$ would be positive, and $x - x_2$ would be negative. It should be pointed out, however, that P might be in such a position that both

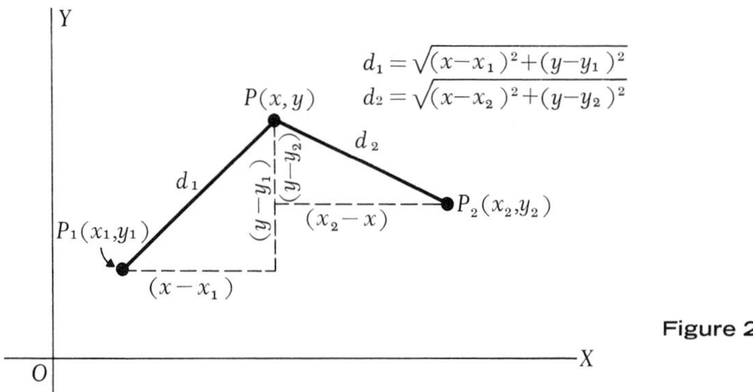

Figure 20-1

$x - x_1$ and $x - x_2$ could both be positive, or both negative. In any case, since only the squares of these distances are involved, the order of subscripts would be immaterial, because obviously $(x - x_2)^2 = (x_2 - x)^2$. Since this is true, by keeping the subscripts in the same order the form of the equation is made somewhat simpler and easier to remember.

There is one other matter that should be discussed in connection with this problem. It should be pointed out that in Figure 20-1 the positions of P, P_1, and P_2 were taken essentially at random and so lead to the most general form of the equation. However, unless the coordinates of the fixed point are definitely specified, no harm is done by taking the axes in the most convenient position with respect to the given points. This is usually done in textbooks in developing the type form of the equation for this locus. If the given points P_1 and P_2 are taken on an axis with the origin midway between them, the form of the equation is simplified and important properties of the locus come to light readily from inspection of the equation.

Thus, by using conventional notation and assuming that d_1 and d_2 are not both zero, the fixed points may be designated as $(c,0)$ and $(-c,0)$, so that the distance between them is $2c$. Then if the sum $d_1 + d_2$ is designated as $2a$ for convenience, we immediately have $d_1 + d_2 = 2a$, and, unless $d_1 = 0$ or $d_2 = 0$, this means that $2a > 2c$. Then

$$d_1 + d_2 = 2a = \sqrt{(x + c)^2 + y^2} + \sqrt{(x - c)^2 + y^2}$$

By straight algebraic manipulation this yields the equation

$$\frac{x^2}{a^2} + \frac{y^2}{a^2 - c^2} = 1$$

and by designating $a^2 - c^2 = b^2$, the equation becomes $x^2/a^2 + y^2/b^2 = 1$.

Not only is this the simplest form for the equation of an ellipse, but the equation itself yields directly some important geometrical information about the locus. If $|a| \neq |c|$ and if $y = 0$, the equation becomes

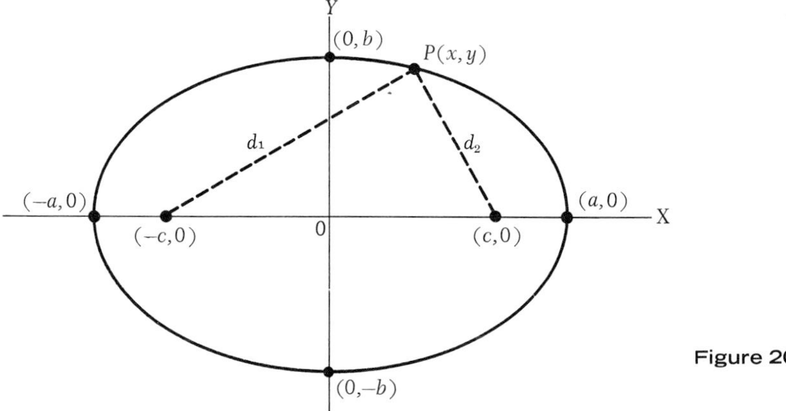

Figure 20-2

$x^2/a^2 = 1$, which yields the coordinates of the vertexes as $(a,0)$ and $(-a,0)$. If we take $x = 0$, we get $y = \pm b$, and we have the ordinates of the points where the locus intersects the y axis. Thus with the equation in the form indicated above, the intercepts on the axes are known at a glance, and the coordinates of the foci are immediately determined from the defining relation $c = \sqrt{a^2 - b^2}$. The extent of the locus is readily determined, since if $|x| > |a|$ or if $|y| > |b|$, the values of y and x, respectively, become imaginary. The form of the equation makes it clear that there are no horizontal or vertical asymptotes, and the absence of any odd powers of either variable shows that the locus is symmetrical with respect to both axes and, hence, with respect to the origin. Hence this equation provides immediately all information needed to sketch the graph of this locus and locate its foci. It is of interest, in passing, to consider the special case that arises when $c = 0$ and the ellipse becomes a circle, and to notice how easily one reaches this conclusion by merely inspecting the equation.

It is most important, of course, for the students to understand that this simplest form of the equation represents only a very special case, i.e., when the center is at the origin and the major axis lies on the x axis. Under other circumstances the equation will be more complicated and can be thrown into this simple standard form and made to yield the geometrical information which the simple form gives only through the laborious work of referring the coordinates and the equation to a new system of axes which *are* in standard position with respect to the curve.

In the beginning most students need some supervised practice in setting up equations of loci. A little extra time explicitly on this in the early part of the course can develop insight and appreciation which will pay good dividends later on. The same insight which enables a student to translate geometrical conditions into algebraic equations is likely also to be a powerful aid to him in inferring geometrical conditions when the equations are given.

The straight line The objectives for the study of the straight line may be set down as follows:

1. To understand that a straight line is uniquely determined if any of the following pairs of conditions is specified:
   a. Two fixed points through which it passes.
   b. One fixed point through which it passes with a given slope.
   c. Its intercepts on the two axes, provided these are not both zero. This is a special case of (*a*).
   d. Its slope and its intercept on one of the axes. This is a special case of (*b*).
   e. Its slope and its directed distance from the origin.
2. To know and be able to write or develop the type equation of a straight line for each of these sets of conditions.
3. To recognize and identify the equation of a straight line from the form and the characteristic constants in its equation.
4. To be able to convert the equation of a line from one type form into another type form.

Development of the formulas for the first four sets of conditions given under (1) should involve little difficulty; it requires only the proportionality property of similar triangles and the concept of slope as the tangent of the angle of inclination. Nearly all students can follow the details of these developments readily when they are given by the instructor. A good many, however, do not know how to proceed if they are called on to redevelop these formulas, and the common reason is that they do not have clearly in mind where the details are leading. They have seen the trees but not the forest. They have verified the details without sensing clearly the goal and the plan. If in their explanation instructors would rapidly sketch out the objective and the plan of each development before filling in the details, it would do much to clarify the derivations in the students' minds and give point and direction to the sequence of detailed steps.

Students should learn and use the names commonly given to these formulas: the two-point form, the point-slope form, the intercept form, the slope-intercept form, the normal form. These names are helpful in at least three ways. First, the name suggests the proper approach to the derivation of that particular formula because it indicates the geometric considerations which define the line and so suggests the form of equation which is stated in terms of those characteristics. Second, if a line is known to satisfy a given pair of independent conditions and if the student knows the various forms, the appropriate one can be written down at once. The given conditions can then be inserted to complete the equation of the particular line in question. Third, if the type form of a given equation can be recognized, the associated name suggests at once what geometrical characteristics of the line can be inferred directly from the equation.

Of course the importance of the type forms of the equation of a straight line lies not only in setting up specific equations from given geometric conditions but also in interpreting particular equations in terms of geometric properties of the locus. This consists in identifying certain constants in the equation directly with the particular geometric information which they afford. Thus the equation $y + 7 = (5/9)(x - 4)$ should yield at once the information that this particular line passes through the point $(4, -7)$ and that its slope is $5/9$. Students need practice in this sort of interpretation, but as a rule they get too little of it. Such interpretation can do a great deal to build understanding and appreciation of the geometrical significance of key elements in the equation of a locus, and this is one of the over-all objectives of analytic geometry. It need not take a great deal of time, but it does need to be given more attention than it has customarily received in the past.

The normal form for the equation of a straight line will require some special attention to both its derivation and its interpretation. Here a new element, the *normal axis*, is introduced, and along with it the meanings of the *normal intercept* and the *normal angle* (the angle of inclination of the normal axis). Different textbooks exhibit somewhat different methods of deriving the normal equation of a line. A few writers favor the use of direction cosines as the counterpart of what is done in solid analytic geometry, but most textbooks develop the formula in terms of the sine and cosine of the normal angle. These are subsequently transformed into terms of numbers which form the constants in the equivalent linear form of the equation.

Derivation of the normal form is not so simple as the derivation of the other four forms. Here the students may experience difficulty even in following some of the details. However, this difficulty again can be traced in large measure to their failing to sense the aim and the plan, i.e., to their failing to see what this form of the equation can tell them that the other forms cannot. This is one of the hard spots in this course, but the normal form is also one of the most important of all the formulas, since it gives the distance from a straight line to a given point. Few students can successfully get all that they should about it merely from the discussion in their textbooks. Whether the students are held responsible for redeveloping this formula or not, they need to know its form, understand the geometrical significance of its elements, and understand how to reduce an ordinary linear equation in two variables to its normal form in order to find the normal angle and the normal intercept of the straight line which it represents. These aims will be achieved about in proportion to the clearness of the instructor's explanations and the opportunity afforded to the students for interpretation of particular equations.

Families of straight lines: parameters The equation of any straight line, given in one of the standard forms, contains certain constants, and these constants determine which one of all the straight lines in the coordinate plane is represented by that equation. When all the necessary constants are explicitly given, the line is determined uniquely. For example, the equation $y = 7x - 2$ represents the one line whose slope is 7 and whose y intercept is -2. The equation $y = 7x + 1$ represents a different line. It has the same slope as the first one but a different y intercept. Similarly, the equation $y = 4x - 2$ represents still another line. This line has the same y intercept as the first one but a different slope.

The general form of the slope-intercept equation of a line is usually written $y = mx + b$, where m and b represent constants which in turn represent respectively the slope and the y intercept of the line. In this general form, however, it is not specified what constant values m and b have. Numerical values may be assigned to m and b at will. By keeping m fixed and assigning different values to b, we can represent arbitrarily many lines having different y intercepts. In other words, we represent a set of parallel lines, one line for each value assigned to b. For example, the equation $y = \frac{1}{2}x + b$ represents the set of all parallel lines in the plane with slope $\frac{1}{2}$. Similarly, by keeping b fixed but assigning different values to m, we represent a set of lines all of which have the same y intercept but different slopes. For example, the equation $y = mx + 2$ represents all lines in the plane (except, of course, the y axis, whose slope is undefined) which pass through the point (0,2).

Letters such as m and b in the slope-intercept formula are called *arbitrary constants*, or *undetermined constants*, or *parameters* in the formulas. Whenever a slope-intercept equation contains a single such parameter, as, for example, $y = 7x + b$ or $y = mx + 5$, it represents a whole *set* or *system* or *family* of lines. These will all differ in the one characteristic ascribable to that parameter, and they will all be alike in the characteristic determined by the fixed constant. Such a system is a *one-parameter* family of lines. If both m and b are allowed to take on all admissible values, we get a *two-parameter* family of lines which clearly includes every line in the plane except the y axis and those lines parallel to it. No value for m can be ascribed to these lines.

These notions represent generalizations which are important for more than one reason. In the first place, they are important because they *are* generalizations. As such they can deepen the student's understanding and expand his mathematical horizons. Moreover, if properly explained, they seem to fascinate many students and increase interest in the subject as a whole. They afford unlimited opportunity and variety for illustrations which are easy to give and which can be most illuminating. Then, too, the notions of parameters and families of loci are pervasive concepts which will play important roles later on in this and subsequent courses. They should be solidly established and firmly clinched here where they are first encountered.

The general equation of the straight line We have seen that any straight line which is not parallel to the y axis can be represented by an equation of the form $y = mx + b$, where m and b are parameters. For every line which can be represented in this way, y is a *function*. That is to say, for any given values of m and b, a unique value of y is determined for each admissible value of x. If $m \neq 0$, the line is oblique to the coordinate axes and is the graph of the linear function $y = mx + b$ $(m \neq 0)$. If $m = 0$, the line is parallel to the x axis and is the graph of the *constant function*, since its equation is $y = 0x + b$, or simply $y = b$. Thus any line in the plane which is not parallel to the y axis is the graph of an equation of the form $y = mx + b$.

There is one set of straight lines, however, whose members cannot be represented by equations of the form $y = mx + b$. This is the set of lines parallel to the y axis. For such lines the slope is undefined, and the equation of such a line is $x = k$, where k is some real number. Therefore any line parallel to the y axis is the graph of a *relation* but not of a *function*. Its mapping from x to y is not one-to-one but one-to-many.

Thus the straight lines in the coordinate plane fell into three classes: (1) those not parallel to either axis and whose type equation is $y = mx + b$, with $m \neq 0$, (2) those parallel to the y axis and whose type equation is $x = k$, and (3) those parallel to the x axis and whose type equation is $y = b$. At first thought it might appear that there could be no type equation that could properly represent lines in all three of these classes. However, we shall see that this is not the case.

Consider the general equation of the first degree in x and y: $Ax + By + C = 0$, where A and B are not both zero. If neither is zero, the solution of this equation is $y = (-A/B)x + (-C)/B$, which is of the form $y = mx + b$, where $m = -A/B$ and $b = -C/B$. Hence the general equation $Ax + By + C = 0$ clearly represents a straight line. If $A \neq 0$ and $B \neq 0$, the line is oblique to the coordinate axes. Moreover, if $A = 0$ and $B \neq 0$, this equation becomes $y = -C/B$, which is the equation of the constant function whose graph is a line parallel to the x axis. Finally, if $B = 0$ and $A \neq 0$, the equation $Ax + By + C = 0$ becomes $x = -C/A$, which is the graph of the relation $x = k$. Hence the general equation $Ax + By + C = 0$ with A and B not both zero is the general equation of the straight line, since it subsumes the equation of a line parallel to the y axis (the graph of a relation) as well as that of any line not parallel to the y axis (the graph of a function).

The circle

Of all the loci studied in elementary analytic geometry, the circle probably offers the least difficulty to students. Once they have grasped the idea of how the equations of loci are set up in terms of coordinates from given geometric conditions, they are not likely to experience difficulty either in setting up the equation from given geometric conditions or in inferring the essential geometric properties of the locus from its equation.

Once the coordinates of the center and the length of the radius are known, a sketch shows clearly that a single application of the distance formula is sufficient to give the equation. The right triangle constructed as shown in Figure 20-3 yields at once the equation

$$(x - h)^2 + (y - k)^2 = r^2$$

This is the generalized standard form in terms of the three parameters h, k, and r and thus represents a three-parameter family of circles.

When a fixed value is assigned to just one of these parameters, say to r, the equation still defines a family of circles in the plane; but this is a two-parameter family of circles because, although r is fixed, both h and k may take on any values whatever. It is the family of all circles lying in the plane and having a fixed radius but arbitrary centers. There are also one-parameter families of circles in the plane. For example, if r is arbitrary while both h and k are fixed, we get the family of concentric circles whose center is at (h,k). Thus when specific values are assigned to one or two of the three parameters, the family of circles defined by the equation is less inclusive than that defined when all three parameters are left arbitrary. On the other hand, when all three parameters are assigned particular values, a single or unique circle is defined. With these understandings established, it is easy for students to see why the simplest form of all is obtained when both h and k are assigned the value zero.

Figure 20-3

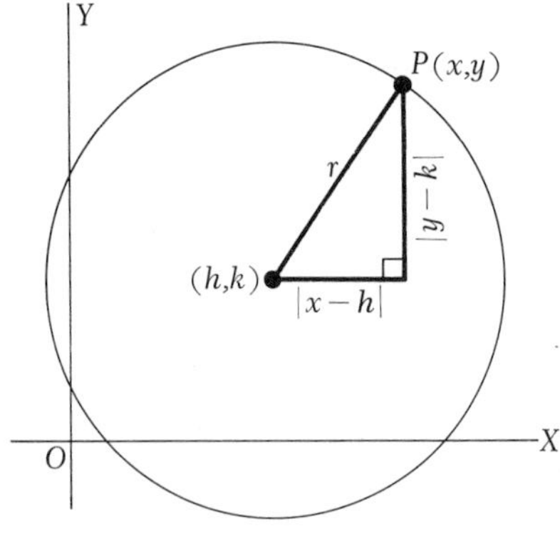

This, in turn, provides motivation for study of the translation of axes, which may well be undertaken at this time. It should involve no serious difficulty on the part of the students, provided the instructor makes three things clear: (1) the reason for making the translation (to simplify the equation of the locus), (2) the fact that the general coordinates (x,y) must now be replaced by expressions involving coordinates $(x'y')$ referred to the new axes, and (3) why, in the case of the circle, these replacements are of the form $x = x' + h$, $y = y' + k$, where h and k are the coordinates of the center as referred to the original axes. Once these points are grasped, and with h and k being known, the translation is easily effected and the simplified equation is obtained.

It must be remembered, however, that this is but one side of the coin. Interpretation of the new equation is no less important than its derivation, and there can be little assurance of full understanding unless both receive proper emphasis. Suppose, for example, that the equation of a particular circle is given as $(x - 4)^2 + (y + 1)^2 = 26$ and that through the usual transformation procedures associated with the translation of axes the students arrive at the simpler equation $x'^2 + y'^2 = 26$. Unless they can interpret this new form correctly, little will have been gained. They need to be made to understand that this change in the form of the equation does not imply any change in the characteristics of the circle itself (the location of the center and the length of the radius) because these remain invariant for any particular circle, but merely that $x'^2 + y'^2 = 26$ should be interpreted as $(x' - 0)^2 + (y' - 0)^2 = 26$. In a word, the students must understand that the equation $(x - 4)^2 + (y + 1)^2 = 26$ and $x'^2 + y'^2 = 26$ are merely two representations of the same circle when referred to two sets of respectively parallel axes one of which has its origin at the center of the circle.

There are certain problems associated with the study of circles which do sometimes prove troublesome for students. Among those which commonly are included in current textbooks may be mentioned the following:

1. Deriving the equation of the circle through three given points not on a line (understanding why it takes three such points to provide the necessary data, why these data are also sufficient, and why the routine work of deriving the equation takes the form it does)
2. Finding the equation of a family of circles through the points of intersection of two given circles
3. Finding the length of a tangent to a given circle from a given point outside the circle

This catalog of associated problems is by no means exhaustive but it is representative. It may be expected that each of the problems mentioned will prove troublesome to some students. Also, it is almost certain that trouble with such problems stems from lack of insight, i.e., from failure to understand what the problem really is, what the given conditions imply, and what the plan is for using what is known to establish what is required.

To explain the approach to these problems successfully, attention should be focused first on the things of major concern rather than upon details of notation. By rapidly sketching out the problem and the plan of attack in broad, bold, rapid strokes, it should be possible to get across to the students a basic understanding of both in a very short time. The explanation may be lacking in elegance, and it may be superficial from the standpoint of rigor and completeness of detail. Elegance and rigor can come later. The important consideration at the moment is that the explanation shall present clearly and as simply as possible the essential considerations and the line of argument leading to the conclusion or solution. Any student who has a modicum of skill in algebraic technique can fill in the necessary details and the proper notation once the essential framework has been built in his mind. Textbooks, however, too seldom use this approach. Authors do not always bother to make clear this framework and plan at the outset, and this is probably responsible for much of the trouble which students experience in this subject. Most students can supply necessary detail to complete a proof or to solve a problem when they have the plan of work well in mind more successfully than they can discover the plan by studying the detail.

As a single example of a broad, quick outline of a plan, we shall consider the problem of finding the length of a tangent, say, from the point (9,2) to the circle $(x - 2)^2 + (y + 1)^2 = 17$. A sketch can be quickly made to show that the required distance t is merely one leg of a right triangle, Figure 20-4. The length of the other leg, being the radius of the circle, is known, and the length of the hypotenuse can be found immediately by use of the distance formula. It is clear, then, that

$$t^2 + (\text{radius})^2 = (\text{hypotenuse})^2$$

and this equation can easily be solved to give the length t which is required.

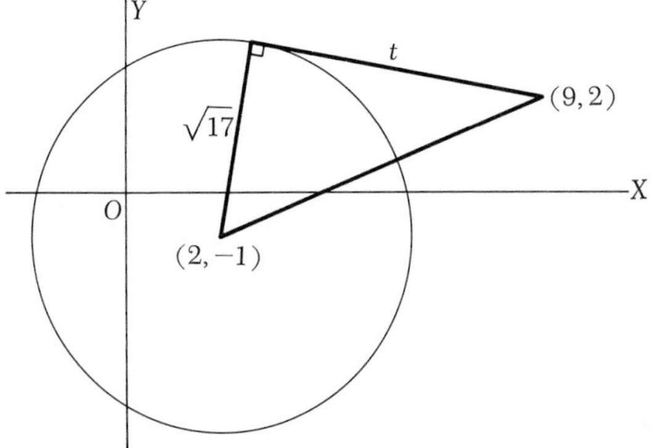

Figure 20-4

This explanation can be given in about two minutes at the chalkboard. It involves no subtleties. There is no need for students to ask, "Why do you do it that way?" It lays out the essential plan for attacking this problem in simple, familiar terms, and once the students grasp the plan they should have no trouble in supplying the details needed for the numerical solution.

The conic sections Study of the conic sections has traditionally occupied a place of prominence in analytic geometry. It represents an important class of loci, and the study of these loci affords excellent opportunity for applying analytic methods as well as for determining the properties of the loci and their equations. The latter should include awareness of both the common characteristics which bind them together in a class and the special characteristics which distinguish them from each other.

If the coordinate axes are chosen to give the equations of these loci in simplest form, if the definitions are given very clearly and are supplemented by good illustrations, and if the geometrical meanings and the notation of the characteristic elements are made perfectly clear, then any intelligent student should attain these objectives without serious difficulty. The explanations of the instructor, however, are very important here, as, indeed, they are throughout this course. Many students do not read very effectively. Moreover, diagrams in the textbooks are necessary and good as far as they go, but they are static. It is hard even to suggest motion and variation in a textbook diagram. On the other hand this can be done well by the instructor sketching at the chalkboard and actually building the diagram and discussing it at the same time. In this way he can give the locus a dynamic character and can highlight the things he wants to emphasize much more effectively than an author can simply by placing an already-made diagram in the textbook. Thus the ability of the instructor to "chalk-talk" effectively is a tremendous asset, and it can do a great deal to promote understanding and facilitate learning.

There is practically complete uniformity among textbooks in their definitions of the parabola, which invariably seem to be in terms of the equality of two distances. The ellipse and the hyperbola are initially defined in most textbooks in terms of the sum or difference of two distances, but this is not always the case. Some authors prefer to define first the eccentricity in terms of the *ratio* of two distances and then the ellipse and hyperbola in terms of the eccentricity. Doubtless each of these approaches has its advantages, and it is not possible to state categorically that either is better than any other.

Logically the two approaches have equal validity. From the viewpoint of the immature learner there are some considerations which seem to favor the former. Perhaps this is because the sum or difference of two distances can be visualized and apprehended more readily than their ratio. Also, this way of defining these loci stresses the fact, from the outset, that an ellipse or hyperbola has two foci. On the other hand, the directrixes play no part in this definition. In contrast, the second approach ensures that these concepts are established at the outset but gives no hint of the important property upon which the first definition is based. If time permits, it is well, at least for one of these curves, to give derivations from both definitions and to point out that the equations and the properties at which one arrives in the two cases are equivalent.

Study of the hyperbola involves some special features which have to be given special attention. In the ellipse both axes terminate in the curve itself; in the hyperbola they do not. Moreover, in the ellipse the major axis (the line segment joining the vertexes) is always longer than the minor axis; their counterparts (the transverse and conjugate axes) in the hyperbola are not subject to this condition. The length of the conjugate axis can be depicted only by means of an auxiliary rectangle which in turn is determined by the curve and its asymptotes. The asymptotes themselves and their relation to the locus require special definition and study, and the considerations involved are often troublesome to students. The directrixes of a hyperbola lie between the vertexes, but the vertexes of an ellipse lie between the directrixes. Every hyperbola has associated with it a conjugate hyperbola, but there is no counterpart of this for the ellipse.

Students sometimes forget or confuse these numerous and special characteristics and the conventional notation generally used. It has been found helpful to have them make type diagrams showing these things geometrically in typical form and actually refer to these diagrams if they need to do so when working problems. A specimen diagram of this sort is shown in Figure 20-5.

The general equation of the second degree in x and y takes the form $Ax^2 + Bxy + Cy^2 + Dx + Ey + F = 0$ and always represents a conic section or a degenerate or limiting case of a conic, provided A, B, and C are not all zero. In an equation of this kind the coefficients can reveal much information about the nature of the locus, sometimes even through casual examination, if the students have been taught how to discover it. This fact needs to be emphasized. Thus if $B = 0$ while A and C are not equal and neither is zero, the curve will be an ellipse or hyperbola. If A and C have like signs, the curve will be an ellipse; if they have unlike signs, the curve will be a hyperbola. In either case the principal axes of the locus will be parallel to the coordinate axes. If $B = 0$ and either $A = 0$ or $C = 0$ but not both, the curve is a parabola with its axis parallel to one of the coordinate axes.

On the other hand, if $B \neq 0$, then the locus is a conic with its princi-

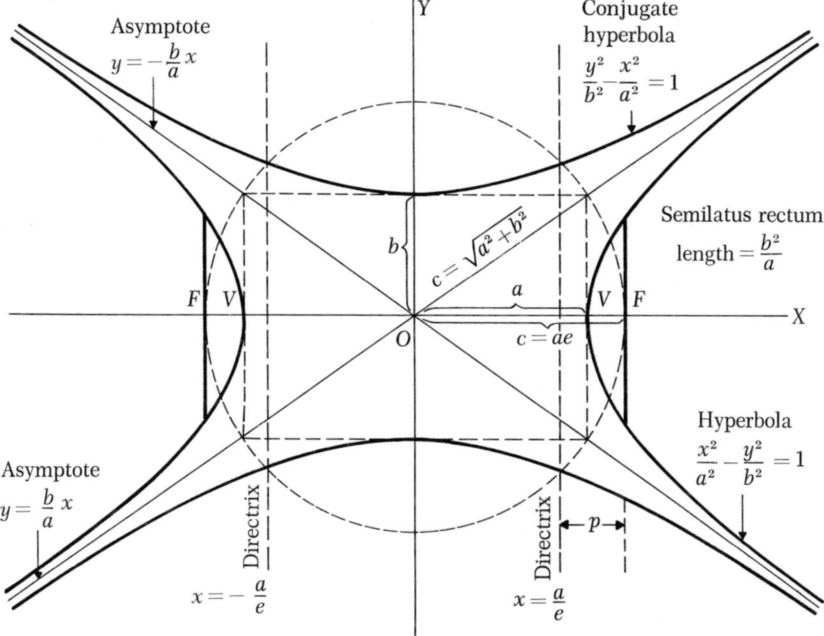

Figure 20-5

pal axis inclined at some angle θ to the x axis. In such cases the product term can be removed and the equation correspondingly simplified by the transformation known as "rotation of axes." This is not inherently difficult, but it is a long, laborious process if done by direct substitution of the transformation formulas and the subsequent algebraic work necessary to determine the angle θ for which $B = 0$. The labor of simplifying such equations can be greatly reduced by having the students use the not-too-well-known relation $\tan 2\theta = B/(A - C)$. This should be proved, of course, and most textbooks contain proofs of this theorem, but the relation is often neglected, even though it provides an efficient means for simplifying such equations.

With one exception[3] both the translation and rotation of axes have the effect of changing the coordinates of every point on the locus and consequently of changing the form of the equation of the locus. On the other hand, these transformations do not change the metric or geometrical properties of the locus at all. These properties are said to be *invariant* under the transformations indicated. It is also true that, when the equation is written in the general form

$$Ax^2 + Bxy + Cy^2 + Dx + Ey + F = 0$$

[3]The single exception is that the coordinates of the origin are not changed under rotation about the origin.

the values of certain expressions involving some of the coefficients remain unaltered by these transformations. Thus the coefficients of the second-degree terms are invariant under the translation of axes. Under rotation, the sum of the coefficients $A + C$ of the terms in x^2 and y^2 is invariant, and the value of the expression $B^2 - 4AC$ is also invariant under rotation. In view of the fact, noted above, that A, B, and C are individually invariant under translation, it follows that the values of the expressions $A + C$ and $B^2 - 4AC$ are invariants under both transformations.

This rather remarkable fact is interesting, if for no other reason than just because it is so. Additional interest, however, attaches to the invariant $B^2 - 4AC$ because it provides a means of identifying the type of conic represented by the equation. It is sometimes called the *characteristic* of the equation $Ax^2 + Bxy + Cy^2 + Dx + Ey + F = 0$ and is designated by the symbol Δ. If $\Delta < 0$, the equation represents an ellipse; if $\Delta = 0$, the equation represents a parabola; if $\Delta > 0$, the equation represents a hyperbola. This criterion does not distinguish between typical conics and their degenerate or limiting forms, but it is useful anyway, and the students should not be left unaware of it.

Lack of space makes it impossible to discuss all the important matters or all the interesting problems associated with the conic sections. To mention a few of them, there are the matters of examining the equation for evidence of symmetry, limitations on extent of the locus, axis intercepts, and horizontal and vertical asymptotes; the invariants in the equation under translation and rotation of axes; the interesting correspondence exhibited by the inequalities associated with the invariant $B^2 - 4AC$ and the eccentricity; the polar equations of the conics; and physical applications of the loci.

Each of these topics has its points of difficulty for students. However, the trouble lies not so much in the difficulty of the concepts or considerations themselves as in the fact that most students cannot readily translate into concepts what they read in their textbooks. The role of the instructor as an expositor in helping to make these ideas emerge and stand out is most important. The instructor who is able to highlight key ideas and help his students crystallize them and make them stand out in their minds will have contributed greatly to their understanding.

The many interesting aspects and properties of the conics could easily lead one to devote a disproportionate amount of time to their study. It must not be forgotten, however, that there are other parts of the course which are also interesting and important and which must not be neglected. Therefore, in the study of the conic sections it may be necessary at times to sacrifice the merely interesting to make time for things that are relatively more important in relation to subsequent work.

Families of conics In a previous section attention was called to the fact that the equation of the general linear function, $y = mx + b$, involves two parameters, m and b. When specific values are assigned to both parameters, the resulting equation defines one particular line. If, however, specific values are not assigned to both parameters, the equation represents a whole family of lines. Similarly, the general equation of the circle, $(x - h)^2 + (y - k)^2 = r^2$, involves the three parameters h, k, and r. Assignment of a number to any one parameter places one restriction on the set of circles defined by the equation. Assigning a number to a second parameter imposes a second restriction on the set, and if a number is assigned also to the third parameter, this imposes a final restriction on the set, and the equation selects and defines one particular circle out of all the circles in the plane.

Like considerations apply to the equations of all conic sections. The equation of the general conic is $Ax^2 + Bxy + Cy^2 + Dx + Ey + F = 0$ where A, B, and C cannot all be zero. Since all coefficients may be divided by any nonzero coefficient, it is evident that the equation contains five independent constants, or parameters. Assignment of values to any number of these parameters imposes specific restrictions on the characteristics of the conic represented. For example, if $A = C \neq 0$ and $B = 0$, the equation may be written as $x^2 + y^2 + px + qy + s = 0$, or, in equivalent form, as $(x - h)^2 + (y - k)^2 = r^2$.

Probably most students sense this in a vague sort of way, but too often textbooks and teachers neglect to focus attention deliberately and explicitly on the generalizing effect of the parameters and the restricting effect of replacing any of the parameters by particular constants. The concept of families of curves and of the role of parameters in relation to the descriptions of families of curves is important to a full understanding of analytic geometry. Teachers have a responsibility for bringing this concept out of the shadow of vagueness and for giving their students a clear appreciation of its meaning and its implications.

Polar coordinates Probably the key to success in working with polar coordinates and polar equations is to develop clear understandings of the meaning and terminology and the relations between polar and rectangular coordinate systems. To this end it is a good thing to start by sketching a set of axes as for an ordinary rectangular system and putting in a single point P in a representative position, giving it the usual rectangular coordinates (x,y). The pole and the polar axis are identified with the origin and the positive half of the x axis. The line segment joinging P with the origin is the radius vector r, and the angle it makes with the polar axis is the vectorial angle θ. Reference to the diagram, Figure 20-6, gives at once the fundamental relations between the two systems of coordinates. It should be pointed out, however, that

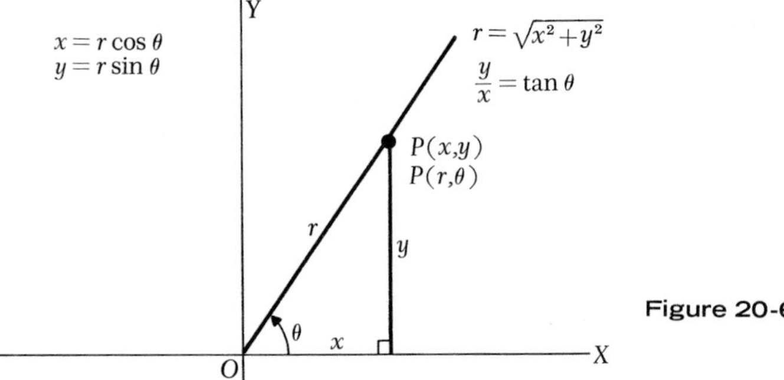

Figure 20-6

whereas the rectangular coordinates of a point are unique, the polar coordinates are not. For example, the point whose rectangular coordinates are (1,1) has infinitely many pairs of polar coordinates: $(\sqrt{2},45°)$, $(\sqrt{2},405°)$, $(\sqrt{2},-315°)$, $(-\sqrt{2},225°)$, etc.

With these things in mind students should easily convert an equation from rectangular form to polar form simply by making the appropriate substitutions. Thus $y^2 = 3 + 6x$ becomes $(r\sin\theta)^2 = 3 + 6(r\cos\theta)$. In similar fashion one may convert an equation from polar form to rectangular form. Thus $r = 10\cos\theta$ becomes $\sqrt{x^2+y^2} = 10x/\sqrt{x^2+y^2}$, whence $x^2 + y^2 - 10x = 0$.

It is usually easier for students to make these conversions than to plot the graphs of equations in polar form. Typically, constructing a graph requires a point-by-point plotting of enough points to give a good sketch of the locus, and this in turn requires the construction of a table of values of θ and r. Except for the simplest equations this table may need several columns. For example, let it be required to plot the graph of

$$r = 1 + 4\cos 2\theta$$

The table should be similar to the following one.

θ	2θ	$\cos 2\theta$	$4\cos 2\theta$	$1 + 4\cos 2\theta$
0°	0°	1	4	5
30°	60°	1/2	2	3
45°	90°	0	0	1
60°	120°	−1/2	−2	−1

etc.

A good many students have to be shown how to plan and construct such a table. Also, they frequently need to be reminded that, as in the present case, even if r is given as a function of 2θ, the values of r must be plotted against the corresponding values of θ itself, not against the values of 2θ. The use of polar-coordinate paper facilitates the actual plotting, though good sketches can often be made by use of a protractor or even by careful estimates of the sizes of the angles.

Certain additional considerations may be helpful to students in determining characteristics of some loci given in polar coordinates, and they should be emphasized:

1. If r occurs only in the form r^2, then the curve will be symmetrical with respect to the pole.
2. If an equivalent equation is obtained when θ is replaced by $180° - \theta$, then the curve is symmetrical with respect to the 90° axis. An example of this situation occurs with the locus of the equation $r = 3 \sin \theta$. It may be noted that this particular replacement is a sufficient but not a necessary condition for symmetry about the 90° axis, since the same symmetry will result if we replace θ by $540° - \theta$, $900° - \theta$, $-(180° + \theta)$, etc.
3. If an equivalent equation is obtained when θ is replaced by $-\theta$, the curve is symmetrical with respect to the polar axis. Thus the locus of $r = 3 \cos \theta$ is symmetrical in this way. From considerations such as those above, it can be seen that this particular replacement also is a sufficient but not a necessary condition for symmetry about the polar axis.
4. The intercepts on the lines whose equations are $\theta = 0°$, 90°, 180°, 270°, and 360° can usually be found readily.
5. Sometimes values of θ for which r becomes infinite can be found easily, and this fact may be very helpful in sketching.
6. Finding maximum and minimum values of r, with the corresponding values of θ, can be helpful in determining the extent of the curve. Limitations on the extent of the curve may also often be determined by solving the equation for r in terms of θ to see whether there are any values of θ that will make r imaginary. Thus, for the locus $r^2 = \cos \theta$ we find that r is imaginary for $90° < \theta < 270°$.
7. Sometimes the form of the locus is revealed by converting the equation from polar to rectangular form. Thus the equation $r = 10 \cos \theta$ becomes $x^2 + y^2 = 10x$, which is clearly the equation of a circle.

To determine points of intersection of the graphs of two polar equations, one may solve the equations simultaneously for the two variables, as is done with equations in rectangular form. However, in seeking common solutions for two polar equations it is always advisable to plot the graphs of the equations. This may suggest at once solutions that can be tested directly in the equations. But even more importantly, it will sometimes reveal one or more points of intersection that are not brought to light in the algebraic solution of the equations. A simple example of this is the pair of equations $r = 2 \sin \theta$ and $r = 2 \cos \theta$. Algebraic solution gives $\tan \theta = 1$, $\theta = 45°$, $r = \sqrt{2}$. Thus it yields only a single point of intersection, $(\sqrt{2}, 45°)$. The graph will show, however, that the pole also lies on both curves.

Parametric equations The one concept which will be essentially new or unfamiliar to students when they take up the study of parametric equations is the notion of a parameter used as an auxiliary variable. In previous work there has been exhibited a direct relation between the independent and dependent variables, the one being expressible as a function of the other. It is not at all hard for students to recognize that each of the original variables, say x and y, may in certain cases be defined as some function of a third variable; it simply is a new idea to which they need to become accustomed. The best way to bring about this feeling of familiarity is by having tables and graphs made for several rather simple cases. Such pairs of equations as $x = t$, $y = 1/t$ or $x = t^2$, $y = 3 + t$ can be used to illustrate how the table of values is to be formed and the corresponding values of x and y are to be used to plot points on the locus.

Converting a pair of parametric equations into an equivalent equation in rectangular form by eliminating the parameter is usually interesting to students. It strengthens the feeling of a direct relation between the original variables, even though it may not be apparent in the parametric forms in which they are both expressed. For some loci this rectangular form of the equation may be very simple. For example, the parametric equations $x = 5 \cos \theta$, $y = 5 \sin \theta$ yield the equation $x^2 + y^2 = 25$, which is recognizable immediately as a circle with center at the origin and radius 5 units. But even though the rectangular form will not always be simple, students should work out a number of such cases as a means of giving explicit form to the implicit relation between the original variables. A useful by-product of this is some excellent incidental practice in algebraic manipulation and equation solving.

Students often ask, "Why use the parametric form at all? Why not simply use the rectangular form?" In answer to this question it should be pointed out that there may be several possible advantages in using the parametric equations. For one thing, the parametric equations may sometimes convey more information than the rectangular equations, as in the case of the trajectory of a projectile. Thus they are often needed in physics and engineering. Again, in calculus the derivatives of some functions can be obtained more easily from parametric equations of the loci than from the rectangular equations. However, the principal reason for the use of parametric equations in analytic geometry lies in the fact that for certain loci the parametric equations are simpler than the rectangular equations. Indeed, for some loci parametric equations can be set up directly from the geometrical descriptions of the loci, although it may be impossible to set up the rectangular equations for the loci directly. In such cases the rectangular equation may be derived from the parametric equations if the parameter can be eliminated. The cycloid curves are fairly simple examples of such loci.

Loci in three-dimensional space Lack of time usually imposes severe limitations on the study of space loci in analytic geometry, and justice can be done to this topic only in a separate course. At the same time it is highly desirable that some topics from three-dimensional geometry be included in the elementary course. In particular, if time permits, it is desirable to give some attention to the analytic geometry of the straight line, the plane, cylindrical surfaces and projections on the coordinate planes, surfaces of revolution with emphasis on the sphere, and discussion of surfaces from their traces and their intercepts. This admittedly is a large order, and it can be regarded as realistic only if time is economized in the earlier part of the course; but it is a worthwhile goal to attempt to reach.

There are a good many places in solid analytic geometry where students may be expected to have difficulty. Many of these difficulties stem from three general limitations which are common to many students: (1) poor space imagination and inability to visualize three-dimensional figures well, (2) inability to sketch good diagrams to represent space configurations realistically, and (3) difficulty in translating given geometric conditions into algebraic form and in interpreting the latter in terms of the former. Lacking adequate skill in these things, students are tempted to rely on sheer memorization, and this contributes nothing to understanding. There are, of course, certain formulas which do need to be memorized in the interest of economy, but to memorize a formula without understanding how it is derived and what it means is of little lasting benefit. The ability of the instructor to draw good diagrams and to explain how the formulas are derived, what they mean, and how they are used is of crucial importance.

Textbooks on analytic geometry are remarkably uniform in respect to the topics of solid analytic geometry which they include. These may be listed substantially as follows:

General

Projections of a line segment on the coordinate axes
Distance between two points
Direction cosines of a straight line
Direction numbers of a straight line
Angle between two lines
Conditions for parallel and perpendicular lines
Definition of a locus in space

The Plane

Normal equation of a plane
General equation of a plane
Conditions for parallel and perpendicular planes

Intercepts and traces of a plane
Angle between two planes
Distance from a plane to a point
Intercept equation of a plane

The Straight Line

Projection equations of a line
Symmetric equations of a line
Two-point equations of a line

Nonplanar Surfaces

Cylindrical surfaces; projecting cylinders
Surfaces of revolution
Quadric surfaces in standard position
Study of surfaces through their traces and their intercepts

There is a high degree of essential sequence in the development of these topics, and thorough development of all of them would require more time than is available in many cases. Often a choice may be forced upon the instructor, and such a choice is not easy. It would require careful weighing of the topics with respect to their relative importance in future use. From this viewpoint the following would surely find a place among those chosen: (1) the general forms and significance of the equations of the plane, cylindrical surfaces, and the standard quadric surfaces; (2) the characteristics of a surface of revolution, as these are exhibited through the equation of the surface; (3) the study of surfaces through study of their intercepts and their traces in the coordinate planes and in other, parallel planes.

Solid analytic geometry is rather hard for most students. Nearly every topic will have its potential difficulties. In view of the pressure of time, it is especially important that the instructor examine each topic in detail and plan his discussion to highlight the important ideas, bypass the nonessential ideas, and try to find ways to make the hard parts understandable.

Analytic geometry and calculus Since about the middle of the century there has been a growing tendency to merge analytic geometry and calculus into a single course. Actually, some attempts at this were made even earlier, but the tendency has been more pronounced since that time. Indeed, judging from the titles of the new textbooks for calculus published since 1960, it would appear that the combined course is becoming the typical course. The close relation of the two subjects and the role of analytic geometry in calculus provide strong arguments for such a combination. The principal advantages claimed for fusing the two into a single course appear to be about as follows:

1. It makes possible an earlier introduction of some of the fundamental notions, techniques, and applications of calculus, thus making calculus available as an instrument for the study of physics earlier than would otherwise be the case.
2. Certain parts of the work in analytic geometry itself can be simplified by the use of derivatives.
3. Many of the topics of analytic geometry that are needed in calculus can be taken up just before they are needed, and in this way time can be gained.
4. The simultaneous study of the two subjects gives the students a feeling of their interrelation.

These arguments present a good case for a combined course, and there is some evidence that it is being viewed with increasing favor. However, upon examination of some of the textbooks, it is not always apparent that there is much organic correlation of the two subjects. Sometimes the parts on analytic geometry are distinctly subordinated to the calculus, and sometimes their relation to immediately subsequent parts of the calculus is far from clear. Probably the intention in these books is to consider the calculus course as the prime objective and develop only such parts of the analytic geometry as are needed for the calculus. Undoubtedly some time can be saved in such an arrangement. It can be expected that the combined course will be tried out extensively in the years ahead.

EXERCISES

1. Why should stress be laid on the concept of *ordered* pairs of numbers in connection with the coordinates of points in a plane, and of *ordered* triples of numbers in connection with the coordinates of a point in three-space?

2. Give a brief but clear exposition of the derivation of the formula for the distance from one point to another in terms of the coordinates of these points (a) in a plane and (b) in three-dimensional space. Use the chalkboard and make clear the importance of the notion of the projection of one line on another in this connection.

3. Explain the derivation of the general point-of-division formulas for the coordinates of a point dividing a given line segment in a given ratio. Show why the midpoint formulas are merely special cases of the general formulas.

4. One main problem of analytic geometry is to infer certain geometric properties of loci from the equations of these loci without actually drawing the graphs. Give an example. Point out what elements of the equation provide geometric information directly and list information they provide.

5. What advantage is there in reducing the equations of straight lines, circles, and conic sections to standard forms? Illustrate the advantage.

6. Describe the loci represented by each of the following equations:

$$y = \frac{3}{4}x - 2 \qquad \frac{x}{5} + \frac{y}{8} = 1$$

$$(x - 5)^2 + (y + 2)^2 = 9$$

7. It has been said that one really understands the method of analytic geometry when and only when he has attained a genuine appreciation of the interrelations between loci and their equations. Comment on this.

8. Explain and illustrate the steps to be taken in setting up the equation of a locus when the geometrical conditions are specified.

9. Set up the equation for the locus of a point which is three units further from the point (2,3) than it is from the point (9,6). Follow the outline of steps described in the preceding exercise.

10. If (x_1,y_1) and (x_2,y_2) are two points, the distance between them can be found by using either of these formulas:

$$d^2 = (x_1 - x_2)^2 + (y_1 - y_2)^2 \text{ or}$$
$$d^2 = (x_2 - x_1)^2 + (y_2 - y_1)^2$$

Explain why the order of the subscripts makes no difference in this case.

11. What geometric information about a conic section is yielded by the equation $x^2/a^2 + y^2/(a^2 - c^2) = 1$? Be explicit.

12. Write the five type forms for the equation of a straight line. In each of these identify the two parameters and explain what information each parameter gives about the line.

13. What advantage is there in knowing how to write or how to interpret the equation of a straight line in the various forms called for in exercise 12. Be specific.

14. Write the intercept form and the slope-intercept form for the equation of the line $7x + 2y + 1 = 0$. What geometric information would each provide?

15. Derive the normal form for the equation of a straight line and interpret it. Illustrate your interpretation by an example.

16. Describe the locus of points represented by each of the following: $y = 3 + \frac{1}{2}x$, $y < 3 + \frac{1}{2}x$, $y > 3 + \frac{1}{2}x$, $y \leqq 3 + \frac{1}{2}x$.

17. Why does the family of lines represented by $y = mx + b$ not include the y axis or any straight line perpendicular to the x axis? Does it include all other straight lines in the plane? Explain.

18. Write the equation of the family of circles whose centers are at (−3,8).

19. Describe the family of circles represented by the inequality

$$(x - 5)^2 + (y - 2)^2 \leqq 4$$

20. Describe the family of circles represented by the inequality

$$(x - a)^2 + (y - b)^2 \neq 12$$

Does this include all circles in the plane?

21. Explain how to find the length of a tangent from a fixed point to a given circle whose equation is given.

22. What is meant by the eccentricity of a conic section? What is the numerical value of the eccentricity of a circle?

23. The general equation of the second degree in x and y can be written in the form $Ax^2 + Bxy + Cy^2 + Dx + Ey + F = 0$. Give the name of the locus in each of the following cases: $B = 0, A > 0, C < 0$; $B = 0, A = C$; $B = 0, A > 0, C > 0, A \neq C$; $B = 0, C = 0, A \neq 0$. Are the principal axes of all these curves necessarily parallel to the coordinate axes?

24. In the general equation above, let $B \neq 0$ and $A \neq C$. What information does this provide about the principal axis of the curve? Can the curve be a circle?

25. Derive and explain the transformation formulas for the translation of axes. For what purposes are these used in simplifying equations of the second degree in two unknowns? Illustrate.

26. Derive and explain the transformation formulas for the rotation of axes. For what purpose are these used?

27. What is meant by saying that the geometric or metric properties of a locus are invariant under translation and rotation of axes?

28. The expression $B^2 - 4AC$ is invariant

under translation and rotation of axes. Explain how the value of this invariant provides a means for identifying at once the kind of conic section represented by any particular equation of the second degree in x and y.

29. Take the equation of some locus given in rectangular coordinates and transform it into polar coordinates.

30. Transform $r = 5 - 3 \cos \theta$ into rectangular coordinates. Note that the polar equation is the simpler of the two.

31. Assume that you are teaching a course in analytic geometry and that you have time for about twelve lessons on solid analytic geometry at the end of the course. What topics do you think you would include?

32. Much of the study of three-dimensional surfaces is made through studying the intercepts of these surfaces on the axes and the traces of these surfaces in the coordinate planes and planes parallel to the coordinate planes. Take the equation of some nonplanar surface and show how this can be done.

BIBLIOGRAPHY

Ballantine, J. P., and A. P. Jerbert: Distance from a Line, or Plane, to a Point, *American Mathematical Monthly*, **59** (1952), 242–244.

Bourne, S.: Coordinate Geometry from the Vector Point of View, *American Mathematical Monthly*, **59** (1952), 245–248.

Boyer, C. B.: History of Analytic Geometry, *Scripta Mathematica* (1956).

Bureau of Secondary Curriculum Development: "Mathematics 10-11-12" (Albany, N.Y.: The State Education Department, 1959), pp. 12, 19, 30–32, 69, 72–74.

Commission on Mathematics, Report of: "Program for College Preparatory Mathematics" (New York: College Entrance Examination Board, 1959), pp. 25–28.

———: "Appendices" (New York: College Entrance Examination Board, 1959), pp. 36–58, 120–139.

Dubisch, Roy, with the Assistance of Vernon E. Howes: "The Teaching of Mathematics" (New York: John Wiley & Sons, Inc., 1963), pp. 71–80.

Evans, Trevor, and Bevan K. Youse: "How to Solve Problems in Analytic Geometry and Calculus," vol. I (Englewood Cliffs, N.J.: Prentice-Hall, Inc., 1961).

Eves, Howard: The Names 'Ellipse,' 'Parabola,' and 'Hyperbola,' *Mathematics Teacher*, **53** (1960), 280–281.

Gallego-Diaz, J.: A Note on the Conics, *American Mathematical Monthly*; **66** (1959), 225–228.

Greenspan, Donald: On Rapid Sketching of Polar Curves, *Mathematics Teacher*, **50** (1957), 267–271.

Hoffman, A. A. J., and Roger Osborn: Concerning Simultaneous Solutions of Polar Equations by the Graphical Method, *Mathematics Teacher*, **53** (1960), 133–134.

Huff, G. B.: On Defining Conic Sections, *American Mathematical Monthly*, **62** (1955), 250–251.

Karst, O. J.: Two Methods for Finding the Angle of Rotation, *American Mathematical Monthly*, **63** (1956), 416–417.

Lange, Luise: Deriving the Equations of the Sections of a Cone, *American Mathematical Monthly*, **63** (1956), 488–491.

Levy, H.: Analytic Geometry and the Calculus, *American Mathematical Monthly*, **68** (1961), 925–927.

Meserve, Bruce E., and Max A. Sobel: "Mathematics for Secondary School Teachers" (Englewood Cliffs, N.J.: Prentice-Hall, Inc., 1962), pp. 241–289.

Porges, A.: The Rotation of Axes, *American Mathematical Monthly*, **64** (1957), 37.

———: Rapid Sketching of a Conic, *American Mathematical Monthly*, **64** (1957), 41–42.

Rippey, Robert M.: Rotation of Axes with Complex Numbers, *Mathematics Teacher*, **53** (1960), 197.

Schaaf, William L.: "Basic Concepts of Elementary Mathematics" (New York: John Wiley & Sons, Inc., 1960), pp. 88–96.

Yates, Robert C.: The Cardioid, *Mathematics Teacher*, **52** (1959), 10–15.

TWENTY-ONE

The teaching of calculus

RECENT YEARS have witnessed an increasing concern over the problems of grade placement and instructional procedures as they are related to calculus. Examples can be found in which the first course in calculus is presented at the sophomore college level, at the freshman college level, and in the upper grades of the senior high school. At present the major evidence seems to support the freshman level of instruction as the most generally accepted interpretation of proper grade placement for this extremely important mathematical experience. There are those, however, who feel that the basic concepts and techniques of the calculus are of such great significance that they should be placed in the high school program so that the course would precede the student selection which takes place in passing from high school to college; some even feel that certain aspects of the calculus should be incorporated in the instructional program prior to the selection of the later years of the high school.

Of no less consequence to the program of effective instruction in calculus is the problem of subject-matter selection, organization, and presentation. There are arguments, with supporting textbooks, that the first course in calculus should be a coordinated program of calculus and analytic geometry. Just as strong arguments, and with supporting texts, call for a course devoted entirely to the development of calculus concepts and techniques preceded by a separately organized strong course in analytic geometry. Similarly, there are those who argue for the physical orientation out of which the basic concepts, principles, and techniques of differentiation and integration are shown to evolve. Others argue just as strongly that first one should develop such calculus properties in their theoretical structure and then proceed to the mechanics of their physical application. Regardless of which of these two widely different instructional patterns is followed, a strong mixture of an intuitive approach followed by a rigorous deductive treatment seems to be the generally accepted pattern of development.

In such a context of debatable issues related to grade placement and instructional pattern it is not surprising that the present decade finds a professional literature much richer than in previous years in articles dealing with problems related to the teaching of calculus.

Calculus in high school Since the turn of the century, various leaders in mathematical education have advocated that elements of the calculus be introduced in the last year of the senior high school. It was not contemplated that this work should comprise the complete course in differential and integral calculus usually offered in the junior college. It was thought that such a course would require more adequate mastery of algebra, trigonometry, and analytic geometry than could be reasonably expected at the end of the eleventh grade. Rather, the idea was that just as there are certain parts of trigonometry that are simple enough to be successfully understood by junior high school students, so there are certain parts of calculus which can be understood by twelfth-grade students, even if they do not have all the prerequisites for a complete systematic course.

This position was well stated in the suggestions of the National Committee on Mathematical Requirements regarding calculus in the high school:[1]

> In connection with the recommendations concerning the calculus, such questions as the following may arise: Why should a college subject like this be added to a high school program? How can it be expected that high school teachers will have the necessary training and attainments for teaching it? Will not the attempt to teach such a subject result in loss of thoroughness in earlier work? Will anything be gained beyond a mere smattering of the theory? Will the boy or girl ever use the information or training secured? The subsequent remarks are intended to answer such objections as these and to develop more fully the point of view of the committee in recommending the inclusion of elementary work in the calculus in the high school program.
>
> By the calculus we mean for the present a study of *rates* of change. In nature all things change. How much do they change in a given time? How fast do they change? Do they increase or decrease? When does a changing quantity become largest or smallest? How can rates of changing quantities be compared?

[1]Report of the National Committee on Mathematical Requirements, "The Reorganization of Mathematics in Secondary Education" (Boston: Houghton Mifflin Company, 1923), pp. 57–59.

These are some of the questions which lead us to study the elementary calculus. Without its essential principles these questions cannot be answered with definiteness.

The following are a few of the specific replies that might be given in answer to the questions listed at the beginning of this note: The difficulties of the college calculus lie mainly outside the boundaries of the proposed work. The elements of the subject present less difficulty than many topics now offered in advanced algebra. It is not implied that in the near future many secondary school teachers will have any occasion to teach the elementary calculus. It is the culminating subject in a series which only relatively strong schools will complete and only then for a selected group of students. In such schools there should always be teachers competent to teach the elementary calculus here intended. No superficial study of calculus should be regarded as justifying any substantial sacrifice of thoroughness. In the judgment of the committee the introduction of elementary calculus necessarily includes sufficient algebra and geometry to compensate for whatever diversion of time from these subjects would be implied.

The calculus of the algebraic polynomial is so simple that a boy or girl who is capable of grasping the idea of limit, of slope, and of velocity, may in a brief time gain an outlook upon the field of mechanics and other exact sciences and acquire a fair degree of facility in using one of the most powerful tools of mathematics, together with the capacity for solving a number of interesting problems. Moreover, the fundamental ideas involved, quite aside from their technical applications, will provide valuable training in understanding and analyzing quantitative relations—and such training is of value to everyone.

With reference to the content of such a course as was contemplated, the committee stated[2]

The work should include:

a. The general notion of a derivative as a limit indispensable for the accurate expression of such fundamental quantities as velocity of a moving body or slope of a curve.

b. Applications of derivatives to easy problems in rates and in maxima and minima.

c. Simple cases of inverse problems; e.g., finding distance from velocity, etc.

d. Approximate methods of summation leading up to integration as a powerful method of summation.

e. Applications to simple cases of motion, area, volume, and pressure.

Work in the calculus should be largely graphic and may be closely related to that in physics; the necessary technique should be reduced to a minimum by basing it wholly or mainly on algebraic polynomials. No formal study of analytic geometry need be presupposed beyond the plotting of simple graphs.

It is important to bear in mind that, while the elementary calculus is sufficiently easy, interesting, and valuable to justify its introduction, special pains should be taken to guard against any lack of thoroughness in the fundamentals of algebra and geometry; no possible gain could compensate for a real sacrifice of such thoroughness.

[2]*Ibid.*, pp. 54–55.

It should also be borne in mind that the suggestion of including elementary calculus is not intended for all schools nor for all teachers in any school. It is not intended to connect in any direct way with college entrance requirements. The future college student will have ample opportunity for calculus later. The capable boy or girl who is not to have the college work ought not on that account to be prevented from learning something of the use of this powerful tool. The applications of elementary calculus to simple concrete problems are far more abundant and interesting than those of algebra. The necessary technique is extremely simple.

This Report of the National Committee gave some impetus to the inclusion of certain concepts and techniques from calculus in the high school program. The attempts, however, were scattered and sporadic, and, while a certain amount of interest and success was reported in some instances, there appears to have been little general enthusiasm for the idea. No important subsequent report made any recommendation concerning a course in calculus for the high school until the Joint Commission, in its 1940 report, suggested "introducing study of differentiation, limited to polynomials, with applications to slopes, maxima and minima, rates of change, velocity, acceleration, and related problems" in connection with algebra in the twelfth grade.[3] Much more recently (1959) the College Entrance Examination Board's Commission on Mathematics recommended ". . . that well-staffed schools offer their ablest students a year of college-level calculus and analytic geometry as recommended in the Advanced Placement Program." It also pointed out that few high schools at present are sufficiently well staffed to teach a full course of college-level calculus effectively. The commission deprecated the practice of exposing high school students to formal calculus for a short time.[4] Concurrently with this report the Secondary School Curriculum Committee issued its report in which a college-preparatory program for grades nine through twelve was proposed. As a portion of the recommendation for the twelfth grade this sentence occurred:[5] "Some schools might find desirable a strong course in analytic geometry and calculus as preparation for the Advanced Placement examinations." This proposal was received with mixed feelings.[6]

A recent report which deals with this major problem is that of the

[3]Joint Commission of the Mathematical Association of America and the National Council of Teachers of Mathematics, "The Place of Mathematics in Secondary Education," *Fifteenth Yearbook* (Washington, D.C.: National Council of Teachers of Mathematics, 1940), pp. 97–98.

[4]College Entrance Examination Board, Report of the Commission on Mathematics (New York: College Entrance Examination Board, 1959), pp. 14–15.

[5]Secondary School Curriculum Committee, Report of, The Secondary Mathematics Curriculum, *Mathematics Teacher,* **52** (1959), 405–406.

[6]See, for example, articles by Blank, Ferguson, Hildebrandt, and Neeley, listed in the bibliography of this chapter.

Cambridge Conference on School Mathematics.[7] In their discussion of the mathematics curriculum for grades seven through twelve they proposed two topical outlines for the content of the program.[8] Each outline contains "a logically complete course" in analysis (calculus) for grades eleven and twelve, with one of them being prefaced on a "heuristic and brief introduction to the calculus in the 9th grade." This entire program for grades seven through twelve is posited on one proposed for the elementary grades (kindergarten through sixth) which was designed to give the student "a thorough grounding in both arithmetic and intuitive geometry." The philosophy supporting this entire program seems to have been that the high school program in mathematics should provide: (1) "the foundations upon which applications to the sciences, engineering, and mathematics itself are built"; (2) opportunity for students to become informed in those areas of mathematics which "have become part of what every person should know in order to understand the complex world in which he lives"; and (3) to give those students who drop out of the mathematical program of instruction some opportunity to develop an understanding and appreciation of the structure and usefulness of mathematics.

Importance of emphasizing fundamental concepts Any thorough mastery of the calculus has two fundamental aspects, namely, (1) the understanding of the basic concepts that are involved in the development of the subject and familiarity with the many special formulas that are needed and (2) the acquisition of ability and ready facility in the use of these special formulas and methods. Both are fundamental to a balanced mastery of the subject.

It is possible for an individual to acquire a high degree of skill in the latter aspect of the work without understanding much about what he is doing or why he is doing it. Indeed this situation is often found. The relatively enormous amount of formal work that must be done begets a tendency on the part of instructors to emphasize this aspect, often to the detriment of understanding. Many students acquire high proficiency in performing difficult feats of formal differentiation or integration without having any clear conception of the meaning of a derivative or an integral or of the real significance of what they are doing. Proficiency in this mechanical aspect of the work, although it is indispensable, tends to produce complacency on the part of both student and teacher. This is not unnatural, but it is unfortunate. Such a

[7]Cambridge Conference on School Mathematics, Report of, "Goals for School Mathematics" (Boston: Houghton Mifflin Company, 1963).

[8]*Ibid.*, pp. 43–46.

one-sided development indicates not a balanced mastery of the subject but rather mere proficiency in rote performance. It is precisely the sort of thing against which so much criticism of the teaching of elementary algebra has been directed. The reason we hear so little of this criticism leveled at the teaching of calculus is simply that the matter of improving the teaching of college mathematics has as yet received too little attention, at least in the way of published suggestions.

It is true that most of the actual work of differentiation and integration must be carried on by formal methods and that these must be learned and mastered by the students. At the same time, these formal methods and devices can be developed in such a way as to give them meaning, and this should be regarded as a major responsibility of the instructor. The student who gains a real understanding of the meanings of function,[9] variation, increment, limits,[10] infinitesimals, continuity, derivative, rates, maxima and minima, an integral as an antiderivative and as a summation, indefinite and definite integrals, and other basic concepts will derive a far richer experience and a far more adequate basis for further work in either applied or theoretical mathematics than the student who works by rote alone.

The teaching of variables, limits, and infinitesimals

Variables, limits, and infinitesimals are primary concepts in calculus, and serious effort should be made to ensure that the students will have a good understanding of their meanings. Normally the students will have gained considerable familiarity with the meanings of "function" and "variable" through their previous work in trigonometry and algebra. Care should be taken that variables and constants are thought of as symbols and not as quantities: a *variable* is a symbol which may represent any one of a set of values called its *domain,* or *replacement set;* a *constant* is a symbol which represents the same value throughout a particular discussion, or, maybe better said, if the replacement set for a symbol contains only one element the symbol is called a *constant.*

The student should become familiar with the concept of a set (domain, range) of values and with the nature of, and the distinction between, *arbitrary constants (parameters)* and *absolute constants.*

It is important that a clear distinction between independent and dependent variables be made. Furthermore, when these concepts are used in the context of a defined functional relation, they should be associated respectively with the domain and the range of the function.

[9]See "Insights into Modern Mathematics," *Twenty-third Yearbook* (Washington, D.C.: National Council of Teachers of Mathematics, 1957), Chap. 8.

[10]*Ibid.*, Chap. 7.

Consider a set of ordered pairs (x,y) and define a function as a rule which specifies the functional relationship between the members of the set of first elements x and the members of the set of second elements y, or which associates with each element of the set of first elements exactly one element from the set of second elements. Then a symbol (in this case x) which may represent any member of the set of first elements is called the *independent variable*, and a symbol (in this case y) which may represent any member of the set of second elements is called the *dependent variable*.

The function itself (defined above as a rule) may also be thought of as the set of ordered pairs (x,y), where for each x in the domain of the function (i.e., each value of the independent variable) the corresponding element y in the range of the function (i.e., the corresponding value of the dependent variable) is determined by the rule which defines the function. Thus the dependent variable represents the set of values of the function over its domain.

In spite of the presumption of familiarity with these notions, it is advisable at the beginning of the course in calculus to review them, giving numerous and varied illustrations involving both algebraic and transcendental functions. It is not anticipated that students will have much difficulty in establishing these concepts, but as a means of ensuring understanding some practice should be given in identifying independent variables and dependent variables and in building tables and making graphs to illustrate the variation of each of these and the relationship of functions to their independent variables. The student should also become thoroughly familiar with the generalized functional notation. He should learn to recognize $f(x)$ in all its variations and with all its implications.

The concepts of a limit[11] and an infinitesimal and the application of these concepts are vital to an understanding of the calculus and are indeed the foundation stones upon which the calculus is built. These are the concepts which make the study of calculus fundamentally different from any other areas of study which the student may have experienced. They provide the foundation for basic extensions in the domain of mathematical operations and lead to the introduction of the two new inversely related operations, differentiation and integration. As a result the student will not only have to become proficient in the manipulative techniques of these two operations but also learn the new methods which they provide for attacking problem situations.

The difficulty which students most often experience in this connection is not so much in acquiring intuitive concepts of limits and infinitesimals as in understanding the technical definitions. The concept of

[11]*Ibid.*, Chap. 7.

a limit can be illustrated by various situations drawn from elementary geometry or algebra. For example, let there be a polygon inscribed in or circumscribed about a circle. As the number of sides is increased, the difference between the length of the perimeter of the polygon and the circumference of the circle obviously becomes less than it was at the outset. As the process is indefinitely continued, the difference between these two lengths becomes and remains less than any value we may care to assign; i.e., the difference approaches zero as a limit. In other words, the length of the perimeter of the polygon becomes always more nearly equal to the circumference of the circle; the one approaches the other as a limit.

Again, let there be a series of terms of the form $1/2^n$, where $n = 0, 1, 2, 3, 4$, etc. The first term of this series is 1, and, if successive terms are added, the sum of the series becomes $1 + 1/2 + 1/4 + 1/8 + \cdots$. The addition of successive terms brings the sum nearer and nearer to 2. No finite number of terms can make the sum equal to 2, but by taking n sufficiently large, the difference between the sum of the series and 2 can be made as small as desired. Thus we say that, as the number of terms is indefinitely increased, the sum approaches 2 as a limit.

The fundamental idea involved in these illustrations is that of a variable difference, diminishing progressively toward zero, between the value of the varying function and the constant which it approaches as a limit. This idea should be emphasized in all the illustrations that are used, because it is only when it is well understood that the somewhat technical definition of a limit, as it is usually given, takes on real meaning. In general, when a variable or function approaches zero as a limit, it is called an "infinitesimal." It must be made clear that an infinitesimal is not merely "a very small quantity" but a *variable* quantity which can be made smaller than any previously assigned value, no matter how small this value may be; i.e., it approaches zero as a limit. It was the failure to sense this distinction which prevented the ancients from understanding the real nature of continuous variation, and it is precisely the conception of this distinction which enables us to understand the nature of continuity, infinitesimals, and limits, which are the very taproots of calculus.

With this concept of an infinitesimal clearly in mind, the limit of a variable may now be technically defined as follows: If x is a variable and a is a constant and if it is true that, as the values which x may take so change that $|x - a|$ becomes and remains less than h, where h is an arbitrarily small positive quantity, then x is said to approach a as a limit.[12]

[12]The symbol $|x - a|$ is to be read "the absolute value of $x - a$" or "the numerical value of $x - a$." It is to be interpreted as meaning the difference between x and a without regard to sign.

Evidently this definition can be extended to define the limit of a function. Thus: If $f(x)$ is a function of x, and a and A are constants, and if for any arbitrarily chosen small positive quantity d there exists another small positive quantity h such that, when $|x - a| < h$, it is true that $|f(x) - A| < d$, then $f(x)$ is said to approach A as a limit as x approaches a as a limit.

Every effort should be made to make these definitions meaningful to the students. To this end graphic and numerical illustrations should be used in the explanations, which should be more than perfunctory. These definitions are of great importance in that they provide the analytical means of defining the important property of continuity of a function or a variable as well as the indispensable concept of a derivative.

The students should be made familiar with the customary notation used in connection with limits. They should also become familiar with certain theorems concerning limits. These may be, and usually are, given without proof, but their statements should be accompanied by ample illustrative explanation to ensure that their meanings are really understood by the students.

Teaching the meaning of a derivative and a differential

The late Prof. Louis Ingold once said that whoever really understands the meaning of a derivative has learned the most of calculus. He referred, of course, not to operational facility but rather to the fact that an understanding of the derivative underlies the conception of what calculus is all about. The importance of the concept of a derivative and the associated concept of a differential cannot be too greatly emphasized. Therefore, if calculus is to be taught with the idea of giving the students something more than a rote mastery of its techniques, it is highly important that every effort be made to give them at the outset a clear understanding of these two fundamental concepts.

A derivative might be thought of as the instantaneous rate of change of a function with respect to its independent variable. The usual method of defining the derivative in terms of increments, ratios, and limits, with variation in details, is substantially the same in nearly all textbooks. Like many careful definitions, however, this one is difficult for many students to comprehend. There seems to be something mysterious about the process of passing to the limit and of determining the limiting value of the ratio of the increment of the function to the increment of the independent variable when the latter approaches zero as a limit. The student reasons that, if the one increment approaches zero, the other will also approach zero, and the ratio will be reduced in this way to the form 0/0 which, in form, appears meaningless because of the division by zero.

In order to clarify this concept, it is absolutely necessary to make the student understand that the increment of the dependent variable can and must be expressed *in terms of the independent variable and its increment* and that the ratio of the increment of the dependent variable to the increment of the independent variable thus becomes a function of the increment of the independent variable. Furthermore, it should be emphasized that it is the limit of this ratio that is sought and not the ratio of the limits of the numerator and denominator as separate functions. Thus let $y = f(x)$ be a continuous function of x. If x takes on an increment Δx, then y will also take on an increment Δy, such that

$$y + \Delta y = f(x + \Delta x)$$

or $\Delta y = f(x + \Delta x) - y$, or $\Delta y = f(x + \Delta x) - f(x)$. In this way Δy is expressed entirely in terms of x and Δx. Then the ratio $\Delta y/\Delta x$ becomes $[f(x + \Delta x) - f(x)]/\Delta x$, which is reducible in general to a determinate form and should be so reduced *before the limit is taken*. Graphic representations such as are given in nearly all textbooks help greatly in giving concreteness to the concepts of these increments and ratios, and full advantage should be taken of this means of illustrating and clarifying the concepts.

The notation also is confusing to the students, who are puzzled about such questions as these: What is the distinction between Δy and dy and between Δx and dx? Why is it that Δy is not in general equal to dy, while Δx is in general equal to dx? How does Δy become dy? What does dy mean? If dy/dx is defined as the limit of $\Delta y/\Delta x$ as Δx approaches zero, why can it not be thought of as a quotient? Are dy and dx infinitesimals? Are Δy and Δx infinitesimals? What is the distinction between an infinitesimal and an increment and between an increment and a differential?

It is recommended that the notation dy/dx not be used for the derivative until after the concept of differential is developed. A good notation for the derivative of y with respect to x is $D_x y$; similarly, the derivative of $f(x)$ with respect to x would be $D_x f(x)$. There are other good notations that do not introduce the confusion of thinking of a quotient where there is no quotient. It seems probable that a good deal of the confusion and uncertainty concerning the distinction between increment, differential, and derivative could be avoided if, contrary to custom, at least an intuitive notion of the meaning of a differential were to be developed along with the discussion of the derivative. This can be done easily by means of geometric considerations and an arbitrary definition. In Figure 21-1 suppose that P is some point (x,y) on the curve $y = f(x)$. If x takes on an increment Δx, then y must take on an

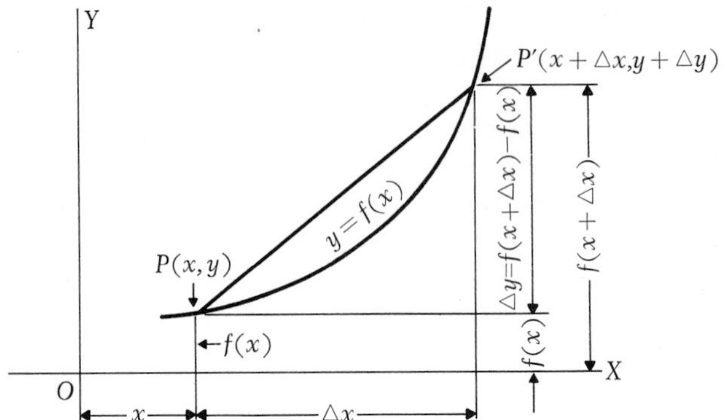

Figure 21-1

increment Δy whose value depends upon the value of Δx. Therefore the ratio $\Delta y/\Delta x$ would give the average rate of change of y with respect to x over the interval Δx, but not the instantaneous rate of change at the beginning of the interval. The instantaneous rate of change at any point on the curve is given by the slope of the curve at that point, and the slope of a curve at a given point is defined as the slope of the tangent to the curve at that point. Thus the derivative of a function at a point, which is defined to be $\lim\limits_{\Delta x \to 0} \dfrac{\Delta y}{\Delta x}$ and which gives the instantaneous rate of change for the corresponding value of the dependent variable, also gives the slope of the tangent to the curve at that point.

If we draw PT tangent to the curve at $P(x,y)$, the distance dy, Figure 21-2, represents the increment which y would have taken if its rate of change with respect to x had become constant exactly at the point $P(x,y)$. As P' moves along the curve to the position of P, Figure 21-2, both Δx and Δy approach zero as a limit. If the ratio $\Delta y/\Delta x$ represents the average rate of change for any of the intervals Δx and the ratio dy/dx the rate of change for the tangent line PT, it is evident that $\Delta y/\Delta x$ is changing in value as Δy and Δx approach zero while dy/dx is remaining constant. For each new position of P', the Δx and dx are the same in value, while Δy and dy differ. Furthermore, $\lim\limits_{\Delta x \to 0} \dfrac{\Delta y}{\Delta x} = \dfrac{dy}{dx}$. By agreement we shall call dx, which is the same as Δx, *the differential of x*, and we shall call *dy the differential of y* corresponding to dx. We have shown that the ratio dy/dx of the differentials dy and dx is the same as the *derivative of y with respect to x*. The value of this ratio will vary accordingly as P takes different positions on the curve, but for any particular position of P (i.e., for any given value of x) the value of the derivative dy/dx remains constant and is entirely independent of the value of dx.

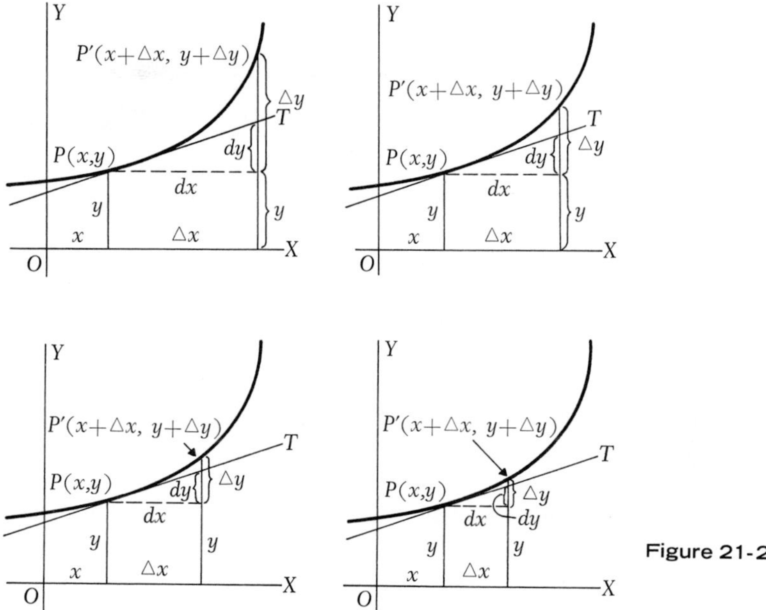

Figure 21-2

Now, if we wish to let dx become an infinitesimal and approach zero as a limit, dy will also become an infinitesimal and approach zero as a limit, but the ratio dy/dx remains the same, even in the limit. However, it is no longer necessary to regard the differentials dy and dx as infinitesimals unless we so wish. They may be regarded simply as tangible, finite increments, dx being any arbitrary increment of x and dy being the increment which y *would take on* if the slope of the curve (or the rate of change of y with respect to x) had become constant at the point $P(x,y)$.

It is believed that an approach to the concept of the derivative along with this intuitive notion of the differential as a finite, measurable quantity rather than an infinitesimal would dispel much of the mystery and uncertainty so often associated with the meaning of derivatives and differentials. The student's understanding will be strengthened if he is asked to take various curves, select arbitrary values and arbitrary increments for the independent variable, and by drawing and actual measurement determine dx, $f(x)$, $f(x + \Delta x)$, Δy, and dy. Then by actual division, dy/dx, he can get approximations to the values of the derivatives. To develop the rules for differentiation, of course, the usual analytic procedure will need to be employed. However, if a preliminary approach such as has just been described can make this analytic procedure more meaningful to the student, it will be exceedingly worthwhile.

Teaching the rules for differentiation The student will soon find that the process of finding the derivative of a function by the graphical method gives only approximations at isolated points and does not give any general expression for the derivative. He will also find that the detailed application of the formula

$$D_x y = \lim_{\Delta x \to 0} \frac{f(x + \Delta x) - f(x)}{\Delta x}$$

while it does give a general and exact expression for the derivative, is a clumsy and laborious process. The practical limitations of time demand that he learn and use the special rules or formulas which are available for differentiating various kinds of functions.

There are two points of view with regard to the introduction, learning, and use of these rules for differentiation. Considered solely from the standpoint of logical sequence and mathematical consistency, it would seem necessary that each of these formulas should be completely developed and proved before being used. This is the position taken by the authors of most textbooks on calculus. On the other hand, there are some authors and many teachers who hold that it is a sounder and more economical pedagogical procedure to introduce without proof certain of these rules in which the meaning is clear and to let the students use these empirically for the time being, the proofs being reserved until later, and special attention being given at the time only to the matter of making sure that the concepts involved are understood by the students. Prof. E. V. Huntington once expressed this point of view as follows:[13]

Now the simplest function is the polynomial,

$$y = A + Bx + Cx^2 + Dx^3 + \cdots$$

I should begin the second day, therefore, by stating, without proof, the rule for differentiating a polynomial, namely:

$$dy = (B + 2Cx + 3Dx^2 + \cdots)dx$$

Equipped with this rule, we can proceed at once to solve a multitude of problems in maxima and minima, which serve better than anything else to convince the student that here is a new tool which is mighty convenient to have at hand. . . .

The study of the polynomial naturally leads to problems involving the quotient of two polynomials, and to problems involving the solution of a quadratic equation. In order to handle such problems, it is well to introduce at this point the statement, without proofs, of the general rules for differentiating a sum, a product, and a quotient, and also the special rules

$$d\left(\frac{1}{x}\right) = -\frac{1}{x^2}dx, \qquad d(\sqrt{x}) = \frac{dx}{2\sqrt{x}}$$

[13]Edward V. Huntington, Teaching the Calculus: Four Papers on the Teaching of Mathematics, *Bulletin* 19 (Lancaster, Pa.: Society for the Promotion of Engineering Education, 1932), pp. 39–41.

in which x may be the independent variable, or itself a function of some other variable. . . .

If the meaning of a theorem is clear, as in the case of the rules for differentiation, the formal proof may often be postponed to advantage, but . . . the meaning of a new concept cannot safely be postponed. . . .

With regard to the subsequent proofs of the rules for differentiation, Huntington continued:[14]

If the time-saving program above outlined has been followed, the student should now have a good working knowledge of the properties of all the elementary functions including the rules for differentiation. If he has a spark of scientific curiosity, he will be interested to know how these rules, whose utility he has come to appreciate, were ever discovered, and how we know they are true. . . .

To indicate how much time can be saved, by taking up the proofs in the most effective order, I may say that the proofs of all the rules for differentiation can easily be disposed of in two classroom periods. First establish the rule for the sine and the rule for the logarithm, for the general case of a function of a function. Then the rules for kx, x^n, e^x, uv, u/v, $\cos x$, $\tan x$, and the inverse functions follow by a turn of the hand.

This will doubtless be regarded by many teachers as an overstatement and an oversimplification of the situation, and it may be that it is. There are also those who will object to it on the grounds that it lacks the sequential rigor of the prove-as-you-go plan, though the basis for this objection may be more apparent than real. However, regardless of whether or not one subscribes wholly to the suggestions made by Huntington, it seems probable that whatever sacrifice of mathematical order they would entail might be largely compensated by increased interest and operational efficiency.

If the student is to use the differentiation formulas with efficiency and dispatch, he will need to memorize them and memorize them thoroughly. As soon as a rule is given, whether with or without proof, it should be applied immediately, and considerable practice should be given in finding derivatives of functions under this rule. This will do a great deal toward enabling the student to fix the rule in his mind. However, as the number of new formulas increases, the difficulty of keeping them straight becomes greater, and the student will in general have to resort to actual and thorough memorization. Careful inspection of a tabulated list of the formulas will perhaps enable the student to discover certain relationships among them and to set up various mnemonics to aid in remembering them and to avoid confusing them with each other.

Some of the formulas are special cases of others. For example, $D_x(cu)$ is a special case of $D_x(uv)$; $D_x(e^u)$ is a special case of $D_x(a^u)$;

[14]*Ibid.*, pp. 46–47.

and other similar instances may be found. Again, certain similarities may be found among the derivatives of certain related inverse functions. The derivative of the arccos x is minus the derivative of the arcsin x; that of the arccot x is minus that of the arctan x; and that of the arccsc x is minus that of the arcsec x.

These and perhaps other relationships that might be found among the formulas will reduce the amount of sheer memorizing that will need to be done, and the very search for such mnemonic devices is itself an excellent exercise in familiarizing the students with the formulas.

Some critical points in developing the proofs of certain rules for differentiation We have already discussed the matter of teaching the meanings of derivative and differential. A clear concept of the meanings of these terms is prerequisite to any real understanding of the proofs of the formulas for the elementary derivatives. These concepts, in turn, involve an understanding of the meanings of increments, limits, and infinitesimals, which have also been discussed. It is probable that teachers, in developing the formulas for derivatives, are inclined to be too generous in their assumptions regarding the students' mastery of the meanings of these concepts.

The general method of finding a derivative needs to be stressed. Its almost mechanical form and the one-two-three order of its steps, together with the reasons for this order, need to be explained and illustrated, not once but numerous times, until the students are able to apply it independently and with facility to simple functions. It is easy for them to follow and verify, step by step, the illustration of it, but it is by no means equally apparent to them *why* the particular steps are taken in that particular order. Consider the typical order in the general development:

$$(1) \qquad y = f(x)$$

$$(2) \qquad y + \Delta y = f(x + \Delta x)$$

$$(3) \qquad \Delta y = f(x + \Delta x) - y = f(x + \Delta x) - f(x)$$

$$(4) \qquad \frac{\Delta y}{\Delta x} = \frac{f(x + \Delta x) - f(x)}{\Delta x}$$

$$(5) \qquad \lim_{\Delta x \to 0} \frac{\Delta y}{\Delta x} = \lim_{\Delta x \to 0} \frac{f(x + \Delta x) - f(x)}{\Delta x} = D_x y = D_x f(x)$$

(by definition)

From a synthetic standpoint it is perfect, each step being a justified consequence of the preceding one. However, it cannot be said that each step *suggests* the following one, and herein lies the rub. The steps and their order suggest themselves only if one has in mind the end toward which he is working. It must be the task of the teacher to point out what this goal is and how and why this particular sequence of steps does lead to it. It is well to carry along this general synthesis with the illustrations of its application to particular functions while pointing out the parallel development and repeatedly calling attention to the reason for performing each step in its particular place.

The explanation may be somewhat as follows: Let us assume that we have given a variable y which is a function of x. Our task is to find the derivative of y with respect to x, or to find $D_x y$. By definition $D_x y$ means $\lim_{\Delta x \to 0} \frac{\Delta y}{\Delta x}$. We must therefore find some way of getting an expression $\Delta y / \Delta x$ in terms of x and Δx in order that we may determine its limit and thus find the derivative.

General Case

$$y = f(x)$$
$$y + \Delta y = f(x + \Delta x)$$

Example

$$y = 3x + 7$$
$$y + \Delta y = 3(x + \Delta x) + 7$$

Since we want to get an expression $\Delta y / \Delta x$, we must first get an expression for Δy itself. This we can do by subtracting y from each member of the above equation:

$$\Delta y = f(x + \Delta x) - y \qquad\qquad \Delta y = 3(x + \Delta x) + 7 - y$$

We may now substitute for y its value $f(x)$ (or $3x + 7$) and express Δy entirely in terms of x and Δx.

$$\Delta y = f(x + \Delta x) - f(x)$$

$$\begin{aligned} \Delta y &= 3(x + \Delta x) + 7 - (3x + 7) \\ &= 3x + 3\,\Delta x + 7 - 3x - 7 \\ &= 3\,\Delta x \end{aligned}$$

Now in order to get an expression for $\Delta y / \Delta x$, we must divide both members of the equation by Δx.

$$\frac{\Delta y}{\Delta x} = \frac{f(x + \Delta) - f(x)}{\Delta x} \qquad\qquad \frac{\Delta y}{\Delta x} = \frac{3\,\Delta x}{\Delta x} = 3$$

Finally, since we want $D_x y$, and since this means $\lim_{\Delta x \to 0} \frac{\Delta y}{\Delta x}$, we must take the limit of $\Delta y / \Delta x$ as Δx approaches zero as a limit.

$$\begin{aligned} D_x y &= \lim_{\Delta x \to 0} \frac{\Delta y}{\Delta x} \\ &= \lim_{\Delta x \to 0} \frac{f(x + \Delta x) - f(x)}{\Delta x} \end{aligned}$$

$$\begin{aligned} D_x y &= \lim_{\Delta x \to 0} \frac{3\,\Delta x}{\Delta x} \\ &= \lim_{\Delta x \to 0} 3(1) \\ &= \lim_{\Delta x \to 0} 3 = 3 \end{aligned}$$

Several illustrations carried through in this manner, with specific attention to the order of procedure and the reasons that each step comes in its particular place, will be extremely helpful to the students. It will go far toward giving them a real understanding of the fundamental meaning and method of finding derivatives and developing the general derivative formulas.

Proof of the formula for the derivative of a logarithm This is one of the particularly tough spots which students encounter. The method is perfectly general, but the proof involves certain facts and relations with which students often lack familiarity, although presumably they will have encountered them beforehand. We shall give a proof of the general formula and then analyze some of its difficulties.

$$(1)\qquad \text{Let } y = \log_a u, \text{ where } u \text{ is a function of } x$$

$$(2)\qquad y + \Delta y = \log_a (u + \Delta u)$$

$$(3)\qquad \Delta y = \log_a (u + \Delta u) - y$$

$$(4)\qquad = \log_a (u + \Delta u) - \log_a u$$

$$(5)\qquad = \log_a \frac{u + \Delta u}{u}$$

$$(6)\qquad \frac{\Delta y}{\Delta u} = \frac{1}{\Delta u} \log_a \frac{u + \Delta u}{u}$$

$$(7)\qquad \frac{\Delta y}{\Delta u} = \frac{1}{\Delta u} \log_a \left(1 + \frac{\Delta u}{u}\right)$$

$$(8)\qquad = \frac{1}{u} \cdot \frac{u}{\Delta u} \log_a \left(1 + \frac{\Delta u}{u}\right)$$

$$(9)\qquad = \frac{1}{u} \log_a \left(1 + \frac{\Delta u}{u}\right)^{\frac{u}{\Delta u}}$$

$$(10)\qquad D_u y = \lim_{\Delta u \to 0} \frac{\Delta y}{\Delta u} = \frac{1}{u} \log_a \left[\lim_{\Delta u \to 0} \left(1 + \frac{\Delta u}{u}\right)^{\frac{u}{\Delta u}}\right]$$

$$= \frac{1}{u} \log_a e$$

$$(11)\qquad = \frac{1}{u} \cdot \frac{1}{\log_e a}$$

$$(12)\qquad D_x y = D_u y \cdot D_x u = \frac{1}{u \log_e a} \cdot D_x u$$

It must be kept in mind that the proof of this formula necessarily follows some pattern of intuitive justification of the existence of $e = 2.71828 \ldots$ as the limit of $(1 + x)^{1/x}$ as x approaches zero. Although the proof of the existence of this limit is quite beyond the scope of any first course in calculus, satisfactory intuitive rationalization of its existence is not too difficult.

The first four steps involve no particular difficulties, but throughout the rest of the proof there are several places where the development is likely to be hard for students to follow. The first of these trouble spots occurs in step 5. Here the student must learn to recognize the application of the principle $\log m - \log n = \log m/n$. The principle itself will be familiar, but there is possibility that in this unfamiliar dress the student may fail to recognize it unless it is pointed out by the teacher.

Step 6 then follows naturally in the process of finding $\Delta y/\Delta u$ before passing to the limit. But here we run into trouble. In the present form of the expression on the right we have the problem of finding the limit of a product in which one of the factors becomes infinite and the other approaches 0 as Δu approaches 0. Careful examination of the factors will reveal the fact that if $\dfrac{u + \Delta u}{u}$ is written in the equivalent form $\left(1 + \dfrac{\Delta u}{u}\right)$, this factor has close resemblance to the binomial in the expression $(1 + x)^{1/x}$, for which the limit e exists as x approaches 0. This observation leads to the further investigation of the possibility of converting the expression given in step 7 into a form equivalent to $\lim\ (1 + x)^{1/x}$. If x is used to represent $\Delta u/u$, then $1/x = u/\Delta u$. The question is then raised as to whether there is any legitimate manipulation which can be used to transform the right side of step 7 into an equivalent expression of the form $\left(1 + \dfrac{\Delta u}{u}\right)^{u/\Delta u}$. Recalling the inverse relation between multiplication and division and the logarithmic property that $m \log n = \log (n)^m$, we are led through steps 8 and 9 to step 10. Here we recognize the expression whose limit is e as Δu approaches 0.

Substitution of e for this limit leads to the formula of step 11 for $D_u y$. However, since we are required to find $D_x y$ and since u is a function of x, we must make use of the formula for the derivative of a function of a function: $D_x y = D_u y \cdot D_x u$. We may assume that this has been previously developed, so in passing to step 12 we need only recall this rule and point out its application in the present situation.

Finally, it should be pointed out that we have developed the formula for the most general case: $y = \log_a u$. If we take e as the base (as a special case of a), then $\log_e a$, in the denominator of 12, becomes $\log_e e$, and the formula itself becomes

$$D_x(\log_e u) = \frac{1}{u} \cdot D_x u$$

since $\log_e e = 1$. This is the form in which it is usually found and in which it is generally used.

We have thus seen that the proof of this formula holds numerous specific difficulties for students. In addition to these it has the general difficulty of being somewhat long and involving numerous transformations and substitutions, the reasons for which are not immediately obvious to the students. Only a few of the better students will be able to dig it all out for themselves. Whether the majority really get it or not will depend largely upon how skillfully and clearly it is explained by the teacher.

The proof of the formula for the derivative of the exponential $y = a^u$ follows easily after the formula for the derivative of a logarithm has been established. Conversely, if the formula for the derivative of the exponential is independently developed first, as can be done, it may be used to simplify the development of the formula for the derivative of a logarithm. The order varies with different textbooks. Either may be used. In general it may be said that the one which is developed first, and independently of the other, will be more difficult for the students than the one which makes use of the first. The formulas depend ultimately upon the evaluation of

$$\lim_{x\to 0} \frac{a^x - 1}{x} = \log_e a \qquad \text{or} \qquad \lim_{x\to 0} (1 + x)^{1/x} = e$$

Proof of the formula for the derivative of the sine of an angle This is another of the basic derivatives and a proverbial trouble spot for students. The steps in the proof may be given as follows:

$$\begin{aligned}
&(1) & \text{Let } y &= \sin u, \text{ where } u \text{ is some function of } x \\
&(2) & y + \Delta y &= \sin(u + \Delta u) \\
&(3) & \Delta y &= \sin(u + \Delta u) - y \\
&(4) & &= \sin(u + \Delta u) - \sin u \\
&(5) & &= \sin u \cos \Delta u + \cos u \sin \Delta u - \sin u \\
&(6) & \frac{\Delta y}{\Delta u} &= \frac{\cos u \sin \Delta u}{\Delta u} - \frac{\sin u(1 - \cos \Delta u)}{\Delta u} \\
&(7) & &= \cos u \frac{\sin \Delta u}{\Delta u} - \sin u \frac{1 - \cos \Delta u}{\Delta u} \\
&(8) & D_u y &= \lim_{\Delta u\to 0} \frac{\Delta y}{\Delta u} = \cos u \left[\lim_{\Delta u\to 0} \frac{\sin \Delta u}{\Delta u}\right] \\
& & &\qquad - \sin u \left[\lim_{\Delta u\to 0} \frac{1 - \cos \Delta u}{\Delta u}\right] \\
&(9) & &= \cos u(1) - (0) \\
& & &= \cos u \\
&(10) & D_x y &= D_u y \cdot D_x u = \cos u \cdot D_x u
\end{aligned}$$

The first four steps involve no difficulty whatever. In step 5 there is a substitution to be made, and in steps 6 and 7 there are certain rearrangements of terms and the insertion of the divisor Δu; but these, again, involve no special difficulty so far as the operations themselves are concerned. There is, however, the question *why* these particular substitutions and rearrangements are made, and the reasons should be explained clearly to the students. In order to present these reasons, however, one must recall that it is necessary, in setting up the derivative, to evaluate $\lim_{\Delta u \to 0} \frac{\Delta y}{\Delta u}$. It should be explained that, in order to do this, we need to use $\lim_{\Delta u \to 0} \frac{\sin \Delta u}{\Delta u}$ and $\lim_{\Delta u \to 0} \frac{1 - \cos \Delta u}{\Delta u}$ because these expressions can be evaluated and their use affords the only way to evaluate $\lim_{\Delta u \to 0} \frac{\Delta y}{\Delta u}$. Indeed, the limiting values of these expressions will already have been determined, but as a matter of refreshing the minds of the students on these points it will be well to review them before substituting them in the formula. As a matter of fact, the two most difficult parts of the whole proof are (1) the preliminary establishment of the limiting values of these two expressions, and (2) sensing the role which they play in the proof. Step 9 merely involves the substitution of the numerical limiting values for these expressions.

It will be noted that this development gives the derivative of y with respect to u, where u is some function of x. In order to get the derivative of y with respect to x, we must again make use of the relation

$$D_x y = D_u y \cdot D_x u$$

This is done in step 10, which completes the proof.

Successive differentiation; maxima and minima A few illustrations will suffice to make it clear to the students that in general the derivative of a function of x with respect to x is itself a function of x which may in turn be differentiated and that, by differentiating successive derivatives in this way, there are obtained the so-called higher derivatives of the function. The students should be made acquainted with the various forms of notation for these higher derivatives, and in particular they should be given an interpretation of the second derivative as the rate at which the first derivative is changing, or graphically, as the rate of change of the slope of the curve. That is, the student should come to understand that, if the second derivative is positive at a given point, it means that the first derivative is increasing at that point; a negative value of the second derivative indicates a decreasing first derivative; and a zero value of the second derivative indicates that the first derivative is neither increasing nor decreasing.

The most important immediate application of the second derivative is in connection with the determination of maximum, minimum, and inflection points. It will be obvious to the student from a consideration of the graphs of functions that the first derivative at a maximum or a minimum point must be zero. The converse does not necessarily hold true, however; even if it did, this would not enable one to distinguish between a maximum and minimum. In order to make a certain test of this, the second derivative must also be employed. The student must be shown that, if $f'(x) = 0$ and is decreasing [i.e., if at the same time $f''(x)$ is negative], then a maximum is indicated at that point, while if $f'(x) = 0$ and is increasing [i.e., if at the same time $f''(x)$ is positive], then a minimum is indicated. If $f'(x) = 0$ and $f''(x) = 0$, also, then at that point the function has neither a maximum nor a minimum, but a point of inflection. Careful explanation of these matters should be given and should be accompanied by graphic illustrations to ensure that the students understand them clearly.

The students should be warned against concluding wrongly that $f'(x)$ for a certain x, or at a certain point, will necessarily be zero just because $f''(x)$ is zero. Since $f''(x) < 0$ indicates that the curve is *concave downward* and $f''(x) > 0$ indicates it is *concave upward*, it follows that at the point where the sense of concavity changes, $f''(x) = 0$ if it has a value. This point is called a "point of inflection," or "flex point." That these are not sufficient conditions for a flex point may be seen by examining the curves $f(x) = x^4$ and $f(x) = x^{2/3}$. A simple illustration of how $f'(x)$ and $f''(x)$ may be used in graphing a function is the graph of $f(x) = 3x^3 - 2x + 5$ given in Figure 21-3.

The study of maxima and minima offers a wealth of interesting applications of the theory to geometrical and physical situations. These

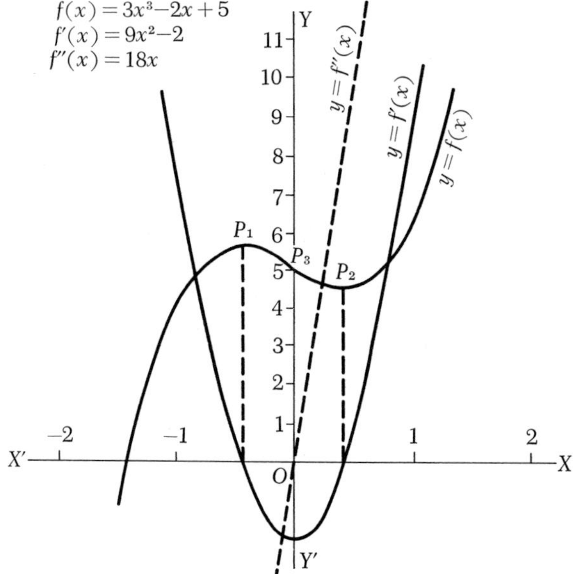

Figure 21-3

problems not only give practice in formal differentiation but also give to the work a high degree of motivation and afford excellent training in interpreting geometric and physical situations and in translating these into the formal language of the derivative.

The indefinite integral; formal integration Up to the present we have considered only matters which are related to derivation and differentiation of functions. We must now give some attention to that part of calculus which is concerned with the inverse problem of finding a primitive function of which the given function is the derivative. It should be pointed out to the students that many of the most important applications of calculus give rise to problems of this nature, particularly those involving definite integrals. No student should have any difficulty in understanding the meaning of integration if it is explained simply as the process of antidifferentiation; i.e., if it is clearly pointed out that in differentiation we are given the function and required to find the derivative, while in integration we are given the derivative and required to find the function. The two processes are absolutely inverse to each other, just as division and multiplication or addition and subtraction are. Either one *un*does the other.

In taking up the study of integration, then, the first task of the instructor should be to make this clear to the students so that their work in integration will not be devoid of meaning. It will help greatly toward achieving this understanding if the instructor and students together work out a few of the fundamental integrals. The finding of a derivative is, of course, a direct process; on the other hand, the finding of an integral form is essentially a matter of trial. In view of the fact that the two processes are exactly inverse to each other, the test for the correctness of an integral is whether or not it can be differentiated to give the original expression.

By using this basic principle, it is possible to take the fundamental formulas for derivatives and, by reversing the reasoning and the notation, arrive at some of the fundamental formulas for integration. A number of these should be set down and tested in this way by the students with the assistance of the instructor. Thus, since $D_x(\sin x) = \cos x$, it is seen at once that $\int(\cos x)\, dx = \sin x + C$, because by applying the test for an integral it is apparent that the derivative of $\sin x + C$ is $\cos x$. In like manner the integrals corresponding to the other fundamental derivative formulas should be set down, explained, and verified. If this is done, the students can hardly help sensing the relation between derivatives and integrals.

In connection with the development of these integration formulas the student will note the appearance of the constant of integration. The necessity and meaning of the constant of integration must be carefully explained by the instructor. This may be done by use of the theorem "If two functions have the same derivative, they differ only by a constant" and its converse; these may easily be illustrated by examples. It should be pointed out that in many of the applications of integration the determination of the constant of integration to satisfy initial conditions is of extreme importance.

Use of the table of integrals There are a few of the fundamental integrals with which the student should become perfectly familiar. The lists of these vary in different textbooks, the number usually being between 12 and 25 and depending mainly upon the author's inclination toward generalization or specialization of the forms. The discussion of these forms in each textbook presumably will be consistent with the author's views in this respect, so the precise number of formulas listed in any case is of less consequence than the fact that there *are* certain of these which the student must know thoroughly. These formulas should be tested by differentiation and should be memorized.

In addition to these fundamental integrals there are many special integrals which are often useful. Textbooks usually contain more or less extensive lists or tables of these special integrals. Separately published tables, which are much more complete even than those given in the textbooks, are also available. There is no general agreement among instructors on the extent to which students should use these tables of special integrals. Some feel that, since much of integration is formal anyway, the free use of the tables speeds up the work and allows more to be accomplished without any detriment to the student. Others feel that the student will gain more insight and understanding if he performs most of these integrations for himself by means of the fundamental integrals. Nobody knows just what the optimum is with regard to this question, but it would seem that a middle ground or reasonable balance of these views would perhaps be more defensible than either extreme position. To this end, Huntington's suggestion that "no formula in the table should be used until it has at least been verified by 'differentiating back' "[15] seems appropriate.

In using an extensive table of integrals, the student will need to familiarize himself with the way in which the integrals are classified so that he can readily locate and identify the form corresponding to any given integrand.

Sometimes it may be impossible to find in the table a formula which corresponds to the given integrand. In such cases it is sometimes possible to transform the given expression into usable form through such special devices as resolution of the expression into partial fractions, the substitution of a new variable, application of the rule for integra-

[15]Huntington, *op. cit.*, p. 55.

tion by parts, or use of the reduction formulas. These special devices involve special procedures the reasons for which, and the real significance of which, will probably not be clear to the students unless the underlying principles and considerations are carefully explained by the instructor. In order that the students may appreciate and become familiar with the nature of these devices, ample illustration and explanation of them should be given. In connection with trigonometric substitutions and the transformation of trigonometric expressions into integrable forms, it may be advisable to give again a brief summary and review of certain of the trigonometric identities, notably the addition formulas and the functions of half angles and double angles. The extreme generality of the reduction formulas makes it desirable that illustrative examples be worked out by the instructor to familiarize the students with the precise manner in which these formulas are applied to particular functions and with the effect which is produced in the integrand through the application of these formulas.

The definite integral As in the case of the indefinite integral many students employ the definite integral without clearly understanding its nature and interpretation. The indefinite integral was defined merely as an antiderivative. The definite integral, on the other hand, is to be interpreted in a different way, viz., as a summation of elements having the characteristic form $f(x)\ \Delta x$, or, more precisely, as the limit of the sum of these elements as Δx approaches zero as a limit. The justification for identifying the limit of such a sum with an integral rests, of course, upon the fundamental theorem for definite integrals, and this must be made clear to the students in due time. Here is a case, however, in which the concept of the definite integral may justifiably be developed, explained, illustrated, defined, associated with its characteristic symbolism, and actually used before proceeding to a proof of the fact that its use is justified.

In general there are three phases to problems involving definite integrals: (1) setting up the element of integration, (2) performing the formal integration, and (3) substituting limits and evaluating the integral. The third of these is mere labor. The second involves the knowledge and ability required to perform the integration correctly. This presumably will have been developed in connection with the work on indefinite integrals. The first phase, setting up the formula for the element of integration, is the part of the work which is likely to cause the students the most difficulty. Since ideas seem to be most readily acquired and assimilated when they are associated with graphic representations, the most effective illustration of the method of setting up the formula for the element of integration is probably in connection with the problem of finding the area under a curve, Figure 21-4. Here it is

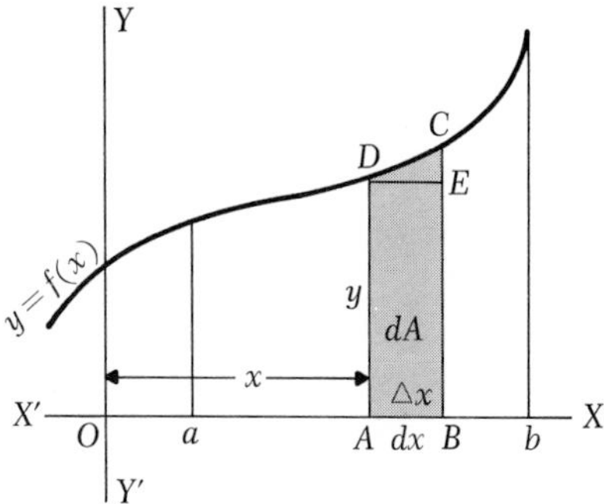

Figure 21-4

apparent that the element of area, ΔA or $ABCD$, is approximately equal to the area of the rectangle $ABED$, this area being given by $y\ \Delta x$, or $f(x)\ \Delta x$. On passing to the differential notation, we have $dA = f(x)\ dx$, which is the characteristic form for the differential of area or the element of integration, whence $A = \int dA = \int f(x)\ dx$. The important thing here is that the element of integration is always of the form $dA = f(x)\ dx$, and the area itself is given as $A = \int f(x)\ dx$, or $F(x)$. If $x = a$, we have $A = F\ (a)$; if $x = b$, we have $A = F\ (b)$. The area under the curve and *between* the ordinates erected at a and b will evidently be $F\ (b) - F\ (a)$, which, as we have seen, is given by

$$\int_{x=b} f(x)\ dx - \int_{x=a} f(x)\ dx$$

It is to be noted that the constant of integration would appear in both of these integrals but would disappear in the subtraction, so it may be disregarded.

The customary notation for the definite integral, $\int_a^b f(x)\ dx$, should be clearly explained, and the student should observe and keep in mind the meaning of every detail of this notation. In particular, the student should be aware of the fact that for a given function $f(x)$ the value of the definite integral $\int_a^b f(x)\ dx$ depends entirely upon the values of a and b.

The fact that such an integral should produce the measure of the area bounded by the curve, the x axis, and the two specified ordinates is not always completely accepted by a class. This possibly is due to incomplete acceptance of the technique of integration, previously developed and used exclusively as a technique for finding antiderivatives, as having any direct association with the limit of a sum of infinitesimal strips of area under the curve. Help in overcoming this difficulty can be obtained from a pattern of rationalization that consists in creating certain areas which can be computed independently of the definite integral and then checking this computation against the result obtained by using the definite integral.

Example: (*a*) Find the area bounded by the straight line $y = 2x + 4$, the x axis, and the line $x = 4$.

If the graph of this line is drawn, the area described will be seen to be that of a right triangle with a base of 6 units and an altitude of 12 units. Its area is therefore 36 square units. From the integral we have

$$A = \int_{-2}^{4} (2x + 4)\, dx = x^2 + 4x + c \Big|_{-2}^{4} = (16 + 16 + c) - (4 - 8 + c) = 36$$

(*b*) If one desires a more involved illustration of this same type, the example can be that of finding the area of a circle with its center at the origin and with any specified radius. For the area enclosed by the circle $x^2 + y^2 = 25$ we have $A = 25\pi$.

To find the area by integration, first find the area in the first quadrant and then multiply this result by 4.

$$\begin{aligned} A &= 4\int_{0}^{5} \sqrt{25 - x^2}\, dx \\ &= 2\Big[x\sqrt{25 - x^2} + 25 \sin^{-1} x/5\Big]_{0}^{5} \\ &= 2(25 \sin^{-1} 1) = 25\pi \end{aligned}$$

It should be pointed out to the student that in general the element of integration for any solid can be readily set up provided it is possible to get a characteristic expression for the area of all the sections made by planes parallel to a coordinate plane. If the solid is cut into slices of thickness dh by planes parallel to this plane and if the sections thus made can all be represented by the same algebraic form, then, denoting a typical section by A_i, the element of integration is given by $A_i dh$. The meaning of this should be made clear by drawings, as should the fact that, if A_i can now be expressed in terms of h, then a definite integral for the volume can be set up. Probably the most common and simplest application of this is in connection with solids of revolution.

Other type forms for the element of integration are encountered in problems involving length of arc, surfaces of solids, plane areas in polar coordinates, moments of mass and inertia, and centroids. Whenever a new type form is to be considered, the instructor should make a special point of explaining and illustrating how the new special form fits into, and in fact derives from, the fundamental concept and definition of an element of integration. If this is done, the student will gradually acquire the ability to interpret problems and set up integrals for himself, and the application of the definite integral will come to have meaning for him instead of seeming to be merely an assortment of tricks to be learned. If the student once gets a clear concept of the meaning of the element of integration for single definite integrals, the subsequent extension to double, triple, or multiple integrals in general will be plausible and comparatively easy for him.

The foregoing discussion has dealt mainly with the matter of developing meanings and concepts. The illustrations used have dealt with simple functions, and rigorous treatment has not been attempted. This is not to say that rigorous work has no place in connection with the advanced study of the definite integral. On the contrary, if one is to justify completely the use of this important mathematical tool, it is absolutely necessary that a rigorous proof of the fundamental theorem be given.

It should be kept in mind, however, that there is an important distinction between understanding and using this tool and justifying its use. As has been said before, it seems that in this case there is a substantial advantage to be gained by undertaking a thorough development of the concept and application of the definite integral before, perhaps even without, requiring a rigorous analytical proof of the theorem which justifies its use. Indeed, most elementary textbooks make no pretense of giving a rigorous proof of the theorem but rest the case upon explanations which give understanding and plausibility but which involve a considerable amount of intuition.

All students should be required to understand the line of reasoning which underlies the proof of the fundamental theorem. If the customary geometrical interpretation is used as a basis for the explanation, the problem resolves itself essentially into showing that the area bounded by the curve $y = f(x)$, the x axis, and the perpendiculars erected to the x axis at the points $x = a$ and $x = b$ is exactly equal to the area given by the limit of the sum

$$f(x_1)\,\Delta x_1 + f(x_2)\,\Delta x_2 + f(x_3)\,\Delta x_3 + \cdots + f(x_n)\,\Delta x_n$$

as n becomes infinite and each Δx approaches zero as a limit; i.e., $\lim\limits_{n\to\infty} \sum\limits_{i=1}^{n} f(x_i)\,\Delta x_i$, where $\Delta x_i \to 0$ as $n \to \infty$. This is done by showing

1. That a certain area, say A, is given by $F(b) - F(a)$, where a and b are particular values of x and $F(x) = \int f(x)\,dx$

2. That $\lim\limits_{n\to\infty} \sum\limits_{i=1}^{n} f(x_i)\,\Delta x_i$ gives *precisely* this same area A

Thus the students should come to see that the summation process may at any time be replaced by the definite integral and that the symbols $\lim\limits_{n\to\infty} \sum\limits_{i=1}^{n} f(x_i)\,\Delta x_i$ and $\int_{x_1}^{x_2} f(x)\,dx$ may be regarded as interchangeable, provided the function is continuous over the interval.

It should be pointed out that neither the conclusion embodied in the theorem nor the line of reasoning leading to it is limited to or dependent upon geometrical considerations, although a geometrical illustration was used and the problem was set up in terms of the summation of elements of area. This is done (1) because the graphic or geometric representation helps to give tangibility and concreteness to a situation otherwise highly abstract and (2) because functions may be represented graphically and interpreted geometrically even though they refer to nongeometric variables, such as forces, heat, and work. It should be emphasized that the definite integral may be used to determine any kind of magnitude, provided the characteristic function can be set up in conformity with the requirements stated above.

Improvement of prerequisite concepts and skills In addition to adding a whole new branch of mathematics to the student's equipment, the study of calculus holds tremendous possibilities for extending and deepening his understanding of the branches previously studied and the perfection of his skills in them. This is especially the case with reference to algebra, trigonometry, and analytic geometry. It has been said that the place where these subjects are really learned is in calculus. That this is more than a mere figure of speech will be evident from a consideration of the completeness with which the concepts and operations peculiar to these branches underlie and permeate the whole structure of calculus. Algebraic processes find application in innumerable connections throughout the course. Indeed, one of the main problems of formal integration is the algebraic transformation of functions into integrable forms. Trigonometric functions, identities, and transformations are also much in evidence, and a good understanding of analytic geometry is certainly a prime requisite, not only in setting up functions and equations for many of the applied problems but in giving the student tangible geometric interpretations of the fundamental concepts of calculus.

Functions of many kinds are met with and are made the subject of various investigations and operations. Incidentally, it may be noted that calculus gives the student a more comprehensive concept of the nature of a function than he will have been able to get in his previous study. He will already have gained an understanding of the general meaning of a function and will have made some study of the variation of functions, but in calculus, for the first time, he will make a systematic study of a new aspect of functions, viz., the rate of change of a function with respect to its independent variable.

The student who, in taking up a study of calculus, lacks an adequate background in algebra, trigonometry, and analytic geometry will find himself at a great disadvantage. Indeed, it is not improbable that a large share of the difficulty which students experience in calculus may be directly traceable to inadequate mastery of the prerequisite branches. On the other hand, nowhere could there be found a finer opportunity for well-motivated review and application of their concepts and techniques. Every student should be made conscious of this and should be urged as a matter of enlightened self-interest to put forth every effort to perfect himself in these concepts and techniques. For students who have difficulty, the instructor may be able to perform a real service by helping them to diagnose their troubles and suggesting appropriate remedial exercises. The importance of perfecting the skills and having ready mastery of the concepts and relationships of algebra, trigonometry, and analytic geometry is a matter which should receive continual emphasis.

Mathematical rigor in calculus The discussion in this chapter has admittedly given special emphasis to the matter of developing concepts and understandings because it has been felt that in general the teaching of calculus more often falls short in this respect than in any other. Intuitive concepts, however, do not provide sufficiently sound mathematical justification for the conclusions upon which much of calculus is based. Moreover, by the time the student has come through a study of calculus, he should have acquired a feeling for the nature of and the necessity for mathematical rigor *as such*. There can be no real appreciation of the nature of mathematical thinking, nor any sound basis for the exploration of higher mathematics, apart from an understanding of what is implied by a rigorous examination of the foundations of mathematics, the nature of the processes employed, and the consequences of given conditions.

Calculus stands more or less in the position of a borderline subject with respect to the matter of mathematical rigor. The courses which precede it are concerned mainly with the development of concepts, the acquisition of rules for operation, and the perfection of skills, although at some points there is an approach to real rigor in the treatment of certain theorems. On the other hand, the higher analytical courses are characterized by essentially rigorous and formal treatment of the subject matter. Thus, whether the student expects to "top off" his work in mathematics with calculus or go on into the domain of higher mathematics, it is important that his study of calculus provide him, both as a matter of appreciation and as a matter of training, with some opportunity for really rigorous examination of certain topics.

Calculus offers numerous opportunities for such work in the analytical definitions associated with the concepts of limits, infinitesimals, continuity, differentials, derivatives, and the like, and in the proofs of certain theorems, such as Rolle's theorem, the theorem of the mean, the fundamental theorem of definite integrals, Taylor's theorem, and Maclaurin's theorem.

It is undoubtedly true that there are many students who will be able to do little with this kind of work, and it must not be assumed merely on this account that the course is worthless to them. This, after all, is but one of the objectives of the course; it must not be forgotten that the use of a theorem and the proof of that same theorem are two entirely different matters and that things may often be extremely useful without being completely understood. On the other hand, students who are able to appreciate the significance of this type of analysis and follow its development will find a satisfying sense of security and finality in their work which must otherwise be lacking. Those who expect to go further in mathematics will find the training afforded in this sort of rigorous treatment of the foundations and theorems of calculus to be of inestimable value to them in their later work.

EXERCISES

1. What have been the main arguments for the introduction of some work in calculus in the high school?

2. Why, in your opinion, has calculus not been more extensively taught in the high school?

3. The opinion has sometimes been advanced that much of the difficulty which students have in calculus is due to inability to handle basic elementary algebra and trigonometric identities with facility and assurance. Comment on this.

4. To what extent do you think students' difficulties in calculus stem from their inability to read and interpret readily the explanations and discussions in their calculus textbooks? Present some examples of material taken from a calculus textbook which you feel might involve difficulty of this nature, and explain what the difficulty is.

5. What do you consider the most serious indictment of the teaching of calculus in colleges and engineering schools?

6. Explain and present illustrations of the following: variable, constant, parameter, domain of a variable, infinitesimal.

7. Give an intuitive explanation or illustration and also a formal definition of what is meant by saying that a variable approaches a constant as a limit. What difficulties do students have with the formal definition?

8. Give a formal definition of a derivative, using the notation of the textbook you use. Then explain and clarify this, using various illustrations.

9. What is a differential? Give three physical illustrations of the differentials of functions.

10. If $y = f(x)$, explain as you would to a class why it is that $\Delta x = dx$, while in general $\Delta y \neq dy$. Under what circumstances does $\Delta y = dy$?

11. Present arguments to justify or refute the assertion that in calculus the trigonometric identities play a more important role than the solution of triangles.

12. By using the definition and assuming the existence of the number e, present to the class a complete derivation of the formula for $D_x y$, where $y = \log_a x$, and show how this formula is simplified when a is taken to be e. (Note that this is where the number e really comes into the mathematical picture as an important constant.)

13. Show how the formula for the derivative of an exponential follows easily from the formula for the derivative of a logarithm.

14. Present to the class a full derivation of the formula for $D_x y$, where $y = \sin x$.

15. By taking u as a function of x and using the formulas for the derivative of $\sin u$ and the derivative of a fraction, show

how to obtain the formulas for the derivatives of cos x and tan x with respect to x.

16. By using the formulas for the derivatives of the trigonometric functions, show how to obtain the formulas for the derivatives of the inverse trigonometric functions.

17. Give a symbolic statement of the law of the mean. Then, using a diagram, explain and illustrate clearly the meaning of this formula. Give one instance in which this important law is used.

18. Give a clear explanation of the role of first and second derivatives in the matter of locating and classifying critical points (relative maxima and minima and inflection points) on the graph of a function.

19. Explain clearly the meaning of an indefinite integral as an antiderivative. Why must an indefinite integral contain a constant of integration?

20. Explain clearly the meaning of a definite integral as the limit of a summation process. Show that the constant of integration is actually accounted for in the process of evaluating a definite integral.

21. Show how the law of the mean is used in establishing L'Hôpital's rule for evaluating indeterminate forms. Give some examples of the application of this rule.

22. By using the trapezoidal rule, find the approximate area bounded by the curve $y = 3x^2$, the x axis, and the ordinates at $x = 2$ and $x = 7$. Use $\Delta x = 1$. Check your result by integration. Explain your work to the class.

23. Give a good, clear geometric interpretation of a partial derivative, and explain your diagram in detail. Do the same thing for a directional derivative.

24. Enumerate five tests for the convergence of infinite series. Explain how and why each of these works and why it is really a test.

25. Cite a problem involving an improper integral, and show how it should be solved.

26. Discuss the role of mathematical rigor in the course in calculus.

27. Pick out five things which seemed to you to present special difficulty when you were taking calculus. Try now to locate and identify the precise reasons these caused you difficulty. Then try to devise teaching procedures by which you would hope to make them clearer to your own students.

BIBLIOGRAPHY

Anderson, A. G.: The Derivative of cos x, *American Mathematical Monthly*, **60** (1953), 255–256.

Apostol, T. M.: Term-wise Differentiation of Power Series, *American Mathematical Monthly*, **59** (1952), 323–326.

Blank, Albert A.: Remarks on the Teaching of Calculus in the Secondary School, *Mathematics Teacher*, **53** (1960), 537–539.

Boyer, Carl B.: "The Concepts of the Calculus" (New York: Columbia University Press, 1939).

———: Analysis: Notes on the Evolution of a Subject and a Name, *Mathematics Teacher*, **47** (1954), 450–462.

Brand, Louis: The Fundamental Theorem of the Calculus, *American Mathematical Monthly*, **62** (1955), 440–441.

Clair, Harry S.: The Theorem of the Mean and Its Application to Problems of Maxima and Minima, *School Science and Mathematics*, **57** (1957), 468–472.

Coffman, Raphael T.: An Elementary Approach to the Use of the Rate of Change Concept for Solving Problems, *Mathematics Magazine*, **30** (1956), 81–90.

Cummins, Kenneth: A Student Experience-Discovery Approach to the Teaching of Calculus, *Mathematics Teacher*, **53** (1960), 162–170.

Dubisch, Roy: "The Teaching of Mathematics" (New York: John Wiley & Sons, Inc., 1963), pp. 81–106.

Duncan, D. G.: Some Standard Problems in Integration Simplified, *American Mathematical Monthly*, **61** (1954), 421–422.

Eaves, J. C.: Off the Beaten Path with Some Differentiation Formulas for the Trigonometric, Exponential, and Logarithmic Functions, *Mathematics Magazine,* **26** (1953), 147–152.

Evans, Trevor, and Bevan K. Youse: "How to Solve Problems in Analytic Geometry and Calculus," vol. I (Englewood Cliffs, N.J.: Prentice-Hall, Inc., 1961).

Ferguson, W. Eugene: Calculus in the High School, *Mathematics Teacher,* **53** (1960), 451–453.

Fort, M. K.: The Maximum value for a Continuous Function, *American Mathematical Monthly,* **58** (1951), 32–33.

———: Differentials, *American Mathematical Monthly,* **59** (1952), 392–395.

Fulton, Curtis M.: Differentiation of Logarithms, *Mathematics Magazine,* **28** (1954), 31–32.

Hamilton, H. J.: Toward Understanding Differentials, *American Mathematical Monthly,* **59** (1952), 398–403.

Hight, Donald W.: The Limit Concept in the Education of Teachers, *American Mathematical Monthly,* **70** (1963), 203–205.

Hildebrand, F. B.: A Simple Problem in Cylindrical Coordinates, *American Mathematical Monthly,* **64** (1957), 194–195.

Hildebrandt, E. H. C.: Remarks on "A Generation of High School Calculus," *American Mathematical Monthly,* **69** (1962), 430–433.

Hoffman, S.: A Classroom Proof of $\lim_{t\to 0} \frac{\sin t}{t}$, *American Mathematical Monthly,* **67** (1960), 671–672.

Hoyt, J. P.: A Natural Approach to the Fundamental Theorem of the Integral Calculus, *American Mathematical Monthly,* **61** (1954), 413–415.

———: A Proof of the Moment-Area Problem, *Mathematics Magazine,* **30** (1956), 95–97.

Karst, Otto J.: The Limit, *Mathematics Teacher,* **51** (1958), 443–499.

Leader, S.: On the Definition of ln *a*, *American Mathematical Monthly,* **66** (1959), 622–623.

Munroe, M. E.: Bringing Calculus Up-to-Date, *American Mathematical Monthly,* **65** (1958), 81–90.

Neeley, J. H.: What to Do about a New Kind of Freshman, *American Mathematical Monthly,* **66** (1959), 584–586.

———: The Generation of Calculus, *American Mathematical Monthly,* **68** (1961), 1004–1005.

Ogilvy, C. S.: A Calculus Problem with Overtones in Related Fields, *American Mathematical Monthly,* **65** (1958), 765–767.

Parker, F. D.: Integrals of Inverse Functions, *American Mathematical Monthly,* **62** (1955), 439–440.

Pascual, M. J.: On the $\lim_{\theta\to 0} \cos \theta$, *American Mathematical Monthly,* **62** (1955), 252–253.

———: The Derivatives of the Trigonometric Functions, *Mathematics Magazine,* **31** (1957), 39–40.

Perry, Gary: Alternate Classroom Proof that $\frac{\sin t}{t} \to 1$ as $t \to 0$, *American Mathematical Monthly,* **70** (1963), 426–427.

Phipps, C. G.: The Relation of Differential and Delta Increments, *American Mathematical Monthly,* **59** (1952), 395–398.

Prenowitz, Walter: Insight and Understanding in the Calculus, *American Mathematical Monthly,* **60** (1953), 32–37.

Randolf, John F.: Limits, *Twenty-third Yearbook* (Washington, D.C.: National Council of Teachers of Mathematics), pp. 200–240.

Ransom, W. R.: The Fundamental Theorem of the Differential Calculus, *American Mathematical Monthly,* **62** (1955), 361–363.

Richmond, D. E.: Calculus: A New Look, *American Mathematical Monthly,* **70** (1963), 415–423.

Spiegel, M. R.: Derivatives of Implicit Functions, *American Mathematical Monthly,* **61** (1954), 120–121.

Thurston, H. A.: A Simple Way of Differentiating Trigonometric Functions and Their Inverses in an Elementary Calculus Course, *American Mathematical Monthly,* **70** (1963), 424.

Walsh, J. L.: "A Rigorous Treatment of Maximum-Minimum Problems in the Calculus" (Boston: D. C. Heath and Company, 1962)

Weiner, L. M.: On the Computation of Definite Integrals, *American Mathematical Monthly,* **61** (1954), 254–255.

Wolfe, James: An Adjusted Trapezoidal

Rule Using Function Values within the Range of Integration, *American Mathematical Monthly*, **66** (1959), 125–127.

Yates, R. C.: Differentiating the Logarithm, *American Mathematical Monthly*, **61** (1954), 120.

———: Developments in Power Series, *American Mathematical Monthly*, **61** (1954), 256–258.

———: The Logarithm and Its Inverse, *Mathematics Teacher*, **51** (1958), 105–106.

———: The Trigonometric Functions, *Mathematics Teacher*, **51** (1958), 191–193.

Zeitlin, David: An Application of the Mean Value Theorem, *American Mathematical Monthly*, **64** (1957), 427.

———: On Plane Area in Polar Coordinates, *American Mathematical Monthly*, **66** (1959), 135–136.

Index